JOURNEYSONGS

THIRD EDITION

Concordat cum originali: † John G. Vlazny, Archbishop of Portland in Oregon

Published with the approval of the Committee on Divine Worship,
United States Conference of Catholic Bishops (USCCB).

Publisher: John J. Limb

Editorial Director: Eric Schumock

Executive Editor: Randall DeBruyn, DMA

Editorial Portfolio Manager: Joanne Osborn

Managing Editors: Amanda Weller, Angela Westhoff-Johnson

Managing Arranger: Rick Modlin

Editorial Assistance: Bari Colombari, Anne Connors, Scot Crandal, Katy Devine, Geraldine Ethen,
    Estela García-López, C. Angelyn Jáuregui, Craig Kingsbury, Travis Powers,
    William Schuster, Alan Tarpinian, Wade Wisler

Typesetting and Layout: Melissa Schmidt

Engraving Manager: Tia Regan

Senior Engravers: Monica Germano, Scott Hall, Bill Straub, Jon Taubman

Engravers: Lars Campbell, Dan Cosley, Laura Kantor, R. Michael Sanchez

Art Direction: Judy Urben

Cover Design and Graphic Icons: Le Vu

© 2012, OCP
5536 NE Hassalo, Portland, OR 97213
Phone: (503) 281-1191
liturgy@ocp.org
ocp.org

Second Printing: November 2012

Assembly	edition 21001
Assembly with Readings	edition 21002
Choir/Cantor	edition 21003
Keyboard Accompaniment	edition 21004
Guitar Accompaniment	edition 21005
Solo Instrument	edition 21006
CD Recording Library	edition 21007

ISBN 978-1-57992-152-1
BP 11/12

PREFACE

Ten years after the publication of the second edition of *Journeysongs*, it became evident that a new edition of this popular and well-received hymnal was necessary. The most compelling reason for a third edition was the introduction of the new English translation of *The Roman Missal* in November 2011. With the new text for the Order of Mass, along with the need for new musical settings of the Mass, plus the growing number of new songs published in these last ten years, the older edition of *Journeysongs* clearly needed a thorough revision.

As a result, we are proud to offer *Journeysongs: 3rd Edition* as our response to this need, especially for those parishes that have come to expect and rely upon OCP's long-established tradition of a perfect balance between new music and a well-known, stable repertoire. The Order of Mass is shown, as required, with the newly-translated chants from *The Roman Missal*. In addition, OCP offers nine Mass settings in a variety of musical styles and designed to meet various parish needs: Latin and English chant, traditional, multicultural and bilingual, and contemporary. Following these, a section of additional service music provides more possibilities for various moments during Mass.

Similar to the second edition, the Rites of Christian Initiation, the Order of Christian Funerals, Eucharistic Exposition and Benediction, as well as Morning and Evening Prayer are given here. The Psalms and Canticles section was also thoroughly analyzed and updated to give a good selection of psalms for all the most important Sundays and feasts. Bilingual English/Spanish psalmody was chosen for those occasions when the entire parish community might gather to worship, such as during Holy Week, or for weddings, funerals, and the RCIA.

In deciding which hymns and songs to carry over from OCP's current hymnals, the hymnal committee looked at both previous editions of *Journeysongs* and *Glory & Praise: 2nd Edition* to make sure that important repertoire from these hymnals was not omitted. Therefore, the best-known music of the St. Louis Jesuits, the Dameans, Michael Joncas, Carey Landry, Bernadette Farrell, Christopher Walker, Bob Hurd, and many others, which has formed the basis for numerous parish music programs over the last thirty years, has been retained. To supplement this, a large number of hymns and songs new to *Journeysongs* was drawn from music that has become known and loved in OCP's missal programs over the last ten years, including a substantial number of songs from the popular *Spirit & Song* repertoire.

As in past editions of *Journeysongs*, a sturdy plastic pocket is attached to the inside back cover of the third edition to allow for custom-made parish music supplements, if desired, or for a variety of music supplements published by OCP for several specialized genres: Latin-language chants, Mass settings and hymns, Spanish-language songs and service music, and youth-oriented contemporary songs. The usual accompaniment editions are also provided: keyboard/vocal, guitar/vocal, assorted C and B-flat instrument parts for those hymns and songs that have them, a CD and digital recording library, and a hardbound Choir/Cantor book. For liturgy preparation, in addition to the complete set of indexes provided in the back and in the accompaniments, OCP now provides song suggestions for this edition in its popular *Today's Liturgy* magazine as well as on liturgy.com.

Journeysongs: 3rd Edition is also available in an edition with the complete three-year cycle of *Lectionary* readings. Music for the responsorial psalms and gospel acclamations in that edition is taken from OCP's popular resource *Respond & Acclaim*, which may be purchased each year as needed or may be ordered as a standing subscription.

We must express our gratitude to the music advisory committee for *Journeysongs: 3rd Edition*, whose recommendations were essential to the final content of this book: Mr. Frank Brownstead, Sr. Jeremy Gallet, SP, Dr. Jennifer Pascual, Sr. Mary Jo Quinn, SCL, and Dr. Elaine Rendler-McQueeney. Additional recognition is once again given to Amanda Weller and her editorial team, without whose assistance and hard work this hymnal would not have been possible.

Journeysongs: 3rd Edition Hymnal Committee:

Randall DeBruyn, D.M.A., Chair
Barbara Bridge, B. Mus.
Rick Modlin, B. Mus.
Joanne Osborn, B. Mus.
Thomas N. Tomaszek, M.A., M.T.S.
Angela Westhoff-Johnson, M. Mus.

CONTENTS

Lectionary Readings

Prayers

Indexes

*These indexes are available in the accompaniment editions.

MORNING PRAYER
(LAUDS)

The Liturgy of the Hours is the Church's public worship of Christ, the communal celebration of praise and thanksgiving of the Church at prayer. The Hours, along with the Eucharist, take their meaning solely from the Paschal Mystery of salvation in Christ. Morning Prayer proclaims the themes of Christ as light of the world and sun of justice. It is the praise of God in creation that unites us with the prayer of Christ.

OPENING VERSE: INVITATORY

1

All make the sign of the cross on their lips as the Cantor/Presiding Minister sings:

Cantor/Presiding Minister: Lord,†open my lips.
All: And my mouth will proclaim your praise.

Cantor/Presiding Minister: Lord, open my lips.
All: And my mouth will pro-claim your praise.

MORNING HYMN

2

1. Dawn's ra-diance wash-es o-ver earth, Re-freshed and rest-ed
2. Em-bla-zoned thus, our earth pro-claims Its first foun-da-tion
3. O Christ, in-dwell-ing source of life, Re-flect-ing fair your
4. With-in your love we sing our praise, Tran-scen-dent God who

1. from the night: The grate-ful world, a-wake, a-ware,
2. and its end. An-oth-er day stirs life a-fresh:
3. Ab-ba's face, Your ra-diance bright-ens all the earth
4. nur-tures all; Day's dawn-ing splen-dor sends us forth

1. Is bathed in Christ's bap - tis - mal light.
2. Its gifts from God to God all tend.
3. As we a - wake in your em - brace.
4. To an - swer with our lives your call. A - men.

Text: 88 88; Aelred-Seton Shanley, d. 1999, © 1999, Aelred-Seton Shanley, from *Hymns for Morning and Evening Prayer*,
Archdiocese of Chicago: Liturgy Training Publications. All rights reserved. Used with permission.
Music: Chant, Mode VI.

PSALMODY*   3

(Water may be used as a baptismal remembrance during the singing of Psalm 63)

Antiphon

As morn - ing breaks I look to you, O God,

to be my strength this day, al - le - lu - ia.

Verses 1-4: Cantor

1. O God, you are my God, for you I long;
   for you my soul is thirsting.
   My body pines for you
   like a dry, weary land without water.

2. So I gaze on you in the temple
   to see your strength and your glory.
   For your love is better than life,
   my lips will speak your praise.

3. So I will bless you all my life,
   in your name I will lift up my hands.
   My soul shall be filled as with a banquet,
   my mouth shall praise you with joy.

4. On my bed I remember you.
   On you I muse through the night
   for you have been my help;
   in the shadow of your wings I rejoice.
   My soul clings to you;
   your right hand holds me fast.

Verse 5: All

5. Glory to the Father and to the Son,
   and to the Holy Spirit:
   as it was in the beginning, is now,
   and will be for ever. Amen.

Text: Psalm 63:2, 3–4, 5–6, 7–9. Antiphon © 1974, ICEL. All rights reserved. Used with permission.
Verses 1–4 © 1963, The Grail (England). All rights reserved. Used with permission of A.P. Watt, Ltd.
Music: Camaldolese Monks, OSB, © 1994, 2001, 2010, Camaldolese Monks, OSB. Published by OCP. All rights reserved.

**Other psalms, canticles and their antiphons may be taken from the proper of the
day (see No. 52–54). On Wednesday, Friday and other penitential days, Psalm 51
may be used (see No. 48–51).*

PSALM-PRAYER

READING

HOMILY/PREACHING

GOSPEL CANTICLE

All make the sign of the cross.

4

1. Blest be the Lord, the God of Is - ra - el,
2. The proph-ets tell a sto - ry just be - gun
3. This is the oath once sworn to A - bra - ham:
4. And you, my child, this day you shall be called
5. The ten - der love God prom-ised from our birth
6. All glo - ry be to God, Cre - a - tor blest,

1. Who brings the dawn and dark - est night dis - pels,
2. Of van-quished foe and glo - rious vic - t'ry won,
3. All shall be free to dwell up - on the land,
4. The prom - ised one, the proph - et of our God,
5. Is soon to dawn up - on this shad-owed earth,
6. To Je - sus Christ, God's love made man - i - fest,

1. Who rais - es up a might - y Sav - ior from the earth,
2. Of prom-ise made to all who keep the law as guide:
3. Free now to praise, un-harmed by the op - pres-sor's rod,
4. For you will go be - fore the Lord to clear the way,
5. To shine on those whose sor - rows seem to nev - er cease,
6. And to the Ho - ly Spir - it, gen - tle Com-fort - er,

1. Of Da - vid's line, a son of roy - al birth.
2. God's faith - ful love and mer - cy will a - bide.
3. Ho - ly and righ - teous in the sight of God.
4. And shep-herd all in - to the light of day.
5. To guide our feet in - to the path of peace.
6. All glo - ry be, both now and ev - er - more.

INTERCESSIONS

5

Intercession/Response

Cantor: ...We pray to the Lord: Lord, have mercy.

Lord, have mer - cy. Lord, have mer - cy; hear our prayer.

THE LORD'S PRAYER 6

Our Fa-ther, who art in heav-en, hal-low-ed be thy name;

thy king-dom come, thy will be done on earth as it is in heav-en.

Give us this day our dai-ly bread, and for-give us our tres-pass-es,

as we for-give those who tres-pass a-gainst us;

and lead us not in-to temp-ta-tion, but de-liv-er us from e-vil.

CONCLUDING PRAYER

The presiding minister says the concluding prayer.

BLESSING 7

Presiding Minister

May the Lord bless us, protect us from all evil

All

and bring us to ever-last-ing life. A - men.

SIGN OF PEACE

All share a sign of Christ's peace as a conclusion.

EVENING PRAYER
(VESPERS)

Evening Prayer is an occasion to give thanks for the blessings of the day and for redemption in Christ. Prayer rises "like incense in the Lord's sight," and "upraised hands" become "an evening sacrifice" (Psalm 141:2). It is appropriate to begin Evening Prayer with the lighting of candles, stemming from the ancient practice known as the Lucernarium, "the lighting of the lamps." In doing so, we call to mind the light of Jesus Christ in our hearts as we offer our thanks.

OPENING VERSE/LUCERNARIUM

8

All make the sign of the cross as the Cantor/Presiding Minister sings:

EVENING HYMN

9

1. O   ra - diant Light, O   Sun   di - vine   Of   God   the   Fa - ther's
2. O   Son   of   God, the source of   life,   Praise is   your   due   by
3. Lord Je - sus Christ, as   day - light fades,   As   shine the   lights   of

1. death - less   face,   O   im - age   of   the   Light   sub - lime
2. night and   day.   Our   hap - py   lips   must raise   the   strain
3. e - ven - tide,   We   praise the   Fa - ther   with   the   Son,

Final

1. That   fills   the heav'n - ly   dwell - ing   place.
2. Of   your   es - teemed and splen - did   name.
3. The   Spir - it   blest,   and with them   one.   A   -   men.

Text: *Phos Hilaron*, Greek, ca. 200; tr. by William G. Storey, b. 1923, © William G. Storey.
All rights reserved. Used with permission.
Music: Chant, Mode VI.

PSALMODY*

10

(Incense may be used during the singing of Psalm 141)

Like burn - ing   in - cense, O   Lord,   let my prayer   rise up   to you.

Verses 1-4: Cantor

1. I have called to you, Lord;
hasten to help me!
Hear my voice when I cry to you.
Let my prayer arise before you like incense,
the raising of my hands
like an evening oblation.

2. Set, O Lord, a guard over my mouth;
keep watch, O Lord, at the door of my lips!
Do not turn my heart
to things that are wrong,
to evil deeds with those who are sinners.

3. Never allow me to share in their feasting.
If the righteous strike or reprove me
it is kindness;

but let the oil of the wicked
not anoint my head.
Let my prayer be ever against their malice.

4. To you, Lord God, my eyes are turned;
in you I take refuge; spare my soul!
From the trap they have laid for me
keep me safe;
keep me from the snares
of those who do evil.

Verse 5: All

5. Glory to the Father and to the Son,
and to the Holy Spirit:
as it was in the beginning, is now,
and will be for ever. Amen.

Text: Psalm 141:1–5, 8–9. Antiphon and verses 1–4, © 1963, The Grail (England).
All rights reserved. Used with permission of A.P. Watt, Ltd.
Music: Camaldolese Monks, OSB, © 1994, 2001, 2010, Camaldolese Monks, OSB. Published by OCP. All rights reserved.

See also No. 111. Other psalms, canticles and their antiphons may be taken from the proper of the day.

Psalm-Prayer

Reading

Homily/Preaching

Gospel Canticle

All make the sign of the cross.

11

1. My soul pro - claims the great-ness of the Lord.
2. Through me great deeds will God make man - i - fest,
3. God's might - y arm, pro - tec - tor of the just,
4. Soon will the poor and hun - gry of the earth
5. All glo - ry be to God, Cre - a - tor blest,

1. My spir - it sings to God, my sav - ing God,
2. And all the earth will come to call me blest.
3. Will guard the weak and raise them from the dust.
4. Be rich - ly blest, be giv - en great - er worth.
5. To Je - sus Christ, God's love made man - i - fest,

1. Who on this day a - bove all oth - ers fa - vored me
2. Un - bound-ed love and mer - cy sure will I pro - claim
3. But might - y kings will swift - ly fall from thrones cor - rupt.
4. And Is - ra - el, as once fore-told to A - bra - ham,
5. And to the Ho - ly Spir - it, gen - tle Com - fort - er,

1. And raised me up, a light for all to see.
2. For all who know and praise God's ho - ly name.
3. The strong brought low, the low - ly lift - ed up.
4. Will live in peace through-out the prom-ised land.
5. All glo - ry be, both now and ev - er - more.

Intercessions

12

Intercession/Response

Cantor: ...We pray to the Lord: Lord, have mercy.

Lord, have mer - cy. Lord, have mer - cy; hear our prayer.

THE LORD'S PRAYER

Our Fa-ther, who art in heav-en, hal-low-ed be thy name;

thy king-dom come, thy will be done on earth as it is in heav-en.

Give us this day our dai-ly bread, and for-give us our tres-pass-es,

as we for-give those who tres-pass a-gainst us;

and lead us not in-to temp-ta-tion, but de-liv-er us from e-vil.

CONCLUDING PRAYER

The presiding minister says the concluding prayer.

BLESSING

Presiding Minister

May the Lord bless us, protect us from all evil

All

and bring us to ever-last-ing life. A - men.

SIGN OF PEACE

All share a sign of Christ's peace as a conclusion.

PSALMS & CANTICLES

Biblical psalms and canticles form the heart of the Church's song. Several kinds of religious lyrics, poems and prayers comprise the psalter. The canticles are poems, other than the psalms, found in the Jewish and Christian scriptures. Usually psalms and canticles are sung responsorially at eucharistic celebrations and antiphonally in the Liturgy of the Hours. These musical settings can help us remember key words and phrases and carry them in our hearts as we walk in the world.

PSALMS

---

15   **PSALM 16: THE PATH OF LIFE**

You will show me the path of life, the de-lights that a-wait me in your pres-ence. With-out you there is noth-ing; no joy can be com-plete un - til at last I sit by your side.

1. O God, you are my refuge,
   do not turn me away;
   I say "You are my God."
   Without you there can be no good.

2. I bless the Lord who guides me
   even in my sleep;

   my face is turned to God.
   With the Lord at my side I shall stand firm.

3. My heart exults, my spirit sings,
   even my body trusts in you;
   for you will not abandon my soul to death,
   nor let me sink into the grave.

Text: Based on Psalm 16:11, 1–2, 7–10; Scott Soper, b. 1961.
Music: Scott Soper.
Text and music © 1991, OCP. All rights reserved.

PSALM 16: YOU ARE MY INHERITANCE 16

You are my in-her-i-tance, O Lord, my in-her-i-tance, O Lord.

1. O LORD, my allotted portion and my cup,
   you it is who hold fast my lot.
   I set the LORD ever before me;
   with him at my right hand
   I shall not be disturbed.

2. Keep me, O God, for in you I take refuge;
   I say to the LORD, "My Lord are you.
   O LORD, my allotted portion and my cup,
   you it is who hold fast my lot."

3. I bless the LORD who counsels me;
   even in the night my heart exhorts me.
   I set the LORD ever before me;
   with him at my right hand
   I shall not be disturbed.

4. Therefore my heart is glad
   and my soul rejoices,
   my body, too, abides in confidence;
   because you will not abandon my soul
   to the netherworld,
   nor will you suffer your faithful one
   to undergo corruption.

5. You will show me the path to life,
   fullness of joys in your presence,
   the delights at your right hand,
   at your right hand forever.

PSALM 16: KEEP ME SAFE, O GOD 17

Keep me safe, O God, I take ref-uge in you.

Keep me safe, O God, I take ref-uge in you.

1. O Lord, it is you who are my portion and cup;
   it is you yourself who are my prize.
   I keep the Lord ever in my sight:
   since he is at my right hand
   I shall stand firm.

2. And so my heart rejoices, my soul is glad;
   even my body shall rest in safety.

For you will not leave my soul among
   the dead,
nor let your beloved know decay.

3. You will show me the path of life,
   the fullness of joy in your presence,
   at your right hand, at your right hand
   happiness for ever.

18   PSALM 18: I LOVE YOU, LORD, MY STRENGTH

I love you, Lord,   I love you, Lord, my strength.

1. I love you, O Lord, my strength,
   O Lord, my rock,
   my fortress, and my Savior.

2. My God, my rock of refuge,
   my shield, my help, my stronghold!

The Lord is worthy of all praise.
When I call I am saved from my foes.

3. Long life to the Lord, my rock!
   Praised be the God who saves me.
   You who gave great victories to your king,
   and love shown to your anointed.

19   PSALM 19: LORD, YOU HAVE THE WORDS

Lord, you have the words of ev-er-last - ing life.

1. The law of the LORD is perfect,
   refreshing the soul;
   the decree of the LORD is trustworthy,
   giving wisdom to the simple.

2. The precepts of the LORD are right,
   rejoicing the heart;
   the command of the LORD is clear,
   enlightening the eye.

3. The fear of the LORD is pure,
   enduring forever;
   the ordinances of the LORD are true,
   all of them just.

4. They are more precious than gold,
   than a heap of purest gold;
   sweeter also than syrup
   or honey from the comb.

20   PSALM 19: YOUR WORDS, LORD, ARE SPIRIT AND LIFE

Your words, Lord, are Spir-it,   Spir - it and life.

1. The law of the LORD is perfect,
   refreshing the soul.
   The decree of the LORD is trustworthy,
   giving wisdom to the simple.

2. The precepts of the LORD are right,
   rejoicing the heart;
   the command of the LORD is clear,
   enlight'ning the eye.

3. The fear of the LORD is pure,
   enduring forever;

the statutes of the LORD are true,
all of them just.

4. They are more precious than gold,
   than a heap of purest gold;
   sweeter also than syrup
   or honey from the comb.

5. Let the words of my mouth
   and the thought of my heart
   find favor before you, O LORD,
   my rock and my redeemer.

PSALM 22: MY GOD, MY GOD
21

My God, my God, why have you a-ban-doned me, my God, my God?

1. All who see me deride me.
   They curl their lips,
   they toss their heads.
   "He trusted in the Lord,
   let him save him;
   let him release him if this is his friend."

2. Many dogs have surrounded me,
   a band of the wicked beset me.
   They tear holes in my hands and my feet.
   I can count every one of my bones.

3. They divide my clothing among them.
   They cast lots for my robe.
   O Lord, do not leave me alone;
   my strength,
   make haste to help me!

4. I will tell of your name to my people,
   and praise you where they are assembled.
   "You who fear the Lord,
   give him praise;
   children of Jacob, give him glory."

PSALM 22: MY GOD, MY GOD
22

My God, my God, why have you a - ban-doned me?

1. All who see me scoff;
   they mock me with parted lips,
   they wag their heads:
   "He relied on the LORD; let him deliver him,
   let him rescue him, if he loves him."

2. Indeed, many dogs surround me,
   a pack of evildoers close upon me;
   They have pierced my hands and feet;
   I can number all my bones.

3. They divide my garments among them,
   for my vesture they cast lots.
   But you, O LORD, be not far from me;
   O my help, hasten to my aid.

4. I will proclaim your name to my brethren;
   amidst the assembly I will praise you:
   "You who fear the LORD, praise him;
   all you descendants of Jacob,
   give glory to him."

23 PSALM 23: THE LORD IS MY SHEPHERD/ I SHALL LIVE IN THE HOUSE OF THE LORD

Refrain

The Lord is my shep-herd; there is noth-ing I shall want.

Alternate Refrain

I shall live in the house of the Lord all the days of my life.

1. The LORD is my shepherd; I shall not want.
   In verdant pastures he gives me repose;
   beside restful waters he leads me;
   he refreshes my soul.

2. He guides me in right paths
   for his name's sake.
   Even though I walk in the dark valley
   I fear no evil; for you are at my side
   with your rod and your staff
   that give me courage.

3. You spread the table before me
   in the sight of my foes;
   you anoint my head with oil;
   my cup overflows.

4. Only goodness and kindness
   follow me all the days of my life;
   and I shall dwell in the house of the LORD
   for years to come.

24 PSALM 23: I SHALL LIVE IN THE HOUSE OF THE LORD/ THE LORD IS MY SHEPHERD

Refrain

I shall live in the house of the Lord all the days

of my life, all the days of my life.

Alternate Refrain

The Lord is my shep-herd; there is noth-ing

I shall want, there is noth-ing I shall want.

1. The LORD is my shepherd; I shall not want.
   In verdant pastures he gives me repose;
   beside restful waters he leads me;
   he refreshes my soul.

2. He guides me in right paths
   for his name's sake.
   Even though I walk in the dark valley
   I fear no evil; for you are at my side
   with your rod and your staff
   that give me courage.

3. You spread the table before me
   in the sight of my foes;
   you anoint my head with oil;
   my cup overflows.

4. Only goodness and kindness follow me
   all the days of my life;
   and I shall dwell in the house of the LORD
   for years to come.

PSALM 23: THE LORD IS MY SHEPHERD/ EL SEÑOR ES MI PASTOR

25

El Se - ñor es mi pas - tor, na - da me fal - ta.

The Lord is my shep-herd; there is noth-ing I shall want.

1. El Señor es mi pastor, nada me falta:
   en verdes praderas me hace recostar;
   me conduce hacia fuentes tranquilas
   y repara mis fuerzas.

2. Me guía por el sendero justo,
   por el honor de su nombre.
   Aunque camine por cañadas oscuras,
   nada temo, porque tú vas conmigo:
   tu vara y tu cayado me sosiegan.

3. Preparas una mesa ante mí,
   enfrente de mis enemigos;
   me unges la cabeza con perfume,
   y mi copa rebosa.

4. Tu bondad y tu misericordia me acompañan
   todos los días de mi vida,
   y habitaré en la casa del Señor
   por años sin término.

1. The LORD is my shepherd;
   I shall not want.
   In verdant pastures he gives me repose;
   beside restful waters he leads me;
   he refreshes my soul.

2. He guides me in right paths
   for his name's sake.
   Even though I walk in the dark valley
   I fear no evil;
   for you are at my side with your rod
   and your staff that give me courage.

3. You spread the table before me
   in the sight of my foes;
   you anoint my head with oil;
   my cup overflows.

4. Only goodness and kindness follow me
   all the days of my life;
   and I shall dwell in the house of the LORD
   for years to come.

26 PSALM 24: LORD, THIS IS THE PEOPLE/LET THE LORD ENTER

Refrain

Lord, this is the peo-ple who long to see your face.

Lord, this is the peo-ple who long to see your face.

Alternate Refrain

Let the Lord en-ter, let the Lord

en-ter, the King of glo-ry.

1. All creation is the work of God.
   The earth and all creatures
   belong to the Lord.
   From mountains to valleys,
   from ocean to land,
   the Lord God made them all.

2. Who will climb the sacred mountain,
   the holy place of God?

   Those who have not done evil,
   whose hearts are pure,
   whose eyes are not blind.

3. God will send a blessing
   to honor his faithful ones.
   Lord, this is the people
   who seek the face of Jacob's God.

27 PSALM 25: TO YOU, O LORD

To you, O Lord, to you, O Lord, I

lift up, I lift up my soul.

1. Your ways, O Lord,
   make known to me;
   teach me your paths.
   Guide me in your truth and teach me,
   for you are God my savior.

2. Good and upright is the Lord;
   thus he shows sinners the way.

   The humble he guides to justice;
   he teaches the humble his way.

3. Kindness and constancy
   the paths of the Lord
   for those who keep covenant with him.
   The friendship of the Lord
   with those who revere him,
   his covenant for their instruction.

Psalm 25: To You, O Lord 28

To you, O Lord, I lift up, I lift up my soul, my God.

1. Your ways, O Lord, make known to me;
   teach me your paths.
   Guide me in your truth, for you are my God,
   and for you I will wait.

2. Good and upright is the Lord;
   he shows us the way.

He guides the meek to justice,
he teaches the humble to follow his ways.

3. Your way, O Lord,
   is kindness to those who are true.
   Your friendship is
   with those who love you;
   you reveal to them your Word.

Psalm 25: To You, O Lord 29

To you, O Lord, I lift my soul, O Lord, I lift my soul.

1. Your ways, O LORD, make known to me;
   teach me your paths,
   guide me in your truth and teach me,
   for you are God my savior.

2. Good and upright is the LORD;
   thus he shows sinners the way.
   He guides the humble to justice,
   and teaches the humble his way.

3. All the paths of the LORD are kindness
   and constancy toward those
   who keep his covenant and his decrees.
   The friendship of the LORD
   is with those who fear him,
   and his covenant, for their instruction.

Psalm 27: The Goodness of the Lord 30

I be-lieve, I be-lieve I shall see the good-ness of the Lord in the land, in the land of the liv-ing.

1. The Lord is my light,
   the Lord is my rock, my salvation.
   The Lord is my refuge, guarding my life;
   of whom should I be afraid?

2. Only one thing I ask:
   may I live in the house of my Lord.

I shall gaze on God's goodness all of my days;
I shall live in the shelter of God.

3. I believe I shall see
   the goodness of God
   in the land of the living.
   Be strong, wait for the Lord.

31   PSALM 27: THE LORD IS MY LIGHT

The Lord is my light, the Lord is my light, the Lord is my light and my sal - va - tion.

1. The Lord is my light and my salvation;
   if God is my help, whom should I fear?
   The Lord is my refuge,
   my stronghold and my strength;
   why should I be afraid?

2. There is but one thing that I want:
   to live in the dwelling place of God;

to look all my days on the beauty of the Lord,
and contemplate God's holy temple.

3. I shall see for myself the grace of God,
   the dawn of that day among the living.
   Wait for the Lord,
   find strength in your hearts;
   have courage and wait for God.

32   PSALM 29: THE LORD WILL BLESS HIS PEOPLE WITH PEACE

The Lord will bless his peo - ple with peace, his peo - ple with peace.

1. Give to the LORD, you sons of God,
   give to the LORD glory and praise,
   give to the LORD the glory due his name;
   adore the LORD in holy attire.

2. The voice of the LORD is over the waters,
   the LORD, over vast waters.

The voice of the LORD is mighty;
the voice of the LORD is majestic.

3. The God of glory thunders,
   and in his temple all say, "Glory!"
   The LORD is enthroned above the flood;
   the LORD is enthroned as king forever.

PSALM 30: I WILL PRAISE YOU, LORD

I will praise you, Lord, you have res-cued me, I will praise you, Lord, for your mer - cy. I will praise you, Lord, you have res-cued me: I will praise you, Lord.

1. I will praise you, Lord,
   you have rescued me
   and have not let
   my enemies rejoice over me.
   O Lord, you have raised my soul
   from the dead,
   restored me to life
   from those who sink into the grave.

2. Sing psalms to the Lord,
   you who love him,
   give thanks to his holy name.

His anger lasts but a moment;
his favor through life.
At night there are tears,
but joy comes with dawn.

3. The Lord listened and had pity.
   The Lord came to my help.
   For me you have changed
   my mourning into dancing;
   O Lord my God,
   I will thank you for ever.

PSALM 31: FATHER, I PUT MY LIFE IN YOUR HANDS

Fa-ther, I put my life in your hands.

1. In you, O Lord, I take refuge;
   let me never be put to shame.
   Into your hands I commend my spirit;
   you will redeem me, faithful God.

2. For all my foes reproach me,
   neighbors laugh and friends stand off.
   I am forgotten like dead unremembered;
   I am like a dish cast down.

3. But my trust is in you, O Lord;
   I say, "You are my God."
   Into your hands I place my future;
   from the clutch of foes you rescue me.

4. Let your face shine on your servant;
   O save me in your love.
   Be stouthearted, and come, take courage,
   all you who now hope in the Lord.

35   PSALM 31: FATHER, INTO YOUR HANDS

Ostinato Refrain

Fa - ther, in - to your hands I com-mend my Spir - it.

1. In you, O Lord, I take refuge.
   Let me never be put to shame.
   In your justice, set me free.
   It is you who will redeem me, Lord.

2. In the face of all my foes
   I am a reproach,
   an object of scorn to my neighbors
   and of fear to my friends.

3. Those who see me in the street
   run far away from me.

I am like the dead, forgotten by all,
a thing thrown away.

4. But as for me, I trust in you, Lord;
   I say, 'You are my God.'
   My life is in your hands,
   deliver me from those who hate me.

5. Let your face shine on your servant.
   Save me in your love.
   Be strong, let your heart take courage,
   all who hope in the Lord.

Text: Luke 23:46; Psalm 31:2 & 6b, 12a, 12b–13, 15–16, 17 & 25. Refrain © 1970, 1997, 1998, CCD. All rights reserved.
Used with permission. Verses © 1963, The Grail (England). All rights reserved. Used with permission of A.P. Watt, Ltd.
Music: Martin Foster, b. 1966, © 1998, Martin Foster. Published by OCP. All rights reserved.

36   PSALM 31: FATHER, INTO YOUR HANDS/ PADRE, EN TUS MANOS

(Español) Pa - dre, _____ en tus ma - nos en - co - mien - do mi es -
(Bilingual) Pa - dre, _____ en tus ma - nos en - co - mien - do mi es -
(English) Fa - ther, ___ in - to your hands __ I com - mend ___ my

pí - ri - tu.
pí - ri - tu.
spir - it.

Pa - dre, _____ en tus
Fa - ther, _____ in - to your
Fa - ther, _____ in - to your

ma - nos en - co - mien - do mi es - pí - ri - tu.
hands __ I com - mend __ my spir - it.
hands __ I com - mend __ my spir - it.

1. A ti, Señor, me acojo:
   no quede yo nunca defraudado;
   tú que eres justo, ponme a salvo.
   En tus manos encomiendo mi espíritu:
   tú, el Dios leal, me librarás.

2. Soy la burla de todos mis enemigos,
   la irrisión de mis vecinos,
   el espanto de mis conocidos;
   me ven por la calle y escapan de mí.
   Me han olvidado como a un muerto,
   me han desechado
   como a un cacharro inútil.

1. In you, O LORD, I take refuge;
   let me not be put to shame.
   In your justice save me.
   Into your hands I commend my spirit;
   you will redeem me, faithful God.

2. I am scorned by all my enemies,
   dreaded by friends and neighbors;
   when they see me they turn away.
   I am like one dead and forgotten,
   like a vessel broken and discarded.

3. Pero yo confío en ti, Señor,
   te digo: "Tú eres mi Dios".
   En tu mano están mis azares;
   líbrame de los enemigos,
   los enemigos que me persiguen.

4. Haz brillar tu rostro sobre tu siervo,
   sálvame por tu misericordia.
   Sean fuertes y valientes de corazón,
   los que esperan en el Señor.

3. *But Lord, I trust in you;*
   I say: "You are my God."
   My life is in your hands;
   save me from my enemies,
   from the hands of those who pursue me.

4. *Let your face shine upon your servant;*
   in your steadfast kindness save me.
   Take courage, be strong of heart,
   all you who wait for the Lord,
   all you who hope in the Lord.

PSALM 33: BLESSED THE PEOPLE — 37

Bless-ed the peo-ple the Lord has cho-sen to be his own.

1. Upright is the word of the LORD,
   and all his works are trustworthy.
   He loves justice and right;
   of the kindness of the LORD the earth is full.

2. By the word of the LORD
   the heavens were made;
   by the breath of his mouth all their host.
   For he spoke, and it was made;
   he commanded, and it stood forth.

3. Exult, you just, in the LORD;
   praise from the upright is fitting.
   Blessed the nation whose God is the LORD,

the people he has chosen
for his own inheritance.

4. See, the eyes of the LORD
   are upon those who fear him,
   upon those who hope for his kindness,
   to deliver them from death
   and preserve them in spite of famine.

5. Our soul waits for the LORD,
   who is our help and our shield.
   May your kindness, O LORD, be upon us
   who have put our hope in you.

Note: Holy Trinity, Year B: Verses 1, 2, 4, 5; 19th Sunday in Ordinary Time: Verses 3, 4, 5

PSALM 33: LORD, LET YOUR MERCY — 38

Lord, let your mer-cy be on us as we place our trust in you.

1. Exult, you just, in the Lord.
   It is good to sound your praises,
   giving thanks to God
   with your strings and voice,
   making music before the Lord.

2. The word of God ever true,
   all the works of God enduring.

Every mountain peak, every ocean floor,
loving labor, loving Lord.

3. Behold, the eyes of the Lord
   look with love on those who hunger,
   bringing health and hope
   to our days of want,
   bringing mercy in every need.

39   PSALM 34: TASTE AND SEE/GUSTEN Y VEAN

(Español) Gus - ten   y   ve - an   qué bue - no es el   Se - ñor.
(Bilingual) Gus - ten   y   ve - an   qué bue - no es el   Se - ñor.
(English) *Taste ___   and   see ___   the good - ness of   the   Lord.*

Gus - ten   y   ve - an ___ qué bue - no es el   Se - ñor.
Taste   and   see ___ the ___ good - ness of   the   Lord.
Taste   and   see ___ the ___ good - ness of   the   Lord.

1. Bendigo al Señor en todo momento,
   su alabanza está siempre en mi boca;
   mi alma se gloría en el Señor:
   que los humildes lo escuchen
   y se alegren.

2. Proclamen conmigo
   la grandeza del Señor,
   ensalcemos juntos su nombre.
   Yo consulté al Señor y me respondió,
   me libró de todas mis ansias.

3. Miren al Señor y quedarán radiantes,
   no asomará en sus caras la vergüenza.
   Si el afligido invoca al Señor,
   lo escuchará y lo salva
   de sus angustias.

4. El ángel del Señor protege y salva
   a los que honran y temen al Señor.
   Gusten y vean qué bueno es el Señor,
   dichoso aquel que se acoge a Dios.

1. *I will bless the LORD at all times,*
   his praise shall be ever in my mouth.
   Let my soul glory in the LORD;
   the lowly will hear me and be glad.

2. *Glorify the LORD with me,*
   let us together extol his name.
   I sought the LORD, [who] answered me
   and delivered me from my fears.

3. *Look to the Lord; be radiant with joy.*
   And let your faces
   not blush with shame.
   The poor called out,
   and the Lord heard and rescued them
   from all their distress.

4. *The angel of the Lord*
   encamps around those who fear God
   and delivers them.
   O taste and see that the Lord is good;
   happy are those who take refuge in God.

Text: Psalm 34 (33):2–3, 4–5, 6–7, 8–9. Spanish refrain and verses 1 and 2 © 1970, Comisión Episcopal Española de Liturgia.
   All rights reserved. Used with permission. English refrain © 1969, 1981, 1997, ICEL. All rights reserved.
   Used with permission. English verses 1 and 2 © 1970, 1986, CCD. All rights reserved. Used with permission.
   English and Spanish verses 3 and 4, Mary Frances Reza, © 1998, Mary Frances Reza.
   Published by OCP. All rights reserved.
Music: Mary Frances Reza, © 1998, Mary Frances Reza. Published by OCP. All rights reserved.

40   PSALM 34: TASTE AND SEE

Taste and   see   the   good - ness   of   the   Lord;

taste and see   the   good - ness of   the   Lord.

1. I will bless the Lord at all times,
   with praise always on my lips;
   in the Lord my soul shall make its boast.
   The humble shall hear and be glad.

2. Glorify the Lord with me.
   Together let us praise his name.
   I sought the Lord and was answered;
   from my terrors God set me free.

3. Look towards the Lord and shine in light;
   let your faces be not ashamed.
   This poor man called; the Lord heard him
   and rescued him from all his distress.

4. The angel of the Lord is encamped
   around those who revere him.
   Taste and see that the Lord is good.
   They are happy who seek refuge in him.

Text: Psalm 34:2–3, 4–5, 6–7, 8–9. Refrain © 1969, ICEL. All rights reserved. Used with permission.
Verses © 1963, The Grail (England). All rights reserved. Used with permission of A.P. Watt, Ltd.
Music: Christopher Willcock, b. 1947, © 1977, 1990, 1997, Christopher Willcock, SJ.
Published by OCP. All rights reserved.

PSALM 34: TASTE AND SEE THE GOODNESS OF THE LORD/ 41
I WILL BLESS THE LORD AT ALL TIMES

1. I will bless the LORD at all times;
   his praise shall be ever in my mouth.
   Let my soul glory in the LORD;
   the lowly will hear me and be glad.

2. Glorify the LORD with me,
   let us together extol his name.
   I sought the LORD, and he answered me
   and delivered me from all my fears.

3. Look to him that you may be
   radiant with joy,
   and your faces may not blush with shame.
   When the poor one called out,
   the LORD heard,
   and from all his distress he saved him.

4. The angel of the LORD encamps
   around those who fear him
   and delivers them.

Taste and see how good the LORD is;
blessed the man who takes refuge in him.

5. The LORD has eyes for the just,
   and ears for their cry.
   The LORD confronts the evildoers,
   to destroy remembrance of them
   from the earth.

6. When the just cry out, the LORD hears them,
   and from all their distress he rescues them.
   The LORD is close to the brokenhearted;
   and those who are
   crushed in spirit he saves.

7. Many are the troubles of the just one,
   but out of them all the LORD delivers him;
   he watches over all his bones;
   not one of them shall be broken.

Text: Psalm 34:2–3, 4–5, 6–7, 8–9, 16–17, 18–19, 20–21. Refrain © 1969, 1981, 1997, ICEL. All rights reserved.
Used with permission. Verses © 1970, 1997, 1998, CCD. All rights reserved. Used with permission.
Music: Kevin Keil (ASCAP), b. 1956, © 2005, Kevin Keil. Published by OCP. All rights reserved.

42   PSALM 34: TASTE AND SEE

Taste and see, taste and see that the Lord is good, the Lord is good.

1. I will bless the Lord at all times,
   his praise always on my lips.
   The Lord shall be the glory of my soul;
   the humble shall hear and be glad.

2. Glorify the Lord with me,
   together let us praise his name.
   I sought the Lord: he answered me;
   he set me free from all my fear.

3. Look upon the Lord and be radiant;
   hide not your face from the Lord.
   He heard the cry of the poor;
   he rescued them from all their woes.

4. The angel of the Lord is with his people
   to rescue those who trust in him.

   Taste and see the goodness of the Lord;
   seek refuge in him and be glad.

5. Saints of the Lord, revere him;
   those who fear him lack nothing.
   Lions suffer want and go hungry,
   but those who seek him lack no blessing.

6. Children of the Lord come and hear,
   and learn the fear of the Lord.
   Who is he who longs for life,
   whose only love is for his wealth?

7. Keep evil words from your tongue,
   your lips from speaking deceit.
   Turn aside from evil and do good;
   seek and strive after peace.

Text: Based on Psalm 34:2–3, 4–5, 6–7, 8–9, 10–11, 12–13, 14–15; Stephen Dean, b. 1948.
Music: Stephen Dean.

43   PSALM 40: HERE I AM/GOD, MY GOD, COME TO MY AID

Refrain

Here I am, Lord, here I am. I come to do your will.

Alternate Refrain

God, my God, come to my aid, come to my

aid, come to my aid; come.

1. Long was I waiting for God,
   and then he heard my cry.
   It was he who taught this song to me,
   a song of praise to God.

2. You asked me not for sacrifice,
   for slaughtered goats or lambs.
   No, my heart,
   you gave me ears to hear you,
   then I said, "Here I am."

3. You wrote it in the scrolls of law
   what you would have me do.
   Doing that is what has made me happy,
   your law is in my heart.

4. I spoke before your holy people,
   the good news that you save.
   Now you know that I will not be silent,
   I'll always sing your praise.

Text: Based on Psalm 40:8, 14, 2, 4, 7–10. Refrains © 1969, 1981, ICEL. All rights reserved. Used with permission.
   Verses, Rory Cooney, b. 1952, © 1971, 1991, OCP. All rights reserved.
Music: Rory Cooney, © 1971, 1991, OCP. All rights reserved.

PSALM 42/43: AS THE DEER LONGS

As the deer longs for run - ning streams, so I long,

so I long, so I long for you.

1. Athirst my soul for you,
   the God who is my life!
   When shall I see, when shall I see,
   see the face of God?

2. Echoes meet
   as deep is calling unto deep,
   over my head, all your mighty waters,
   sweeping over me.

3. Continually the foe delights in taunting me:
   "Where is God, where is your God?"
   Where, O where are you?

4. Defend me, God;
   send forth your light and your truth.
   They will lead me to your holy mountain,
   to your dwelling place.

5. Then I shall go unto the altar of my God.
   Praising you, O my joy and gladness,
   I shall praise your name.

Text: Based on Psalm 42:2, 3, 8, 4; 43:3, 4; Bob Hurd, b. 1950.
Music: Bob Hurd.

PSALM 42/43: LIKE A DEER THAT LONGS/ MY SOUL IS THIRSTING FOR YOU

Refrain

Like a deer that longs for run - ning streams, my

soul longs for you, my God.

Alternate Refrain

My soul is thirst-ing for you, thirst-ing for you, my God.

1. Athirst is my soul for God,
   for God, the living God.
   When shall I go
   and behold the face of God?

2. I went with the throng
   and led them in procession
   to the house of God.
   Amid loud cries of joy and thanksgiving,
   with the multitude keeping festival.

3. Send forth your light and your fidelity;
   they shall lead me on
   and bring me to your holy mountain,
   to your dwelling-place.

4. Then will I go in to the altar of God,
   the God of my gladness and joy;
   then will I give you thanks
   upon the harp,
   give you thanks, O God, my God!

Text: Psalm 42:3, 5; 43:3, 4. Refrain © 1969, 1981, 1997, ICEL. All rights reserved. Used with permission.
Verses © 1970, 1997, 1998, CCD. All rights reserved. Used with permission.
Music: Refrain based on *Sicut cervus desiderat*, Giovanni Pierluigi da Palestrina, 1525–1594; adapt. by
Barbara Bridge, b. 1950. Verses and refrain adapt. © 2010, Barbara Bridge. Published by OCP. All rights reserved.

46   PSALM 45: THE QUEEN STANDS

The queen stands at your right hand, ar-rayed in gold.

1. The queen takes her place
   at your right hand in gold of Ophir.

2. Hear, O daughter and see; turn your ear,
   forget your people and your father's house.

3. So shall the king desire your beauty;
   for he is your lord.

4. They are borne in with gladness,
   borne in with joy;
   they enter the palace of the king.

47   PSALM 47: GOD MOUNTS HIS THRONE

God mounts his throne to shouts of joy: Al-le-lu-ia, al-le-lu-ia!

1. All peoples, clap your hands,
   cry to God with shouts of joy!
   For the Lord Most High we must fear,
   great King over all the earth.

2. God goes up with shouts of joy;
   the Lord goes up with trumpet blast.

   Sing praise for God, sing praise for God,
   sing praise to our King.

3. God is King of all the earth.
   Sing praise with all your skill.
   God is King over the nations;
   he reigns on his holy throne.

48   PSALM 51: CREATE IN ME

Cre-ate in me a clean heart, O God, a
clean heart, O God, cre-ate in me.

1. O God, in your goodness have mercy
   on me.
   In your compassion wipe out my offense.
   Thoroughly wash me from my guilt,
   and cleanse me from my sins.

2. For I acknowledge my offense
   and my sin is always before me;
   against only you have I sinned,
   and done what is evil in your eyes.

3. A clean heart create for me, O God,
   a steadfast spirit renew in me.
   Cast me not out from your presence,
   O God.
   Take not your Holy Spirit from me.

4. Give us back the joy of our salvation,
   and renew in us a willing spirit.
   O Lord, open my lips, Lord, open my lips.
   And we will sing your praise.

PSALM 51: BE MERCIFUL, O LORD/ CREATE A CLEAN HEART IN ME/I WILL RISE AND GO TO MY FATHER

49

Be mer-ci-ful, O Lord, for we have sinned. Be
mer-ci-ful, O Lord, for we have sinned.

Alternate Refrain 1

Cre - ate a clean heart in me, O God. Cre -
ate a clean heart in me, O God.

Alternate Refrain 2

I will rise and go to my fa - ther. I will
rise and go to my fa - ther.

1. Have mercy on me, O God,
   in your goodness;
   in the greatness of your compassion
   wipe out my offense.
   Thoroughly wash me from my guilt
   and of my sin cleanse me.

2. For I acknowledge my offense,
   and my sin is before me always:
   "Against you only have I sinned,
   and done what is evil in your sight."

3. A clean heart create for me, O God,
   and a steadfast spirit renew within me.
   Cast me not out from your presence,
   and your Holy Spirit take not from me.

4. Give me back the joy of your salvation,
   and a willing spirit sustain in me.
   O Lord, open my lips,
   and my mouth shall proclaim your praise.

50 PSALM 51: BE MERCIFUL, O LORD

Be mer-ci-ful, O Lord. Have mer-cy on us, for we have sinned. We come be-fore you; cleanse us from with-in. Have mer-cy on us, Lord.

1. Have mercy on me in your goodness, Lord.
   In your great compassion
   wipe out my offense.
   Wash me from guilt, Lord,
   cleanse me from my sin.
   Have mercy on me, Lord.

2. Create a clean heart for me, O God.
   And a steadfast spirit, renew within me.

   Cast me not out from your presence, O Lord.
   Take not your Spirit from me.

3. Give me the joy of your salvation, Lord,
   and a willing spirit sustain within me.
   Open my lips,
   let my mouth proclaim your praise.
   Have mercy on me, Lord.

51 PSALM 51: CREATE IN ME/OH DIOS, CREA EN MÍ

Oh Dios, cre-a en mí, oh Dios, cre-a en mí, _____
Cre-ate in ___ me, cre-ate in ___ me a
cre-a un co-ra-zón, un co-ra-zón pu-ro.
pure ___ heart, O God, a will-ing spir-it.

1. Piedad de mí, Señor,
   por tu bondad,
   por tu inmensa compasión
   borra mi culpa;
   lava del todo mi delito,
   purifícame, tú, de mi pecado.

2. Oh Dios, crea en mí
   un corazón puro,
   pon en mí un espíritu firme;
   no me arrojes lejos de tu rostro,
   no me quites tu santo espíritu.

1. *Have mercy on me, O God,
   in your kindness
   blot out my offenses;
   wash me, wash away my guilt,
   cleanse me completely of my sin.*

2. *Create in me, God,
   a pure heart
   and give me a steadfast spirit;
   do not cast me out
   from your presence,
   nor remove your holy spirit.*

3. Dame la alegría de tu salvación,
   mantén en mí un alma generosa.
   Enseñaré a los malvados
   tus caminos,
   se volverán a ti los pecadores.

3. *Give me back the joy*
   of your salvation,
   sustain in me a willing spirit.
   Open my lips, O Lord,
   and I shall proclaim your praise.

PSALM 63: MY SOUL IS THIRSTING/AS MORNING BREAKS 52

My soul is thirst-ing for you, O Lord, thirst-
As morn-ing breaks I __ look to you; be

-ing for you, my God. My soul is thirst-
my __ strength this day. As morn-ing breaks

-ing for you, O Lord, thirst-ing for you, my God,
I __ look to you; be my __ strength this day,

thirst-ing for you, my God.
be my __ strength this day.

1. O God, you are my God,
   and I will always praise you.
   In the shadow of your wings
   I cling to you and you hold me high.

2. Through the day you walk with me;
   all the night your love surrounds me.

To the glory of your name I lift my hands,
I sing your praise.

3. I will never be afraid,
   for I will not be abandoned.
   Even when the road grows long and
   weary your love will rescue me.

*Alternate refrain.

53   PSALM 63: AS MORNING BREAKS

As morn-ing breaks   I look to you;   I look to you, O Lord, to be my strength this day,   as morn-ing breaks,   as morn-ing breaks.

1. O God, you are my God, for you I long;
   for you my soul is thirsting.
   My body pines for you,
   like a dry, weary land without water.
   So I gaze on you in your holy place
   to see your strength and your glory.

2. For your love is better than life,
   my lips will speak your praise.
   So I will bless you all my life,
   in your name I will lift up my hands.
   My soul shall be filled as with a banquet,
   my mouth shall praise you with joy.

3. On my bed I remember you.
   On you I muse through the night,
   for you have been my help;
   in the shadow of your wings I rejoice.
   My soul clings to you;
   your right hand holds me fast.

4. Glory to the Father, and to the Son,
   and to the Holy Spirit:
   as it was in the beginning,
   is now, and will be forever. Amen.

54   PSALM 63: MY SOUL IS THIRSTING/AS MORNING BREAKS

My soul   is thirst-ing for you,   O Lord my God.
*As morn - ing breaks   I look to you, O   God.

1. O God, you are my God whom I seek;
   for you my flesh pines and my soul thirsts
   like the earth, parched and barren,
   lifeless without water.

2. Thus have I gazed toward you in the sanctuary
   to see your power and your glory,
   for your kindness is a greater good than life;
   my lips shall glorify you.

3. Thus will I bless you while I live;
   lifting up my hands,
   I will call upon your name.
   As with the riches of a banquet
   shall my soul be satisfied,
   and with exultant lips my mouth shall praise you.

4. I will remember you upon my couch,
   and through the night-watches
   I will meditate on you:
   you are my help,
   and in the shadow of your wings
   I shout for joy.

5. You are my help, and in the
   shadow of your wings I shout for joy.
   My soul clings fast to you;
   your right hand upholds me.

6. Glory to the Father, and to the Son,
   and to the Holy Spirit;
   as it was in the beginning,
   is now, and will be forever. Amen.

*Alternate refrain.

Note: 12th Sunday in Ordinary Time, Year C and 22nd Sunday in Ordinary Time, Year A: Refrain and verses 1–3, 5–6.
32nd Sunday in Ordinary Time, Year A: Refrain and verses 1–4, 6. Morning Prayer: Alternate Refrain and verses 1–4,
the last half of verse 5, and verse 6.

PSALM 66: LET ALL THE EARTH

55

Let all the earth cry out, cry out to God with joy!

Let all the earth cry out, cry out to God with joy!

1. Sing out your joy;
   praise the glory of God's holy name.
   Say to the Lord:
   "Oh, how awesome are your mighty ways."

2. Come now and hear all the things
   our God has done for me.

   Blessed be the Lord who holds me close,
   whose love is surrounding me.

3. All the earth shall bow before you,
   singing to your holy name.
   See the work of God,
   the wonders of his deeds from age to age.

PSALM 66: LET ALL THE EARTH CRY OUT

56

Let all the earth cry out to God with

joy, al - le - lu - ia.

1. Shout joyfully to God, all the earth,
   sing praise to the glory of his name;
   proclaim his glorious praise.
   Say to God,
   "How tremendous are your deeds!"

2. "Let all on earth sing praise and worship you,
   sing praise to the holiest of names!"
   Come and see the Lord's wondrous deeds
   among the children of Adam.

3. He has changed the sea into dry land;
   through the river they passed on foot.
   Let us rejoice in him.
   He rules by his might forever.

4. Hear now, all you who fear God,
   while I declare what he has done for me.
   Blessed be God who refused me not
   my prayer or his kindness.

57   Psalm 66: Let All the Earth Cry Out

Let all the earth cry out to God with joy, with joy.

1. Cry out with joy to God, all the earth!
   O sing to the glory of his name!
   O render him glorious praise,
   say to God:
   "How tremendous your deeds."

2. Before you all the earth shall bow,
   shall sing to you, sing to your name!
   Come and see the works of God!
   Tremendous his deeds among men!

3. He turned the sea into dry land;
   they passed through the river dry-shod.
   Let our joy then be in him—
   he rules evermore by his might!

4. Come and hear,
   all who fear God,
   I will tell what he did for my soul:
   to him I cried aloud,
   with high praise ready on my tongue!

58   Psalm 67: O God, Let All the Nations

O God, let all the na-tions praise your name,
let all the na-tions praise your name.

1. Lord, look with favor on us;
   show us your face.
   Reveal to the faithful your way, Lord,
   salvation for all the world.

2. May the nations sing and be glad,
   for your word governs all the world.

   Your justice will guide all nations,
   all people on the earth.

3. Lord, may we sing your praise;
   may we sing to you all of our days.
   O God, we ask you to bless us,
   as we honor your name.

59   Psalm 72: Justice Shall Flourish/Lord, Every Nation

Refrain   to Verses 1-2, 4-5

Jus-tice shall flour-ish in his time, and full-ness of peace for ev - er.

Alternate Refrain   to Verses 1-4

Lord, ev-'ry na-tion on earth will a - dore you.

1. O God, with your judgment
   endow the king,
   and with your justice, the king's son;
   he shall govern your people
   with justice
   and your afflicted ones with judgment.

2. Justice shall flower in his days,
   and profound peace,
   'til the moon be no more.
   May he rule from sea to sea,
   and from the River to the ends of the earth.

3. From the islands and Tarshish
   shall kings come with gifts;
   from Arabia and Sheba they come.

All the kings of the earth pay him homage;
all the nations shall serve him.

4. For he shall rescue the poor
   when he cries out,
   and the afflicted
   when he has no one to help him.
   He shall have pity for the lowly and poor;
   the lives of the poor he shall save.

5. May his name be blessed forever,
   and while the sun lasts
   his name shall remain.
   In him shall all the tribes
   of the earth be blessed;
   all the nations
   shall proclaim his happiness.

PSALM 80: THE VINEYARD OF THE LORD/   60
LORD, MAKE US TURN TO YOU

Ord. Time The vine-yard of the Lord is the house of Is - ra - el. The
Advent Lord, make us turn to you, show your face, we shall be saved. Lord,

vine-yard of the Lord is the house of Is - ra - el.
make us turn to you, show your face, we shall be saved.

Ordinary Time Verses

1. A vine from Egypt you transplanted;
   you drove away the nations and planted it.
   It put forth its foliage to the Sea,
   its shoots as far as the River.

2. Why have you broken down its walls,
   so that every passer-by plucks its fruit,
   the boar from the forest lays it waste,
   and the beasts of the field feed upon it?

3. Once again, O LORD of hosts,
   look down from heaven, and see;
   take care of this vine,

and protect what your right hand
   has planted,
the son of man whom you yourself
   made strong.

4. Then we will no more withdraw from you;
   give us new life,
   and we will call upon your name.
   O LORD, God of hosts, restore us;
   if your face shine upon us,
   then we shall be saved.

Advent Verses

1. O shepherd of Israel, hearken,
   from your throne upon the cherubim,
   shine forth.
   Rouse your power,
   and come to save us.

2. Once again, O LORD of hosts,
   look down from heaven, and see;
   take care of this vine,
   and protect what your right hand
   has planted,

the son of man whom you yourself
   made strong.

3. May your help be with the man
   of your right hand,
   with the son of man whom you yourself
   made strong.
   Then we will no more withdraw from you;
   give us new life,
   and we will call upon your name.

61 PSALM 84: HOW LOVELY IS YOUR DWELLING PLACE

How love-ly is your dwell-ing place, O Lord God of Hosts!

1. My soul yearns and pines
   for the courts of the Lord,
   my heart and my flesh cry out;
   Even the sparrow may find a home,
   the swallow a nest for her young;
   Your altars, my king and my God!

2. How happy are they
   who may dwell in your courts,
   how happy when you are their strength;

Though they might go through
   the valley of death,
they make it a place of springs.
Your first rain will bring it to life.

3. O Lord of Hosts, hear my cry,
   and hearken, O God of Jacob;
   One day in your house
   is worth much more to me
   than ten thousand anywhere else;
   The Lord is my sun and my shield!

Text: Based on Psalm 84:2–7, 9, 11–12; Michael Joncas, b. 1951.
Music: Michael Joncas.
Text and music © 1979, OCP. All rights reserved.

62 PSALM 85: LET US SEE YOUR KINDNESS

Let us see your kind-ness, O Lord, grant us your sal-va-tion, O God.

1. God, how I long
   for the peace you proclaim,
   your salvation and glory
   near to all who revere your name.

2. Kindness and truth shall meet,
   justice and peace shall kiss;

truth shall spring forth from the earth
   and justice look down from heaven.

3. You, yourself, will give these gifts;
   our land shall yield its fruit.
   Justice shall walk before you,
   and salvation along your way.

Text: Based on Psalm 85:8, 9–10, 11–12, 13–14; Dominic MacAller, b. 1959.
Music: Dominic MacAller.
Text and music © 1988, Dominic MacAller. Published by OCP. All rights reserved.

63 PSALM 85: LORD, LET US SEE YOUR KINDNESS

Lord, let us see your kind-ness, and grant us your sal - va - tion.

1. I will hear what God proclaims;
   the LORD—for he proclaims
   peace to his people.
   Near indeed is his salvation
   to those who fear him,
   glory dwelling in our land.

2. Kindness and truth shall meet;
   justice and peace shall kiss.

Truth shall spring out of the earth,
   and justice shall look down from heaven.

3. The LORD himself will give his benefits;
   our land shall yield its increase.
   Justice shall walk before him,
   and prepare the way of his steps.

Text: Psalm 85:9–10, 11–12, 13–14. Refrain © 1969, 1981, 1997, ICEL. All rights reserved. Used with permission.
   Verses © 1970, 1997, 1998, CCD. All rights reserved. Used with permission.
Music: John Schiavone, b. 1947, © 2001, John Schiavone. Published by OCP. All rights reserved.

PSALM 85: LORD, LET US SEE YOUR KINDNESS

64

Lord, let us see your kind-ness; Lord, let us see your kind-ness.

Your kind - ness and sal - va - tion grant us, O Lord.

1. I will hear what the Lord proclaims:
peace and salvation close at hand,
always near to those who fear him;
glory dwelling in our land.

2. Kindness and truth shall meet at last;
justice and peace embrace in love.

Truth shall spring up from the earth,
and justice shall look down from heaven above.

3. God will grant abundant grace;
earth will spring up with boundless life.
Blessings flow ever before him
to prepare his way.

Text: Based on Psalm 85:9–10, 11–12, 13–14; Scott Soper, b. 1961.
Music: Scott Soper.
Text and music © 2003, Scott Soper. Published by OCP. All rights reserved.

PSALM 89: FOR EVER I WILL SING
THE GOODNESS OF THE LORD

65

For ev - er I will sing the good-ness of the Lord.

1. I have made a covenant
with my chosen one,
I have sworn to David my servant:
forever will I confirm your posterity
and establish your throne
for all generations.

2. Blessed the people who know
the joyful shout;
In the light of your countenance,
O LORD, they walk.
At your name they rejoice all the day,
and through your justice they are exalted.

3. He shall say of me,
"You are my father,
my God, the rock, my savior."

Forever I will maintain
my kindness toward him,
and my covenant with him stands firm.

4. The promises of the LORD
I will sing forever,
through all generations my mouth
shall proclaim your faithfulness.
For you have said, "My kindness
is established forever";
in heaven you have confirmed
your faithfulness.

5. You are the splendor of their strength,
and by your favor our horn is exalted.
For to the LORD belongs our shield,
and to the Holy One of Israel, our king.

Note: 4th Sunday in Advent, Year B: Verses 4, 1, 3; Christmas: Verses 1, 2, 3;
13th Sunday in Ordinary Time, Year A: Verses 4, 2, 5.

Text: Psalm 89:4–5, 16–17, 27, 29, 2–3, 18–19. Refrain © 1969, 1981, 1997, ICEL. All rights reserved. Used with permission.
Verses © 1970, 1997, 1998, CCD. All rights reserved. Used with permission.
Music: Owen Alstott, b. 1947, © 1977, 1990, OCP. All rights reserved.

66

PSALM 89: FOREVER I WILL SING

For - ev - er   I   will   sing,   I will sing the

good - ness   of   the   Lord.

1. I have made a covenant with my chosen one,
   I have sworn to David my servant:
   forever will I confirm your posterity
   and establish your throne for all generations.

2. Blessed the people who know the joyful shout;
   in the light of your countenance, O LORD,
   they walk.

At your name they rejoice all the day,
and through your justice they are exalted.

3. He shall say of me, "You are my father,
   my God, the rock, my savior."
   Forever I will maintain
   my kindness toward him,
   and my covenant with him stands firm.

67

PSALM 90: IN EVERY AGE

In   ev - 'ry   age,   O   Lord,   you have been our

ref - uge,   you have been our   ref - uge.

1. You return us to dust,
   saying, "Return, O children, to earth."
   For to you a thousand years
   are like yesterday passed,
   or as a watch of the night.

2. You sweep us away in a dream.
   At dawn we are like morning grass
   that rises to the morning sun,
   then withers and fades.

3. Teach us to treasure our days.
   Give wisdom to our hearts.
   Return, O Lord, how long must we wait?
   Pity your servants.

4. Fill our day-break with your love
   that we may rejoice in song.
   May your gracious eye watch over us
   and the work of our hands.

PSALM 91: BE WITH ME, LORD

68

Be with me, Lord, when I am in trou-ble.

Be with me, Lord, be with me.

1. You who dwell in the shelter
   of the Most High,
   who abide in the shadow
   of the Almighty, say to the LORD,
   "My refuge and my fortress,
   my God in whom I trust."

2. No evil shall befall you,
   no affliction come near your tent,
   for God commands the angels
   to guard you in all your ways.

3. Upon their hands they shall bear you up,
   lest you dash your foot against a stone.
   You shall tread upon the asp and the viper;
   you shall trample down the lion and the dragon.

4. Because he clings to me, I will deliver him;
   I will set him on high
   because he acknowledges my name.
   He shall call upon me, and I will answer him;
   I will be with him in distress;
   I will deliver him and glorify him.

PSALM 91: BE WITH ME, LORD

69

Be with me, Lord, when I am in trou - ble.

When I am in trou - ble, be with me, Lord.

1. If you seek a shelter,
   then come to the Lord, our God.
   Say to the Lord,
   "My refuge, I place my trust in you."

2. No evil shall snare you,
   no harm come upon your home.
   God sends to you his angels
   to guard you on your way.

3. Your feet shall not stumble;
   the angels will lift you high.
   You shall defy the viper
   and those who cause you harm.

4. Because of your love,
   because of your faithfulness,
   God will indeed be with you
   to save you from all fear.

70   PSALM 91: BE WITH ME, LORD

Be with me, Lord; be with me, Lord, when I am in trou-ble and need.

1. You who dwell in the shelter
of God, Most High,
who abide in Almighty's shade,
say to the Lord: "My refuge, my
stronghold, my God in whom I trust."

2. Evil shall never befall you,
nor affliction come near to your tent.
Unto his angels he's given command
to guard you in all your ways.

3. On their hands the angels will bear you up,
lest you dash your foot 'gainst a stone.
Lion or viper might strike at your life,
but you will not come to harm.

4. Cling to the Lord and
he'll surely deliver you;
he raises up all who call on his name.
He will bring joy to your hearts and
bless you with peace in all your days.

Text: Based on Psalm 91:15, 1–2, 10–11, 12–13, 14–16; Michael Joncas, b. 1951.
Music: Michael Joncas.
Text and music © 1981, 1982, Jan Michael Joncas Trust. Published by OCP. All rights reserved.

71   PSALM 95: IF TODAY YOU HEAR HIS VOICE

If to-day you hear his voice, hard-en not your

hearts, hard-en not your hearts.

1. Come, let us sing with joy,
sing praise to the Rock who saves us.
Come now with open hearts,
singing songs of thanks,
singing songs of praise.

2. Come, let us kneel to God,
bow down to the Lord who made us.
We are the flock of God;

God who shepherds us,
God who guides us home.

3. If you should hear God's voice,
do not let your hearts be hardened
as in that desert land;
there they saw my works,
still they tested me.

Text: Based on Psalm 95:1–2, 6–7, 8–9. Refrain © 1969, 1981, 1997, ICEL. All rights reserved. Used with permission.
  Verses, Scott Soper, b. 1961, © 2002, Scott Soper. Published by OCP. All rights reserved.
Music: Scott Soper, © 2002, Scott Soper. Published by OCP. All rights reserved.

72   PSALM 95: IF TODAY YOU HEAR GOD'S VOICE

If to-day you hear God's voice, hard-en not your hearts.

If to-day you hear God's voice, hard-en not your hearts.

1. Come, let us sing joyfully to the LORD;
   let us acclaim the Rock of our salvation.
   Let us come into his presence with
   thanksgiving;
   let us joyfully sing psalms to him.

2. Come, let us bow down and worship;
   let us kneel before the LORD who
   made us.
   For he is our God,
   and we are the people he shepherds,
   the flock he guides.

3. O, that today you would
   hear his voice:
   "Harden not your hearts
   as at Meribah,
   as in the day of Massah in the desert."
   Where your fathers tempted me;
   they tested me though they had seen
   my works.

PSALM 95: IF TODAY YOU HEAR HIS VOICE 73

If to-day you hear his voice, hard-en not your hearts.

1. Come, let us sing joyfully to the LORD;
   let us acclaim the Rock of our salvation.
   Let us come into his presence
   with thanksgiving;
   let us joyfully sing psalms to him.

2. Come, let us bow down in worship;
   let us kneel before the LORD who made us.
   For he is our God,

   and we are the people he shepherds,
   the flock he guides.

3. Oh, that today you would hear his voice:
   "Harden not your hearts as at Meribah,
   as in the day of Massah in the desert,
   where your fathers tempted me;
   they tested me
   though they had seen my works."

PSALM 96: TODAY OUR SAVIOR IS BORN 74

To-day our Sav-ior is born! To-day our Sav-ior is born!

This is the day, this is the day, Christ, our Sav-ior is born!

1. Sing to our God a joyful song!
   Everyone bless God's name.
   Tell of God's wondrous deeds;
   sing to all the world.

2. Heaven be glad and earth rejoice,
   let every ocean roar!

   Every forest, every tree
   joins the song of joy!

3. Cry out with joy for God has come,
   come to rule the earth.
   God will rule the world with love,
   righteousness and truth.

75   PSALM 96: TODAY IS BORN OUR SAVIOR/ALLELUIA

Refrain: 1st time: Cantor/All; thereafter: All

Resp. Psalm   To - day   is born   our Sav-ior   Je - sus Christ   the
Gospel Acc. Al - le - lu - ia, al - le - lu - ia,   al - le - lu -

Lord.   Lord.   Lord.   Je - sus Christ   the Lord.
ia!   ia!   ia,   al - le - lu - ia!

*Verses (Responsorial Psalm only)

1. Sing to the LORD a new song;
   sing to the LORD, all the earth.
   Sing to the LORD; bless his holy name.

2. Announce his salvation, day after day.
   Tell his glory among all the nations;
   among all peoples
   his marvelous deeds.

3. Let the heavens be glad
   and the earth rejoice;

let the sea and what fills it resound;
let the plains be joyful
and all that is in them be joyful.
Then let all the trees
of the forest rejoice.

4. They shall rejoice before the LORD,
   who comes to govern the earth,
   to govern the world with justice
   and all the peoples with faithfulness.

*Gospel Acclamation verse is available in accompaniment books.

76   PSALM 96: PROCLAIM HIS MARVELOUS DEEDS

Pro-claim his mar-vel-ous deeds   to   all   the   na-tions.

1. Sing to the LORD, sing a new song;
   sing to the LORD, all you lands.
   Sing to the LORD; bless his name.

2. Announce his salvation, day after day.
   Tell his glory among all the lands;
   among all peoples, his wondrous deeds.

3. Give to the LORD, you families of nations,
   give the LORD glory and praise;
   give to the LORD the glory due his name!

4. Worship the LORD in holy attire.
   Tremble before him, all the earth;
   say among the nations: The LORD is king.
   He governs his people with equity.

PSALM 96: TODAY A SAVIOR IS BORN 77

To - day, to - day a Sav-ior has been born; a
Sav-ior has been born to us. He is Christ the Lord,
Christ the Lord, Je - sus Christ the Lord.

1. Sing a new song to the Lord.
   Sing to the Lord, all the earth.
   Sing to the Lord, sing to the Lord.
   Sing to the Lord, bless his name!

2. Proclaim his help day by day.
   Tell among the nations his glory.

Tell of his works, tell of his works,
and his wonders among all the peoples.

3. Let the heavens rejoice and earth be glad,
   let the sea and all within it thunder praise.
   All of the land, all that it bears:
   rejoice at the presence of the Lord.

PSALM 97: THE LORD IS KING 78

The Lord is King! The Lord is King,
the Most High o - ver all the earth.

1. Let earth rejoice, the Lord God reigns.
   Exult, you shores; be glad, you plains.
   Justice serves as God's high throne, alleluia!

2. The skies proclaim that God is just:
   God's glory plain to all of us.

Unseen spirits, join our song, alleluia!

3. You alone bring hope to birth:
   greater you than all the earth.
   Far beyond all other gods, alleluia!

79   PSALM 98: ALL THE ENDS OF THE EARTH

1. Let us sing a new song
   for the wondrous deeds of our God,
   whose holy arm has prevailed,
   bringing salvation and victory.

2. All the ends of the earth
   have seen the power of God.

   Ring out your joy, break into song;
   all you lands sing praise.

3. Sing the praises of God;
   with the harp and song give praise.
   O trumpets sound! Joyfully sing;
   sing to the ruler of all.

Text: Based on Psalm 98:3, 1, 3–6; Bob Hurd, b. 1950.
Music: Bob Hurd.

80   PSALM 98: THE LORD HAS REVEALED

1. Sing a new song, all you lands,
   of the marvelous deeds of the Lord.
   Salvation is born of God's right hand
   and holy arm.

2. The saving power of God
   has been revealed to all the lands.
   His kindness and truth
   forever faithful to the house of Israel.

3. All of the ends of the earth
   have seen the salvation of God.
   Shout to the Lord, dance for joy,
   sing your praise.

4. Play out your song on the harp,
   create a melodious song.
   With trumpets and horn
   acclaim our King and our God.

Text: Based on Psalm 98:1, 2–3, 3–4, 5–6. Refrain © 1969, 1981, ICEL. All rights reserved. Used with permission.
   Verses, Timothy R. Smith, b. 1960, © 1996, 2000, Timothy R. Smith. Published by OCP. All rights reserved.

PSALM 98: ALL THE ENDS OF THE EARTH

81

All the ends of the earth have seen the sav-ing pow-er of God.

1. Sing to the LORD a new song,
   for he has done wondrous deeds;
   his right hand has won vict'ry for him,
   his holy arm.

2. The LORD has made
   his salvation known:
   in the sight of the nations
   he has revealed his justice.
   He has remembered his kindness
   and his faithfulness
   toward the house of Israel.

3. All the ends of the earth have seen
   the salvation by our God.
   Sing joyfully to the LORD, all you lands;
   break into song; sing praise.

4. Sing praise to the LORD with the harp,
   with the harp and melodious song.
   With trumpets and
   the sound of the horn
   sing joyfully before the King, the LORD.

PSALM 98: ALL THE ENDS OF THE EARTH

82

All the ends of the earth have

seen the sav-ing pow-er of God.

1. O sing to the Lord a new song,
   for he has done wondrous deeds.
   Yes, his right hand and holy arm
   have won the victory.

2. The Lord has revealed salvation;
   his justice prevails on earth.

And to the house of Israel
the Lord bestows his love.

3. Give praise with a soaring melody;
   O sing with the strings and harp.
   With trumpets and the sound of horn,
   acclaim the King, the Lord.

PSALM 100: WE ARE HIS PEOPLE

83

We are his peo-ple: the sheep of his flock.

1. Sing joyfully to the LORD, all you lands;
   serve the LORD with gladness;
   come before him with joyful song.

2. Know that the LORD is God,
   he made us, his we are;

his people, the flock he tends.

3. The LORD is good:
   his kindness endures forever,
   and his faithfulness, to all generations.

84   PSALM 100: WE ARE GOD'S PEOPLE

We are God's peo-ple, the flock of the Lord.

1. Let all the earth shout for joy.
   Serve the Lord with gladness.
   Sing to the Lord with joyful song.

2. Know that the Lord is God.
   He made us, to him we belong,
   and we are the sheep of his flock.

3. Enter his gates with thanks,
   the courts of the Lord with praise.
   Give thanks and bless his name.

4. Forever God is good.
   His love is everlasting,
   faithful for all generations.

Text: Based on Psalm 100:3b, 1–2, 4, 5; Timothy R. Smith, b. 1960.
Music: Timothy R. Smith.
Text and music © 1996, 2000, Timothy R. Smith. Published by OCP. All rights reserved.

85   PSALM 103: THE LORD IS KIND AND MERCIFUL

The Lord is kind, the Lord is kind and mer - ci - ful.

The Lord is kind and mer - ci - ful, mer - ci - ful;

mer - ci - ful is the Lord.

1. O my soul,
   bless the Lord and praise his holy name.
   Bless the Lord, O my soul
   keep in mind what God has done for me.

2. God forgives,
   healing all our pain and sinfulness;
   saves us from an empty life,
   covers us with gentleness and love.

3. Full of grace,
   full of mercy and abundant love,
   slow to anger is the Lord;
   God does not repay us for our sins.

4. Far as the east from the west,
   God placed our sin from us.
   God's compassion rests on us
   like a father's mercy for his own.

Text: Based on Psalm 103:1–2, 3–4, 8–9, 12–13. Refrain © 1969, 1981, 1997, ICEL. All rights reserved. Used with permission.
Verses, Rick Modlin, b. 1966, © 1999, Rick Modlin. Published by OCP. All rights reserved.
Music: Rick Modlin, © 1999, Rick Modlin. Published by OCP. All rights reserved.

PSALM 103: THE LORD IS KIND AND MERCIFUL 86

The Lord is kind and mer - ci - ful.

The Lord is kind and mer - ci - ful.

1. Bless the LORD, O my soul;
   and all my being, bless his holy name.
   Bless the LORD, bless the LORD, O my soul,
   and forget not all his benefits.

2. He pardons all your iniquities,
   he heals all your ills.
   He redeems your life from destruction,
   he crowns you with kindness
   and compassion.

3. Merciful and gracious is the LORD,
   slow to anger and abounding in kindness.
   Not according to our sins
   does he deal with us,
   nor does he requite us
   according to our crimes.

4. As far as the east is from the west,
   so far has he put our transgressions from us.
   As a father has compassion on his children,
   so the LORD has compassion
   on those who fear him.

PSALM 103: THE LORD IS KIND AND MERCIFUL 87

The Lord is kind and mer - ci - ful; mer-ci-ful is the Lord.

1. Bless the LORD, O my soul;
   and all my being, bless his holy name.
   Bless the LORD, O my soul,
   forget not all his benefits.

2. He pardons all your iniquities,
   he heals all your ills.
   He redeems your life from destruction,
   and crowns you with kindness
   and compassion.

3. The LORD secures justice
   and the rights of all the oppressed.
   He has made known his ways to Moses,
   and his deeds to the children of Israel.

4. Merciful and gracious is the LORD,
   slow to anger and abounding in kindness.
   For as the heavens are high above the earth,
   so surpassing is his kindness
   toward those who fear him.

88   Psalm 104: Send Forth Your Spirit, O Lord

Send forth your Spir- it, O Lord, and re - new the face of the earth.

1. Bless the Lord, O my soul,
   O Lord, how great you are!
   How many are your works, O Lord,
   the earth is full of your riches!

2. You take back your Spirit, they die,
   back to the dust from which they came;

Alternate Verses for the Easter Vigil

1. Bless the Lord, O my soul,
   O Lord, how great you are!
   With glory and with majesty clothed;
   you are covered with light!

2. Foundation of earth you made sure,
   standing firm from age to age.
   You placed the ocean like a robe,
   the waters covered the hills.

3. The valleys are flowing with springs;
   rivers run between the hills;

you send forth your Spirit,
they are created, the whole earth is renewed!

3. Your glory will last forever,
   may you rejoice in all your works.
   May my thoughts be pleasing to you,
   I find my joy in you, Lord.

the birds of heaven dwell on their banks,
they make their nests as they sing.

4. You send down your rain on the hills.
   All your blessings fill the earth.
   You give the cattle grass for their food,
   and plants for crops to be grown.

5. In wisdom you made all these things.
   Lord, they are numberless.
   Your riches fill the whole of the earth.
   Bless the Lord, O my soul!

Text: Based on Psalm 104:1, 24, 29–30, 31, 34; 1–2, 5–6, 10, 12, 13–14, 24, 35; Christopher Walker, b. 1947.
Music: Christopher Walker.
Text and music © 1984, 1985, Christopher Walker. Published by OCP. All rights reserved.

89   Psalm 104: Lord, Send Out Your Spirit

Lord, send out your Spir-it, and re - new the face of the earth.

1. Bless the LORD, O my soul!
   O LORD, my God, you are great indeed!
   How manifold are your works, O LORD!
   The earth is full of your creatures.

2. If you take away their breath,
   they perish and return to their dust.
   When you send forth your spirit,

they are created,
and you renew the face of the earth.

3. May the glory of the LORD endure forever;
   may the LORD be glad in his works!
   Pleasing to him be my theme;
   I will be glad in the LORD.

Text: Psalm 104:1, 24, 29–30, 31, 34. Refrain © 1969, 1981, 1997, ICEL. All rights reserved. Used with permission.
  Verses © 1970, 1997, 1998, CCD. All rights reserved. Used with permission.
Music: Ken Canedo, b. 1953, © 2007, Ken Canedo. Published by OCP. All rights reserved.

PSALM 104: LORD, SEND OUT YOUR SPIRIT 90

Lord, send out your Spir-it, and re-new the face of the earth.

1. Bless the LORD, O my soul!
O LORD, my God, you are great indeed!
How manifold are your works, O LORD!
The earth is full of your creatures;

2. May the glory of the LORD endure forever;
may the LORD be glad in his works!

Pleasing to him be my theme;
I will be glad in the LORD.

3. If you take away their breath, they perish
and return to their dust.
When you send forth your spirit,
they are created,
and you renew the face of the earth.

PSALM 110: YOU ARE A PRIEST FOR EVER 91

You are a priest for ev-er, in the line of Mel-chiz-e-dek.

1. The LORD said to my Lord:
"Sit at my right hand
till I make your enemies your footstool."

2. The scepter of your power
the LORD will stretch forth from Zion:
"Rule in the midst of your enemies."

3. "Yours is princely power
in the day of your birth,
in holy splendor;
before the daystar,
like the dew, I have begotten you."

4. The LORD has sworn,
and he will not repent:
"You are a priest forever,
according to the order of Melchizedek."

PSALM 113: BLESSED BE THE NAME OF THE LORD 92

Bless-ed be the name of the Lord for ev-er, for ev-er.

1. Praise, you servants of the LORD,
praise the name of the LORD.
Blessed be the name of the LORD
both now and forever.

2. From the rising to the setting of the sun
is the name of the LORD to be praised.
High above all nations is the LORD;
above the heavens is his glory.

3. Who is like the LORD, our God,
who is enthroned on high
and looks upon the heavens
and the earth below?

4. He raises up the lowly from the dust;
from the dunghill he lifts up the poor
to seat them with princes,
with the princes of his own people.

93

PSALM 116: OUR BLESSING-CUP/
I WILL WALK WITH THE LORD/THE CUP OF SALVATION

Refrain I

Our bless-ing-cup is a com-mu-nion with the Blood, the Blood of Christ.

Refrain II

I will walk with the Lord in the land, the land of the liv-ing.

Refrain III

The cup of sal-va-tion I will take, and call the name of the Lord.

Verses

1. How shall I make a return
   for the goodness God has done for me?
   The cup of salvation I will take
   and call God's name.

2. Precious in the eyes of the Lord
   is the dying of his faithful one.

   I am the servant of the Lord
   who set me free.

3. Sacrifice and thanks I will give
   in the presence of God's chosen ones.
   My vow to the Lord I shall fulfill
   and call God's name.

94

PSALM 116: OUR BLESSING-CUP

Our bless-ing-cup is a com-mu-nion in the Blood of Christ.

1. How shall I make a return to the LORD
   for all the good he has done for me?
   The cup of salvation I will take up,
   and I will call upon the name of the LORD.

2. Taste and see, taste and see
   the sweetness of the Lord,
   the goodness of the Lord.

3. Every time you eat of this bread,
   every time you drink of this cup
   you proclaim the death of the Lord
   until he comes.

PSALM 116: OUR BLESSING-CUP/
EL CÁLIZ QUE BENDECIMOS

*Estribillo

El cá - liz que ben - de - ci - mos
es la co - mu - nión de la san - gre de Cris - to.

*Refrain

Our bless-ing-cup is a com-mu-nion with the Blood of Christ.

1. ¿Cómo pagaré al Señor
   todo el bien que me ha hecho?
   Alzaré la copa de la salvación,
   invocando tu nombre, Señor.

2. Tenía fe, aún cuando dije:
   "Cómo soy de desgraciado".
   Mucho le cuesta al Señor
   la muerte de sus fieles.

3. Señor, yo soy tu siervo,
   el hijo de tu esclava;
   tú rompiste mis cadenas.
   A ti ofrezco un sacrificio de alabanza,
   invocando tu nombre, Señor.

4. Mis votos al Señor cumpliré
   en presencia de todo su pueblo;
   en el atrio de la casa del Señor,
   en medio de ti, Jerusalén.

1. *What shall I return to the LORD*
   for all his bounty to me?
   I will lift the cup of salvation
   and call on the name of the LORD.

2. *I believed, even when I said,*
   "I am greatly afflicted."
   Precious in the eyes of the LORD
   the dying of his faithful ones.

3. *O LORD, I am your servant,*
   your servant, the son of your handmaid;
   you have brought me freedom.
   To you will I offer sacrifice of thanksgiving
   and call upon your name, O LORD.

4. *My vows to the LORD I will pay*
   in the presence of all his people,
   in the courts of the house of the LORD,
   in the midst of you, Jerusalem.

*The response may be sung in only one language or bilingually. It is repeated in either case.

96   PSALM 116: IN THE PRESENCE OF GOD

Verses: Ordinary Time

1. Love you, I love you;
   you have heard my voice.
   I will call your name, cry out your name,
   as long as I shall live.

2. Comfort me, you care for me,
   you have rescued me.
   You have heard my cry,
   have heard my plea.
   You save my soul from death.

3. Gracious is your hand, O God,
   merciful and just.
   God, your love protects the lowly ones;
   your kindness has no end.

4. Deliver me, deliver me.
   Deliver my soul from death,
   my eyes from tears, my feet from snares.
   In the land of the living, I shall walk.

Verses: Lent

1. In my grief, in my pain
   I believed in you.
   How precious is our death to you,
   how precious in your eyes.

2. Here I am, your servant, Lord,
   free to speak your name.

   Words of thanks and praise be on my lips,
   and ever in my heart.

3. I will pay my vows to you,
   here among your people.
   In the presence of your faithful ones,
   I give my life to you.

97   PSALM 117: GO OUT TO ALL THE WORLD
AND TELL THE GOOD NEWS

1. Praise the LORD, all you nations;
   glorify him, all you peoples!

2. For steadfast is his kindness toward us,
   and the fidelity of the LORD endures forever.

PSALM 118: THIS IS THE DAY   98

This is the day the Lord has made; let us re-joice and be glad.

This is the day the Lord has made; let us re-joice and be glad.

1. Give thanks to the LORD, for he is good,
   his mercy endures forever.
   Let the house of Israel say,
   "His mercy endures forever."

2. The LORD's right hand has struck with pow'r;
   the LORD's right hand is exalted.

I shall not die, but live, and
declare the works of the LORD.

3. The stone which the builders rejected
   has become the cornerstone.
   By the LORD has this been done;
   it is wonderful in our eyes.

Text: Psalm 118:24, 1–2, 16–17, 22–23. Refrain © 1969, 1981, ICEL. All rights reserved. Used with permission.
   Verses © 1970, CCD. All rights reserved. Used with permission.
Music: Michael Joncas, b. 1951, © 1981, 1982, 1988, Jan Michael Joncas Trust. Published by OCP. All rights reserved.

PSALM 118: THIS IS THE DAY   99

This is the day that the Lord has made; let us re-joice

and be glad; for this is the day that the Lord has

1-4   1st time: repeat
                   to Verses

made; al - le - lu - ia, al - le - lu - ia!

Final

ia! Al - le - lu - ia, al - le - lu - ia!

1. Give thanks to God; the Lord is good.
   God's mercy endures forever.
   Let the house of Israel say:
   "God's mercy endures forever."

2. The Lord's right hand is lifted up;
   the hand of the Lord is mighty.

I shall not die, but live to tell
the marvelous works of God.

3. The stone which the builders rejected
   has become the cornerstone.
   This is the work of the Lord;
   how wonderful, how wonderful in our eyes!

Text: Based on Psalm 118:24, 1–2, 16–17, 22–23. Refrain © 1969, 1981, ICEL. All rights reserved. Used with permission.
   Verses, Scott Soper, b. 1961, © 1990, OCP. All rights reserved.
Music: Scott Soper, © 1990, OCP. All rights reserved.

100   PSALM 118: GIVE THANKS TO THE LORD FOR HE IS GOOD

Give thanks to the Lord for he is good, his love is ev-er-last-ing.

1. Let the house of Israel say,
"His mercy endures forever."
Let the house of Aaron say,
"His mercy endures forever."
Let those who fear the LORD say,
"His mercy endures forever."

2. I was hard pressed and was falling,
but the LORD helped me.
My strength and my courage is the LORD,

and he has been my savior.
The joyful shout of victory
in the tents of the just:

3. The stone which the builders rejected
has become the cornerstone.
By the LORD has this been done;
it is wonderful in our eyes.
This is the day the LORD has made;
let us be glad and rejoice in it.

101   PSALM 118: THE STONE WHICH THE BUILDERS REJECTED

The stone which the build-ers re-ject-ed has be-come the cor-ner-stone.

Al-le-lu - ia, al-le-lu - ia, has be-come the cor-ner-stone.

1. Let the family of Israel say:
"God's love has no end,
God's love has no end."
Let the family of Aaron say:
"God's love has no end,
God's love has no end."
And let all who fear God,
and let all who fear God
say his love is without end.
Alleluia, alleluia,
say his love is without end.

2. I called to the Lord in my distress,
he answered me and set me free.
God is at my side, God is at my side,
God is here to help me now.
Alleluia, alleluia,
God is here to help me now.

3. Open to me the gates of holiness;
I will enter and give thanks.
This is the Lord's own gate,
the gate where the just may enter in.
I will thank you, Lord,
I will thank you, Lord,
for you hear and answer me.
Alleluia, alleluia,
for you hear and answer me.

4. Go forward with branches,
go forward processing,
go to the altar of the Lord
and give thanks to God,
and give thanks to God
for his love is without end.
Alleluia, alleluia,
for his love is without end.

PSALM 122: LET US GO REJOICING 102

Let us go re-joic-ing, re-joic-ing to the house of the Lord. Let us go re-joic-ing to the house of the Lord.

1. How I rejoiced to hear them say,
"Let us go to the house of the Lord."
And now within your walls
we are standing, O Jerusalem.

2. Jerusalem, a city firmly built,
knit together in unity and strength.
There the tribes go up,
the tribes of the Lord,
making pilgrimage.

3. There the tribes give thanks
to the name of the Lord,
according to the law of Israel.

There are set the thrones of judgment
for the house of David.

4. Let us pray for the good of Jerusalem,
and for those who love you
prosperity and peace,
peace within your ramparts and your towers,
peace in your dwellings.

5. For the sake of my people and my friends,
I say peace be to you, Jerusalem.
For love of God's house
I pray for you and your prosperity.

PSALM 122: LET US GO REJOICING 103

Let us go re-joic-ing to the house of the Lord.

1. I rejoiced because they said to me,
"We will go up to the house of the LORD."
And now we have set foot
within your gates, O Jerusalem.

2. A city that the LORD has joined fast,
unity is yours, O Jerusalem.
And to it all of the tribes go up,
the tribes of the LORD.

3. According to the decree for Israel,
to give thanks to the name of the LORD.

In it there are set up judgment seats,
seats for the house of David.

4. Pray for peace in you, Jerusalem!
May those who love you prosper and grow!
And may peace prevail within your walls,
prosperity in your buildings.

5. Because of friends and relatives I say,
"Peace be always within you!"
Because of this house of the LORD, our God,
I will pray for your good.

104   PSALM 126: THE LORD HAS DONE GREAT THINGS

The Lord has done great things for us; we are filled with joy.

1. When the LORD brought back
   the captives of Zion,
   we were like *people dreaming.
   Then our mouth was filled with laughter,
   and our tongue with rejoicing.

2. Then they said among the nations,
   "The LORD has done great things for them."
   The LORD has done great things for us;
   we are glad indeed.

3. Restore our fortunes, O LORD,
   like the torrents in the southern desert.
   Those that sow in tears
   shall reap rejoicing.

4. Although they go forth weeping,
   carrying the seed to be sown,
   They shall come back rejoicing,
   carrying their sheaves.

*Original text "men."

105   PSALM 128: O BLESSED ARE THOSE

O blessed are those who fear the Lord and walk in his ways.

1. O blessed are those who fear the Lord
   and walk in his ways!
   By the labor of your hands you shall eat.
   You will be happy and prosper.

2. Your wife like a fruitful vine
   in the heart of your house;

   your children like shoots of the olive
   around your table.

3. Indeed thus shall be blest
   all those who fear the Lord.
   May the Lord bless you from Zion
   all the days of your life!

106   PSALM 130: WITH THE LORD THERE IS MERCY

With the Lord there is mer-cy and full-ness of re-

| 1-5 | 1st time: repeat to Verses | Final |

demp-tion.   demp-tion,   re-demp-tion.

1. Out of the depths I cry to you, O Lord.
Hear my voice.
Turn not your ears from the sound
of my voice pleading.

2. Lord, who could stand
if you recalled our sins?
But because of your mercy
we bow to your name.

3. I hold fast to God, I cling to his word.
Like watching for dawn I wait for the Lord.
My soul longs for the Lord.

4. With the Lord is mercy and redemption.
For the Lord's great kindness
and the Lord's compassion
will set Israel free.

PSALM 130: WITH THE LORD THERE IS MERCY   107

With the Lord there is mer-cy and full-ness of re-demp-tion, full-ness of re-demp-tion.

1. Out of the depths I cry to you, O LORD;
LORD, hear my voice!
Let your ears be attentive
to my voice in supplication.

2. If you, O LORD, mark iniquities,
LORD, who can stand?
But with you is forgiveness,
that you may be revered.

3. I trust in the LORD;
my soul trusts in his word.
More than sentinels wait for the dawn,
let Israel wait for the LORD.

4. For with the LORD is kindness
and with him is plenteous redemption;
and he will redeem Israel
from all their iniquities.

PSALM 130: WITH THE LORD THERE IS MERCY   108

With the Lord there is mer-cy, and full-ness of re-demp-tion.

1. Out of the depths I cry to you, O LORD;
LORD, hear my voice!
Let your ears be attentive
to my voice in supplication.

2. If you, LORD, mark our iniquities,
LORD, who can stand?
But with you is forgiveness,
and so you may be revered.

3. I trust in the LORD;
my soul trusts in his word.
My soul waits for the LORD
more than sent'nels wait for the dawn.

4. For with the LORD is kindness
and with him is plenteous redemption;
and he will redeem Israel
from all their iniquities.

109   PSALM 130: OUT OF THE DEPTHS

Out of the depths, I cry to you, O Lord.

1. From out of the depths,
   I cry to you, Lord;
   O hear the sound of my voice.
   Lord, open your ears and listen to me;
   I plead for your kindness, O God.

2. If you, O Lord, should number our sins,
   then Lord, who would survive?
   But you are forgiveness for our sins;
   for this we adore you, O God.

3. I trust in you, Lord, my soul looks to you
   as watchmen wait for the dawn.
   And more than the watchmen
   wait for the dawn,
   let Israel wait for the Lord.

4. For with you is found forgiveness of sin;
   you show your mercy to all.
   And you will deliver your chosen ones;
   deliver your people, O God.

110   PSALM 138: ON THE DAY I CALLED

Lord, on the day I called for help, you an-swered me, you an-swered me.

1. I shall thank you, God of my heart,
   you have heard my troubled word.
   While angels watch, your name I praise;
   I dance before your holy place.

2. For your love and your faithfulness,
   I thank your name,
   your promise surpasses your fame.
   I called for your help
   all night and day long:
   you heard me, and made me strong.

3. From on high,
   from the heavens the poor you see,
   you drive the proud to their knees.
   Though I live
   in the midst of trouble and woe,
   you save me, and foil my foe.

4. Your strong hand shall come to my aid:
   you shall be all good to me.
   Forever shall your love abide;
   do not cast your child aside.

111   PSALM 141: O LORD, LET MY PRAYER RISE

Refrain

O Lord, let my prayer rise be-fore you like in-cense,
my hands like an eve - ning of - fer - ing.

Verses

1. Lord, I am calling: hasten to help me.
   Listen to me as I cry to you.
   Let my prayer rise before you like incense,
   my hands like an evening offering.

2. Lord, set a guard at my mouth,
   keep watch at the gate of my lips.
   Let my heart not turn to things that
   are wrong,
   to sharing the evil deeds done by the sinful.
   No, I will never taste their delights.

3. The good may reprove me,
   in kindness chastise me,
   but the wicked shall never anoint my head.
   Every day I counter their malice with prayer.

4. To you, Lord my God, my eyes are turned:
   in you I take refuge; do not forsake me.
   Keep me safe from
   the traps they have set for me,
   from the snares of those who do evil.

Doxology

5. Praise to the Fa-ther, praise to the Son, all praise to the

5. life-giv-ing Spir-it. As it was, is now and shall

to Refrain

5. al-ways be for a-ges un-end-ing. A-men.

Text: Based on Psalm 141:1–5, 8–9, Doxology; Paul Inwood, b. 1947.
Music: Paul Inwood.
Text and music © 1984, 1985, Paul Inwood. Published by OCP. All rights reserved.

PSALM 145: I WILL PRAISE YOUR NAME   112

I will praise your name for ev-er, my king and my God.

1. I will give you glory, O God my king,
   I will bless your name for ever.
   I will bless you day after day
   and praise your name for ever.

2. The Lord is kind and full of compassion,
   slow to anger, abounding in love.
   How good is the Lord to all,
   compassionate to all creation.

3. All your creatures
   shall give you thanks, O Lord,
   and your friends shall repeat their blessing.
   They shall speak of the glory of your reign
   and declare your might, O God.

4. The Lord is faithful in all his words
   and loving in all his deeds.
   The Lord supports all who fall
   and raises up all who are bowed down.

Text: Psalm 145:1–2, 8–9, 10–11, 13–14. Refrain © 1969, ICEL. All rights reserved. Used with permission.
Verses © 1963, The Grail (England). All rights reserved. Used with permission of A.P. Watt, Ltd.
Music: Christopher Willcock, b. 1947, © 1977, 1990, Christopher Willcock, SJ. Published by OCP. All rights reserved.

113   PSALM 145: I WILL PRAISE YOUR NAME/ THE HAND OF THE LORD

I will praise your name for ev-er, my king and my God.

The hand of the Lord feeds us, and an-swers all our needs.

1. God is merciful and gracious,
   slow to anger, full of kindness.
   The Lord is faithful to all his people,
   compassionate to all creation.

2. Lord, we lift our eyes to the heavens,
   and you feed us in due season.
   The treasures, Lord, that you impart
   fulfill every desire.

3. All of your people bless your name
   in a holy song of thanksgiving,
   singing of your eternal reign,
   declaring your holy power.

4. Lord, your justice lasts forever,
   your loving deeds from age to age.
   You are near to all who call,
   never far from faithful hearts.

114   PSALM 145: THE LORD IS NEAR/ I WILL PRAISE YOUR NAME

The Lord is near to all who call him.
(Alternate Refrain) I will praise your name for-ev-er,

The Lord is near to all who call in truth. truth.
I will praise my king and my God. God.

1. Ev'ry day will I bless you,
   I will praise your name forever and ever.
   Great is the LORD
   and highly to be praised.

2. His greatness is unsearchable.
   The LORD is gracious and merciful,

   slow to anger
   and of great kindness.

3. The LORD is good to all
   and compassionate toward all his works.
   The LORD is just in all his ways
   and holy in all his works.

PSALM 145: I WILL PRAISE YOUR NAME/ THE HAND OF THE LORD FEEDS US

115

1. I will praise you, God and king;
   I will bless your name forever.
   Every day I will bless you,
   praise your name forever.

2. You are grace and mercy, Lord,
   slow to anger, filled with kindness.
   You are good to all your children,
   loving all creation.

3. Let your works give thanks to you;
   let your faithful ever bless you;
   let them praise your strength, your glory,
   and proclaim your kingdom.

4. Every word you speak in faith,
   every work you do is holy.
   You lift up all who stumble,
   you raise up the lowly.

PSALM 146: PRAISE THE LORD, MY SOUL

116

1. The God of Jacob keeps faith forever,
   secures justice for the oppressed,
   gives food to the hungry.
   The LORD sets captives free.

2. The LORD gives sight to the blind;
   the LORD raises up
   those who were bowed down.

   The LORD loves the just;
   the LORD protects strangers.

3. The fatherless and the widow the LORD sustains,
   but the way of the wicked he thwarts.
   The LORD shall reign forever;
   your God, O Zion, through all generations.
   Alleluia.

117 EXODUS 15: TO GOD BE PRAISE AND GLORY

Verses
Cantor/Choir ... All

1. I sing ___ to ___ God, tri - um - phant is he.
2. O Pha-roah, your ___ ar - my, they sink like a stone. } To
3. By wa - ter and the Spir-it, all blest with new birth,
4. ⅞ In sav - ing ___ wa-ters we sink like a stone.

Cantor/Choir

1-4. God be praise and glo - ry!

The horse ___ and char - iot he
My God, ___ he plunged them in the
we work to re - new ___ the
From death in - to liv - ing we

All

1. cast in - to the sea.
2. Red Sea all a - lone. }
3. face of the earth.
4. each must go a - lone.

To God be praise and

Cantor/Choir

1-4. glo - ry!

My strength ___ and cour - age
We come to this land, the
As Je - sus was raised, now
But stand in the light of this

All ... Cantor/Choir

1. comes from the Lord.
2. moun - tain of the free. } To God be praise and glo - ry! }
3. all death must die.
4. great fam - i - ly;

All
The
Come
God's

All

1. clothed ___ in glo - ry, for ev - er be a - dored.
2. peo - ple give thanks in your sanc - tu - ar - y. } To
3. lift up your voice ___ in one joy - ful cry:
4. love will u - nite us and make us all free.

1-4. God be praise and glo - ry! I am free!

Refrain

I will sing to the Lord, tri -

um - phant is he: the horse and char - i - ot he

cast in - to the sea! I will cast in - to the sea!

Text: Based on Exodus 15:19–21; Janèt Sullivan Whitaker, b. 1958.
Music: Janèt Sullivan Whitaker.

ISAIAH 12: WE SHALL DRAW WATER 118

We shall draw wa - ter joy - ful-ly, sing-ing joy - ful-ly,

sing-ing joy - ful-ly; we shall draw wa - ter

joy - ful-ly from the well - springs of sal - va - tion.

1. Truly God is our salvation;
we trust, we shall not fear.
For the Lord is our strength,
the Lord is our song;
he became our Savior.

2. Give thanks, O give thanks to the Lord;
give praise to his holy name!
Make his mighty deeds known to
all of the nations; proclaim his greatness.

3. Sing a psalm, sing a psalm to the Lord
for he has done glorious deeds.
Make known his works to all of the earth;
people of Zion, sing for joy,
for great in your midst, great in your midst
is the Holy One of Israel.

Text: Based on Isaiah 12:3, 2, 4–6; Paul Inwood, b. 1947.
Music: Paul Inwood.

119   DANIEL 3: GLORY AND PRAISE FOR EVER

Refrain

Glo-ry and praise, glo-ry and praise, glo-ry and praise for ev-er!

1. Blessed are you, O Lord, the God of our fathers,
   praiseworthy and exalted above all forever;
   and blessed is your holy and glorious name, **(to Response I)**

All   to Refrain

Resp. I: praise-wor-thy and ex - alt-ed a-bove all for all   a - ges.
Resp. II: praise-wor-thy and ex - alt-ed a-bove__ all for - ev - er.

2. Blessed are you in the temple of your holy glory, **(to Response II)**

3. Blessed are you on the throne of your kingdom, **(to Response II)**

4. Blessed are you who look into the depths
   from your throne upon the cherubim, **(to Response II)**

120   LUKE 1: MY SOUL REJOICES

Refrain

My soul re-joic-es in God, my Sav-ior. My spir-it finds its

Verses

joy in God, the liv-ing God.

1. My soul pro-claims your
2. Your mer-cy flows through-
3. You cast the might - y
4. You fill the hun - gry
5. Just as you prom - ised

to Refrain

1. might-y deeds. My spir-it sings the great-ness of your name.
2. out the land and ev-'ry gen-er-a-tion knows your love.
3. from their thrones and raise the poor and low-ly to new life.
4. with good things. With emp-ty hands you send the rich a-way.
5. A-bra-ham, you come to free your peo-ple, Is-ra-el.

Luke 1: Magnificat

1. Sing out, my soul, for God has raised and
2. The proud of heart he shall make low and
3. Glo - ry to you, the God of all cre -

1. blessed me And looked on me with kind - ly, lov - ing
2. hum - ble. The gen - tle, poor and hun - gry shall be
3. a - tion. Glo - ry to you, O Christ, the prom - ised

1. eyes. A ser - vant low - ly, yet am I be - lov - ed.
2. filled. O Is - ra - el! God shall up - hold the prom - ise
3. one. Glo - ry to you, O Spir - it of Com - pas - sion.

1. This won - drous God has done great things for me.
2. Made long a - go to you and A - bra - ham.
3. In - spire our hearts to sing our moth - er's song.

1-3. For - ev - er - more, O might - y God of mer - cy,

1-3. I will sing praise, for ho - ly is your name!

Text: 11 10 11 10 11 10; based on Luke 1:46–55; Janèt Sullivan Whitaker, b. 1958, © 2006, Janèt Sullivan Whitaker.
Published by OCP. All rights reserved.
Music: FINLANDIA; Jean Sibelius, 1865–1957.

122   LUKE 1: CANTICLE OF ZACHARY

Verses 1, 3, 5

1. Blest be the God of Is - ra - el, The ev - er - liv - ing Lord, Who
3. Of old he gave his sol - emn oath To Fa - ther A - bra - ham; His
5. The ris-ing sun shall shine on us To bring the light of day To

1. comes in pow'r to save his own, His peo - ple Is - ra - el. For
3. seed a might-y race should be And blest for-ev - er-more. He
5. all who dwell in dark - est night And shad-ow of the grave. Our

1. Is - ra - el he rais-es up Sal - va-tion's tow'r on high In
3. vowed to set his peo-ple free From fear of ev - 'ry foe, That
5. foot-steps God shall safe-ly guide To walk the ways of peace; His

1. Da-vid's house who reigned as king And ser - vant of the Lord.
3. we might serve him all our days In good-ness, love, and peace.
5. name for - ev - er-more be blest, Who lives and loves and saves.

Verses 2, 4

2. Through ho - ly proph-ets did he speak His Word in days of old,
4. O ti - ny child, your name shall be The proph-et of the Lord;

2. That he would save us from our foes And all who bear us ill.
4. The way of God you shall pre - pare To make his com-ing known.

2. To our an - ces-tors did he give His cov - e - nant of love,
4. You shall pro-claim to Is - ra - el Sal - va-tion's dawn-ing day,

to Verses 3, 5

2. So with us all he keeps his Word In love that knows no end.
4. When God shall wipe a - way all sins In his re - deem-ing love.

LUKE 1: BENEDICTUS

123

1. Blest be the God of Is - ra - el who comes to set us free
2. With prom-ised mer - cy will God still the cov - e - nant re - call,
3. My child, as proph-et of the Lord you will pre - pare the way,

1. and rais - es up new hope for us: a Branch for Da-vid's tree.
2. the oath once sworn to A - bra - ham from foes to save us all;
3. to tell God's peo - ple they are saved from sin's e - ter-nal sway.

1. So have the proph-ets long de - clared that with a might-y arm
2. that we might wor - ship with - out fear and of - fer lives of praise,
3. Then shall God's mer - cy from on high shine forth and nev - er cease

1. God would turn back our en - e - mies and all who wish us harm.
2. in ho - li - ness and righ-teous-ness to serve God all our days.
3. to drive a - way the gloom of death and lead us in - to peace.

Text: CMD; based on Luke 1:68–79; adapt. by Carl P. Daw, Jr., b. 1944, © 1989, Hope Publishing Co.
   All rights reserved. Used with permission.
Music: FOREST GREEN; trad. English Melody; collected and adapt. by Ralph Vaughan Williams, 1872–1958.

124   ## LUKE 2: SONG OF SIMEON

Now, O God, let your ser-vant go.

Let me go in peace ac-cord-ing to your word.

For my eyes be-hold your sav-ing work:

a light for all the world, al-le-lu-ia.

Final

Al-le-lu-ia, al-le-lu-ia.

Text: Based on Luke 2:29–32; *Nunc dimittis*; Janèt Sullivan Whitaker, b. 1958.
Music: Janèt Sullivan Whitaker.

LUKE 2: CANTICLE OF SIMEON

Refrain

Christ is the light of all the na-tions and the glo-ry of his peo-ple Is-ra-el.

Verses

1. Now, __ Lord, you have kept __ your __ word: __ let __
2. With my own eyes I have seen __ the sal - va-tion which __
3. A __ light to re - veal you to the na-tions and the

to Refrain
2

1. your __ ser-vant go in peace.
2. you pre-pared __ in the sight __ of us all.
3. glo-ry of your peo-ple Is - ra - el.

RITES OF CHRISTIAN INITIATION

DISMISSAL OF THE CATECHUMENS/ELECT

When the catechumens and the elect are present at liturgy, they are usually dismissed after the homily or preaching. After the dismissal, the catechumens and elect gather with their catechists to pray and break open the scriptures of the day. The following acclamation may be sung during the dismissal to accompany those who are preparing for the sacraments of initiation.

126

Go in peace, and may God's Word light your way.

Go in peace, and know that for you we pray.

Go in peace to fol-low Christ day by day.

Or

127

May you jour-ney in faith by the light of Christ. May you

live by his gos-pel in spir-it and truth.

SCRUTINIES

The scrutinies occur on the third, fourth and fifth Sundays of Lent and are accompanied by the readings from Year A. The elect are called before the community to pray for the spirit of repentance. The following song may be sung as the elect are dismissed to continue their reflection on the word of God.

128

Refrain

May we see you in faith, may we know you in faith. Lord of life, may we love you in faith.

Verses

1. May our eyes be o-pened to see those in need.
2. May our hearts be o-pened to love those in need.
3. May our ears be o-pened to hear your ho - ly Word.
4. May our minds be o-pened, im - plant your Word, O Lord.

to Refrain

1. May your Spir - it guide us to tend to all in need.
2. May your pres - ence guide us to give to all in need.
3. May your Word give us cour-age to bring your love to all.
4. May your love bring us peace, your peace to com - fort all.

Text: Based on John 9:1–12; Gerard Chiusano, b. 1965.
Music: Gerard Chiusano.

ORDER OF CHRISTIAN FUNERALS

VIGIL FOR THE DECEASED

INTRODUCTORY RITES

GREETING

OPENING SONG

129

1. I know that my Re - deem - er lives! What joy the
2. He lives tri - um - phant from the grave; He lives e-
3. He lives to si - lence all my fears; He lives to
4. He lives, all glo - ry to his name! He lives my

1. blest as - sur - ance gives! He lives, he lives, who
2. ter - nal - ly to save; He lives in maj - es -
3. wipe a - way my tears; He lives to calm my
4. Sav - ior, still the same; What joy this blest as -

1. once was dead; He lives, my ev - er - liv - ing head!
2. ty a - bove; He lives to guide his church in love.
3. trou - bled heart; He lives all bless - ings to im - part.
4. sur - ance gives: I know that my Re - deem - er lives!

Text: LM; based on Job 19:25; Samuel Medley, 1738–1799, alt.
Music: DUKE STREET; John Hatton, ca. 1710–1793.

INVITATION TO PRAYER

OPENING PRAYER

LITURGY OF THE WORD

FIRST READING

RESPONSORIAL PSALM

130

Note: Verses available in the accompaniment books.
Text: Psalm 27:1, 4, 7 and 8b and 9a, 13–14. Refrains © 1969, 1981, 1997, ICEL. All rights reserved. Used with permission.
Music: John Schiavone, b. 1947, © 2001, John Schiavone. Published by OCP. All rights reserved.

GOSPEL

HOMILY/PREACHING

PRAYER OF INTERCESSION

LITANY

131

Response: 1st time: Cantor, All repeat; thereafter: All

Text: *Order of Christian Funerals*, © 1985, ICEL. All rights reserved. Used with permission.
Music: Based on *Dies Irae*; Chant, Mode I; Michael R. Prendergast, b. 1955, © 2002, Michael R. Prendergast.
   Published by OCP. All rights reserved.

THE LORD'S PRAYER

CONCLUDING PRAYER

A member or friend of the family may speak in remembrance of the deceased.

CONCLUDING RITE

BLESSING

The vigil may conclude with a song or a few moments of silent prayer or both.

RITE OF RECEPTION AT THE CHURCH

The presiding minister greets the mourners at the entrance of the church. As a baptismal remembrance the coffin is sprinkled with holy water and the pall may be placed on the coffin. The funeral procession then moves into the church accompanied by the following or another appropriate song.

PROCESSIONAL SONG

132

Grant them e-ter-nal rest, O Lord, and let per-pet-u-al light shine up-on them.

Note: Verses available in the accompaniment books.
Text and music: Owen Alstott, b. 1947, © 1983, OCP. All rights reserved.

A symbol of Christian life may be carried in procession, then placed on the coffin.

If the introductory rites have not taken place at the church door, the liturgy begins in the usual manner with a song, the greeting, and the penitential rite.

OPENING PRAYER

LITURGY OF THE WORD

Appropriate readings should be chosen from those provided in the Order of Christian Funerals or the Lectionary.

READINGS

Either one or two readings from scripture may be read before the Gospel reading.

RESPONSORIAL PSALM

133

The Lord is my shep-herd; there is noth-ing I shall want.

Note: Verses available in the accompaniment books.
Text: Psalm 23:1–3a, 3b–4, 5, 6. Refrain © 1969, 1981, 1997, ICEL. All rights reserved. Used with permission.
Music: John Schiavone, b. 1947, © 2001, John Schiavone. Published by OCP. All rights reserved.

GOSPEL ACCLAMATION

GOSPEL

HOMILY

GENERAL INTERCESSIONS

LITURGY OF THE EUCHARIST

FINAL COMMENDATION

If the Final Commendation takes place in church, the ministers go to a place near the coffin. After a silent prayer, the coffin may be sprinkled with holy water and honored with incense. Meanwhile, the following or another appropriate hymn (see Funeral section, No. 550–562) may be sung.

SONG OF FAREWELL　　　　　　　　　　　　　　　　**134**

1. Come to his/her aid, O saints of God; Come meet him/her,
2. May Christ, who called you, take you home, And an - gels
3. Give him/her e - ter - nal rest, O Lord. May light un -
4. I know that my Re - deem - er lives; The last day

1. an - gels _ of the Lord.
2. lead you to A - bra - ham.
3. end - ing _ shine on him/her.
4. I shall _ rise a - gain.
{ Re - ceive his/her soul, O

1-4. ho - ly ones; Pre - sent him/her now to God, Most High.

Text: LM; *Subvenite sancti Dei; Requiem aeternam; Credo quod Redemptor*; tr. by Dennis C. Smolarski, SJ, b. 1947,
　© 1981, Dennis C. Smolarski, SJ. All rights reserved. Used with permission.
Music: OLD HUNDREDTH; *Genevan Psalter*, 1551; attr. to Louis Bourgeois, ca. 1510–1561, alt.

PRAYER OF COMMENDATION

PROCESSION TO THE PLACE OF COMMITTAL

After the prayer, the following or another appropriate psalm or hymn is sung while the coffin is being carried to the place of committal.

135

Response: 1st time: Cantor, All repeat; thereafter: All

Lord, have mer - cy. Lord, have mer - cy.

Note: Intercessions available in the accompaniment books.
Text: *Order of Christian Funerals*, © 1985, ICEL. All rights reserved. Used with permission.
Music: Based on *Dies Irae*; Chant, Mode I; Michael R. Prendergast, b. 1955, © 2002, 2006, Michael R. Prendergast.
　Published by OCP. All rights reserved.

Or

136

In pa - ra - dí - sum de - dú - cant te án - ge - li:
May an - gels guide you and bring you in - to par - a - dise:

in tu - o ad - vén - tu su - scí - pi - ant te már - ty - res,
and may all the mar - tyrs come forth to wel - come you home;

et per - dú - cant te in ci - vi - tá - tem san - ctam
and may they lead you in - to the ho - ly cit - y,

Je - rú - sa - lem. Cho - rus an - ge - ló - rum te ___
Je - ru - sa - lem. May the an - gel cho - rus sing ___

su - scí - pi - at, et cum Lá - za - ro quon - dam
to wel - come you, and like Laz - a - rus, for - got -

páu - pe - re ae - tér - nam há - be - as ré - qui - em.
ten and poor, you shall have ev - er - last - ing rest.

Text: *In paradisum* and *Chorus angelorum*; Latin, 11th cent.; English tr. by Owen Alstott, b. 1947, © 1987, OCP.
   All rights reserved.
Music: Chant, Mode VII and Mode VIII.

EUCHARISTIC EXPOSITION & BENEDICTION

During the celebration of this rite there should be prayers, songs, readings, silent prayer and a homily or preaching to direct the attention of the faithful to the worship of Christ the Lord.

EXPOSITION

137

The following or another suitable eucharistic song or seasonal psalm is sung.

1. O sav - ing Vic - tim, o - pen wide The gate of
2. To your great name be end - less praise, Im - mor - tal
1. *O sa - lu - tá - ris Hó - sti - a, Quae cae - li*
2. *U - ni tri - nó - que Dó - mi - no Sit sem - pi -*

1. heav'n to us be - low, Our foes press on from
2. God - head, One in Three; Grant us, for end - less
1. *pan - dis ó - sti - um: Bel - la pre - munt ho -*
2. *tér - na gló - ri - a, Qui vi - tam si - ne*

1. ev - 'ry side; Your aid sup - ply, your strength be - stow.
2. length of days, In our true na - tive land to be.
1. *stí - li - a, Da ro - bur fer au - xí - li - um.*
2. *tér - mi - no No - bis do - net in pá - tri - a.*

Text: LM; *O Salutaris*; St. Thomas Aquinas, 1227–1274; tr. by Edward Caswall, 1814–1878, alt.
Music: DUGUET; attr. to Abbé Dieudonne Duguet, 1794–1849.

ADORATION

The Liturgy of the Hours may be celebrated during the period of exposition, or there may be prayers, songs, readings from the Word of God and a brief homily or preaching along with time for silent prayer.

Psalms 23, 34, 72, 84, 85, 122 or 128 may be sung during the period of adoration (see Psalms section, No. 15–116).

BENEDICTION

℣. You have given them Bread from heaven. (Easter: alleluia)
℟. **Having within it all Sweetness. (Easter: alleluia)**

The minister incenses the Blessed Sacrament while the following or another appropriate song is sung.

138

1. Tan - tum er - go Sac - ra - mén - tum Ve - ne - ré - mur
2. Ge - ni - tó - ri, Ge - ni - tó - que Laus et ju - bi -
1. *Ho - ly sac - ra - ment, most ho - ly, Let us bow on*
2. *God Be - get - ter and Be - got - ten, Yours be praise and*

1. cér - nu - i: Et an - tí - quum do - cu - mén - tum
2. lá - ti - o, Sa - lus, ho - nor, vir - tus quo - que
1. *bend - ed knee: Vi - sions of the an - cient prom - ise*
2. *maj - es - ty, Hon - or, glo - ry and sal - va - tion,*

1. No - vo ce - dat rí - tu - i: Prae - stet fi - des
2. Sit et be - ne - dí - cti - o: Pro - ce - dén - ti
1. *Now ful - filled in mys - te - ry. Faith de - clares what*
2. *Bless - ing for e - ter - ni - ty, With the One pro -*

1. sup - ple - mén - tum Sén - su - um de - fé - ctu - i.
2. ab u - tró - que Com - par sit lau - dá - ti - o.
1. *none dare fath - om; Faith re - veals what none may see.*
2. *ceed - ing al - ways, E - qual - ly in u - ni - ty.*

Text: 87 87 87; *Tantum ergo*; St. Thomas Aquinas, 1227–1274; tr. by Harry Hagan, OSB, b. 1947,
© 1990, St. Meinrad Archabbey. Published by OCP. All rights reserved.
Music: ST. THOMAS (TANTUM ERGO); John F. Wade, 1711–1786.

After a prayer, the priest or deacon blesses those present with the Blessed Sacrament.

REPOSITION

While a minister places the Blessed Sacrament in the tabernacle the people may sing or recite the following or other appropriate acclamations or hymns.

139

Cantor sings each invocation first; assembly repeats

Bless'd be God. Bless'd be his Ho - ly Name.

Bless'd be Je-sus Christ, true God and true Man.

Bless'd be the Name of Je-sus. Bless'd be his most Sa-cred Heart.

Bless'd be his most Pre-cious Blood. Bless'd be Je-sus in the most Ho-ly

Sac-ra-ment of the Al - tar. Bless'd be the Ho - ly

Spir - it, the Par - a-clete. Bless'd be the great Moth-er of God,

Ma - ry most ho - ly. Bless'd be her ho - ly and Im-

ma-cu-late Con - cep-tion. Bless'd be her glo - ri-ous As-sump-tion.

Bless'd be the name of Ma - ry, Vir-gin and Moth - er.

Bless'd be Saint Jo - seph, her most chaste spouse.

(⌒) (Fine)

Bless'd be God in his an - gels. Bless'd be God in his saints.

Text: The Divine Praises.
Music: John Schiavone, b. 1947, © 1990, John Schiavone. Published by OCP. All rights reserved.

THE ORDER OF MASS

At the Eucharist, the Church comes together to hear the Word of the Lord, to pray for the world's needs, to offer the sacrifice of the Cross in praise and thanks to God, to receive Christ Jesus in Communion, and then to be sent forth in the Spirit as disciples of the Gospel. Through the experience of these sacred mysteries in the liturgy, the "summit toward which the activity of the Church is directed," the people of God are renewed and given new strength to live out the Christian faith daily (Sacrosanctum Concilium, No. 10).

140   THE INTRODUCTORY RITES

As the Church gathers, "the faithful, who come together as one, establish communion and dispose themselves properly to listen to the Word of God and to celebrate the Eucharist worthily" (GIRM, No. 46).

ENTRANCE CHANT   *STAND*

A processional chant or hymn may be sung.

GREETING

After the Entrance Chant, all make the Sign of the Cross.

In the name of the Father, and of the Son, and of the Holy Spirit.

A - men.

Any of the three forms of Greeting may be used.

The grace of our Lord Jesus Christ,…be with you all.

Or   Grace to you and peace from God our Father
and the Lord Jesus Christ.

Or   The Lord be with you.

Or　　　*(A Bishop says, "Peace be with you.")*

And with your spir-it.

Rite for the Blessing and Sprinkling of Water

From time to time on Sundays, especially in Easter Time, there may be a blessing and sprinkling of holy water to recall Baptism. This replaces the Penitential Act below. For music during the sprinkling, see No. 166, 167, 242, 254–256. Continue with the "Gloria," No. 146, except on Sundays of Advent, Ash Wednesday and Sundays of Lent.

Penitential Act *(Omit on Ash Wednesday)*

The celebration of God's mercy takes one of the following forms:

141

I confess to almighty God
and to you, my brothers and sisters,
that I have greatly sinned,
in my thoughts and in my words,
in what I have done and in what I have failed to do,
(Strike breast) **through my fault, through my fault,**
through my most grievous fault;
therefore I ask blessed Mary ever-Virgin,
all the Angels and Saints,
and you, my brothers and sisters,
to pray for me to the Lord our God.

May almighty God have mercy on us,
forgive us our sins,
and bring us to everlasting life.

A - men.

Continue with the "Lord, Have Mercy/Kyrie," No. 144 or No. 145.

142

Or Have mercy on us, O Lord.

For we have   sinned a - gainst you.

Show us, O Lord, your mercy.

And grant us   your sal - va - tion.

May almighty God have mercy on us,
forgive us our sins,
and bring us to everlasting life.

A - men.

Continue with the "Lord, Have Mercy/Kyrie," No. 144 or No. 145.

143

Or *Invocation…*

Priest/Deacon/Other Minister;
All respond

Lord,   have   mer - cy.

Or

Priest/Deacon/Other Minister;
All respond

Kýrie,   e - lé - i - son.

Invocation…

Priest/Deacon/Other Minister;
All respond

Christ,   have   mer - cy.

Or

Priest/Deacon/Other Minister;
All respond

Christe,   e - lé - i - son.

Invocation…

Priest/Deacon/Other Minister;
All respond

Lord,   have   mer - cy.

Or

Priest/Deacon/Other Minister;
All respond

Kýrie,   e - lé - i - son.

May almighty God have mercy on us,
forgive us our sins,
and bring us to everlasting life.

A - men.

Continue with the "Gloria," No. 146, except on Sundays of Advent,
Ash Wednesday and Sundays of Lent.

LORD, HAVE MERCY/KYRIE 144

Or **145**

GLORIA

Except on Sundays of Advent, Ash Wednesday and Sundays of Lent, all sing or say:

146

Glo-ry to God in the high-est, and on earth peace to peo-ple of good will.

We praise you, we bless you, we a-dore you, we glo-ri-fy you,

we give you thanks for your great glo-ry, Lord God, heav-en-ly King,

O God, al-might-y Fa-ther. Lord Je-sus Christ, On-ly Be-got-ten Son,

Lord God, Lamb of God, Son of the Fa-ther, you take a-way the sins of the world,

have mer-cy on us; you take a-way the sins of the world,

re-ceive our prayer; you are seat-ed at the right hand of the Fa-ther,

have mer-cy on us. For you a-lone are the Ho-ly One, you a-lone are the Lord,

you a-lone are the Most High, Je-sus Christ, with the Ho-ly Spir-it,

in the glo-ry of God the Fa - ther. A - men.

Or **Glory to God in the highest,
and on earth peace to people of good will.**

**We praise you,
we bless you,
we adore you,
we glorify you,
we give you thanks for your great glory,
Lord God, heavenly King,
O God, almighty Father.**

**Lord Jesus Christ, Only Begotten Son,
Lord God, Lamb of God, Son of the Father,
you take away the sins of the world,
    have mercy on us;
you take away the sins of the world,
    receive our prayer;
you are seated at the right hand of the Father,
    have mercy on us.**

**For you alone are the Holy One,
you alone are the Lord,
you alone are the Most High,
Jesus Christ,
with the Holy Spirit,
in the glory of God the Father.
Amen.**

COLLECT

After a period of silence, the Priest says the Collect, and all respond:

Amen.

THE LITURGY OF THE WORD   147

The Lectionary *(book of readings) and the* Book of Gospels *open the rich trea-
sure of God's word from the Jewish and Christian Scriptures. Sunday readings
follow a three-year cycle: Year A emphasizes the Gospel of Matthew, Year B the
Gospel of Mark, Year C the Gospel of Luke. The Church proclaims the Gospel of
John especially during the seasons of Lent and Easter.*

FIRST READING *SIT*

After the reading, the reader says, "The word of the Lord," and all respond:

Thanks be to God.

RESPONSORIAL PSALM

For music for the responsorial psalm see No. 15–125.

SECOND READING

After the reading, the reader says, "The word of the Lord," and all respond:

Thanks be to God.

GOSPEL ACCLAMATION *STAND*

The assembly welcomes the proclamation of the Gospel by singing an acclamation. If it cannot be sung, it is to be omitted. For music, see Mass Settings and No. 259–264 . During Lent, see Mass Settings and No. 265–266.

GOSPEL

Before the Gospel, the Deacon/Priest says, "The Lord be with you," and all respond:

And with your spirit.

The Deacon/Priest says, "A reading from the holy Gospel according to N.," and all respond:

Glory to you, O Lord.

After the Gospel reading, the Deacon/Priest says, "The Gospel of the Lord," and all respond:

Praise to you, Lord Jesus Christ.

HOMILY *SIT*

The Priest or Deacon preaches the good news of Christ's saving mystery.

DISMISSAL OF THE CATECHUMENS AND THE ELECT

In Masses at which catechumens or elect are present for the Liturgy of the Word, the Priest may use these or similar words:

> My dear friends, this community now sends you forth to reflect more deeply upon the word of God which you have shared with us today. Be assured of our loving support and prayers for you. We look forward to the day when you will share fully in the Lord's Table.

A song may be sung while the catechumens/elect are dismissed (see No. 126, 127, 520).

PROFESSION OF FAITH   **148**

On Sundays and solemnities, all sing or say the Nicene Creed (for music, see No. 267):

> I believe in one God,
> the Father almighty,
> maker of heaven and earth,
> of all things visible and invisible.
>
> I believe in one Lord Jesus Christ,
> the Only Begotten Son of God,
> born of the Father before all ages.
> God from God, Light from Light,
> true God from true God,
> begotten, not made, consubstantial with the Father;
> through him all things were made.
> For us men and for our salvation
> he came down from heaven,

At the words that follow, up to and including "and became man," all bow.

> and by the Holy Spirit was incarnate of the Virgin Mary,
> and became man.
>
> For our sake he was crucified under Pontius Pilate,
> he suffered death and was buried,
> and rose again on the third day
> in accordance with the Scriptures.
> He ascended into heaven
> and is seated at the right hand of the Father.
> He will come again in glory
> to judge the living and the dead
> and his kingdom will have no end.
>
> I believe in the Holy Spirit, the Lord, the giver of life,
> who proceeds from the Father and the Son,
> who with the Father and the Son is adored and glorified,
> who has spoken through the prophets.
>
> I believe in one, holy, catholic and apostolic Church.
> I confess one Baptism for the forgiveness of sins
> and I look forward to the resurrection of the dead
> and the life of the world to come. Amen.

Instead of the Nicene (Niceno-Constantinopolitan) Creed, especially during Lent and Easter Time, the baptismal Symbol of the Roman Church, known as the Apostles' Creed, may be used.

STAND

**I believe in God,
the Father almighty,
Creator of heaven and earth,
and in Jesus Christ, his only Son, our Lord,**

At the words that follow, up to and including "the Virgin Mary," all bow.

**who was conceived by the Holy Spirit,
born of the Virgin Mary,
suffered under Pontius Pilate,
was crucified, died and was buried;
he descended into hell;
on the third day he rose again from the dead;
he ascended into heaven,
and is seated at the right hand of God the Father almighty;
from there he will come to judge the living and the dead.**

**I believe in the Holy Spirit,
the holy catholic Church,
the communion of saints,
the forgiveness of sins,
the resurrection of the body,
and life everlasting. Amen.**

UNIVERSAL PRAYER *(Prayer of the Faithful)*

As a priestly people, we unite with one another to pray for today's needs in the Church and the world. The Deacon, cantor or other minister offers the petitions and then says or sings:

We pray to the Lord.
Lord, hear our prayer.

149

Deacon/Cantor/Other Minister   All

(Intercessions)   Let us pray   to the Lord.   **Lord, hear our prayer.**

Music: Byzantine chant.

Christians are baptized into the paschal mystery of Christ's death and resurrection for the forgiveness of sin and fullness of salvation. This mystery is celebrated at every Mass, remembering Christ's loving deed and giving thanks and praise to God. By this action the "Sacrifice of the Cross is continuously made present in the Church" (GIRM, No. 72).

PRESENTATION AND PREPARATION OF THE GIFTS   *SIT*

The gifts are brought forward. If no chant is sung, the Priest may pray aloud, and all may respond:

Blessed be God for ever.

The Priest prays "…that my sacrifice and yours may be acceptable to God, the almighty Father," and all respond:

STAND

151

May the Lord accept the sacrifice at your hands   for the praise and glory of his name,   for our good   and the good of all his ho - ly Church.

Or   **May the Lord accept the sacrifice at your hands**
for the praise and glory of his name,
for our good
and the good of all his holy Church.

PRAYER OVER THE OFFERINGS

The Priest says the Prayer over the Offerings; following this, the people respond:

Amen.

THE EUCHARISTIC PRAYER

PREFACE

The Eucharistic Prayer begins with a dialogue between the Priest and the assembly.

152

Priest

The Lord be with you.

All

And with your spir - it.

Priest

Lift up your hearts.

All

We lift them up to the Lord.

Priest

Let us give thanks to the Lord our God.

All

It is right and just.

At the conclusion of the Preface, the following acclamation is sung or said by all:

HOLY

153

Ho - ly, Ho - ly, Ho - ly Lord God of hosts. Heav-en and earth are full of your glo-ry. Ho-san-na in the high-est. Bless-ed is he who comes in the name of the Lord. Ho - san - na in the high - est.

KNEEL

After the words of institution of the Eucharist, the Priest sings or says:

The mystery of faith.

All respond:

154

We pro-claim your Death, O Lord, and pro-fess your Res-ur-rec-tion

un-til you come a-gain.

Or **155**

When we eat this Bread and drink this Cup, we pro-claim your

Death, O Lord, un-til you come a-gain.

Or **156**

Save us, Sav-ior of the world, for by your Cross and Res-ur-rec-tion

you have set us free.

The Eucharistic Prayer culminates and concludes when the Priest sings or says:

Through him, and with him, and in him,
O God, almighty Father,
in the unity of the Holy Spirit,
all glory and honor is yours,
for ever and ever.

A - men.

THE COMMUNION RITE

THE LORD'S PRAYER

STAND

The Priest invites all to join in the Lord's Prayer:

157

Our Fa - ther, who art in heav - en, hal-lowed be thy name;

thy king-dom come, thy will be done on earth as it is in heav-en.

Give us this day our dai - ly bread, and for-give us our tres-pass-es,

as we for-give those who tres-pass a - gainst us; and lead us

not in - to temp - ta - tion, but de - liv - er us from e - vil.

Deliver us, Lord, we pray, from every evil,
graciously grant peace in our days,
that, by the help of your mercy,
we may be always free from sin
and safe from all distress,
as we await the blessed hope
and the coming of our Savior, Jesus Christ.

For the king-dom, the power and the glo-ry are yours now and for ev - er.

Music: Chant; adapt. by Robert J. Snow, 1926–1998.

SIGN OF PEACE

Lord Jesus Christ,
who said to your Apostles:
Peace I leave you, my peace I give you,
look not on our sins,
but on the faith of your Church,
and graciously grant her peace and unity
in accordance with your will.
Who live and reign for ever and ever.

A - men.

The peace of the Lord be with you always.

And with your spir-it.

Let us offer each other the sign of peace.

The people exchange a sign of peace, according to local custom.

LAMB OF GOD

During the breaking of the bread and the commingling, the following litany is sung and may be repeated several times until the fraction rite is completed, ending only the final time with "grant us peace."

158

Lamb of God, you take a - way the sins of the world, have mer-cy on us.

Lamb of God, you take a - way the sins of the world, grant us peace.

The faithful kneel after the "Agnus Dei" ("Lamb of God") unless the Diocesan Bishop determines otherwise.

COMMUNION

KNEEL

Behold the Lamb of God,
behold him who takes away the sins of the world.
Blessed are those called to the supper of the Lamb.

All respond:

159

Lord, I am not worthy that you should enter un - der my roof,

but only say the word and my soul shall be healed.

Or **Lord, I am not worthy**
that you should enter under my roof,
but only say the word
and my soul shall be healed.

COMMUNION CHANT

While the Priest is receiving the Sacrament, the Communion Chant or song is begun.

The minister of Communion says,   *STAND*

> *"The Body of Christ" or "The Blood of Christ"*

and the communicant answers:

Amen.

PERIOD OF SILENCE OR SONG OF PRAISE   *SIT (OR KNEEL)*

A period of silence may now be observed, or a psalm or song of praise may be sung.

PRAYER AFTER COMMUNION   *STAND*

The Communion Rite concludes with a prayer to which all respond:

Amen.

On Thursday of the Lord's Supper, the Evening Mass concludes at this point with the Transfer of the Most Blessed Sacrament.

---

160 THE CONCLUDING RITES

GREETING

The Lord be with you.

And with your spir-it.

FINAL BLESSING

May almighty God bless you,
the Father, and the Son, † and the Holy Spirit.

A - men.

A Solemn Blessing or Prayer over the People may be chosen by the Priest, in place of the above blessing.

DISMISSAL

The Deacon/Priest invites all to go in the peace of Christ:

161

Go forth, the Mass is end-ed. **Thanks be to God.**

Or **162**

Go and an-nounce the Gos-pel of the Lord. **Thanks be to God.**

Or **163**

Go in peace, glorifying the Lord by your life. **Thanks be to God.**

Or **164**

Go in peace. **Thanks be to God.**

At the Easter Vigil in the Holy Night, Easter Sunday during the Day, the Octave of Easter, and the Vigil Mass and Mass during the Day on Pentecost Sunday:

165

Go forth, the Mass is end-ed, al-le-lu - ia, al-le - lu - ia.

Or

Go in peace, al-le-lu - ia, al-le - lu - ia.

Thanks be to God, al-le-lu - ia, al-le - lu - ia.

A final psalm or hymn may be sung.

MASS SETTINGS

HOLY
HOLY
HOLY

The music with which the Church celebrates the Eucharist has developed over the centuries, clothing ancient ritual elements in idioms expressive of the assembly's faith. A broad range of settings — contemporary, gospel, and traditional — invigorates the assembly's celebration and expands its vocabulary of praise. Each of these offers a unified musical approach to the Order of Mass.

CHANT MASS

166 **ASPERGES ME**

Antiphon: All
A - spér - ges me, Dó - mi - ne, hys-só - po, et mun-dá - bor: la - vá - bis me, et su - per ni-vem de - al - bá - bor.

Verse: Cantor(s)
Mi - se - ré - re me - i, De - us, se - cún - dum ma-gnam mi - se - ri - cór - di - am tu - am.
to Antiphon

Note: For use in all seasons but Eastertide.
English translation of antiphon: *Sprinkle me with hyssop, O Lord, and I shall be cleansed; wash me and I shall be whiter than snow.*
Translation of the verse (Psalm 51:1): *Have mercy on me, O God, according to your great compassion.*
English translation of the antiphon © 2010, ICEL. All rights reserved. Used with permission.

Text and music: *Chant Mass*; Chant, Mode VII; *Graduale Romanum*, 1974.

Vidi Aquam

Verse (Cantor): Confitémini Dómino…misericórdia eius. **(to Antiphon)**

Note: For use during Eastertide
English translation of antiphon: *I saw water flowing from the Temple, from its right-hand side, alleluia;
    and all to whom this water came were saved and shall say: Alleluia, alleluia.*
The verse appears in the Choir/Cantor edition and accompaniment editions.
English translation of the verse (Psalm 118:1): *Give thanks to the Lord, for he is good, for his mercy endures forever.*
English translation of the antiphon © 2010, ICEL. All rights reserved. Used with permission.
    English translation of the verse © 1969, 1981, 1997, ICEL. All rights reserved. Used with permission.

Text and music: *Chant Mass; Graduale Romanum*, 1974.

168 KYRIE

Text and music: *Chant Mass; Mass XVI*; Chant, Mode III; *Graduale Romanum*, 1974.

169 GLORIA

Qui tol-lis pec-cá-ta mun - di, mi-se-ré - re no-bis.

Qui tol-lis pec-cá-ta mun - di, sú-sci-pe de-pre-ca-ti-ó-

nem no - stram. Qui se-des ad déx-te-ram Pa - tris,

mi-se-ré-re no - bis. Quó-ni-am tu so-lus San - ctus.

Tu so-lus Dó - mi - nus. Tu so-lus Al - tís - si-mus,

Je - su Chri - ste. Cum San-cto Spí - ri - tu,

in gló-ri-a De-i Pa - tris. A - men.

Text and music: *Chant Mass; Mass VIII*; Chant, Mode V; *Graduale Romanum*, 1974.

SANCTUS 170

San-ctus, San-ctus, San-ctus Dó-mi-nus De-us Sá-

ba-oth. Ple-ni sunt coe-li et ter-ra gló-ri-a tu-a.

Ho-sán-na in ex-cél-sis. Be-ne-dí-ctus qui ve-nit in

nó-mi-ne Dó-mi-ni. Ho-sán - na in ex-cél - sis.

Text and music: *Chant Mass; Mass XVIII*; *Graduale Romanum*, 1974.

171   Post Consecrationem

My-sté - ri - um fí - de - i.   My-sté - ri - um   fí   -   de - i.

Mor-tem tu - am an-nun-ti - á-mus, Dó - mi-ne, et tu - am

re-sur-re-cti - ó-nem con-fi - té - mur, do - nec vé-ni - as.

Text and music: *Chant Mass; Graduale Romanum*, 1974.

172   Amen

...per ó - mni - a sáe - cu - la sae - cu - ló - rum. A-men.

Text and music: *Chant Mass; Graduale Romanum*, 1974.

173   Pater Noster

Pa - ter no-ster, qui es in cae-lis: san-cti - fi - cé-tur no - men

tu - um; ad-vé-ni - at re-gnum tu-um; fi - at vo-lún-tas tu - a,

sic - ut in cae - lo, et in ter - ra.

Pa-nem no-strum co - ti - di - á - num da no - bis hó - di - e;

et di - mít - te no - bis dé - bi - ta no-stra, sic - ut et nos di - mít - ti - mus de - bi - tó - ri - bus no - stris;   et   ne   nos

in - dú - cas in ten - ta - ti - ó - nem;   sed lí - be - ra nos a ma - lo.

Priest: Libera nos, quaesumus, Domine...
        et adventum Salvatoris nostri Jesu Christi.

All
Qui - a   tu - um   est   re - gnum,   et   po - té -

stas,   et   gló - ri - a   in   sáe - cu - la.

Priest   All
Pax Dó - mi-ni sit sem-per vo-bís - cum.   Et cum spí-ri-tu tu-o.

Text and music: *Chant Mass; Graduale Romanum*, 1974.

AGNUS DEI   174

A - gnus De - i,   qui tol - lis pec - cá - ta mun - di: mi - se -

ré - re no - bis.   A - gnus De - i,   qui tol - lis pec - cá - ta

mun - di: mi - se - ré - re no - bis.   A - gnus De - i,

qui tol - lis pec - cá - ta mun - di: do - na no - bis pa - cem.

Text and music: *Chant Mass; Mass XVIII; Graduale Romanum*, 1974.

MASS OF RENEWAL

175 KYRIE, ELEISON/LORD, HAVE MERCY

Cantor; All repeat

Ký - ri - e, e - lé - i - son.   Chri - ste, e -
Lord,_____ have mer - cy.   Christ,_____ have

lé - i - son.   Ký - ri - e, e - lé - i - son.
mer - cy.   Lord,_____ have mer - cy.

176 GLORY TO GOD

Glo - ry to God in the high - est,   and on earth peace to peo-ple

of good will.   We praise you, we bless you, we a -

dore you,   we glo - ri-fy you,   we give you

thanks for your great glo - ry, Lord God, heav-en - ly

King,   O God,   al-might-y Fa - ther.

Lord Je - sus Christ, On-ly Be - got-ten Son,   Lord God,

Lamb of God, Son of the Fa - ther,   you take a -

way the sins of the world, have mer - cy on us; you take a -
way the sins of the world, re - ceive our prayer; you are seat - ed
at the right hand of the Fa - ther, have mer -
cy, have mer - cy on us. For you a - lone are the
Ho - ly One, you a - lone are the Lord, you a - lone are the
Most High, Je - sus Christ, with the Ho - ly Spir - it,
in the glo - ry of God the Fa - ther. A - men, a - men.

Music: *Mass of Renewal*; Curtis Stephan, b. 1973, © 2009, Curtis Stephan. Published by OCP. All rights reserved.

ALLELUIA 177

Al - le - lu - ia, al - le - lu - ia, al - le - lu - ia.
Al - le - lu - ia, al - le - lu - ia, al - le - lu - ia.

Note: Verses available in accompaniment books.

Music: *Mass of Renewal*; Curtis Stephan, b. 1973, © 2009, Curtis Stephan. Published by OCP. All rights reserved.

178   LENTEN GOSPEL ACCLAMATION

Glo-ry to you, O Word of God, Lord____ Je-sus Christ!
Glo-ry to you, Lord Je-sus Christ, Son of the liv-ing God.

Glo-ry to you, O Word of God, Lord____ Je-sus Christ!
Glo-ry to you, Lord Je-sus Christ, Son of the liv-ing God.

Note: Verses available in accompaniment books.

179   HOLY

Ho - ly, Ho - ly, Ho - ly Lord God of hosts. Heav-en and

earth are full of your glo - ry. Ho-san-na in the high - est.

Bless-ed is he who comes in the name of the Lord. Ho-

san-na in the high-est. Ho-san-na in the high - est.

180   WE PROCLAIM YOUR DEATH

We pro - claim your Death, O Lord, and pro - fess your

Res - ur - rec - tion un - til you come a - gain.

WHEN WE EAT THIS BREAD 181

When we eat this Bread and drink this Cup, we pro-

claim your Death, O Lord, un-til you come a-gain.

SAVE US, SAVIOR 182

Save us, Sav-ior of the world, for by your Cross and Res-ur-

rec-tion you have set us free, you have set us free.

AMEN 183

A - men, a - men, a - men.

LAMB OF GOD 184

Lamb of God, you take a-way the sins of the world, have mer-cy,

have mer-cy on us. world, grant us, grant us peace.

MASS OF CHRIST THE SAVIOR

185   LORD, HAVE MERCY/KYRIE, ELEISON

Lord,____ have mer-cy.   Christ,____ have mer-cy.
Ký - ri - e, e - léi-son.   *Chri - ste, e - léi-son.*

Lord,____ have mer-cy, have mer-cy on us.
Ký - ri - e, e - léi-son, e - lé - i - son.

Music: *Mass of Christ the Savior*; Dan Schutte, b. 1947, © 2007, 2009, Daniel L. Schutte.
Published by OCP. All rights reserved.

186   GLORY TO GOD

Glo-ry to God. Glo-ry to God. Glo-ry to God in the high -

est, and on earth peace, on earth peace to peo-ple of good

will.   will.   A - men. A - men.

1. We praise you, we bless you, we a-dore you, we

1. glo-ri-fy you, we give you thanks for your great glo-ry,

1. Lord God, heav'n-ly King, O God, al-might-y Fa-ther.

2. Lord Je-sus Christ, On - ly Be-got - ten Son, Lord God,

2. Lamb of God, Son of the Fa-ther, you take a-way the sins of the world,

2. have mer-cy on us; you take a-way the sins of the world,

2. re-ceive our prayer; you are seat - ed at the right hand,

to Verse 3 or Refrain

2. the right hand of the Fa-ther, have mer-cy on us.

Verse 3

3. For you a-lone are the Ho - ly One, you a-lone are the Lord,

3. you a - lone are the Most High, Je - sus Christ, with the Ho - ly

to Coda or Refrain

3. Spir - it, in the glo - ry of God the Fa - ther.

Music: *Mass of Christ the Savior*; Dan Schutte, b. 1947, © 2007, 2009, Daniel L. Schutte.

ALLELUIA 187

Al - le-lu - ia. Al - le-lu - ia. Al - le-lu - ia.

Note: Verses available in accompaniment books.

Music: *Mass of Christ the Savior*; Dan Schutte, b. 1947, © 2007, 2009, Daniel L. Schutte.

188 **LENTEN GOSPEL ACCLAMATION**

Glo-ry to you, Word of God, Lord Je-sus Christ!

Note: Verses available in accompaniment books.

189 **HOLY**

Ho - ly, Ho - ly, Ho - ly Lord God of hosts. Heav-en and

earth are full, are full of your glo - ry. Ho - san - na! Ho -

san - na! Ho - san - na in the high - est. Bless - ed is

he who comes, who comes in the name of the Lord. Ho -

190 **WE PROCLAIM YOUR DEATH**

We pro - claim your Death, O Lord, and pro - fess your

Res - ur - rec - tion un - til you come a - gain.

WHEN WE EAT THIS BREAD 191

When we eat this Bread and drink this Cup, we pro-

claim your Death, O Lord, un-til you come a - gain.

SAVE US, SAVIOR 192

Save us, save us, Sav-ior of the world, for by your

Cross and Res - ur - rec - tion you have set us free.

AMEN 193

A - men. A - men. A - men.

LAMB OF GOD 194

*Lamb of God, you take a - way the sins of the

1... Final

world, have mer-cy on us. world, grant us peace.

*Other Invocations available in accompaniment books.

195   PENITENTIAL ACT WITH INVOCATIONS

Lord, have mer - cy.

Christ, have mer - cy.

Lord, have mer - cy. (Absolution) A - men.

196   GLORY TO GOD

Glo-ry to God in the high-est, and on earth peace to

peo-ple of good will. We praise you, we bless

you, we a-dore you, we glo-ri-fy you, we give you

thanks for your great glo-ry, Lord God, heav-en-ly King,

O God, al-might - y Fa-ther. Lord Je-sus Christ,

On-ly Be-got-ten Son, Lord God, Lamb of God, Son of the

Fa-ther, you take a-way the sins of the world,

have mer-cy on us;
re-ceive our prayer; you are seat-ed at the right hand

of the Fa - ther, have mer-cy on us. For

you a-lone are the Ho - ly One, you a-lone

are the Lord, you a-lone are the Most High,

Je - sus Christ, with the Ho - ly Spir-it, in the

glo-ry of God the Fa-ther. A - men.

Music: *Mass of Spirit and Grace*; Ricky Manalo, CSP, b. 1965, © 2007, 2009, Ricky Manalo, CSP.
   Published by OCP. All rights reserved.

ALLELUIA

197

Al - le - lu - ia! Al - le-lu - ia! Al - le-lu - ia!

Note: Verses available in accompaniment books.

Music: *Mass of Spirit and Grace*; Ricky Manalo, CSP, b. 1965, © 2007, 2009, Ricky Manalo, CSP.
   Published by OCP. All rights reserved.

198 LENTEN GOSPEL ACCLAMATION

Glo-ry to you, Lord Je-sus Christ, Son of the liv-ing God.

Glo-ry to you, Lord Je-sus Christ, Son of the liv-ing God.

Note: Verses available in accompaniment books.

199 HOLY

Ho-ly, Ho-ly, Ho-ly Lord God of hosts.

Heav-en and earth are full of your glo-ry. Ho-

(Fine)

san - na, ho-san - na, ho-san-na in the high-est.

Bless-ed is he who comes in the name of the Lord. Ho-

200 WE PROCLAIM YOUR DEATH

We pro-claim your Death, O Lord, and pro-

fess your Res - ur - rec - tion un - til you come a -

gain, un - til you come a - gain.

When We Eat This Bread 201

When we eat this Bread and drink this Cup,

we pro - claim your Death, O Lord, un - til you

come a - gain, un - til you come a - gain.

Save Us, Savior 202

Save us, Sav - ior of the world, for by your Cross and Res - ur -

rec - tion you have set us free, you have set us free.

Amen 203

A - men! A - men! A - men! A - men!

204   LAMB OF GOD

Lamb of God, you take a - way the sins of the

1, 2   **4**

world, have mer - cy on us.

Final

world, grant us peace, grant us peace.

BELMONT MASS

205   PENITENTIAL ACT WITH INVOCATIONS

Priest/Deacon/Cantor   Cantor; All repeat   Priest/Deacon/Cantor

(Invocation)   *Ký - ri - e, e - lé - i - son.*   (Invocation)
               Lord, have mer - cy.

Cantor; All repeat   Priest/Deacon/Cantor

Chri - ste, e - lé - i - son.   (Invocation)
Christ, have mer - cy.

Cantor; All repeat   Priest   All

Ký - ri - e, e - lé - i - son.   (Absolution)   A - men.
Lord, have mer - cy.

206   GLORY TO GOD

Glory to God in the highest, and on earth peace to people of good will.

We praise you, we bless you, we a - dore you, we glorify you, we give you thanks for your great glory, Lord God, heav-en-ly King, O God, al-might-y Father. Lord Jesus Christ, Only Be-got-ten Son, Lord God, Lamb of God, Son of the Father, you take away the sins of the world, have mer-cy on us; you take away the sins of the world, re-ceive our prayer; you are seated at the right hand of the Father, have mer-cy on us. For you a-lone are the Holy One, you a-lone are the Lord, you alone are the Most High, Je - sus Christ, with the Ho-ly Spirit, in the glory of God the Father. A-men, a - men.

ALLELUIA
207

Al - le - lu - ia, al - le - lu - ia, al - le - lu - ia.

Note: Verses available in accompaniment books.

208   **Lenten Gospel Acclamation**

Praise and hon-or to you, Lord Je - sus Christ!

Note: Verses available in accompaniment books.

209   **Holy**

Ho-ly, Ho - ly, Ho - ly Lord God of hosts. Heav-en and

earth are full of your glory. Ho - san - na in the high-est.

Bless - ed is he who comes in the name of the Lord.

Ho - san - na in the high-est, ho - san - na in the high - est.

210   **We Proclaim Your Death**

We pro - claim your Death, O Lord, and pro - fess your

Res - ur - rec - tion un - til you come a - gain.

When We Eat This Bread 211

When we eat this Bread and drink this Cup, we proclaim your Death, O Lord, un - til you come a - gain.

Text © 2010, ICEL. All rights reserved. Used with permission.
Music: *Belmont Mass*; Christopher Walker, b. 1947, © 2007, 2010, Christopher Walker.
    Published by OCP. All rights reserved.

Save Us, Savior 212

Save us, Sav - ior of the world, for by your
Cross and Res - ur - rec - tion you have set us free.

Text © 2010, ICEL. All rights reserved. Used with permission.
Music: *Belmont Mass*; Christopher Walker, b. 1947, © 2007, 2010, Christopher Walker.
    Published by OCP. All rights reserved.

Amen 213

Priest   All
...for ev - er and ev - er. A - men, a - men.

Music: *Belmont Mass*; Christopher Walker, b. 1947, © 2007, 2010, Christopher Walker.
    Published by OCP. All rights reserved.

Lamb of God 214

Cantor or All   (All)
*Lamb of God, you take a - way the sins of the world,

1...   Repeat as needed   Final
have mer - cy on us.   grant us peace, grant us peace.

*Other Invocations available in accompaniment books.

Music: *Belmont Mass*; Christopher Walker, b. 1947, © 2007, 2010, Christopher Walker.
    Published by OCP. All rights reserved.

215   PENITENTIAL ACT WITH INVOCATIONS

216   GLORY TO GOD

ceive our prayer; you are seat-ed at the right hand of the Fa-ther,

have mer-cy on us. For you a-lone are the Ho-ly One,

you a-lone are the Lord, you a-lone are the Most High,

Je-sus Christ, with the Ho-ly Spir-it, in the glo-ry, the glo-ry of

God the Fa-ther. A - men. A - men.

Text © 2010, ICEL. All rights reserved. Used with permission.
Music: *Mass of the Resurrection*; Randall DeBruyn, b. 1947, © 2002, 2009, Randall DeBruyn.
   Published by OCP. All rights reserved.

ALLELUIA   217

Al-le - lu - ia, al - le-lu - ia, al-le-lu - ia, al-le-lu-

ia, al-le-lu-ia, al - le-lu-ia, al-le-lu - ia, al-le-lu - ia!

Note: Verses available in accompaniment books.
Music: *Mass of the Resurrection*; Randall DeBruyn, b. 1947, © 2002, 2009, Randall DeBruyn.
   Published by OCP. All rights reserved.

LENTEN GOSPEL ACCLAMATION   218

Praise to you, Lord Je - sus Christ, King of end - less glo - ry.

Praise to you, Lord Je - sus Christ, King of end - less glo - ry.

Note: Verses available in accompaniment books.

Text © 1969, 1981, 1997, ICEL. All rights reserved. Used with permission.
Music: *Mass of the Resurrection*; Randall DeBruyn, b. 1947, © 2002, 2009, Randall DeBruyn.
   Published by OCP. All rights reserved.

219 **HOLY**

Ho - ly, Ho - ly, Ho - ly Lord God of hosts.

Heav-en and earth are full of your glo - ry. Ho -

san - na, ho - san - na, ho - san-na in the high-est.

Bless-ed is he who comes in the name of the Lord. Ho -

220 **WE PROCLAIM YOUR DEATH**

We pro-claim your Death, O Lord, and pro-fess your Res - ur -

rec-tion un - til you come a - gain, un - til you come a - gain.

221 **WHEN WE EAT THIS BREAD**

When we eat this Bread and drink this Cup, we pro -

claim your Death, O Lord, un - til you come a - gain.

SAVE US, SAVIOR 222

Save us, Sav-ior of the world, for by your Cross and Res-ur-rec-tion you have set us free, you have set us free.

AMEN 223

A - men, a - men, a - men, a - men.

LAMB OF GOD 224

Lamb of God, you take a-way the sins of the

1, 2
world, have mer-cy on us.

Final
world, grant us peace.

HERITAGE MASS

LORD, HAVE MERCY 225

Lord, have mer - cy. Christ, have mer - cy. Lord, have mer - cy.

226 GLORY TO GOD

Glo - ry to God in the high - est, and on earth peace to
peo-ple of good will. We praise you, we bless you, we a - dore you,
we glo - ri-fy you, we give you thanks for your great glo - ry,
Lord God, heav'n-ly King, O God, al-might-y Fa - ther.
Lord Je-sus Christ, On - ly Be-got - ten Son, Lord God,
Lamb of God, Son of the Fa-ther, you take a-way the
you take a-way the
sins of the world, have mer - cy on us; you are seat-ed at the
sins of the world, re - ceive our __ prayer;
right hand of the Fa - ther, have mer - cy on us.
For you a-lone are the Ho - ly One, you a - lone are the Lord,
you a-lone are the Most High, Je - sus Christ, with the Ho - ly
Spir - it, in the glo - ry of God the Fa - ther. A - men.

Music: *Heritage Mass*; Owen Alstott, b. 1947, © 1987, 2009, OCP. All rights reserved.

HOLY

Ho-ly, Ho-ly, Ho - ly Lord God of hosts. Heav'n and earth are full of your glo - ry. Ho - san-na! Ho-san-na in the high - est. Blessed is he who comes in the name of the Lord.

WE PROCLAIM YOUR DEATH

We pro - claim your Death, O Lord, and pro - fess your Res - ur - rec - tion un - til you come, un - til you come a - gain.

WHEN WE EAT THIS BREAD

When we eat this Bread and drink this Cup, we pro-claim your Death, O Lord, un - til you come a - gain.

230   SAVE US, SAVIOR

Save us, Sav-ior of the world, for by your
Cross and Res-ur-rec-tion you have set us free.

231   AMEN

A - men, a - men, a - men.

232   LAMB OF GOD

Lamb of God, you take a-way the sins of the

1, 2
world, have mer-cy on us.

3
world, grant us peace.

MISA SANTA FE

233   ACTO PENITENCIAL, FORMULARIO 3/ PENITENTIAL ACT WITH INVOCATIONS

Sacerdote/Diácono/Cantor
Priest/Deacon/Cantor
        Cantor/All

(Invocación/
Invocation)

Se - ñor, ten pie-dad.   Se - ñor, ten pie-dad.
℣ Lord, have mer-cy.   ℣ Lord, have mer-cy.

Sacerdote/Diácono/Cantor
Priest/Deacon/Cantor
Cantor/All
(Invocación/ Invocation)

Cris-to, ten pie-dad.   Cris-to, ten pie-dad.
Christ, have mer-cy.   Christ, have mer-cy.

Sacerdote/Diácono/Cantor
Priest/Deacon/Cantor
Cantor/All
(Invocación/ Invocation)

Se-ñor, ten pie-dad.   Se-ñor, ten pie-dad.
Lord, have mer-cy.   Lord, have mer-cy.

GLORIA/GLORY TO GOD   234

Estribillo/Refrain

Glo — ria a Dios en el cie-lo, y en la tie — rra
Glo — ry to God in the high-est, and on earth

paz a los hom-bres que a-ma el Se-ñor.
peace to peo-ple, to peo-ple of good will.

Estrofas

1. Por tu inmensa gloria te alabamos,
   te bendecimos, te adoramos,
   te glorificamos, te damos gracias,
   Señor Dios, Rey celestial,
   Dios Padre todopoderoso.

2. Señor, Hijo único, Jesucristo,
   Señor Dios, Cordero de Dios,
   Hijo del Padre,
   tú que quitas el pecado del mundo,
   ten piedad de nosotros;
   tú que quitas el pecado del mundo,
   atiende nuestra súplica;
   tú que estás sentado
   a la derecha del Padre,
   ten piedad de nosotros.

3. Porque sólo tú eres Santo,
   sólo tú Señor,
   sólo tú Altísimo, Jesucristo,
   con el Espíritu Santo
   en la gloria de Dios Padre. Amén.

Verses

1. *We praise you, we bless you,*
   we adore you, we glorify you,
   we give you thanks for your great glory,
   Lord God, heavenly King,
   O God, almighty Father.

2. *Lord Jesus Christ, Only Begotten Son,*
   Lord God, Lamb of God,
   Son of the Father,
   you take away the sins of the world,
   have mercy on us;
   you take away the sins of the world,
   receive our prayer;
   you are seated at the right hand
   of the Father,
   have mercy on us.

3. *For you alone are the Holy One,*
   you alone are the Lord,
   you alone are the Most High, Jesus Christ,
   with the Holy Spirit,
   in the glory of God the Father. Amen.

235   Aclamación al Evangelio/Gospel Acclamation

¡A - le - lu - ya, a - le - lu - ya,   a - le - lu - ya!
Cuaresma   A - la-ban - za a ti, oh Cris-to,   Rey de e-ter - na glo-ria.
Al - le - lu - ia, al - le - lu - ia,   al - le - lu - ia!
Lent   Praise to you, Lord Je - sus Christ,   King of end-less glo-ry!

236   Santo/Holy

Español   San - to, San - to, San-to es el Se - ñor,   Dios del U - ni - ver - so.
English   Ho - ly, Ho - ly, Ho - ly   Lord God of hosts.
Biling.   San - to, San - to, San-to es el Se - ñor,   Dios del U - ni - ver - so.

Lle - nos es -tán el cie - lo y la tie - rra de tu glo - ria. Ho -
Heav - en and earth are full of your glo - ry. Ho -
Heav - en and earth are full of your glo - ry. Ho -

san - na en el cie - lo. Ho - san - na en el cie - lo. Ben-
san - na in the high-est. Ho - san - na in the high - est.
san - na en el cie - lo. Ho - san - na en el cie - lo.

di - to el que vie - ne en nom - bre del Se - ñor. Ho -
Bless - ed is he who comes in the name of the Lord. Ho -
Bless - ed is he who comes in the name of the Lord. Ho -

san - na en el cie - lo. Ho - san - na en el cie - lo.
san - na in the high-est. Ho - san - na in the high-est.
san - na en el cie - lo. Ho - san - na en el cie - lo.

Anunciamos Tu Muerte/We Proclaim Your Death   237

A - nun - cia - mos tu muer - te, pro - cla -
We pro - claim your Death, O Lord, and pro -

ma - mos tu re - su - rrec - ción. ¡Ven, Se - ñor Je -
fess your Res - ur - rec - tion un - til you come a -

sús! ¡Ven, Se - ñor Je - sús!
gain, un - til you come a - gain.

Cada Vez que Comemos/When We Eat This Bread   238

Ca - da vez que co - me - mos de es - te pan y be -
When we eat this Bread and

be - mos de es - te cá - liz, a - nun - cia - mos tu
drink this Cup, we pro - claim your

muer - te, Se - ñor, has - ta que vuel - vas.
Death, O Lord, un - til you come a - gain.

239 **POR TU CRUZ/SAVE US, SAVIOR**

Por tu cruz, por tu cruz y re -

Save us, Sav - ior of the world, for by your

su - rrec - ción nos has sal - va - do, Se -

Cross and Res-ur - rec - tion you have set us

ñor, nos has sal - va - do, Se - ñor.

free, you have set us free.

Text: Spanish © 1975, 1991, Comisión Episcopal de Pastoral Litúrgica de la Conferencia del Episcopado Mexicano. All rights reserved. Sole US agent: US Conference of Catholic Bishops. Used with permission.
English © 2010, ICEL. All rights reserved. Used with permission.
Music: *Misa Santa Fe*; Mary Frances Reza, © 2009, 2011, Mary Frances Reza. Published by OCP. All rights reserved.

240 **AMÉN/AMEN**

A - mén, a-mén, a - mén. A - mén, a-mén, a - mén.
A - men, a-men, a - men. A - men, a-men, a - men.

Music: *Misa Santa Fe*; Mary Frances Reza, © 2009, 2011, Mary Frances Reza. Published by OCP. All rights reserved.

241 **CORDERO DE DIOS/LAMB OF GOD**

1-3. Cor - de - ro de Dios, que qui-tas el pe - ca - do del mun-do,
1-3. Lamb of God, you take a-way the sins of the world,

1, 2. ten pie-dad de no - so-tros, 𝄾 ten pie-dad de no - so-tros.
3. 𝄾 da - nos la paz, 𝄾 da - nos la paz.
1, 2. *have mer - cy on us,* 𝄾 *have mer - cy on us.*
3. 𝄾 *grant us peace,* 𝄾 *grant us peace.*

MASS OF GLORY

COME TO THE RIVER

242

Refrain

Come, O come, come to the riv - er

flow - ing from the bod - y of Christ.

We'll go down, deep in the wa - ter,

but in the Lord we shall a - rise.

Verses

1. Washed in wa - ters of re-birth,
2. Priest - ly peo - ple are ___ we,
3. Blest are those ___ who ___ thirst
4. Let us walk ___ in the light
5. Those who sow ___ in ___ tears

to Refrain

1. we have put on Christ Je - sus.
2. sealed and sent by the Spir - it.
3. for the reign of God's jus - tice.
4. of God's ho - ly prom - ise.
5. reap the har - vest re - joic - ing.

*Repeat last phrase final time.

243   PENITENTIAL ACT WITH INVOCATIONS

1. Lord, have mer-cy. Lord, have
2. Christ, have mer-cy. Christ, have

1. mer-cy on us.
2. mer-cy on us.

3. Lord, have mer-cy.

3. Lord, have mer-cy. Lord, have mer-cy on us.

Note: Invocations from *The Roman Missal*, 3rd Edition are in the accompaniment books.

Music: *Mass of Glory*; Bob Hurd, b. 1950, © 1991, 2009, Bob Hurd. Published by OCP. All rights reserved.

244   GLORY TO GOD

Refrain: 1st time: Cantor, All repeat; thereafter: All

Glo-ry to God, glo-ry to God, glo-ry to God in the high - est,

and on earth peace to peo-ple of good will.

Last time

Glo - ry to God, glo - ry to God, glo-ry to God in the

high-est, and on earth peace to peo-ple of good will.

A - men, a - men, a - men.

Verses

1. We praise you, we bless you,
   we adore you, we glorify you,
   we give you thanks for your great glory,
   Lord God, heavenly King,
   O God, almighty Father.

   you take away the sins of the world,
   receive our prayer;
   you are seated at the right hand
     of the Father,
   have mercy on us.

2. Lord Jesus Christ, Only Begotten Son,
   Lord God, Lamb of God,
   Son of the Father,
   you take away the sins of the world,
   have mercy on us;

3. For you alone are the Holy One,
   you alone are the Lord,
   you alone are the Most High, Jesus Christ,
   with the Holy Spirit,
   in the glory of God the Father.

Text © 2010, ICEL. All rights reserved. Used with permission.

Music: *Mass of Glory*; Ken Canedo, b. 1953, and Bob Hurd, b. 1950, © 1998, 2009, Ken Canedo and Bob Hurd.
Published by OCP. All rights reserved.

Alleluia! Give the Glory

Al - le - lu - ia! Al - le - lu - ia!

Al - le - lu - ia! Give the glo - ry

1
and the hon - or to the Lord!

2
and the hon - or to the Lord!

Note: Gathering, Gospel Acclamation and Easter Vigil Psalm 118 verses are available in the accompaniment books.

Text: Ken Canedo, b. 1953, and Bob Hurd, b. 1950.
Music: *Mass of Glory*; Ken Canedo.

Lenten Gospel Acclamation

Praise and hon - or to you, O Lord Je - sus Christ.

Note: Verses available in accompaniment books.

Music: *Mass of Glory*; Ken Canedo, b. 1953, and Bob Hurd, b. 1950, © 1998, Ken Canedo and Bob Hurd.

Universal Prayer/Prayer of the Faithful

Refrain: 1st time: Cantor, All repeat; thereafter: All

Hear our prayer. Hear our prayer.

God of mer - cy, hear our prayer.

Note: Verses available in accompaniment books.

248   HOLY

Ho - ly, Ho - ly, Ho - ly   Lord   God   of

hosts.   Heav - en and earth are full of your

glo - ry.   Ho - san-na,   ho - san-na,   ho - san - na

in the high-est.   Bless-ed is   he who comes

in the name   of   the Lord.   Ho -

249   WE PROCLAIM YOUR DEATH

We   pro - claim your Death, O Lord,   and pro - fess your

Res - ur - rec - tion   un - til you come a - gain.

250   WHEN WE EAT THIS BREAD

When we eat this Bread   and drink   this Cup,

we pro - claim your Death, O   Lord,   un - til you

come a - gain, un - til you come a - gain.

SAVE US, SAVIOR 251

Save us, Sav - ior of the world, for by your Cross and

Res - ur - rec - tion you have set us free.

AMEN 252

A - men. A - men. Al - le - lu - ia, a - men. men.
During Lent: Praise and glo-ry,

LAMB OF GOD 253

Cantor or Choir   All

*Lamb of God, you take a-way the sins of the world,

1, etc.   (repeat as needed)

have mer - cy on us; have mer - cy on us.

Final

grant us peace; grant us peace.

*Other Invocations available in accompaniment books.

GUIDELINES FOR THE
RECEPTION OF COMMUNION

For Catholics: As Catholics, we fully participate in the celebration of the Eucharist when we receive Holy Communion. We are encouraged to receive Communion devoutly and frequently. In order to be properly disposed to receive Communion, participants should not be conscious of grave sin and normally should have fasted for one hour. A person who is conscious of grave sin is not to receive the Body and Blood of the Lord without prior sacramental confession except for a grave reason where there is no opportunity for confession. In this case, the person is to be mindful of the obligation to make an act of perfect contrition, including the intention of confessing as soon as possible *(Code of Canon Law, canon 916)*. A frequent reception of the Sacrament of Penance is encouraged for all.

For our fellow Christians: We welcome our fellow Christians to this celebration of the Eucharist as our brothers and sisters. We pray that our common baptism and the action of the Holy Spirit in this Eucharist will draw us closer to one another and begin to dispel the sad divisions which separate us. We pray that these will lessen and finally disappear, in keeping with Christ's prayer for us "that they may all be one" *(Jn 17:21)*.

Because Catholics believe that the celebration of the Eucharist is a sign of the reality of the oneness of faith, life, and worship, members of those churches with whom we are not yet fully united are ordinarily not admitted to Holy Communion. Eucharistic sharing in exceptional circumstances by other Christians requires permission according to the directives of the diocesan bishop and the provisions of canon law *(canon 844 ¶ 4)*. Members of the Orthodox Churches, the Assyrian Church of the East, and the Polish National Catholic Church are urged to respect the discipline of their own Churches. According to Roman Catholic discipline, the Code of Canon Law does not object to the reception of communion by Christians of these Churches *(canon 844 ¶ 3)*.

For those not receiving Holy Communion: All who are not receiving Holy Communion are encouraged to express in their hearts a prayerful desire for unity with the Lord Jesus and with one another.

For non-Christians: We also welcome to this celebration those who do not share our faith in Jesus Christ. While we cannot admit them to Holy Communion, we ask them to offer their prayers for the peace and the unity of the human family.

ADDITIONAL SERVICE MUSIC

To foster the assembly's sung participation in the ritual moments of the Eucharistic Celebration, the following selection of acclamations, litanies and other music allows additional choices to suit the community and the occasion. "Authentic sacred music supports the Church's prayer by enriching its elements." (Sing to the Lord, No. 15)

SPRINKLING RITE

AGUA DE VIDA/WATER OF LIFE   254

Estribillo/Refrain: Todos/All

A - gua de vi - da, _____ san - to re - cuer - do;
Wa - ter of life, _____ ho - ly re - mind - er;

1
u - ne y re - nue - va _____ al cuer - po de Cris - to. _____
touch - ing, re - new - ing _____ the bod - y of Christ. _____

2
al cuer - po de Cris - to. _____
the bod - y of Christ. _____

Note: Verses available in accompaniment books.

Text and music: *Misa del Pueblo Inmigrante*; Jaime Cortez, b. 1963, © 1994, Jaime Cortez.
    Published by OCP. All rights reserved.

255   WATER OF LIFE

Refrain

Wa-ter of life, cleanse and re-fresh us; raise us to life in Christ Je - sus.

Verses: Cantor

1. All you who thirst, come to the wa - ters,
2. As rain from heav'n, so is God's word, _____ it
3. Dy - ing with Christ, so we shall rise with him,
4. Turn to the Lord, cast off your wick - ed - ness,

to Refrain

1. and you will nev - er be thirst - y a - gain.
2. wa - ters the earth ____ and brings ____ forth life.
3. death shall no long - er have pow'r o - ver us.
4. you will find peace in his in - fi - nite love.

Text and music: Stephen Dean, b. 1948, © 1981, Stephen Dean. Published by OCP. All rights reserved.

256   I SAW WATER FLOWING

Refrain: 1st time: Cantor, All repeat; thereafter: All

I saw wa-ter flow - ing from the right side of the tem - ple, Al - le -

lu - ia! Al - le - lu - ia!

Verses

1. The wa - ter flowed,
2. It brought God's life,
3. The peo - ple sang,

to Refrain

1. Al - le - lu - ia! Flowed from the tem - ple, Al - le - lu - ia!
2. Al - le - lu - ia! And his sal - va - tion, Al - le - lu - ia!
3. Al - le - lu - ia! They sang in joy - ful praise, Al - le - lu - ia!

Text: Based on Ezekiel 47:1–2, 9; © 1973, ICEL. All rights reserved. Used with permission.
Music: Randall DeBruyn, b. 1947, © 1987, OCP. All rights reserved.

LORD, HAVE MERCY

LORD, HAVE MERCY   257

1, 3. Lord, have mer - cy. Lord, have mer - cy.
2. Christ, have mer - cy. Christ, have mer - cy.

1, 3. Lord, have mer - cy, have mer - cy.
2. Christ, have mer - cy, have mer - cy.

Music: *Missa Oecumenica*; after Alexander Archangelsky, 1846–1924; arr. by Richard Proulx, 1937–2010,
© 1999, Richard Proulx. Published by TRINITAS. All rights reserved.

GLORY TO GOD

A CHRISTMAS GLORIA   258

*Refrain: All

Glo - ri - a

in ex - cel - sis De - o, De - o.

*Verses available in accompaniment books.

Music: GLORIA; trad. French Carol; verses arr. by Paul Gibson, b. 1952.

ALLELUIA

ADVENT GOSPEL ACCLAMATION   259

Al - le - lu - ia, al - le - lu - ia, al - le - lu - ia, al - le - lu - ia,

al - le - lu - ia, al - le - lu - ia, al - le - lu - ia, al - le - lu - ia.

Note: Verses for each Sunday of Advent are available in the accompaniment books.

Music: Andrew Wright, b. 1955, © 1999, Andrew Wright. Published by OCP. All rights reserved.

260   ADVENT/CHRISTMAS GOSPEL ACCLAMATION

Refrain: 1st time: Cantor, All repeat; thereafter: All

Al-le - lu - ia, al-le-lu - ia.   Al-le - lu - ia, al-le-lu - ia.

*Verses 1-4
Cantor   4   All   to Refrain

1. You are the joy of ev'ry human heart,   Lord   Je-sus,   come!
   king of all the nations.
2. You are Lord, our justice and our mercy.
   Show us how to live:
3. Eternal light, and sun of justice,
   shine in all our darkness:
4. Emmanuel, the joy of all nations,
   come to us and save us:

*Verses 5-7
Cantor   4   All   to Refrain

5. Born today, our justice and our mercy,   Lord,   Je-sus   Christ!
   God in flesh among us:
6. You are light that shines in the darkness,
   star to guide the nations:
7. You are born of water and the Spirit,
   fountain of our dreams:

*Verses 1–4, Advent; verse 5, Christmas; verse 6, Epiphany; verse 7, Baptism of the Lord.

Text and music: David Haas, b. 1957, © 1986, David Haas. Published by OCP. All rights reserved.

261   CHRISTMAS SEASON GOSPEL ACCLAMATION

Al - le - lu - ia,   al - le - lu-ia!   Al - le - lu - ia, al - le - lu - ia!

Note: Verses available in accompaniment books.

Music: Adapt. fr. *Sussex Carol*; Barbara Bridge, b. 1950, © 2005, Barbara Bridge. Published by OCP. All rights reserved.

262   ALLELUIA FOR THE EASTER SEASON/ALELUYA PARA PASCUA

Al - le - lu - ia!   Al - le - lu - ia!   Al - le - lu - ia!
A - le - lu - ya!   A - le - lu - ya!   A - le - lu - ya!

Note: Verses available in accompaniment books.

Music: O FILII ET FILIAE; Chant, Mode II; *Airs sur les hymnes sacrez, odes et noëls*, 1623.

EASTERTIDE ALLELUIA 263

Al - le - lu - ia, al - le - lu - ia, al - le - lu - ia.

Note: Verses available in accompaniment books.

Music: Chant, Mode VI.

CELTIC ALLELUIA 264

Al - le - lu - ia, al - le - lu - ia.

Al - le - lu - ia, al - le - lu - ia.

Note: Verses available in accompaniment books.

Music: *Celtic Mass*; Fintan O'Carroll, d. 1977, and Christopher Walker, b. 1947, © 1985, Fintan O'Carroll and Christopher Walker. Published by OCP. All rights reserved.

LENTEN GOSPEL ACCLAMATION

GLORY AND PRAISE 265

Glo - ry and praise to you, Word of Life! Je - sus!

Je - sus Christ! Glo - ry and praise to you,

Word of Life! Je - sus! Je - sus Christ!

Note: Verses available in accompaniment books.

Text and music: Jesse Manibusan, b. 1958, © 1993, Jesse Manibusan. Published by OCP. All rights reserved.

266   **LENTEN GOSPEL ACCLAMATION**

Praise to you, Lord_ Je-sus Christ,   King of end-less glo-ry!

Alt. Ref.: *Praise and glo - ry to you, O   Christ, to - day__ and for - ev - er!*

Note: Verses available in accompaniment books.

Text: Refrain © 1969, 1981, 1997, ICEL. All rights reserved. Used with permission. Alternate refrain,
   Michael R. Prendergast, b. 1955, © 1999, Michael R. Prendergast. Published by OCP. All rights reserved.
Music: Michael R. Prendergast and Joseph B. Sullivan, b. 1956, © 1999, Michael R. Prendergast and Joseph B. Sullivan.
   Published by OCP. All rights reserved.

PROFESSION OF FAITH

267   **CREDO III**

Priest/Cantor/Choir   All

I be-lieve in one God, the Fa-ther al-might-y, mak-er of heav-en and earth,

of all things vis-i-ble and in-vis - i-ble. I be-lieve in one Lord Je - sus Christ,

the On-ly Be-got-ten Son of God, born of the Fa - ther be-fore all a - ges.

God from God, Light from Light, true God from true God, be-got-ten, not made,

con - sub - stan - tial with the Fa - ther; through him all things were made.

For us men and for our sal - va - tion he came down from heav - en,

At the words that follow, up to and including "and became man," all bow.

and by the Ho - ly Spir - it was in-car-nate of the Vir-gin Mar - y, and be-came man. For our sake he was cru - ci-fied un - der Pon-tius Pi - late,

he suf-fered death and was bur - ied, and rose a-gain on the third day

in ac-cord-ance with the Scrip-tures. He as-cend-ed in - to heav - en

and is seat-ed at the right hand of the Fa - ther. He will come a-gain in glo-ry

to judge the liv - ing and the dead and his king-dom will have no end.

I be-lieve in the Ho - ly Spir - it, the Lord, the giv - er of life, who pro -

ceeds from the Fa-ther and the Son, who with the Fa-ther and the Son

is a-dored and glo - ri-fied, who has spo-ken through the proph - ets.

I be-lieve in one, ho-ly, ca-tho-lic and a-pos-tol-ic Church. I con-fess one Bap-tism

for the for-give-ness of sins and I look for-ward to the res-ur-rec-tion of

the dead and the life of the world to come. A - men.

Universal Prayer (Prayer of the Faithful)

268

O God, Hear Us

O God, hear us; hear our prayer.

Note: Verses available in accompaniment books.

269

Óyenos, Señor/Listen to Your People

Estribillo Ostinato/Ostinato Refrain

Ó - ye - nos, Se - ñor.   Ó - ye - nos, Se - ñor.
Ding - gin mo ka - mi.
(Filipino)

Lis - ten to your peo - ple.   Ó - ye - nos, Se - ñor.
Chúng con cầu xin Ngài.
(Vietnamese)

Note: Verses available in accompaniment books.

Eucharistic Acclamation: Amen

270

Danish Amen

A - men, a - men, a - men.

Lamb of God

271

Advent Lamb of God

Cantor

1-5
All

1. Lamb of God,
2. Lord of Light,
3. Morn - ing Star,
4. God With Us,
5. Prince of Peace,
6. Lamb of God,

you take a - way the sins of the world, have

1-5. mer - cy on us, have mer - cy on us.

Final | **All**
6. world, grant us your peace, O grant us your peace.

LAMB OF GOD   272

Lamb of God, you take a - way the sins of the

1, 2 world, have mer - cy on us. **Final** world, grant us peace.

AGNUS DEI   273

Latin	1. A - gnus	De - i,	
Vietnamese	2. Chi - en Thi - en	Chu - a,	
Hmong	3. Yaj Txiv	Tswr Ntuj,	
	(Yah dzee	jer ndu,)	qui
Laotian	4. O pra sum pa noy	kog pra jau,	
Spanish	5. Pan	de Vi - da,	
English	6. Cup of Sal -	va - tion,	
Latin	7. A - gnus	De - i,	

tol - lis pec-ca-ta mun - di: mi-se-re-re no - bis.
(Final) do-na no-bis pa - cem.

HYMNS & SONGS

"Thankfully sing to God psalms, hymns and holy songs" (Colossians 3:16). From the earliest centuries of Christianity, hymns and songs have played a major role in the liturgies and devotions of the faithful. A hymn is a song of praise or thanksgiving to God. All hymns are songs; but in contemporary liturgy the term "song" includes a wide variety of other musical forms: verse-refrain, litany, ostinato, chant, acclamation, spiritual and call-response. Often, but not always, liturgical song is based on scripture. Songs bring to expression and realize externally the inner attitudes of adoration, joy, sadness or petition, and they draw together in unity the diverse dispositions of community members. "A liturgical celebration can have no more solemn or pleasing feature than the whole assembly's expressing its faith and devotion in song." (Musicam Sacram, No. 16) St. Augustine said simply, "They who love, sing."

SEASONS AND SOLEMNITIES OF THE LORD

274   O COME, O COME, EMMANUEL

Verses

1. O	come, O	come, Em - man		u -	el,
2. O	come, O	Wis - dom	from	on	high,
3. O	come, O	come, great	Lord	of	might,
4. O	come, O	Rod	of	Jes -	se's	stem,
5. O	come, O	Key	of	Da -	vid,	come,
6. O	come, O	Day - spring	from	on	high
7. O	come, De -	sire	of	na -	tions,	bind

1. And	ran - som	cap - tive	Is -	ra -	el,
2. Who	or - dered	all things	might -	i -	ly;
3. Who	to	your tribes	on	Si -	nai's	height
4. From	ev - 'ry	foe	de - liv -	er	them
5. And	o - pen	wide	our	heav'n -	ly	home;
6. And	cheer	us	by your	draw -	ing	nigh;
7. In	one	the hearts	of	hu -	man - kind;

1. That mourns in lone - ly ex - ile here
2. To us the path of knowl - edge show,
3. In an - cient times did give the law,
4. That trust your might - y pow'r to save,
5. Make safe the way that leads on high,
6. Dis - perse the gloom - y clouds of night,
7. Make all our sad di - vi - sions cease,

1. Un - til the Son of God ap - pear.
2. And teach us in her ways to go.
3. In cloud, and maj - es - ty, and awe.
4. And give them vic - t'ry o'er the grave.
5. And close the path to mis - er - y.
6. And death's dark shad - ow put to flight.
7. And be for us our King of Peace.

Refrain

Re - joice! Re - joice! Em - man - u - el

Shall come to you, O Is - ra - el!

Text: LM with refrain; Latin, 9th cent.; verses 1, 3–6, para. in *Psalteriolum Cantionum Catholicarum*, Cologne, 1710;
    tr. by John Mason Neale, 1818–1866; verses 2, 7 tr. fr. *The Hymnal 1940*, alt.
Music: VENI, VENI, EMMANUEL; Chant, Mode I; *Processionale*, French, 15th cent.;
    adapt. by Thomas Helmore, 1811–1890.

MARANATHA! COME, LORD JESUS   275

*Refrain: 1st time: Cantor, All repeat; thereafter: All

Ma - ra - na - tha! Come, Lord Je - sus. Al - le - lu - ia! Al - le - lu - ia!

Ma - ra - na - tha! Come, Lord Je - sus. Al - le - lu - ia! A - men!

*Verses available in accompaniment books.

276

A VOICE CRIES OUT

Verse 1

1. Con - sole my peo - ple, the ones dear to me; speak to the

1. heart of Je - ru - sa - lem: the time of your mourn - ing is

1. end - ed now, the Lord of life will come.

Refrain

A voice cries out in the wil - der - ness: "Pre - pare a

way for the Lord!" A voice cries out in the wil - der -

ness: "Make straight a high - way for God!"

Verses 2, 4

2. Ev - 'ry val - ley is made a plain, ev - 'ry moun - tain is
4. Zi - on, shout from the moun-tain top, lift up your voice, O Je -

2. lev - eled; the glo - ry of God __ shall then be re -
4. ru - sa - lem, and say to the peo - ple of God's __ own

to Refrain

2. vealed, and the na - tions will sing in praise.
4. land, "Be - hold, be - hold your God!"

Verse 3

3. A voice shouts: "Cry!" O what shall I cry? All flesh is like

3. grass and its flow - ers: the grass may with - er, the

3. flow-ers may fade, but the Word of the Lord is for - ev - er.

Verse 5

5. The Lord will ap - pear as a shep - herd, hold-ing his

5. lambs in his arms, keep-ing his flock so

to Refrain

5. close to his heart, lead-ing them all, old and young.

Text: Based on Isaiah 40:1–11; Michael Joncas, b. 1951.
Music: Michael Joncas.

PATIENCE, PEOPLE 277

Refrain

Pa-tience, peo-ple, till the Lord is come.

Verses

1. See ___ the farm - er a - wait the yield of the soil. He
2. You ___ have seen ___ the pur - pose of the Lord. You
3. Stead - y your hearts, for the Lord is close at hand. And

1. watch - es it in win - ter and in spring rain.
2. know of his com-pas - sion and his mer - cy.
3. do not grum - ble, one a-gainst the oth - er.

1-3. Pa - tience, peo - ple, for the

2

1-3. Lord is com - ing.

Text: Based on James 5:7–9, 11; John Foley, S.J., b. 1939.
Music: John Foley, S.J.

278   ON JORDAN'S BANK

1. On Jor - dan's bank the Bap - tist's cry An -
2. Then cleansed be ev - 'ry soul from sin; Make
3. We hail you as our Sav - ior, Lord, Our
4. To heal the sick stretch out your hand, And
5. To God the Son all glo - ry be, Whose

1. nounc - es that the Lord is nigh; A - wake and heark - en,
2. straight the way of God with - in, And let each heart pre -
3. ref - uge, and our great re - ward; With - out your grace we
4. bid the fall - en sin - ner stand; Shine forth, and let your
5. ad - vent set your peo - ple free; Whom with the Fa - ther

1. for he brings Glad tid - ings of the King of kings.
2. pare a home, Where such a might - y guest may come.
3. waste a - way Like flow'rs that with - er and de - cay.
4. light re - store Earth's own true love - li - ness once more.
5. we a - dore, And Ho - ly Spir - it, ev - er - more.

Text: LM; Charles Coffin, 1676–1749; tr. by John Chandler, 1806–1876, alt.
Music: WINCHESTER NEW; Georg Wittwe's *Musicalishes Hand-Buch,* Hamburg, 1690;
    adapt. by William H. Havergal, 1793–1870.

279   O COME, DIVINE MESSIAH

Verses

1. O come, di - vine Mes - si - ah; The world in
2. O Christ, whom na - tions sigh for, Whom priest and
3. You come in peace and meek - ness And low - ly

1. si - lence waits the day When hope shall sing its
2. proph - et long fore - told, Come, break the cap - tive's
3. will your cra - dle be; All clothed in hu - man

1. tri - umph And sad - ness flee a - way.
2. fet - ters, Re - deem the long - lost fold.
3. weak - ness Shall we your God - head see.

Refrain

Dear Sav - ior, haste! Come, come to earth. Dis-pel the
night and show your face, and bid us hail the dawn of grace. O
come, di-vine Mes - si - ah; the world in si-lence waits the day when
hope shall sing its tri - umph and sad-ness flee a - way.

Text: 78 76 with refrain; Abbé Simon-Joseph Pellegrin, 1663–1745; tr. by Sr. Mary of St. Philip, 1825–1904.
Music: VENEZ, DIVIN MESSIE; trad. French Carol, 16th cent.

THE ANGEL GABRIEL FROM HEAVEN CAME   280

1. The an - gel Ga - bri - el from heav - en came, His
2. "For know a bless - ed Moth - er you shall be, All
3. Then gen - tle Ma - ry meek - ly bowed her head; "To
4. Of her, Em - man - u - el, the Christ, was born In

1. wings as drift - ed snow, his eyes as flame; "All
2. gen - er - a - tions praise con - tin - ual - ly, Your
3. me be as it pleas - es God!" she said. "My
4. Beth - le - hem, all on a Christ - mas morn; And

1. hail," said he, "O low - ly maid - en Ma - ry,"
2. Son shall be Em - man - u - el, by seers fore-told."
3. soul shall laud and mag - ni - fy his ho - ly name."   "Most
4. Chris - tian folk through-out the world will ev - er say:

1-4. high-ly fa - vored la - dy!" Glo - ri - a!

Text: 10 10 12 10; *Birjina gaztettobat zegoen*; trad. Basque Carol; tr. by Sabine Baring-Gould, 1834–1924.
Music: GABRIEL'S MESSAGE; trad. Basque Carol Melody.

281   WHEN THE KING SHALL COME AGAIN

1. When the King shall come a - gain All his pow'r re - veal - ing,
2. In the des - ert trees take root Fresh from his cre - a - tion;
3. Strength-en fee - ble hands and knees, Faint - ing hearts, be cheer-ful!
4. There God's high-way shall be seen Where no roar - ing li - on,

1. Splen-dor shall an-nounce his reign, Life and joy and heal - ing;
2. Plants and flow'rs and sweet-est fruit Join the cel - e - bra - tion;
3. God who comes for such as these Seeks and saves the fear - ful;
4. Noth - ing e - vil or un-clean Walks the road to Zi - on:

1. Earth no long - er in de - cay, Hope no more frus - trat - ed;
2. Riv - ers spring up from the earth, Bar - ren lands a - dorn - ing;
3. Deaf ears, hear the si - lent tongues Sing a - way their weep-ing;
4. Ran-somed peo - ple home-ward bound All your prais - es voic - ing,

1. This is God's re - demp-tion day Long - ing - ly a - wait - ed.
2. Val - leys, this is your new birth, Moun-tains, greet the morn-ing!
3. Blind eyes, see the life - less ones Walk - ing, run-ning, leap-ing.
4. See your Lord with glo - ry crowned, Share in his re - joic-ing!

Text: 76 76 D; Isaiah 35; Christopher Idle, b. 1938, © 1982, The Jubilate Group. All rights reserved.
    Administered by Hope Publishing Co. Used with permission.
Music: GAUDEAMUS PARITER; Johann Horn, ca. 1495–1547.

282   THE KING SHALL COME WHEN MORNING DAWNS

1. The King shall come when morn - ing dawns And
2. Not, as of old, a lit - tle child, To
3. O bright - er than the ris - ing morn When
4. O bright - er than that glo - rious morn Shall
5. The King shall come when morn - ing dawns And

1. light tri - um - phant breaks, When beau - ty gilds the
2. bear, and fight, and die, But crowned with glo - ry
3. he, vic - to - rious, rose And left the lone-some
4. this fair morn - ing be, When Christ, our King, in
5. light and beau - ty brings. Hail, Christ, the Lord! Thy

1. east - ern   hills   And   life   to   joy   a - wakes.
2. like   the   sun   That   lights   the   morn - ing   sky.
3. place   of   death,   De - spite   the   rage   of   foes.
4. beau - ty   comes,   And   we   his   face   shall   see!
5. peo - ple   pray: Come   quick - ly   King   of   kings.

Text: CM; Greek; tr. by John Brownlie, 1859–1925, alt.
Music: MORNING SONG; *Sixteen Tune Settings*, Philadelphia, 1812; *Kentucky Harmony*, 1816.

MARANATHA 283

Refrain

Ma - ra - na - tha, we long for your peace.

Ma - ra - na - tha, we long for your mer - cy. Ma - ra - na -

tha, we long for your com - ing, O God.

Verses

1. In your im - age you have fash - ioned us, in the
2. In our weak-ness we have turned from you, turned from
3. In your love ___ you have sent your Son, your sal -
4. We a - wait your day of glo - ry, Christ ___

1. gar - den you made ___ us; you have giv - en us your
2. light to the dark - ness, ev - er long-ing for sal -
3. va - tion for ev - 'ry-one; Word in - car-nate, God's com -
4. Je - sus, re - turn for us. Gen - tle King, ___ Just De -

to Refrain

1. breath of life, voice to praise your name, voice to praise your name.
2. va - tion, O ___ Lord of light, O ___ Lord of light.
3. pas - sion, hope for hu - man-kind, hope for hu - man - kind.
4. liv - er-er, you will bring us home, you will bring us home.

Text and music: Gerard Chiusano, b. 1965, © 2000, Gerard Chiusano. Published by OCP. All rights reserved.

284   CHRIST, CIRCLE ROUND US

Verses

1. Come, O Ra-diant Dawn, splen-dor of the morn-ing
2. Come, O Flow'r of Love, ho-ly branch of Jes-se's
3. Come, O Word of Truth, font of know-ledge from on
4. Come, O Gate of Hope, ho-ly door of heav-en's
5. Come, O Might-y Lord, mas-ter of the stars of
6. Come, Em-man-u-el, cher-ished hope of Is-ra-
7. Come, Lord Je-sus Christ, long a-wait-ed Prince of

1. light. Come, Sun of Jus-tice,
2. tree. Come, Bough of Bless-ing,
3. high. Come, Ho-ly Wis-dom,
4. throne. Come, Key of Da-vid,
5. night. Come, Strength of Pil-grims,
6. el. Come, live a-mong us,
7. Peace. Come, Hope of Na-tions,

1. turn a-way the pow'r of night.
2. bloom for all the world to see.
3. be our faith-ful friend and guide.
4. o-pen wide the path-way home.
5. keep us in your lov-ing sight.
6. ev-er in our hearts to dwell.
7. ev-er make our love in-crease.

Refrain

Christ, cir-cle round us. Christ, may your light sur-
round us. Shine in our liv-ing. Fill our hearts
with great thanks-giv-ing.

Text: Based on Advent 'O' Antiphons; Dan Schutte, b. 1947.
Music: Based on *Salve Regina* (Chant, Mode V); Dan Schutte.

LET THE KING OF GLORY COME

Refrain

Lift up, you gates, lift up your arch - es: let the
King of glo - ry come! Lift up your hearts and
sing, you peo - ple: let the King of glo - ry come!

Last time to Coda ⊕

Verses

1. Who is the King of glo - ry? Our God,
2. Come, O___ come, Em - man - u - el: come and
3. Come, O___ come, bright Wis - dom: come and
4. Come, you___ Key of Da - vid, come: o - pen our

1. ho - ly and strong! Who is the Lord of
2. dwell___ with us! Come, O___ come, you
3. make___ us wise! Come, O___ come, you
4. heav - en - ly home! Come, De - sire of

to Refrain

1. ma - jes - ty? Our God, might - y and strong!
2. Lord of might: ban - ish death___ and fear!
3. Day - spring: love, un - close___ our eyes!
4. na - tions, come: bring us in - to your peace!

⊕ **Coda**

Let the King of glo - ry come!

286   LIFT UP YOUR HEADS, YE MIGHTY GATES

1. Lift up your heads, ye might-y gates; Be-hold the
2. O blest the land, the cit-y blest, Where Christ the
3. Fling wide the por-tals of your heart; Make it a
4. So come, my Sov-'reign; en-ter in! Let new and

1. King of glo-ry waits! The King of kings is draw-ing
2. rul-er is con-fest! O hap-py hearts and hap-py
3. tem-ple, set a-part From earth-ly use for heav'n's em-
4. no-bler life be-gin; Thy Ho-ly Spir-it guide us

1. near; The Sav-ior of the world is here.
2. homes To whom this King of tri-umph comes!
3. ploy, A-dorned with prayer and love and joy.
4. on, Un-til the glo-rious crown be won.

Text: LM; based on Psalm 24; George Weissel, 1590–1635; tr. by Catherine Winkworth, 1827–1878.
Music: TRURO; Williams' *Psalmodia Evangelica, Part II*, 1789.

287   THE ADVENT OF OUR KING

1. The ad-vent of our King Our thoughts must _ now em-ploy;
2. The co-e-ter-nal Son A maid-en's _ off-spring see;
3. Daugh-ter of Si-on rise To greet thine _ in-fant King;
4. In glo-ry from his throne A-gain will _ Christ de-scend,
5. Let deeds of dark-ness fly Be-fore the ap-proach-ing morn,
6. Our joy-ful prais-es sing To Christ, who _ set us free;

1. Then let us meet him on the road With songs of ho-ly joy.
2. A ser-vant's form Christ put-teth on, To set his peo-ple free.
3. Nor let thy stub-born heart de-spise The par-don he doth bring.
4. And sum-mon all who are his own To joys that nev-er end.
5. For un-to sin 'tis ours to die And serve the Vir-gin-born.
6. Like trib-ute to the Fa-ther bring, And Ho-ly Ghost, to thee.

Text: SM; Charles Coffin, fr. *Paris Breviary*, 1736; tr. by Robert Campbell, 1814–1868, alt.
Music: ST. THOMAS (WILLIAMS); *New Universal Psalmodist*, 1770; Aaron Williams, 1731–1776.

READY THE WAY

Verses

1. "Read - y the way of the Lord! Read - y the
2. "Let ev - 'ry val - ley be filled. Let ev - 'ry
3. Des - ert and waste-land will bloom. Des - ert and
4. Those who are blind will then see. Those who are
5. Strength-en the ones who are weak. Strength-en the

1. way of the Lord!" A voice ___ cries out in the wil - der-
2. val - ley be filled. Let ev - 'ry moun-tain be hum -
3. waste-land will bloom. Glo - ry and splen - dor will fill the
4. deaf will then hear. Those who are lame will then leap for
5. ones who are weak. Say to the fright-ened: "Have cour -

1. ness: "Read - y the way of the Lord!" (to Verse 2)
2. bled; let ev - 'ry val - ley be filled." (to Refrain)
3. land. Des - ert and waste-land will bloom. (to Verse 4)
4. joy. Those who are mute will then sing. (to Refrain)
5. age." Strength-en the ones who are weak. (to Refrain)

Refrain

Here is your God, com-ing with your vin-di-ca - tion.

Look and be-hold the sav - ing pow - er of God.

1, 2 to Verses 3, 5 | Final

2

The sav - ing pow - er of God.

Text: Based on Isaiah 35:1–6; 40:1–5, 9–11; Ezekiel 11:19–20; Bob Hurd, b. 1950.
Music: Bob Hurd.
Text and music © 1986, Bob Hurd. Published by OCP. All rights reserved.

289   **EVERY VALLEY**

Refrain

Ev-'ry val-ley shall be ex-alt-ed and ev-'ry hill made low. And all God's peo-ple shall see to-geth-er the glo-ry of the Lord.

Verses 1, 3

1. A voice cries out in the wil-der-ness, "Pre-pare the way
3. Stand up-on the moun-tain-top. O lift your voice

1. of the Lord. Make straight in the des-ert a
3. to the world. Sing joy-ful-ly, Je-

1. high-way, a high-way ____ for our God."
3. ru-sa-lem: "Be-hold, ____ be-hold your God."

Verse 2

2. Com-fort all my peo-ple. The time for war is gone. The
2. blind shall see, the deaf shall hear, the lame shall leap for joy.

Text: Based on Isaiah 40:1, 3, 4, 9; Bob Dufford, SJ, b. 1943.
Music: Bob Dufford, SJ.
Text and music © 1970, Robert J. Dufford, SJ. Published by OCP. All rights reserved.

290   **CREATOR OF THE STARS OF NIGHT**

1. Cre-a-tor of the stars of night, Your peo-ple's
2. In sor-row that the an-cient curse Should doom to
3. When this old world drew on toward night, You came; but
4. At your great Name, O Je-sus, now All knees must
5. Come in your ho-ly might, we pray, Re-deem us
6. To God Cre-a-tor, God the Son, And God the

1. ev - er - last - ing light, O Christ, Re - deem - er
2. death a u - ni - verse, You came, O Sav - ior,
3. not in splen - dor bright, Not as a mon - arch,
4. bend, all hearts must bow: All things on earth with
5. for e - ter - nal day; De - fend us while we
6. Spir - it, Three - in - One, Praise, hon - or, might, and

1. of us all, We pray you hear us when we call.
2. to set free Your own in glo - rious lib - er - ty.
3. but the child Of Ma - ry, blame - less moth - er mild.
4. one ac - cord, Like those in heav'n, shall call you Lord.
5. dwell be - low From all as - saults of our dread foe.
6. glo - ry be From age to age e - ter - nal - ly.

Text: LM; Latin, 9th cent.; tr. fr. *The Hymnal 1982* © 1985, The Church Pension Fund. All rights reserved.
Used with permission of Church Publishing, Inc., New York, NY.
Music: CONDITOR ALME SIDERUM; Chant, Mode IV.

ADVENT LITANY/LETANÍA DE ADVIENTO 291

O come, O come.   O come, O come.
Oh ven, oh ven.   *Oh ven, oh ven.*

1. True light of the world.
Promised one from God.
Wonder Counselor.
Holy Prince of Peace.

2a. Shoot from Jesse's tree.
King from David's throne.
Heaven's brightest star.
Light amidst the darkness.

2b. Fullness of God's glory.
Son of the Most High.
Eternal Word made flesh.
Recompense divine.

3a. Lover of the just.
Protector of the stranger.
Sustainer of the widow.
Justice for the world.

3b. Food for those who hunger.
Freedom for the captives.
Day of vindication.
Anointed One, Emmanuel.

1. *Luz verdadera.*
Prometido de Dios.
Consejero admirable.
Príncipe de paz.

2a. *Linaje de Jesé.*
Hijo de David.
La estrella más brillante.
Luz en las tinieblas.

2b. *Gloria de los cielos.*
Hijo del Altísimo.
Verbo encarnado.
Divina recompensa.

3a. *Amor para el que es justo.*
Protector del forastero.
Aliento para la viuda.
Justicia para el mundo.

3b. *Sustento de los pobres.*
Liberación para los cautivos.
Día de venganza.
El Ungido, Emmanuel.

*Verses available in accompaniment books.

Text: Based on Isaiah 11; 12; 35 and 'O' Antiphons; Jaime Cortez, b. 1963.
Music: Jaime Cortez.
Text and music © 2005, Jaime Cortez. Published by OCP. All rights reserved.

292   LET THE VALLEYS BE RAISED

Refrain

Let the val - leys be raised and the moun - tains made low. Ev-'ry mead-
- ow and field o-ver-turn. Make the path - way straight
and the high-way run smooth for the com - ing of God in our day.

Verses

1. God, ___ you come to your peo - ple   as you prom-
2. You, lit-tle _ child, go be - fore   him   like the proph-
3. God, ___ you come like the morn - ing   on the dark-

1. - ised of old.   You have raised   up a Sav-
2. - ets of old,   bring-ing news   of his com-
3. - ness of night,   as a light   to the peo-

to Refrain

1. - ior   in the sight   of us   all.
2. - ing   by the mer - cy of   God.
3. - ple,   like the break - ing of   day.

Text: Based on Isaiah 40:3–5; Luke 1:68–79; Dan Schutte, b. 1947.
Music: Dan Schutte.

293   LITANY OF THE WORD

Cantor   All   Cantor   All

1. Word of jus - tice,   Al-le-lu - ia,   Come to dwell here.   Ma-ra-na-tha!
2. Word of mer - cy,   Al-le-lu - ia,   Live a-mong us.   Ma-ra-na-tha!
3. Word of pow - er,   Al-le-lu - ia,   Live with - in us.   Ma-ra-na-tha!
*4. Word of free-dom,   Al-le-lu - ia,   Save your peo - ple.   Ma-ra-na-tha!

*Additional verses available in accompaniment books.

READY THE WAY

Refrain

Read-y the way, read-y the way, read-y the way

1. / 2. of the Lord. of the Lord.

Verse 1

1. Make straight the road, raise the val - leys, and

1. moun-tains make low. Turn-ing from sin, let the bro-ken be whole,

to Refrain

1. and read-y the way of the Lord.

Verses 2, 3

2. As we wait for you, give us the strength to walk
3. Let us see your face; in ___ our hearts we pre-

2. in your truth, so we may love_____ more like__ you
3. - pare a place. Come bring this world__ your mer - cy and grace

to Refrain

2. and } read-y the way for you, Lord.
3. as we }

Text: Based on Isaiah 40:3, 4a; Curtis Stephan, b. 1973.
Music: Curtis Stephan.

295   COMFORT, COMFORT, O MY PEOPLE

1. Com - fort, com - fort, O my peo - ple, Speak of peace, now
2. Hark, the voice of one who's cry - ing In the des - ert
3. O make straight what long was crook - ed, Make the rough - er

1. says our God; Com - fort those who sit in dark - ness,
2. far and near, Bid - ding all to full re - pent - ance
3. plac - es plain; Let your hearts be true and hum - ble,

1. Mourn-ing 'neath their sor-rows' load. Speak un - to Je - ru - sa -
2. Since the king-dom now is here. O that warn - ing cry o -
3. As be - fits his ho - ly reign. For the glo - ry of the

1. lem Of the peace that waits for them; Tell of all the
2. bey! Now pre - pare for God a way; Let the val - leys
3. Lord Now o'er earth is shed a-broad; And all flesh shall

1. sins I cov - er, And that war - fare now is o - ver.
2. rise to meet him And the hills bow down to greet him.
3. see the to - ken That his word is nev - er bro - ken.

Text: 87 87 77 88; based on Isaiah 40:1–8; Johann G. Olearius, 1611–1684; tr. by Catherine Winkworth, 1827–1878, alt.
Music: GENEVA 42; Claude Goudimel, ca. 1514–1572; *Genevan Psalter*, 1551.

296   COME, O LONG-EXPECTED JESUS

1. Come, O long - ex - pect - ed Je - sus, Born to
2. Is - rael's strength and con - so - la - tion, Hope to
3. Born your peo - ple to de - liv - er, Born a
4. By your own e - ter - nal Spir - it Rule in

1. set your peo - ple free! From our fears and
2. all the earth im - part; Dear de - sire of
3. child and yet a king: Born to reign in
4. all our hearts a - lone; By your all - suf -

1. sins   re - lease   us,   You   in   whom our   rest   shall   be.
2. ev - 'ry   na - tion,   Joy   of   ev - 'ry   long - ing   heart.
3. us   for - ev - er,   Now   your   gra - cious   king - dom   bring.
4. fi - cient   mer - it   Raise   us   to   your   glo - rious   throne.

Text: 87 87; Charles Wesley, 1707–1788, alt.
Music: STUTTGART; Christian F. Witt's *Psalmodia Sacra*, Gotha, 1715; adapt. by Henry J. Gauntlett, 1805–1876.

PEOPLE, LOOK EAST 297

1. Peo - ple,   look   East.   The   time   is   near   Of   the
2. Fur - rows,   be   glad,   though earth   is   bare.   One   more
3. Birds, though   you   long   have   ceased   to   build,   Guard   the
4. Stars,   keep   the   watch   when   night   is   dim.   One   more
5. An - gels,   an - nounce   on   this   great   feast: Him   who

1. crown - ing   of   the   year.   Make your house   fair   as   you   are
2. seed   is   plant - ed   there;   Give   up   your strength the   seed   to
3. nest   that must   be   filled.   E - ven   the   hour   when wings   are
4. light   the   bowl   shall   brim.   Shin - ing   be - yond   the   frost - y
5. com - eth   from   the   East.   Set   ev - 'ry   peak   and   val - ley

1. a - ble. Trim   the hearth   and   set   the   ta - ble. Peo - ple, look
2. nour - ish, That   in   course   the flow'r   may flour - ish. Peo - ple, look
3. fro - zen He   for   fledg - ing   time   has   cho - sen. Peo - ple, look
4. weath - er, Bright   as   sun   and moon   to - geth - er. Peo - ple, look
5. hum - ming With   the word,   the Lord   is   com - ing. Peo - ple, look

1. East,   and   sing   to - day: Love,   the   Guest,   is   on   the   way.
2. East,   and   sing   to - day: Love,   the   Rose,   is   on   the   way.
3. East,   and   sing   to - day: Love,   the   Bird,   is   on   the   way.
4. East,   and   sing   to - day: Love,   the   Star,   is   on   the   way.
5. East,   and   sing   to - day: Love,   the   Lord,   is   on   the   way.

Text: 87 98 87; *Oxford Book of Carols*, 1928; Eleanor Farjeon, 1881–1965, © 1957, Eleanor Farjeon. All rights reserved.
   Reprinted by permission of Harold Ober Assoc., Inc.
Music: BESANÇON; Trad. French Carol.

298   WAKE, O WAKE, AND SLEEP NO LONGER

1. Wake, O wake, and sleep no long - er, For he who calls you
2. Zi - on hears the sound of sing - ing; Our hearts are thrilled with
3. Glo - ry, glo - ry, sing the an - gels, While mu - sic sounds from

1. is no strang - er: A - wake, God's own Je - ru - sa - lem!
2. sud - den long - ing: She stirs, and wakes, and stands pre - pared.
3. strings and cym - bals; All hu - man - kind, with songs a - rise!

1. Hear, the mid - night bells are chim - ing The sig - nal for his
2. Christ, her friend, and lord, and lov - er, Her star and sun and
3. Twelve the gates in - to the cit - y, Each one a pearl of

1. roy - al com - ing: Let voice to voice an - nounce his name!
2. strong re - deem - er — At last his might - y voice is heard.
3. shin - ing beau - ty; The streets of gold ring out with praise.

1. We feel his foot - steps near, The Bride - groom at the
2. The Son of God has come To make with us his
3. All crea - tures round the throne A - dore the ho - ly

1. door — Al - le - lu - ia! The lamps will shine with
2. home: Sing ho - san - na! The fight is won, the
3. One With re - joic - ing: A - men be sung by

1. light di - vine As Christ the Sav - ior comes to reign.
2. feast be - gun; We fix our eyes on Christ a - lone.
3. ev - 'ry tongue To crown their wel - come to the King.

Text: 898 898 664 88; based on Matthew 25:1–13; tr. and adapt. by Christopher Idle, b. 1938, © 1982, The Jubilate Group.
All rights reserved. Administered by Hope Publishing Co. Used with permission.
Music: WACHET AUF; Philipp Nicolai, 1556–1608; adapt. by Johann Sebastian Bach, 1685–1750.

EMMANUEL

Refrain

Come, come, Em-man-u-el! Son of God, ap-pear. Heav-en and earth, re-joice! Sal-va-tion is draw-ing near.

Verses

1. O come, O come, Em-man-u - el,
   ___ That mourns in lone-ly ex-ile here
2. O come, O Wis-dom from on high,
   ___ To us the path of knowl-edge show,
3. O come, O Rod of Jes-se's stem;
   ___ That trust your might-y pow'r to save,
4. O come, De - sire of na-tions, bind
   ___ Make all our sad di - vi - sions cease,
5. Re - joice! Em - man - u - el
   Re - joice! Em - man - u - el

(to Refrain)

1. And ran-som cap-tive Is-ra - el,
   ___ Un - til the Son of God ap - pear.
2. Who or - dered all things might - i - ly;
   ___ And teach us in her ways to go.
3. From ev - 'ry foe de - liv - er them
   ___ And give them vic - t'ry o'er the grave.
4. In one the hearts of hu - man - kind;
   ___ And be for us the King of Peace.
5. shall come to thee, O Is-ra - el.
   shall come to thee, O Is-ra - el. *(Fine)*

Text: Refrain, Steve Angrisano, b. 1965, © 2004, Steve Angrisano. Published by OCP. All rights reserved.
   Verses based on Advent 'O' Antiphons.
Music: Steve Angrisano, © 2004, Steve Angrisano. Published by OCP. All rights reserved.

300

O COME, ALL YE FAITHFUL

Verses

1. O come, all ye faith - ful, joy - ful and tri - um - phant, O
2. God of __ God, __ Light __ of __ Light, __
3. Sing, choirs of an - gels, sing in ex - ul - ta - tion,
4. Yea, Lord, we greet thee, born this hap- py morn - ing,

1. *Ad - é - ste fi - dé - les, laé - ti tri-um-phán - tes, Ve -*
2. *De - um de De - o, Lu - men de Lú - mi-ne*
3. *Can - tet nunc i - o, cho-rus an - ge - ló - rum,*
4. *Er - go qui na - tus Di - e ho-di - ér - na,*

1. come ye, O come __ ye to Beth - le - hem;
2. Lo! he comes forth __ from the Vir - gin's womb.
3. Sing, all ye cit - i - zens of heav'n a - bove!
4. Je - sus, to thee __ be all glo - ry giv'n;

1. *ní - te, ve - ní - te in Béth - le - hem.*
2. *Ge - stant pu - él - lae __ ví - sce - ra.*
3. *Can - tet nunc au - la cae - lés - ti - um.*
4. *Je - su __ ti - bi sit gló - ri - a.*

1. Come and be - hold him, born the King of an - gels;
2. Our ver - y God, be - got - ten, not cre - a - ted;
3. Glo - ry to God, all glo - ry in the high - est;
4. Word of the Fa - ther, now in flesh ap - pear - ing;

1. *Na - tum vi - dé - te Re - gem an - ge - ló - rum.*
2. *De - um __ ve - rum, Gé - ni - tum, non fa - ctum.*
3. *Gló - ri - a, gló - ria, in ex - cél - sis De - o.*
4. *Pa - tris ae - tér - nae ver - bum ca - ro fa - ctum.*

Refrain

O come, let us a - dore him, O come, let us a - dore him, O

Ve - ní - te, a - do - ré - mus, ve - ní - te, a - do - ré - mus, ve -

come, let us a - dore him, Christ, the Lord!

ní - te, a - do - ré - mus Dó - mi - num.

Text: Irregular with refrain; John F. Wade, ca. 1711–1786; tr. by Frederick Oakeley, 1802–1880, alt.
Music: ADESTE FIDELES; John F. Wade.

WAKE FROM YOUR SLEEP

301

1. Wake from your sleep, a Sav - ior is born. God's ho - ly
2. Come from your fields as shep-herds of old. Wel-come this
3. Stay with us now, O Lord of the earth. Make of our
4. Now shall the earth take joy in her tears. Now shall our

1. child gives light to this morn, all our dark - ness
2. child whom proph - ets fore - told. God has made the
3. hearts a place for your birth. Though our cares be
4. hearts be turned from their fears. All the earth shall

1. to dis - pel. Praise to our God whose glo - ry we tell.
2. earth his home. Praise to our God, the Sav - ior has come.
3. great or small, Je - sus the Lord, be born in us all.
4. sing God's praise. Je - sus the Lord, be born on this day.

Text and music: Dan Schutte, b. 1947, © 1977, 1978, Daniel L. Schutte and OCP. All rights reserved.

LO, HOW A ROSE E'ER BLOOMING

302

1. Lo, how a Rose e'er bloom-ing From ten - der stem hath sprung!
2. I - sai - ah 'twas fore-told it, This Rose I have in mind,
3. O Flow'r, whose fra-grance ten - der With sweet-ness fills the air,

1. Of Jes - se's lin - eage com - ing, As those of old have sung.
2. With Ma - ry we be - hold it, The Vir - gin Moth - er kind.
3. Dis - pel in glo-rious splen-dor The dark-ness ev - 'ry-where;

1. It came, a flow - er bright, A - mid the
2. To show God's love a - right, She bore to
3. True man, yet ver - y God, From sin and

1. cold of win - ter, When half spent was the night.
2. us a Sav - ior, When half spent was the night.
3. death now save us, And share our ev - 'ry load.

Text: 76 76 6 76; based on Isaiah 11:1; trad. German Carol, 15th cent.; tr. by Theodore Baker, 1851–1934, alt.
Music: ES IST EIN' ROS' ENTSPRUNGEN; *Alte Catholische Geistliche Kirchengesänge*, Cologne, 1599.

303   JOY TO THE WORLD

1. Joy to the world! the Lord is come; Let earth re-
2. Joy to the world! the Sav-ior reigns; Let us our
3. No more let sins and sor-rows grow, Nor thorns in-
4. He rules the world with truth and grace, And makes the

1. ceive her King; Let ev-'ry heart pre-pare him
2. songs em-ploy; While fields and floods, rocks, hills and
3. fest the ground; He comes to make his bless-ings
4. na-tions prove The glo-ries of his righ-teous-

1. room, And heav'n and na-ture sing, And heav'n and na-ture
2. plains Re-peat the sound-ing joy, Re-peat the sound-ing
3. flow Far as the curse is found, Far as the curse is
4. ness, And won-ders of his love, And won-ders of his

1. sing, And heav'n, and heav'n and na-ture sing.
2. joy, Re-peat, re-peat the sound-ing joy.
3. found, Far as, far as the curse is found.
4. love, And won-ders, won-ders of his love.

Text: CM with repeats: based on Psalm 98; Isaac Watts, 1764–1748, alt.
Music: ANTIOCH; T. Hawkes' *Collection of Tunes*, 1833; George Frideric Handel, 1685–1759;
   adapt. by Lowell Mason, 1792–1872, alt.

304   GOD REST YOU MERRY, GENTLEMEN

Verses

1. God rest you mer-ry, gen-tle-men, Let noth-ing you dis-may;
2. From God our heav'n-ly Fa-ther A bless-ed an-gel came,
3. "Fear not, then," said the an-gel, "Let noth-ing you af-fright;
4. Now to the Lord sing prais-es, All you with-in this place,

1. Re-mem-ber Christ our Sav-ior Was born on Christ-mas Day
2. And un-to cer-tain shep-herds Brought tid-ings of the same,
3. This day is born a Sav-ior Of Vir-gin pure and bright,
4. And with true love and char-i-ty Each oth-er now em-brace;

1. To save us all from Sa-tan's pow'r When we were gone a - stray.
2. How that in Beth - le - hem was born The Son of God by name.
3. To free all those who trust in him From Sa - tan's pow'r and might."
4. This ho - ly tide of Christ - mas Is filled with heav'n-ly grace.

Refrain

O tid - ings of com - fort and joy, Com-fort and

joy; O tid - ings of com - fort and joy.

Text: 86 86 86 with refrain; trad. English Carol, 18th cent.
Music: GOD REST YOU MERRY; trad. English Carol; melody fr. *Little Book of Christmas Carols*, ca. 1846.

WHILE SHEPHERDS WATCHED THEIR FLOCKS 305

1. While   shep-herds watched their flocks by   night, All   seat - ed
2. "Fear   not," said   he,   for might - y   dread Had   seized their
3. "To   you,   in   Da - vid's town this   day,   Is   born   of
4. "The   heav'n - ly   Babe   you there shall   find   To   hu - man
5. Thus   spoke the   ser - aph, and forth - with Ap - peared   a
6. "All   glo - ry   be   to   God on   high, And   on   the

1. on   the   ground,   The   an - gel   of   the   Lord came   down,
2. trou-bled   mind.   "Glad   tid - ings   of   great   joy   I   bring
3. Da - vid's   line   The   Sav - ior,   who   is   Christ, the   Lord,
4. view dis - played,   All   mean - ly wrapped in   swath-ing   bands,
5. shin - ing   throng   Of   an - gels prais - ing God, who   thus
6. earth be   peace: Good   will hence-forth, from heav'n to   all,

1. And   glo - ry shone a - round,   And   glo - ry shone a - round.
2. To   you   and hu - man-kind,   To   you   and hu - man-kind.
3. And   this   shall be   the sign,   And   this   shall be   the sign:
4. And   in   a   man-ger laid,   And   in   a   man-ger laid."
5. Ad - dressed their joy - ful song,   Ad-dressed their joy - ful song:
6. Be - gin   and nev - er cease!   Be - gin   and nev - er cease!"

Text 86 86 6; based on Luke 2:8–14; Nahum Tate, 1652–1715, alt.
Music: CHRISTMAS; George Frideric Handel, 1685–1759; adapt. in *Harmonia Sacra*, 1812.

306 IT CAME UPON THE MIDNIGHT CLEAR

1. It came up-on the mid-night clear, That glo - rious
2. Still through the clo - ven skies they come, With peace - ful
3. And ye, be-neath life's crush-ing load, Whose forms are
4. For, lo, the days are has-tening on, By proph - et

1. song of old, From an - gels bend - ing near the
2. wings un-furled, And still their heav'n - ly mu - sic
3. bend - ing low, Who toil a - long the climb - ing
4. bards fore-told, When with the ev - er - cir - cling

1. earth To touch their harps of gold: "Peace on the earth, good
2. floats O'er all the wea - ry world: A - bove its sad and
3. way With pain - ful steps and slow, Look now! for glad and
4. years Comes 'round the age of gold; When peace shall o - ver

1. will to all From heav'n's all gra - cious King;" The
2. low - ly plains They bend on hov - 'ring wing, And
3. gold - en hours Come swift - ly on the wing: O
4. all the earth Its an - cient splen - dors fling, And

1. world in sol - emn still-ness lay, To hear the an - gels sing.
2. ev - er o'er its Ba - bel sounds The bless-ed an - gels sing.
3. rest be - side the wea - ry road And hear the an - gels sing.
4. all the world give back the song Which now the an - gels sing.

Text: CMD; Edmund H. Sears, 1810–1876, alt.
Music: CAROL; Richard S. Willis, 1819–1900, alt.

307 A CHILD IS BORN IN BETHLEHEM

Verses

1. A child is born in Beth - le - hem, al - le - lu - ia!
2. In man - ger bare, in for - eign land, al - le - lu - ia!
3. The vir - gin moth - er bore a son, al - le - lu - ia!
4. The an - gels sing to shep-herds near, al - le - lu - ia!
5. The kings of na - tions from a - far, al - le - lu - ia!
6. With won-drous mis - sion now fore - told, al - le - lu - ia!
7. A world once lost in dark - est night, al - le - lu - ia!
8. Let trum - pet sound and cym - bals ring, al - le - lu - ia!

1. Re - joice and sing, Je - ru - sa - lem, al - le - lu - ia, al - le - lu - ia!
2. Ac - cord - ing to th'e - ter - nal plan, al - le - lu - ia, al - le - lu - ia!
3. A child di - vine yet with us one, al - le - lu - ia, al - le - lu - ia!
4. The song that earth so longed to hear, al - le - lu - ia, al - le - lu - ia!
5. Pro - claim the mes - sage of the star, al - le - lu - ia, al - le - lu - ia!
6. By myrrh and frank - in - cense and gold, al - le - lu - ia, al - le - lu - ia!
7. Is now a - flame with bril - liant light, al - le - lu - ia, al - le - lu - ia!
8. Let all on earth in glad - ness sing, al - le - lu - ia, al - le - lu - ia!

Refrain

A sav - ior has been born, the Son of God, the

Prince of Peace. O come, let us a - dore.

Text: 88 with alleluias and refrain; *Puer natus in Bethlehem*; Latin, 14th cent.;
tr. by Owen Alstott, b. 1947, © 2002, OCP. All rights reserved.
Music: PUER NATUS; Chant, Mode I.

ANGELS WE HAVE HEARD ON HIGH 308

Verses

1. An - gels we have heard on high Sweet - ly sing - ing o'er the plains,
2. Shep - herds, why this ju - bi - lee? Why your joy - ous strains pro - long?
3. Come to Beth - le - hem and see Him whose birth the an - gels sing;
4. See him in a man - ger laid Whom the an - gels praise a - bove;

1. And the moun - tains in re - ply Ech - o back their joy - ous strains.
2. Say what may the tid - ings be Which in - spire your heav'n - ly song.
3. Come, a - dore on bend - ed knee Christ, the Lord, the new - born King.
4. Ma - ry, Jo - seph, lend your aid, While we raise our hearts in love.

Refrain

Glo - ri - a in ex - cel - sis De - o!

Glo - ri - a in ex - cel - sis De - o!

Text: 77 77 with refrain; Trad. French Carol, ca. 18th cent.; tr. fr. *Crown of Jesus Music, II*, London, 1862;
tr. by James Chadwick, 1813–1882, and others, alt.
Music: GLORIA; Trad. French Carol.

309   **SILENT NIGHT**

1. Si-lent night! Ho-ly night! All is calm, all is bright Round yon
2. Si-lent night! Ho-ly night! Shep-herds quake at the sight; Glo-ries
3. Si-lent night! Ho-ly night! Son of God, love's pure light Ra-diant

1. Vir - gin Moth-er and child! Ho-ly in-fant so ten-der and mild,
2. stream from heav-en a - far; Heav'n-ly hosts— sing "Al-le-lu-ia!
3. beams from thy ho-ly face, With the dawn of re-deem-ing grace,

1. Sleep in heav-en-ly peace, Sleep in heav-en-ly peace.
2. Christ the Sav-ior is born, Christ the Sav-ior is born."
3. Je - sus, Lord, at thy birth, Je - sus, Lord, at thy birth.

Text: Irregular; Joseph Mohr, 1792–1849; English tr. by John F. Young, 1820–1885.
Music: STILLE NACHT; Franz X. Gruber, 1787–1863.

310   **AWAY IN A MANGER**

1. A - way in a man-ger, no crib for a bed, The
2. The cat-tle are low-ing, the ba-by a - wakes, But
3. Be near me, Lord Je-sus! I ask thee to stay Close

1. lit - tle Lord Je - sus laid down his sweet head. The
2. lit - tle Lord Je - sus, no cry - ing he makes. I
3. by me for - ev - er, and love me, I pray. Bless

1. stars in the bright sky looked down where he lay, The
2. love thee, Lord Je - sus! Look down from the sky, And
3. all the dear chil-dren in thy ten - der care, And

1. lit - tle Lord Je - sus, a - sleep on the hay.
2. stay by my side un - til morn - ing is nigh.
3. fit us for heav - en, to live with thee there.

Text: 11 11 11 11; verses 1–2, *Little Children's Book for Schools and Families*, ca. 1885;
   verse 3, John T. McFarland, 1851–1913; Gabriel's *Vineyard Songs*, 1892, alt.
Music: CRADLE SONG; William J. Kirkpatrick, 1838–1921.

GO, TELL IT ON THE MOUNTAIN 311

Refrain

Go, tell it on the moun-tain, O-ver the hills and ev-'ry-
where; Go, tell it on the moun-tain That Je-sus Christ is born.

Verses

1. While shep-herds kept their watch-ing O'er si-lent flocks by night,
2. The shep-herds feared and trem-bled When high a-bove the earth
3. And lo, when they had heard it, They all bowed down and prayed;
4. Down in a low-ly man-ger The hum-ble Christ was born,

to Refrain

1. Be-hold, through-out the heav-ens There shone a ho-ly light.
2. Rang out the an-gel cho-rus That hailed our Sav-ior's birth.
3. They trav-eled on to-geth-er To where the Babe was laid.
4. And God sent us sal-va-tion That bless-ed Christ-mas morn.

Text: 76 76 with refrain; John W. Work, Jr., 1872–1925, alt.; from *American Negro Songs and Spirituals*, 1940,
© Mrs. John W. Work III.
Music: GO TELL IT; Spiritual.

INFANT HOLY, INFANT LOWLY 312

1. In-fant ho-ly, in-fant low-ly, For his bed a
2. Flocks were sleep-ing, shep-herds keep-ing Vi-gil till the

1. cat-tle stall; Ox-en low-ing, lit-tle know-ing
2. morn-ing new. Saw the glo-ry, heard the sto-ry,

1. Christ the babe is Lord of all. Swift are wing-ing, an-gels sing-ing,
2. Tid-ings of a gos-pel true. Thus re-joic-ing, free from sor-row,

1. No-els ring-ing, tid-ings bring-ing: Christ the babe is Lord of all.
2. Prais-es voic-ing greet the mor-row: Christ the babe was born for you.

Text: 87 87 88 77; Polish Carol; tr. by Edith Margaret Gellibrand Reed, 1885–1933.
Music: W ZLOBIE LEZY; Polish Carol.

313   HARK! THE HERALD ANGELS SING

Verses

1. Hark! the her - ald an - gels sing: "Glo - ry to the
2. Christ, by high - est heav'n a - dored, Christ, the ev - er -
3. Hail the heav'n - born Prince of Peace! Hail the Sun of

1. new - born King; Peace on earth, and mer - cy mild,
2. last - ing Lord; Late in time, be - hold him come,
3. Righ - teous - ness! Light and life to all he brings,

1. God and sin - ners rec - on - ciled!" Joy - ful, all ye
2. Off - spring of a vir - gin's womb. Veiled in flesh the
3. Ris'n with heal - ing in his wings. Mild he lays his

1. na - tions, rise, Join the tri - umph of the skies; With an -
2. God - head see! Hail th'in - car - nate De - i - ty! Pleased as
3. glo - ry by, Born that we no more may die, Born to

1. gel - ic hosts pro - claim: "Christ is born in Beth - le - hem!"
2. man with us to dwell; Je - sus, our Em - man - u - el!
3. raise us from the earth, Born to give us sec - ond birth.

Refrain

Hark! the her - ald an - gels sing, "Glo - ry to the new - born King."

Text: 77 77 D with refrain; Charles Wesley, 1707–1788, alt.
Music: MENDELSSOHN; Felix Mendelssohn, 1809–1847; adapt. by William H. Cummings, 1831–1915.

314   GOOD CHRISTIAN FRIENDS, REJOICE

1-3. Good Chris - tian friends, re - joice, With heart and soul and voice;

1. Give ye heed to what we say: Je - sus Christ is born to - day!
2. Now ye hear of end - less bliss; Je - sus Christ was born for this!
3. Now ye need not fear the grave; Je - sus Christ was born to save!

1. Ox and ass be - fore him bow, And he is in the man-ger now.
2. He has o-pened heav-en's door, And we are blest for ev - er-more.
3. Calls you one and calls you all, To gain his ev - er - last-ing hall.

1. Christ is born to - day! Christ is born to - day!
2. Christ was born for this! Christ was born for this!
3. Christ was born to save! Christ was born to save!

Text: 66 77 78 55; Latin and German, 14th cent.; tr. by John M. Neale, 1818–1866, alt.
Music: IN DULCI JUBILO; J. Klug's *Geistliche Lieder*, Wittenberg, 1535.

RISE UP, SHEPHERD, AND FOLLOW   315

Verses

1. There's a star in the East on __ Christ-mas morn; Rise up,
2. Leave your sheep, leave your sheep, and __ leave your lambs; Rise up,
3. If you take good __ heed to the an - gel's words; Rise up,

1. shep-herd, and fol-low; It will lead to the place where the
2. shep-herd, and fol-low; Leave your ewes and your rams, leave your
3. shep-herd, and fol-low; You'll for - get your __ flocks, you'll for -

Refrain

1. Christ was born;
2. ewes and rams;   Rise up, shep-herd, and fol-low.   Fol - low,
3. get your herds;

fol - low; Rise up, shep-herd, and fol-low.   Fol-low the Star of

Beth - le - hem;   Rise up, shep-herd, and fol - low.

Text: 10 7 11 7 with refrain.
Music: RISE UP, SHEPHERD; Spiritual.

316   O LITTLE TOWN OF BETHLEHEM

1. O lit-tle town of Beth-le-hem, How still we see thee lie!
2. For Christ is born of Ma - ry, And gath-ered all a - bove,
3. How si - lent-ly, how si - lent-ly, The won-drous gift is giv'n!
4. O ho - ly Child of Beth-le-hem! De-scend to us, we pray;

1. A - bove thy deep and dream-less sleep The si - lent stars go by;
2. While mor-tals sleep, the an - gels keep Their watch of won-d'ring love.
3. So God im-parts to hu - man hearts The bless-ings of his heav'n.
4. Cast out our sin and en - ter in; Be born in us to - day.

1. Yet in thy dark streets shin - eth The ev - er - last-ing Light:
2. O morn-ing stars, to - geth - er Pro - claim the ho - ly birth!
3. No ear may hear his com - ing, But in this world of sin,
4. We hear the Christ-mas an - gels The great glad tid-ings tell;

1. The hopes and fears of all the years Are met in thee to - night.
2. And prais - es sing to God the King, And peace to all on earth.
3. Where meek souls will re - ceive him, still The dear Christ en - ters in.
4. O come to us, a - bide with us, Our Lord Em-man - u - el!

Text: 86 86 76 86; Phillips Brooks, 1835–1893, alt.
Music: ST. LOUIS; Lewis H. Redner, 1831–1908.

317   OF THE FATHER'S LOVE BEGOTTEN

1. Of the Fa-ther's love be - got - ten, Ere the worlds be -
2. Bless-ed was the day for ev - er When the Vir - gin,
3. This is he whom seers in old time Chant-ed of with
4. O ye heights of heav'n, a - dore him; An - gel hosts, his
5. Glo - ry be to God the Fa - ther, Glo - ry be to

1. gan to be, He is Al - pha and O - me - ga,
2. full of grace, By the Ho - ly Ghost con-ceiv - ing,
3. one ac - cord, Whom the voic - es of the proph - ets
4. prais - es sing; All do-min-ions, bow be - fore him,
5. God the Son, Glo - ry to the Ho - ly Spir - it,

1. He the source, the end - ing he, Of the things that
2. Bore the Sav - ior of our race, And the child, the
3. Prom-ised in their faith - ful word; Now he shines, the
4. And ex - tol our God and King; Let no tongue on
5. Per - sons three, yet God - head one. Glo - ry be from

1. are, that have been, And that fu - ture years shall see,
2. world's Re - deem - er, First re-vealed his sa - cred face,
3. long - ex - pect - ed; Let cre - a - tion praise the Lord,
4. earth be si - lent, Ev - 'ry voice in con - cert ring,
5. all cre - a - tion While e - ter - nal a - ges run,

1-5. Ev - er-more and ev - er-more. 5. A - men.

Text: 87 87 87 7; verses 1–4, *Corde natus ex parentis*; Marcus Aurelius Clemens Prudentius, 348–413;
tr. by John M. Neale, 1818–1866, and Henry W. Baker, 1827–1877, alt.; verse 5, Horatius Bonar, 1808–1889.
Music: DIVINUM MYSTERIUM; *Sanctus* trope, 11th cent.; Chant, Mode V; adapt. fr. *Piae Cantiones*, 1582.

CHRIST WAS BORN ON CHRISTMAS DAY 318

1. Christ was born on Christ-mas day: Wreathe the hol - ly,
2. He is born to set us free, He is born our
3. Let the bright red ber - ries glow Ev - 'ry-where in
4. Chris - tians all, re - joice and sing, 'Tis the birth - day

1. twine the bay, *Chri - stus na - tus ho - di - e:* The
2. Lord to be, *Ex Ma - ri - a Vir - gi - ne:* The
3. good - ly show: *Chri - stus na - tus ho - di - e:* The
4. of a King, *Ex Ma - ri - a Vir - gi - ne:* The

1. Babe, the Son, the Ho - ly One of Ma - ry.
2. God, the Lord, by all a - dored for ev - er.
3. Babe, the Son, the Ho - ly One of Ma - ry.
4. God, the Lord, by all a - dored for ev - er.

Text: 777 11; Traditional.
Music: RESONET IN LAUDIBUS; German Carol, 14th cent.

319   THE SNOW LAY ON THE GROUND

Verses

1. The snow lay on the ground, the stars shone bright, When
2. 'Twas Ma - ry, Vir - gin pure of ho - ly Anne, That
3. Saint Jo - seph, too was near to tend the child; To
4. And thus that man - ger poor be - came a throne; For

1. Christ our Lord was born on Christ - mas night. Ve - ní - te,
2. brought in - to this world the God made man. She laid him
3. guard him and pro - tect his moth - er mild: The an - gels
4. he whom Ma - ry bore was God the Son. O come, then,

1. a - do - ré - mus Dó - mi - num, Ve - ní - te, a - do-
2. in a stall at Beth - le - hem; The ass and ox - en
3. hov - er'd 'round, and sang this song: Ve - ní - te, a - do-
4. let us join the heav'n - ly host, To praise the Fa - ther,

Refrain

1. ré - mus Dó - mi - num.   Ve - ní - te, a - do - ré - mus
2. shared the roof with them.
3. ré - mus Dó - mi - num.
4. Son, and Ho - ly Ghost.

Dó - mi - num,   Ve - ní - te, a - do - ré - mus   Dó - mi - num.

Text: 10 10 10 10 with refrain; based on Isaiah 7:14; 19th cent.; anon.
Music: VENITE ADOREMUS; trad. Melody; adapt. in *Catholic Hymns*, Albany, New York, 1860.

320   SING WE NOW OF CHRISTMAS

Verses

1. ᵧ Sing we now of Christ - mas, No - el, __ sing we here!
2. ᵧ An - gels called to shep - herds, "Leave your __ flocks at rest,
3. In Beth - le - hem they found him; Jo - seph and Ma - ry mild,
4. ᵧ From the east - ern coun - try Came the __ kings a - far,
5. ᵧ Gold and myrrh they took there, Gifts of __ great - est price;

1. Hear our grate-ful prais - es   To the   Babe so   dear.
2. Jour - ney forth to   Beth - l'em,   Find the   lamb - kin   blest."
3. Seat - ed by the   man - ger,   Near the   ho - ly   child.
4. Bear - ing gifts to   Beth - l'em,   Guid - ed   by a   star.
5. Frank - in - cense to   greet the   Child of   par - a - dise.

Refrain

Sing   we   No - el,   the   King   is   born, No - el!

Sing we now of Christ - mas,   Sing we   now No - el!

Text: 65 65 with refrain; Trad. Provençal Carol.
Music: NOËL NOUVELET; Trad. French Carol.

SEE AMID THE WINTER'S SNOW   321

1. See   a - mid the win - ter's snow,   born for us on earth be - low,
2. Say, you ho - ly shep - herds, say,   tell your joy - ful news to - day.

1. see, the gen - tle lamb ap - pears, prom - ised from e - ter - nal years.
2. Why have you now left your sheep on the lone - ly moun - tain steep?

1. There with - in a man - ger lies   he who built the star - ry skies;
2. "As we watched at dead of night, there ap - peared a won - drous light;

1

to Verse 2

1. he who, throned in heights sub - lime,   sits a - mid the cher - u - bim.

Final

2. an - gels sing - ing 'Peace on earth' told us of   the Sav - ior's birth."

Text: 77 77 D; Edward Caswall, 1814–1878.
Music: WINTER'S SNOW; Kevin Keil, ASCAP, b. 1956, © 1992, Kevin Keil. Published by OCP. All rights reserved.

322

O COME, LITTLE CHILDREN

1. O come, lit-tle chil-dren; come one and come
2. O see in the man-ger so meek and so
3. His bed, lit-tle chil-dren, a man-ger with

1. all, O come to the man-ger in Beth-le-hem's
2. mild, O see in the soft light the heav-en-ly
3. hay; His Moth-er and Jo-seph in ec-sta-sy

1. stall, And see what our Fa-ther in heav-en a-
2. Child, In swad-dling clothes fold-ed, his beau-ty more
3. pray, The shep-herds in won-der their glad wor-ship

1. bove Has sent to us all on this earth with his love.
2. sweet Than an-gels, whose voic-es his low-ly birth greet.
3. bring, While cho-rus of an-gels sweet Glo-ri-as sing.

Text: 11 11 11 11; Johann C. von Schmid, 1768–1854; tr. by Melanie Schute, 1885–1922, alt.
Music: IHR KINDERLEIN, KOMMET; Johann A. Schulz, 1749–1800.

323

CHILDREN, RUN JOYFULLY

Refrain

Chil-dren, run joy-ful-ly, Je-sus is born. Tell all the

moun-tains to sing. Pray to our Fa-ther in

heav-en this day: Thank you, for Je-sus is born.

Verse 1

1. Shep-herds stood watch-ing, keep-ing their sheep, and sud-den-ly

1. an-gels ap-peared. "Don't be a-fraid. We bring you great

1. joy: Your Sav - ior is born this night."

Verse 2
2. "And this will be a sign to you: the ba - by will

2. lie in a man - ger in the cit-y of Da-vid, in

to Refrain
2. Beth - le - hem. Go now, vis - it your Lord."

AWAY IN A MANGER

324

1. A - way in a man-ger, no crib for a bed, The
2. The cat - tle are low - ing, the ba - by a - wakes, But
3. Be near me, Lord Je - sus, I ask thee to stay Close

1. lit - tle Lord Je - sus laid down his sweet head; The
2. lit - tle Lord Je - sus, no cry - ing he makes; I
3. by me for - ev - er, and love me, I pray; Bless

1. stars in the sky ___ looked down where he lay, The
2. love thee, Lord Je - sus! Look down from the sky, And
3. all the dear chil - dren in thy ten - der care, And

1. lit - tle Lord Je - sus, a - sleep on the hay.
2. stay by my cra - dle till morn - ing is nigh.
3. fit us for heav - en to live with thee there.

Text: 11 11 11 11; verses 1–2, *Little Children's Book for Schools and Families*, ca. 1885;
   verse 3, John T. McFarland, 1851–1913; *Gabriel's Vineyard Songs*, 1892, alt.
Music: MUELLER; attr. to James R. Murray, 1841–1905.

325   GOD OF EVE AND GOD OF MARY

1. God of Eve and God of Ma - ry, God of
2. As you came to earth in Je - sus, So you
3. Thank you, that the Church, our Moth - er, Gives us
4. Thank you for be - long - ing shel - ter, Bonds of
5. God of Eve and God of Ma - ry, Christ our

1. love and moth - er earth, Thank you for the
2. come to us to - day; You are pres - ent
3. bread and fills our cup, And the com - fort
4. friend - ship, ties of blood, And for those who
5. broth - er, hu - man son, Spir - it, car - ing

1. ones who with us Shared their life and gave us birth.
2. in the car - ing That pre - pares us for life's way.
3. of the Spir - it Warms our hearts and lifts us up.
4. have no chil - dren, Yet are par - ents un - der God.
5. like a moth - er, Take our love and make us one.

Text: 87 87; Fred Kaan, b. 1929, © 1989, Hope Publishing Co. All rights reserved. Used with permission.
Music: STUTTGART; Christian F. Witt's *Psalmodia Sacra*, Gotha, 1715; adapt. by Henry J. Gauntlett, 1805–1876.

326   GOD OF ADAM, GOD OF JOSEPH

1. God of A - dam, God of Jo - seph, God of
2. God, you make us your com - pan - ions, Shar - ers
3. May your pas - sion for cre - a - tion Be re -
4. Thank you for all men en - trust - ed With the
5. Ab - ba (Fa - ther), God of Jo - seph, Hu - man

1. sow - ing, soil and seed, Thank you for your
2. of your lov - ing cup; Thank you for the
3. flect - ed in our own; For our role in
4. charge of fa - ther - hood, And for those who
5. Christ whose name we bear, Spir - it, womb of

1. world of prom - ise: Milk and hon - ey, wine and bread.
2. gen - er - a - tions, Weave of names and threads of hope.
3. birth and nur - ture Make through us your pres - ence known.
4. have no chil - dren, Yet are par - ents un - der God.
5. life and wis - dom: Thank you, God, for who we are!

Text: 87 87; Fred Kaan, b. 1929, © 1989, Hope Publishing Co. All rights reserved. Used with permission.
Music: STUTTGART; Christian F. Witt's *Psalmodia Sacra*, Gotha, 1715; adapt. by Henry J. Gauntlett, 1805–1876.

ONCE IN ROYAL DAVID'S CITY   327

1. Once in roy - al Da - vid's cit - y
2. He came down to earth from heav - en
3. And through all his won - drous child - hood
4. For he is our child - hood's pat - tern,
5. And our eyes at last shall see him,

1. Stood a low - ly cat - tle shed, Where a
2. Who is God and Lord of all, And his
3. He would hon - or and o - bey, Love and
4. Day by day like us he grew; He was
5. Through his own re - deem - ing love; For that

1. moth - er laid her ba - by In a man - ger
2. shel - ter was a sta - ble, And his cra - dle
3. watch the low - ly maid - en In whose gen - tle
4. lit - tle, weak, and help - less, Tears and smiles like
5. child so dear and gen - tle Is our Lord in

1. for his bed. Mar - y was that moth - er
2. was a stall. With the poor and mean and
3. arms he lay. Chris - tian chil - dren all should
4. us he knew: And he feels for all our
5. heav'n a - bove: And he leads his chil - dren

1. mild, _____ Je - sus Christ her lit - tle Child. _____
2. low - ly Lived on earth our Sav - ior ho - ly.
3. be _____ Kind, o - be - dient, good as he. _____
4. sad - ness, And he shares in all our glad - ness.
5. on _____ To the place where he has gone. _____

Text: 87 87 77; Cecil Frances Alexander, 1818–1895, alt.
Music: IRBY; Henry J. Gauntlett, 1805–1876.

328

THE FIRST NOWELL

Verses

1. The first No - well, the an - gel did say,
2. They look - ed up and saw ___ a star
3. And by the light of that ___ same star
4. This star drew nigh to the ___ north - west,
5. Then en - tered in those wise ___ men three,
6. Then let us all with one ___ ac - cord

1. Was to cer - tain poor shep - herds in fields as they lay;
2. Shin - ing in ___ the east, ___ be - yond ___ them far;
3. Three ___ wise ___ men came ___ from coun - try far;
4. O'er ___ Beth - le - hem ___ it took ___ its rest,
5. Full ___ rev - 'rent - ly ___ up - on ___ the knee,
6. Sing ___ prais - es to ___ our heav - 'nly Lord;

1. In fields where ___ they lay keep - ing their sheep,
2. And to the ___ earth it gave ___ great light,
3. To seek for a king was their ___ in - tent,
4. And there it ___ did both stop ___ and stay,
5. And of - fered ___ there, in his ___ pres - ence,
6. Who with the ___ Fa - ther we ___ a - dore

1. On a cold win - ter's night ___ that was ___ so deep.
2. And ___ so it con - tin - ued both day ___ and night.
3. And to fol - low the star ___ wher - ev - er it went.
4. Right ___ o - ver the place ___ where Je - sus lay.
5. Their ___ gold ___ and myrrh ___ and frank - in - cense.
6. And ___ Spir - it blest ___ for ev - er - more.

Refrain

No - well, No - well, No - well, No - well,

Born is the King of Is - ra - el.

Text: Irregular with refrain; trad. English Carol, 17th cent.; verse 6, alt.
Music: THE FIRST NOWELL; trad. English Carol, 17th cent.

WE THREE KINGS

Verses

1. We three kings of O - ri - ent are; Bear - ing gifts we
2. Born a King on Beth - le-hem's plain, Gold I bring to
3. Frank - in - cense to of - fer have I: In - cense owns a
4. Myrrh is mine; its bit - ter per - fume Breathes a life of
5. Glo - rious now be - hold him a - rise, King and God and

1. tra - verse a - far Field and foun - tain, Moor and moun - tain,
2. crown him a - gain, King for - ev - er, Ceas - ing nev - er
3. De - i - ty nigh; Prayer and prais - ing Glad - ly rais - ing,
4. gath - er - ing gloom; Sor - rowing, sigh - ing, Bleed - ing, dy - ing,
5. Sac - ri - fice; "Al - le - lu - ia, Al - le - lu - ia!"

Refrain

1. Fol - low - ing yon - der star. O star of won - der,
2. O - ver us all to reign.
3. Wor - ship him, God on high.
4. Sealed in the stone - cold tomb.
5. Sounds through the earth and skies.

star of night, Star with roy - al beau - ty bright; West - ward

lead - ing, still pro - ceed - ing, Guide us to thy per - fect light.

Text: 88 44 6 with refrain; based on Matthew 2:1–11; John H. Hopkins, Jr., 1820–1891, alt.
Music: KINGS OF ORIENT; *Carols, Hymns and Songs*, 1863; John H. Hopkins, Jr.

330   WHAT CHILD IS THIS

Verses

1. What child is this, who, laid to rest, On Ma-ry's lap is
2. Why lies he in such mean es - tate Where ox and ass are
3. So bring him in - cense, gold, and myrrh, Come peas-ant, king, to

1. sleep - ing? Whom an - gels greet with an - thems sweet, While
2. feed - ing? Good Chris - tian, fear: for sin - ners here The
3. own him; The King of kings sal - va - tion brings, Let

Refrain

1. shep - herds watch are keep - ing? This, this is Christ the
2. si - lent Word is plead - ing.
3. lov - ing hearts en-throne him.

King, Whom shep-herds guard and an - gels sing; Haste,

haste to bring him laud, the babe, the son of Ma - ry.

Text: 87 87 with refrain; Bramley and Stainer's *Christmas Carols New and Old*, 1871; William C. Dix, 1837–1898.
Music: GREENSLEEVES; trad. English Melody, 16th cent.; Bramley and Stainer's *Christmas Carols New and Old*, 1871.

331   CHILD OF THE POOR

Verses

1. Help-less and hun-gry, low - ly he lies, wrapped in the
2. Who is the strang-er here in our midst, look - ing for
3. Bring all the thirst-y, all who seek peace; bring those with

1. chill of mid - win - ter; comes now a-mong us, born in - to
2. shel - ter a - mong us? Who is the out-cast? Who do we
3. noth-ing to of - fer. Strength-en the fee - ble, say to the

1. pov - er - ty's em - brace, new life for the world.
2. see a - mid the poor, the chil - dren of God?
3. fright-ened heart: "Fear not: here is your God!"

Refrain

Who is this who lives with the low-ly, shar-ing their sor-rows,

know-ing their hun-ger? This is Christ, re-vealed to the

world in the eyes of a child, a child of the poor.

Note: *Child of the Poor* may be sung with *What Child Is This* (No. 330) in the following manner:
  Child of the Poor, verse 1, followed by *What Child Is This*, verse 1; *Child of the Poor*, verse 2, followed by
  What Child Is This, verse 2; both songs sung simultaneously on verse 3.

ANGELS FROM THE REALMS OF GLORY   332

1. An - gels, from the realms of glo - ry, Wing your flight o'er
2. Shep-herds, in the fields a - bid - ing, Watch-ing o'er your
3. Sag - es, leave your con - tem - pla-tions, Bright - er vi - sions
4. Though an in - fant now we view him, He shall fill his
5. All cre - a - tion, join in prais-ing God, the Fa - ther,

1. all the earth; Ye who sang cre - a - tion's sto - ry,
2. flocks by night, God on earth is now re - sid - ing;
3. beam a - far; Seek the great De - sire of Na - tions,
4. Fa - ther's throne, Gath - er all the na - tions to him;
5. Spir - it, Son, Ev - er - more your voic - es rais - ing,

1. Now pro-claim Mes - si - ah's birth:
2. Yon - der shines the in - fant light:
3. Ye have seen his na - tal star: Come and wor-ship,
4. Ev - 'ry knee shall then bow down:
5. To the e - ter - nal Three - in - One:

1-5. come and wor-ship, Wor - ship Christ, the new - born King.

Text: 87 87 87; verses 1–3, James Montgomery, 1771–1854; verse 4, *Christmas Box*, 1825;
  verse 5, *Salisbury Hymn Book*, 1857.
Music: REGENT SQUARE; Henry T. Smart, 1813–1879.

333   SONGS OF THANKFULNESS AND PRAISE

1. Songs of thank-ful-ness and praise, Je - sus, Lord, to thee we raise,
2. Man - i - fest at Jor-dan's stream, Proph-et, Priest, and King su-preme;
3. Man - i - fest in mak-ing whole Pal-sied limbs and faint-ing soul;
4. Grant us grace to see thee, Lord, Mir-rored in thy ho - ly Word;

1. Man - i - fest-ed by the star To the sag - es from a - far;
2. And at Ca - na, wed-ding guest, In thy God-head man - i - fest;
3. Man - i - fest in val - iant fight, Quell-ing all the dev - il's might;
4. May we im - i - tate thee now, And be pure, as pure art thou;

1. Branch of roy - al Da - vid's stem In thy birth at Beth - le-hem;
2. Man - i - fest in pow'r di - vine, Chang-ing wa - ter in - to wine;
3. Man - i - fest in gra-cious will, Ev - er bring-ing good from ill;
4. That we like to thee may be At thy great E - piph - a - ny;

1. Prais - es be to thee ad-dressed,
2. Prais - es be to thee ad-dressed,
3. Prais - es be to thee ad-dressed,
4. And may praise thee, ev - er-blessed,
} God in flesh made man - i - fest.

Text: 77 77 D; Christopher Wordsworth, 1807–1885, alt.
Music: SALZBURG; Jakob Hintze, 1622–1702.

334   AS WITH GLADNESS MEN OF OLD

1. As with glad - ness men of old Did the guid - ing
2. As with joy - ful steps they sped To that low - ly
3. As they of - fered gifts most rare At that man - ger
4. Ho - ly Je - sus, ev - 'ry day Keep us in the
5. In the heav'n - ly coun - try bright Need they no cre -

1. star be - hold, As with joy they hailed its light,
2. man - ger - bed, There to bend the knee be - fore,
3. rude and bare; So may we with ho - ly joy,
4. nar - row way; And, when earth - ly things are past,
5. at - ed light; Thou, its light, its joy, its crown,

1. Lead - ing on - ward, beam - ing bright, So, most gra - cious
2. Him whom heav'n and earth a - dore; So may we with
3. Pure and free from sin's al - loy, All our cost - liest
4. Bring our ran - somed souls at last Where they need no
5. Thou its sun which goes not down; There for ev - er

1. Lord, may we Ev - er - more be led to thee.
2. will - ing feet Ev - er seek the mer - cy - seat.
3. trea - sures bring, Christ! to thee, our heav'n - ly King.
4. star to guide, Where no clouds thy glo - ry hide.
5. may we sing Al - le - lu - ias to our King.

Text: 77 77 77; William C. Dix, 1837–1898.
Music: DIX; Conrad Kocher, 1786–1872; adapt. by William H. Monk, 1823–1889.

In the Bleak Midwinter 335

1. In the bleak mid - win - ter, frost - y wind made moan,
2. Our God, heav'n can - not hold him, nor____ earth sus - tain;
3. An - gels and arch - an - gels may have gath - ered there,
4. What____ can I give him, poor____ as I am?

1. Earth stood hard as i - ron, wa - ter like a stone;
2. Heav'n and earth shall flee a - way when he comes to reign.
3. Cher - u - bim and ser - a - phim throng - ed the air;
4. If I were a shep - herd, I would bring a lamb;

1. Snow had fall - en, snow on snow, snow____ on____ snow,
2. In the bleak mid - win - ter a sta - ble place suf - ficed The
3. But his moth - er on - ly, in her maid - en bliss,
4. If I were a Wise____ Man, I would do my part; Yet

1. In the bleak mid - win - ter, long a - go.
2. Lord____ God Al - might - y, Je - sus Christ.
3. Wor - shiped the be - lov - ed with a kiss.
4. what I can I give him: give my heart.

Text: Irregular; Christina G. Rosetti, 1830–1894.
Music: CRANHAM; Gustav T. Holst, 1874–1934.

336   WHAT STAR IS THIS

1. What star is this, with beams so bright, More love - ly
2. 'Tis now ful - filled what God de - creed, "From Ja - cob
3. O Je - sus, while the star of grace Im - pels us
4. To God the Fa - ther, heav'n - ly Light, To Christ, re -

1. than the noon - day light? 'Tis sent to an - nounce a
2. shall a star pro - ceed;" And lo! the __ east - ern
3. on to seek thy face, Let not our __ sloth - ful
4. vealed in earth - ly night, To God the __ Ho - ly

1. new - born king, Glad tid - ings of our God to bring.
2. sag - es stand To read in heav'n the Lord's com - mand.
3. hearts re - fuse The guid - ance of thy light to use.
4. Spir - it raise An end - less song of thank - ful praise!

Text: LM; *Quem stella sole pulchrior*; Charles Coffin, 1676–1749; tr. by John Chandler, 1806–1876, alt.
Music: PUER NOBIS; *Trier MS*, 15th cent.; adapt. by Michael Praetorius, 1571–1621.

337   WHEN JESUS COMES TO BE BAPTIZED

1. When Je - sus comes to be bap - tized, He
2. The Spir - it of the Lord comes down, A -
3. He will not quench the dy - ing flame, And
4. O Spir - it help us be like Christ: To
5. We praise you, God, source of all life, We

1. leaves the hid - den years be - hind, The years of safe - ty
2. noints the Christ to suf - fer - ing, To preach the word, to
3. what is bruised he will not break, But heal the wound in -
4. live in love and char - i - ty, To walk in truth and
5. praise you, Christ, e - ter - nal Word, We praise you, Spir - it,

1. and of peace, To bear the sins of hu - man - kind.
2. free the bound, And to the mourn - er, com - fort bring.
3. jus - tice dealt, And out of death his tri - umph make.
4. jus - tice now, And grow in Chris - tian dig - ni - ty.
5. gra - cious gift; Your tri - une pres - ence fills our world.

Text: LM. Verses 1–3, alt., © 1974, Stanbrook Abbey. All rights reserved. Used with permission.
    Verses 4–5, © 1989, Concacan Inc. All rights reserved. Used with permission.
Music: WINCHESTER NEW; Georg Wittwe's *Musikalisches Hand-Buch*, Hamburg, 1690;
    adapt. by William H. Havergal, 1793–1870.

WHEN JOHN BAPTIZED BY JORDAN'S RIVER

338

1. When John bap-tized by Jor-dan's riv - er / In faith and
2. There as the Lord, bap-tized and pray - ing, / Rose from the
3. O Son of Man, our na - ture shar - ing, / In whose o -

1. hope the peo - ple came, / That John and Jor - dan might de -
2. stream, the sin - less one, / A voice was heard from heav - en
3. be - dience all are blest, / Sav - ior, our sins and sor - rows

1. liv - er / Their trou-bled souls from sin and shame.
2. say - ing, / "This is my own be - lov - ed Son."
3. bear - ing, / Hear us and grant us this re - quest:

1. They came to seek a new be - gin - ning, / The hu - man
2. There as the Fa - ther's word was spo - ken, / Not in the
3. Dai - ly to grow, by grace de - fend - ed, / Filled with the

1. spir - it's age - less quest, / Re - pen-tance, and an
2. pow'r of wind and flame, / But of his love and
3. Spir - it from a - bove; / In Christ bap-tized, be -

1. end of sin - ning, / Re - nounc-ing ev - 'ry wrong con-fessed.
2. peace the to - ken, / Seen as a dove, the Spir - it came.
3. loved, be-friend - ed, / Chil - dren of God in peace and love.

339 ASHES

1. We rise a-gain from ash-es, from the good we've failed to
2. We of-fer you our fail-ures, we ___ of-fer you at-
3. Then rise a-gain from ash-es, let ___ heal-ing come to
4. ⸓ Thanks be to the Fa-ther, who ___ made us like him-

1. do. We rise a-gain from ash-es, to cre-ate our-selves a-
2. tempts, the gifts not ful-ly giv-en, the ___ dreams not ful-ly
3. pain, though spring has turned to win-ter, and ___ sun-shine turned to
4. self. ⸓ Thanks be to his Son, ___ who ___ saved us by his

1. new. If ___ all our world is ash-es, then ___ must our lives be
2. dreamt. Give our stum-bl-ings di-rec-tion, give our vi-sions wid-er
3. rain. The ___ rain we'll use for grow-ing, and cre-ate the world a-
4. death. ⸓ Thanks be to the Spir-it who cre-ates the world a-

1. true, an ___ of-fer-ing of ash-es, an of-fer-ing to you.
2. view, an ___ of-fer-ing of ash-es, an of-fer-ing to you.
3. new from an of-fer-ing of ash-es, an of-fer-ing to you.
4. new from an of-fer-ing of ash-es, an of-fer-ing to you.

Text and music: Tom Conry, b. 1951, © 1978, OCP. All rights reserved.

340 SIGNED BY ASHES

Ostinato Refrain

Signed by wa-ter; signed by ash-es; se-cure in your love, O God.

Verses

1. Have mercy on us, God, in your compassion.
Wipe out our offenses by your might.
Wash away our guilt;
make us worthy to walk your path in justice.

2. My sinfulness is visible, ever before you.
Against you alone I've transgressed.
But in you is the mighty power of mercy;
when I forgive, I am blest.

3. Cleanse me of my sin and I'll be pure, O Lord.
Wash me so I'm cleaner than the snow.
Let me hear the sounds of joy and gladness
that only those forgiven ever know.

4. Create for me a clean heart,
God of mercy.
Renew a steadfast spirit in me.
Cast me not out
from your loving presence,
that I may worship, sacrifice and sing.

5. O God, my heart and voice
are raised to praise you.
You are not pleased with sacrifice alone.
My sacrifice: a contrite, humble spirit;
I've heard your invitation:
"Child, come home!"

Text: Verses based on Psalm 51. Refrain and verses, Maryanne Quinlivan, OSU,
© 1996, The Ursuline Academy of Cleveland. Published by OCP. All rights reserved.
Music: Kevil Keil (ASCAP), b. 1956, © 1996, Kevin Keil. Published by OCP. All rights reserved.

WITH THESE ASHES

Refrain

With these ash - es, we know your love, O Lord. With these ash-es, we turn our hearts to you. Daugh-ters and sons, we jour-ney as one. With these ash-es, we know your love, O Lord.

Verses

1. Join - ing to - geth - er on this jour-ney with you,
2. With prayer and ser - vice, we will an - swer your call.
3. We give of what we have to all those in need.
4. And for those man - y times we stum - ble and fall,

1. we walk these for - ty days and nights. Called by your
2. With voic - es raised, we share your word. Called by your
3. We give as you would have us do. Called by your
4. your mer - cy rains from heav'n a - bove. Called by your

to Refrain

1. grace, we an-swer in faith; O Lord, lead us to your light.
2. grace, we an-swer in faith; O Lord, let our cry be heard.
3. grace, we an-swer in faith; O Lord, lead us back to you.
4. grace, we an-swer in faith; O Lord, lead us to your love.

Text: Mary Hochman, b. 1967.
Music: Gerard Chiusano, b. 1965.
Text and music © 2006, Gerard Chiusano and Mary Hochman. Published by spiritandsong.com®, a division of OCP.

342   LEAVE THE PAST IN ASHES

Leave the past in ash - es and turn to God, re - turn to God with tears and fast - ing.

*Verses available in accompaniment books.

Text: Joel 2:13; fr. the *Sacramentary*, © 1973, 1985, ICEL. All rights reserved. Used with permission.
Music: Cyprian Consiglio, OSB Cam., b. 1958, © 2004, Cyprian Consiglio, OSB Cam. Published by OCP.
  All rights reserved.

343   NOW IS THE ACCEPTABLE TIME

Now is the ac - cept - a - ble time. Now is the day of sal - va - tion. We are called to be-come the ho - li-ness of God. Be rec-on-ciled with God now! Re-ceive the grace of God.

Verses

1. Break o - pen your hearts of stone. _ Re - turn to the Lord
2. Keep se - cret your deeds of love _ and cheer - ful - ly give
3. With fast-ing and con - stant prayer, _____ strength-en your-selves

1. with your whole heart! God's mer - cy a - waits us all:
2. to the need - y. God's bless-ing is ours to share:
3. on the jour - ney. God walks with us day by day:

to Refrain

1-3. God is gra - cious, rich in kind - ness.

Text: Based on Joel 2:12–13; 2 Corinthians 5:20—6:2; Matthew 6:1–4; Barbara Bridge, b. 1950, © 2003, Barbara Bridge.
  Published by OCP. All rights reserved.
Music: Barbara Bridge, © 2003, Barbara Bridge. Published by OCP. All rights reserved.

PARCE DOMINE/SPARE YOUR PEOPLE, LORD

344

Refrain

Par - ce Dó - mi - ne, par - ce pó - pu - lo ___ tu - o: ___
Spare your peo - ple, Lord, spare your peo - ple in your lov - ing kind - ness!

ne in ae - tér - num i - ra - scá - ris no - bis.
Show us your mer - cy; we have sinned a - gainst you, Lord.

Verses

1. Have mercy on me, God, in your good - ness;
2. For I know my of - fense; ___
3. A clean heart create for me, ___ God;
4. Restore my joy in your sal - va - tion;
5. For you do not de - sire sac - ri - fice;

1. In your abundant compassion blot out my of - fense. ___
2. My sin is always be - fore ___ me.
3. Renew in me a stead - fast spir - it.
4. Sustain in me a will - ing spir - it.
5. A burnt offering you would not ac - cept. ___

1. Wash away all my guilt; ___
2. Against you alone have I sinned; ___
3. Do not drive me away from your pres - ence
4. Lord, open my lips; ___
5. My sacrifice, God, is a bro - ken spir - it;

to Refrain

1. From my sin cleanse me. ___
2. I have done such evil in your sight. ___
3. Nor take from me your ho - ly spir - it. ___
4. My mouth will proclaim your praise. ___
5. God, do not spurn a broken, hum - bled heart. ___

345

TURN TO ME

Refrain

Turn to me, O turn, and be saved, says the Lord, for I am God; there is no oth-er, none be - side me. I call your name.

Verse 1

1. I am God, who com-forts you; who are you to be a-fraid of flesh that fades, is made like the grass of the field, soon to with-er.

Verses 2, 3

2. Lis-ten __ to me, __ my peo-ple; give ear to __ me, __ and my jus-tice for a light to the peo-ple.
3. Lift __ up your eyes to the heav-ens, and look at the earth down be-low. __ The heav-ens will van-ish like smoke, and the earth __ will wear out like a gar-ment.

Text: Based on Isaiah 45:22–23; 51:12, 4, 6; John Foley, S.J., b. 1939.
Music: John Foley, S.J.
Text and music © 1975, John B. Foley, S.J., and OCP. All rights reserved.

HAVE MERCY ON US, LORD/ATTENDE DOMINE

Refrain

Have mer-cy on us, Lord, Je-sus our Sav-ior: Bur-dened with sin, we im-
At - tén- de Dó-mi - ne, et mi - se - ré - re, Qui - a pec-cá - vi-mus

Verses

plore you! 1. O great __ Re-deem-er, King of all cre - a - tion,
ti - bi. 2. Ex - alt - ed Sav-ior, Cor-ner-stone of heav - en,
3. We beg __ you, Je - sus, God im-mense in pow - er:
1. Ad te Rex sum-me, __ óm - ni - um re-dém - ptor,
2. Déx - te - ra Pa - tris, __ la - pis an - gu - lá - ris,
3. Ro - gá-mus, De - us, __ tu - am ma - ie - stá - tem:

1. As we are sin - ners, we de - serve your judg - ment:
2. Gate of sal - va - tion, Way to life im - mor - tal:
3. Lis - ten in kind-ness as we ask for - give - ness:
1. Ó - cu - los nó - stros sub - le - vá - mus flen - tes:
2. Vi - a sa - lú - tis iá - nu - a cae - lé - stis,
3. Áu - ri - bus sa - cris gé - mi - tus ex - áu - di:

to Refrain

1. Je - sus, be gra - cious; hear our prayer of sor - row.
2. Send forth your Spir - it; heal your hum-bled peo - ple!
3. Though sin con-demns us, you are strong to save us!
1. Ex - áu - di, Chri - ste, sup - pli - cán - tum pre - ces.
2. Áb - lu - e no - stri má - cu - las de - lí - cti.
3. Crí - mi - na no - stra plá - ci - dus in - dúl - ge.

4. We stand convicted, owning our offenses;
   Guilty before you, yet we seek your pardon:
   O gentle Savior, great is your compassion!

4. *Tibi fatémur, crímina admíssa:*
   Contríto corde pándimus occúlta:
   Túa redémptor, píetas ignóscat.

5. Remember, Jesus, you gave all to save us;
   Dying for sinners, you endured the Passion:
   Savior, immortal, grant your gift of freedom!

5. *Innocens captus, nec repúgnans ductus,*
   Téstibus falsis, pro ímpiis damnátus:
   Quos redemísti, tu consérva, Christe.

Text: 11 11 11 with refrain; Latin, 10th cent.; tr. by Melvin Farrell, SS, 1930–1986, © 1977, OCP. All rights reserved.
Music: ATTENDE DOMINE; Chant, Mode V; *Paris Processionale*, 1824.

347 THE GLORY OF THESE FORTY DAYS

1. The glo - ry of these for - ty days We cel - e -
2. A - lone and fast - ing Mo - ses saw The lov - ing
3. So Dan - iel trained his mys - tic sight, De - liv - ered
4. Then grant that we like them be true, Con - sumed in
5. O Fa - ther, Son, and Spir - it blest, To you be

1. brate with songs of praise; For Christ, by whom all
2. God who gave the law; And to E - li - jah,
3. from the li - ons' might; And John, the Bride - groom's
4. fast and pray'r with you; Our spir - its strength - en
5. ev - 'ry pray'r ad - dressed; Who are in three - fold

1. things were made, Him - self has fast - ed and has prayed.
2. fast - ing, came The steeds and char - i - ots of flame.
3. friend, be - came The her - ald of Mes - si - ah's name.
4. with your grace, And give us joy to see your face.
5. Name a - dored, From age to age the on - ly Lord.

Text: LM; *Clarum decus jejunii*; St. Gregory the Great, ca. 540–604; tr. fr. the *English Hymnal*, 1906;
    Maurice F. Bell, 1862–1947, alt.
Music: ERHALT UNS, HERR; J. Klug's *Geistliche Lieder*, Wittenberg, 1543;
    adapt. by Johann Sebastian Bach, 1685–1750, alt.

348 THIS SEASON CALLS US

1. This sea - son calls us to re - turn That by re -
2. O may the joy of ho - ly Lent Bring us the
3. Come make our yoke, O Christ, so sweet, Our bur - den

1. pen - tance we may learn To seek but Christ and
2. pa - tience to re - pent, To lose our lives for
3. light, our joy com - plete, That we may praise the

1. Christ a - lone, Who by his cross makes us his own.
2. Christ this day And run by faith the gos - pel way.
3. Trin - i - ty This day and all e - ter - ni - ty.

Text: LM; Harry Hagan, OSB, b. 1947, © 1999, St. Meinrad Archabbey. Published by OCP. All rights reserved.
Music: CONDITOR ALME SIDERUM; Chant, Mode IV.

BEHOLD, BEFORE OUR WONDERING EYES 349

1. Be - hold, be - fore our won - d'ring eyes,
2. Be - hold, be - hold the glo - rious wood
3. Be - hold, a - gainst the wall of night,
4. All glo - ry be to him who died,

1. Be - yond the gates of par - a - dise
2. Up - on which hung our on - ly good;
3. The door - way to e - ter - nal light
4. All hon - or to the Cru - ci - fied,

1. Shines out the Tree of Life a - dored,
2. It bore him up in of - fer - ing,
3. Stands o - pen now: the nar - row way
4. Who lives and reigns e - ter - nal - ly,

1. The cross of Je - sus Christ, our Lord.
2. The Lamb whose praise the an - gels sing.
3. In - vites us in to end - less day.
4. With Fa - ther, Spir - it: One in Three.

FORTY DAYS AND FORTY NIGHTS 350

1. For - ty days and for - ty nights You were fast - ing in the wild;
2. Shall not we your sor-row share And from world - ly joys ab - stain,
3. Then if Sa - tan on us press, Flesh or spir - it to as - sail,
4. So shall we have peace di - vine: Ho - lier glad-ness ours shall be;
5. Keep, O keep us, Sav-ior dear, Ev - er con - stant by your side;

1. For - ty days and for - ty nights Tempt - ed, and yet un - de-filed.
2. Fast- ing with un - ceas-ing prayer, Strong with you to suf - fer pain?
3. Vic - tor in the wil - der-ness, Grant we may not faint nor fail!
4. Round us, too, shall an - gels shine, Such as served you faith-ful - ly.
5. That with you we may ap - pear At th'e - ter - nal Eas-ter-tide.

Text: 77 77; George H. Smyttan, 1822–1870, alt.
Music: HEINLEIN; melody attr. to Martin Herbst, 1654–1681, alt.

351   LED BY THE SPIRIT

1. Led by the Spir-it of our God, we go to fast and
2. Led by the Spir-it, we con-front temp - ta-tion face to
3. Led by the Spir-it, now draw near the wa-ters of re -
4. Led by the Spir-it, now sing praise to God the Trin - i -

1. pray With Christ in - to the wil - der-ness; we join his
2. face, And know full well we must re - ly on God's re -
3. birth With hearts that long to wor-ship God in spir - it
4. ty: The Source of Life, the liv - ing Word made flesh to

1. pas - chal way. "Rend not your gar - ments, rend your hearts. Turn
2. deem - ing grace. On bread a - lone we can - not live, but
3. and in truth. "Who - ev - er drinks the drink I give shall
4. set us free, The Spir - it blow - ing where it will to

1. back your lives to me." Thus says our kind and
2. nour-ished by the Word We seek the will of
3. nev - er thirst a - gain." Thus says the Lord who
4. make us friends of God: This mys - t'ry far be -

1. gra - cious God, whose reign is lib - er - ty.
2. God to do: this is our drink and food.
3. died for us, our Sav - ior, kin and friend.
4. yond our reach, yet near in heal - ing love.

Text: CMD; based on Joel 2:12–13; Matthew 4:1–4; Mark 1:12–15; John 4:5–42; Bob Hurd, b. 1950, © 1996, Bob Hurd. Published by OCP. All rights reserved.
Music: KINGSFOLD; trad. English Melody; *English Country Songs*, 1893; adapt. by Ralph Vaughan Williams, 1872–1958.

352   LORD, WHO THROUGHOUT THESE FORTY DAYS

1. Lord, who through - out these for - ty days, For
2. As you with Sa - tan did con - tend, And
3. As you did hun - ger bear and thirst, So
4. And through these days of pen - i - tence, And
5. A - bide with us that when this life Of

1. us did fast and pray, Teach us with you to
2. did the vic - t'ry win, O give us strength in
3. teach us, gra - cious Lord, To die to self, and
4. through your Pas - sion - tide, For - ev - er - more, in
5. suf - fer - ing is past, An Eas - ter of un -

1. mourn our sins, And close by you to stay.
2. you to fight, In you to con - quer sin.
3. al - ways live By your most ho - ly word.
4. life and death, O Lord, with us a - bide.
5. end - ing joy We may at - tain at last!

Text: CM; Claudia F. Hernaman, 1838–1898, alt.
Music: ST. FLAVIAN; *The Whole Psalmes in Foure Partes*, 1563; adapt. by Richard Redhead, 1820–1901.

AGAIN WE KEEP THIS SOLEMN FAST 353

1. A - gain we keep this sol - emn fast, A gift of
2. The law and proph - ets from of old In fig - ured
3. More spar - ing, there - fore, let us make The words we
4. Let us a - void each harm - ful way That lures the
5. We pray, O bless - ed Three - in - One, Our God while

1. faith from ag - es past, This Lent which binds us
2. ways this Lent fore - told, Which Christ, all ag - es'
3. speak, the food we take, Our sleep, our laugh - ter,
4. care - less mind a - stray; By watch - ful prayer our
5. end - less ag - es run, That this, our Lent of

1. lov - ing - ly To faith and hope and char - i - ty.
2. Lord and Guide, In these last days has sanc - ti - fied.
3. ev - 'ry sense; Learn peace through ho - ly pen - i - tence.
4. spir - its free From schem - ing of the e - ne - my.
5. for - ty days, May bring us growth and give you praise.

Text: LM; *Ex more docti mystico*; ascr. to St. Gregory the Great, ca. 540–604; tr. by Peter J. Scagnelli, b. 1949,
   and John M. Neale, 1818–1866, alt., © Peter J. Scagnelli. All rights reserved. Used with permission.
Music: ERHALT UNS, HERR; J. Klug's *Geistliche Lieder*, Wittenberg, 1543;
   adapt. by Johann Sebastian Bach, 1685–1750, alt.

354   SOMEBODY'S KNOCKIN' AT YOUR DOOR

1, 6. Some-bod - y's knock-in' at your door; Some-bod - y's knock-in' at your

1, 6. door; O sin - ner, why don't you an - swer? Some-bod - y's

(Fine) Cantor

1, 6. knock - in' at your door.

2. Knocks like Je - sus,
3. Can't you hear him?
4. Je - sus calls you,
5. Can't you trust him?

All   Cantor

2-5. Some-bod - y's knock-in' at your door.

2. Knocks like Je - sus,
3. Can't you hear him?
4. Je - sus calls you,
5. Can't you trust him?

All

2-5. Some-bod - y's knock-in' at your door. O sin - ner,

2-5. why don't you an - swer? Some-bod - y's knock-in' at your door.

Text and music: Spiritual.

355   TURN OUR HEARTS

*Ostinato Refrain

Turn our hearts to you, O God. With you there is heal-ing,

whole-ness and for-give-ness, free-dom from fear, last-ing peace.

*Verses available in accompaniment books.

Text: Verses based on Psalm 51:1, 6, 12; Barbara Bridge, b. 1950.
Music: Barbara Bridge.

JESUS WALKED THIS LONESOME VALLEY

356

1. Je - sus walked this lone-some val - ley;
2. We must walk this lone-some val - ley;
3. You must go and stand your tri - al;

1. He had to walk it by him - self.
2. We have to walk it by our - selves.
3. You have to stand it by your - self.

1. Oh, no - bod - y else could walk it for him;
2. Oh, no - bod - y else can walk it for us;
3. Oh, no - bod - y else can stand it for you;

1. He had to walk it by him - self.
2. We have to walk it by our - selves.
3. You have to stand it by your - self.

Text: 88 10 8; Traditional.
Music: LONESOME VALLEY; Spiritual.

FROM THE DEPTHS WE CRY TO THEE

357

1. From the depths we cry to thee, God of sov-'reign maj - es - ty!
2. Gra-cious God, our hearts re-new; Strength-en us thy will to do.
3. Lord, ac - cept our Len-ten fast And for-give our sin - ful past,

1. Hear our prayers and hymns of praise; Bless our Lent of for - ty days.
2. Wash us, make us pure with - in; Cleanse us from the stain of sin.
3. That we may par - take with thee In the Eas - ter mys-ter - y.

Text: 77 77; verses 1, 3, Alan G. McDougall, 1895–1964, alt. Verse 2, Owen Alstott, b. 1947, © 1977, OCP.
All rights reserved.
Music: HEINLEIN; melody attr. to Martin Herbst, 1654–1681, alt.

358 CREATE A CLEAN HEART

Refrain

Cre - ate a clean heart in me, O God.

Re - new in me a stead-fast spir - it.

Verses

1. Have mer - cy, God, in com - pas - sion, and for -
2. You are jus - ti - fied giv - ing sen - tence, and with -
3. Make me hear re - joic - ing and glad - ness, that the
4. Give me back the joy of sal - va - tion, with a
5. When I sac - ri - fice, you re - fuse it, and my

1. get that I have de - fied you. Wash a - way all my
2. out re - proach when you judge. You see me just as I
3. bones you bruised may re - vive! Shut your eyes to my
4. fer - vent spir - it sus - tain me. I will show to oth - ers your
5. ho - lo - causts do not please you. My bro - ken spir - it I

1. sin, and cleanse me from my guilt. Ver - y
2. am, a sin - ner be - fore my birth. Be -
3. sin; make my guilt dis - ap - pear. O Cre -
4. way; those in sin will re - turn to you. O
5. of - fer; you will wel - come my hum - ble heart. In your

1. well do I know what is ev - il, and my sins are al - ways be -
2. hold, you love truth in the heart; in my se - cret heart teach me
3. a - tor, re - shape my heart; put a stur - dy spir - it with -
4. res - cue me, God, be my help - er, and my tongue shall ring out your
5. mer - cy show fa - vor to Si - on, and re - build the walls of your

1. fore me. Done to you a - lone, my of - fens - es,
2. wis - dom. With a sprig of hys - sop and wa - ter,
3. in me. De - prive me not of your spir - it;
4. good - ness. O Lord, o - pen my lips and my
5. cit - y. Then our ho - lo-causts will be pleas-ing

1. crimes com-mit-ted right be-fore your eyes.
2. wash me; make me bright-er than the snow.
3. cast me not a-way from your side.
4. mouth will de-clare your praise.
5. sac-ri-fic-es of-fered in your sight.

REMEMBER NOT THE THINGS OF THE PAST 359

Refrain

Re-mem-ber not the things of the past; now I do some-thing new,

do you not see it? Now I do some-thing new, says the Lord.

Verses

1. In our dis-tress God has grasped us by the hand,
2. In our parched land of hy-poc-ri-sy and hate,
3. And who a-mong us is sin-less in God's sight?
4. Press-ing a-head, let-ting go what lies be-hind,

1. o-pened a path in the sea, and we shall pass o-ver,
2. God makes a riv-er spring forth, a riv-er of mer-cy,
3. Then who will cast the first stone, when he who was sin-less
4. may we be found in the Lord, and shar-ing his dy-ing,

1. we shall pass o-ver, free at last.
2. truth and com-pas-sion; come and drink.
3. car-ried our fail-ings to the cross?
4. share in his ris-ing from the dead.

360   BEYOND THE DAYS

Be - yond the days of hope and mys - t'ry we

see a light of faith re - newed, and in our long - ing

1-4
to Verses

we thirst for guid - ance to walk with you day by day.

Final

day, to walk with you day by day.

Verses

1. For - ty days and
2. Not on bread a -
3. In your hands, O
4. On our Lent - en

1. nights, you guide the steps of our jour - ney. May your
2. lone are we to walk on this jour - ney. Speak the
3. God, we feel the touch of your guid - ance. Keep us
4. path we see the dawn of a new day. Be our

to Refrain

1. pres - ence be felt in the whis - per of your voice.
2. words that give life to the yearn - ings of our hearts.
3. safe in your care: may your gen - tle - ness be there.
4. vi - sion of hope; be the prom - ise of our lives.

361   WITH THE LORD

Verse 1

1. Out of the depths I cry to you, I cry to you, O Lord. Lord,

1. o - pen your ears and hear my voice, at - tend to the sound of my plea.

Refrain

With the Lord there is mer-cy and the full-ness of re-demp-tion, call to him in your tri-als, he will

1, 3 to Vss 2, 4 | *2* to Vs 3 | Final

an-swer when-ev-er you call. call. call.

Verses 2, 4

2. If you ____ O Lord, ___ should mark ___ our guilt, then, Lord, who could
4. More than the sen-ti-nels wait for the dawn, let Is-ra-el

2. hope to sur-vive? But with you is found for-give-ness of
4. wait for the Lord. For kind-ness is his, re-demp-tion for

to Refrain

2. sin, and mer-cy that we might re-vere you.
4. all, for-give-ness of sins for his peo-ple.

Verse 3

3. Trust in the Lord, count on his word, wait for the

3. Lord, my soul. I will wait for the Lord all the

to Refrain

3. days of my life as sen-ti-nels wait for the dawn.

362   IN THESE DAYS OF LENTEN JOURNEY

Refrain

In these days of Len-ten jour-ney we have seen and we have heard
the call to sow jus-tice in the lives of those we serve.

Verses

1. We reach out to those who are home-less, to
2. We o - pen our eyes to the hun - gry and
3. We o - pen our ears to the wea - ry and
4. We call on the Spir - it of Jus - tice and

1. those who live with - out warmth. In the cool-ness of
2. see the fac - es of Christ. As we nour - ish all
3. hear the cry of the poor. To the voic - es that
4. pray for righ-teous-ness' sake. We will sing for the

1. eve - ning we'll shel - ter their dreams; we will
2. peo - ple who hun - ger for food, may their
3. ech - o the song of de - spair, we will
4. free - dom of all the op - pressed; we will

to Refrain

1. clothe them in mer - cy and peace.
2. faith in our God be re - newed.
3. show our com - pas - sion and care.
4. loos - en the bonds of dis - tress.

363   AT THE CROSS HER STATION KEEPING

1. At the cross her sta - tion keep-ing, Stood the mourn-ful
2. Through her heart, his sor - row shar-ing, All his bit - ter
3. O how sad and sore dis-tressed, _ Was that Moth - er

1. Sta - bat Ma - ter do - lo - ró - sa Ju - xta cru - cem
2. Cu - jus á - ni - mam ge - mén-tem, Con - tri - stá - tam
3. O quam tri - stis et af - flí - cta Fu - it il - la

1. Moth - er weep - ing, Close to Je - sus to the last.
2. an - guish bear - ing, Now at length the sword has passed.
3. high - ly blest ___ Of the sole be - got - ten One!

1. *la - cri - mó - sa,* *Dum pen - dé - bat* *Fí - li - us.*
2. *et do - lén - tem,* *Per - tran - sí - vit* *glá - di - us.*
3. *be - ne - dí - cta* *Ma - ter* *U - ni - gé - ni - ti!*

4. Christ above in torment hangs,
She beneath beholds the pangs
Of her dying, glorious Son.

4. *Quae maerébat et dolébat,*
Pia Mater, dum vidébat
Nati poenas íncliti.

5. Is there one who would not weep,
Whelmed in miseries so deep,
Christ's dear Mother to behold?

5. *Quis non posset contristári,*
Piam Matrem contemplári
Doléntem cum Fílio?

6. Can the human heart refrain
From partaking in her pain,
In that Mother's pain untold?

6. *Quis est homo qui non fleret,*
Matrem Christi si vidéret
In tanto supplício?

7. Bruised, derided, cursed, defiled,
She beheld her tender Child,
All with bloody scourges rent.

7. *Pro peccátis suae gentis*
Vidit Jesum in torméntis,
Et flagéllis súbditum.

8. For the sins of his own nation
Saw him hang in desolation
Till his spirit forth he sent.

8. *Vidit suum dulcem Natum*
Moriéntem desolátum,
Dum emísit spíritum.

9. O thou Mother! Font of love,
Touch my spirit from above,
Make my heart with thine accord.

9. *Eia Mater, fons amóris,*
Me sentíre vim dolóris
Fac, ut tecum lúgeam.

10. Make me feel as thou hast felt;
Make my soul to glow and melt
With the love of Christ, my Lord.

10. *Fac ut árdeat cor meum*
in amándo Christum Deum,
ut sibi compláceam.

11. Holy Mother, pierce me through,
In my heart each wound renew
Of my Savior crucified.

11. *Sancta Mater, istud agas,*
Crucifíxi fige plagas
Cordi meo válide.

12. Let me share with thee his pain,
Who for all my sins was slain,
Who for me in torment died.

12. *Tui Nati vulneráti,*
Tam dignáti pro me pati,
Poenas mecum dívide.

13. Let me mingle tears with thee,
Mourning him who mourned for me,
All the days that I may live.

13. *Fac me vere tecum flere,*
Crucifíxo condolére,
Donec ego víxero.

14. By the cross with thee to stay;
There with thee to weep and pray,
All I ask of thee to give.

14. *Juxta crucem tecum stare,*
Ac me tibi sociáre
In planctu desídero.

15. Virgin of all Virgins best!
Listen to my fond request:
Let me share thy grief divine.

15. *Virgo vírginum praeclára,*
Mihi jam non sis amára:
Fac me tecum plángere.

Text: 88 7; *Stabat Mater dolorosa*; Jacopone da Todi, 1230–1306; tr. by Edward Caswall, 1814–1878, alt.
Music: STABAT MATER; *Maintzisch Gesangbuch*, 1661.

364   SAVE YOUR PEOPLE

Refrain

Save your peo-ple, O Lord. Show us the way to come
home. We have been wan-der-ing far from your love. Save your
peo-ple, O Lord.

Verses

1. One thing I ask, ___ O ___
2. For you will hide me in the
3. Lis-ten, O Lord, ___ to the
4. Thus will I bless you all the

1. Lord, ___ this I seek: to dwell for - ev - er in your
2. shel - ter of your wings and from the ar - rows of my
3. sound ___ of my call, for I ac - knowl-edge my of -
4. days ___ of my life. Lift-ing my hands, I call your

1. house, that I may gaze ___ on your love - li - ness
2. foes. You set me high ___ on a moun-tain-top,
3. fense. Wash me and I ___ shall be pur - i - fied.
4. name: "O Lord, re - mem-ber your in - her - i - tance.

to Refrain

1. all ___ the days of my life.
2. saved ___ me from my dis - tress.
3. I shall be whit - er than snow.
4. Save ___ your peo - ple, O Lord!"

Hosanna to the Son of David 365

Ho-san-na to the Son of Da-vid; bless-ed is he who comes
in the name of the Lord, the King of Is -
ra - el. Ho - san - na in the high-est.

Text: Based on Matthew 21:9. English tr. © 2010, ICEL. All rights reserved. Used with permission.
Music: Chant, Mode VII; music adapt. © 2010, ICEL. All rights reserved. Used with permission.

All Glory, Laud, and Honor 366

1-5. All glo-ry, laud, and hon - or To you, Re-deem-er King!

1-5. To whom the lips of chil - dren Made sweet ho-san-nas ring.

1. You are the King of Is - ra - el, And Da-vid's roy - al Son,
2. The com-pa - ny of an - gels Are prais-ing you on high;
3. The peo-ple of the He - brews With palms be - fore you went:
4. To you be-fore your pas - sion They sang their hymns of praise:
5. Their prais-es you ac - cept - ed, Ac - cept the prayers we bring,

1. Now in the Lord's Name com - ing, Our King and Bless-ed One.
2. And mor - tals, joined with all things Cre - a - ted, make re - ply.
3. Our praise and prayers and an - thems Be - fore you we pre-sent.
4. To you, now high ex - alt - ed, Our mel - o - dy we raise.
5. Great source of love and good - ness, Our Sav-ior and our King.

Text: 76 76 D; Theodulph of Orleans, ca. 760–821; tr. by John M. Neale, 1818–1866, alt.
Music: ST. THEODULPH; Melchior Teschner, 1584–1635.

367   HOSANNA TO THE SON OF DAVID

Ho - san - na to the Son of Da - vid! O blest is he, O blest is he who comes in the name of the Lord!

Verses

1. Re - joice, daugh - ter of Zi - on,
2. Re - joice, all who are thirst - ing
3. Re - joice, all who are long - ing
4. Re - joice, all who are search - ing
5. Re - joice, all who are hop - ing
6. Re - joice, all who are wait - ing
7. Re - joice, all who are call - ing
8. Re - joice, all who are hun - gry

1. in the One who brings great joy!
2. for the streams of liv - ing joy!
3. to be - hold the face of God!
4. for the truth of ho - ly light!
5. for the reign of peace and love!
6. for the dawn of heav - en's light!
7. on the name of God on high!
8. for the taste of liv - ing bread!

Sing praise, chil -

to Refrain

1-8. - dren of Ju - dah, for the Lord is close at hand!

Text: Refrain based on Matthew 21:9; Dan Schutte, b. 1947.
Music: Dan Schutte.

368   PASSION ACCLAMATION

There is no great - er love than this: To lay down your life for your friends.

Text: Based on John 15:13; Christopher Walker, b. 1947.
Music: Christopher Walker.

At the Name of Jesus

369

Refrain

At the name of Je - sus ev - 'ry knee shall bend,
at the name of Je - sus ev - 'ry knee shall bend.

Verses

1. 'Tis our God's great plea - sure we should speak God's name,
2. Hum - bled for a sea - son, to re - ceive a name
3. Christ is tru - ly Sav - ior, Christ, the God a - dored,
4. In your hearts en - throne him, there let him sub - due
5. Sis - ters, broth - ers, Je - sus dwells with us a - gain

to Refrain

1. who from the be - gin - ning was for - e'er the same.
2. from the lips of peo - ples un - to whom he came.
3. ev - er to be wor - shiped, ev - er - more a - dored.
4. all that is not ho - ly, all that is not true.
5. now to let his vi - sion o'er our hearts to reign.

Text: Based on Phillippians 2:5–7; Caroline M. Noel, 1817–1877, alt.; Suzanne Toolan, RSM, b. 1927,
© 1995, Suzanne Toolan, RSM. Published by OCP. All rights reserved.
Music: Suzanne Toolan, RSM, © 1995, Suzanne Toolan, RSM. Published by OCP. All rights reserved.

Rite for Receiving the Holy Oils

370

1. Behold the oil of the sick, blessed by our Bishop,
   sent to us for the anointing of all who suffer illness.

Refrain

Thanks be to God! Thanks be to God!
Alt. Refrain Blessed be God for - ev - er! Blessed be God for - ev - er!

2. Behold the oil of the catechumens, blessed by our Bishop,
   sent to us for the anointing of our catechumens in preparation for their baptism.

3. Behold the sacred chrism, oil mixed with sweet perfume,
   and consecrated by our Bishop, sent to us for the anointing
   of the baptized who are to be sealed with the Holy Spirit.

Text and music: John Schiavone, b. 1947, © 1989, John Schiavone. Published by OCP. All rights reserved.

371 JESU, JESU

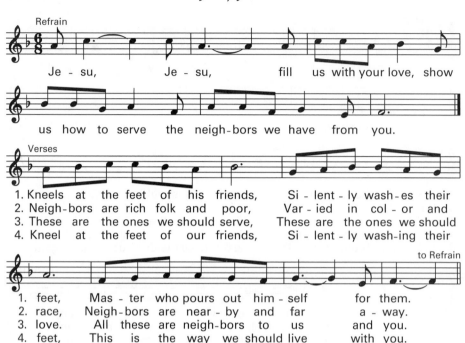

Refrain

Je - su, Je - su, fill us with your love, show us how to serve the neigh-bors we have from you.

Verses

1. Kneels at the feet of his friends, Si - lent - ly wash-es their
2. Neigh-bors are rich folk and poor, Var - ied in col - or and
3. These are the ones we should serve, These are the ones we should
4. Kneel at the feet of our friends, Si - lent - ly wash-ing their

to Refrain

1. feet, Mas - ter who pours out him - self for them.
2. race, Neigh-bors are near - by and far a - way.
3. love. All these are neigh-bors to us and you.
4. feet, This is the way we should live with you.

Note: Jesu is pronounced "yay-zoo"

Text: 779 with refrain; John 13:3–5; Ghanaian Folk Song; tr. by Tom Colvin, b. 1925.
Music: CHEREPONI; Ghanaian Folk Song; adapt. by Tom Colvin.
Text and music © 1969, Hope Publishing Co. All rights reserved. Used with permission.

372 AS I HAVE DONE FOR YOU

Refrain

I, your Lord and Mas-ter, now be-come your ser-vant.

I who made the moon and stars will kneel to wash your feet.

This is my com-mand-ment: to love as I have loved you.

Kneel to wash each oth-er's feet as I have done for you.

Verses

1. All the world will know you are my dis - ci - ples
2. I must leave you now on - ly for a mo - ment.
3. I am like a vine, you are like the branch-es.
4. I have called you friends, now no long - er ser-vants.
5. You will weep for now while the world re - joic - es.
6. I will give you peace; this will be my bless - ing.

1. by the love that you of - fer, the kind - ness you
2. I must go to my Fa - ther to make you a
3. If you cling to my teach - ing you sure - ly will
4. What I told you in se - cret, the world longs to
5. But the tears of your sor - row will soon turn to
6. Though the world churns a - round you, I leave you my

1. show. You have heard the voice of God in the
2. home. On the day of my re - turn, I will
3. live. If you make your home in me, I will
4. know. There can be no great - er love than to
5. joy. As a moth - er cries in child - birth and her
6. peace. I have told you all these things that my

1. words that I have spo - ken. You be - held heav-en's
2. come to take you with me to the place I have
3. come to dwell with - in you. You can count on my
4. give your life for oth - ers. As the Fa - ther has
5. pain is turned to glad - ness, you will know great re -
6. peace may dwell with - in you. Let your faith be un -

to Refrain

1. glo - ry and have seen the face of God.
2. prom - ised where your joy will have no end.
3. mer - cy when you ask for what you need.
4. loved me, so I love you as my own.
5. joic - ing on the day of my re - turn.
6. shak - en and your hope be ev - er strong.

Text: Based on John 13–16; Dan Schutte, b. 1947.
Music: Dan Schutte.

373   IF I, YOUR LORD AND MASTER

Refrain

If I, your Lord and Mas - ter, have washed your feet, you must do the same for one an - oth - er.

Verses

1. The Lord___ Je - sus, when he had
2. But Si - mon Pe - ter asked why the
3. "You call me Mas - ter, but here you

1. eat - en with his dis - ci - ples, took
2. Lord had___ stooped to wash him, and
3. see me___ as your ser - vant. If

1. wa - ter in a ba - sin and knelt down to wash their
2. Je - sus an - swered, "Pe - ter, if I do not wash your
3. I whom you call Mas - ter have done such a thing for

to Refrain

1. feet, say - ing: "This ex - am - ple I leave you."
2. feet for you, you have no part with me."
3. you, you must now do the same for each oth - er."

Text: Based on John 13:4–6, 8, 13–15; Stephen Dean, b. 1948.
Music: Stephen Dean.
Text and music © 2000, Stephen Dean. Published by OCP. All rights reserved.

UBI CARITAS/WHERE TRUE CHARITY AND LOVE DWELL 374

Refrain

U - bi cá - ri - tas est ve - ra De - us i - bi est.
Where true char - i - ty and love dwell, God him-self is there.

Verses

1. Con - gre - gá - vit nos in u - num Chri - sti a - mor.
2. Si - mul er - go cum in u - num con - gre - gá - mur:
3. Si - mul quo - que cum be - á - tis vi - de - á - mus

1. *Since the love of Christ has joined us in one bod - y,*
2. *As we are all of one bod - y, when we gath - er*
3. *Now we pray that with the bless - ed you grant us grace*

1. Ex - sul - té - mus et in i - pso iu - cun - dé - mur.
2. Ne nos men - te di - vi - dá - mur, ca - ve - á - mus.
3. Glo - ri - án - ter vul - tum tu - um, Chri - ste De - us:

1. *Let us all re - joice and be glad now and al - ways.*
2. *Let no dis - cord or en - mi - ty break our one-ness.*
3. *To see your ex - alt - ed glo - ry, O Christ our God,*

1. Ti - me - á - mus et a - mé - mus De - um vi - vum.
2. Ces - sent iúr - gi - a ma - lí - gna, ces-sent li - tes.
3. Gáu - di - um, quod est im-mén - sum at - que pro - bum,

1. *And as we hear and love our Lord, the liv - ing God,*
2. *May all our pet - ty jeal-ous - ies and ha - tred cease*
3. *Our bound-less source of joy and truth, of peace and love,*

1. Et ex cór - de di - li - gá - mus nos sin - cé - ro. **(to Ref.)**
2. Et in mé - di - o no-stri sit Chri-stus De - us. **(to Ref.)**
3. Sáe - cu - la per in - fi - ní - ta sae - cu - ló - rum.

1. *So let us in sin-cer - i - ty love all peo - ple.* **(to Ref.)**
2. *That Christ the Lord may be with us through all our days.* **(to Ref.)**
3. *For ev - er and for ev - er-more, world with - out end.*

Text: 12 12 12 12 with refrain; Latin, 9th cent.; tr. by Joyce MacDonald Glover, b. 1923, © 1982, Joyce MacDonald Glover.
    All rights reserved. Used with permission.
Music: UBI CARITAS; Chant, Mode VI.

375 GLORY IN THE CROSS

Holy Thursday
(Vss. 1–4)

1. Let us ev - er glo - ry in the cross of Christ, our sal-
2. Let us make our jour - ney to the cross of Christ, who sur-
3. Let us tell the sto - ry of the cross of Christ as we
4. Let us stand to - geth - er at the cross of Christ where we

1. va - tion and __ our hope. Let us bow in hom-age to the
2. ren-dered glo - ry and grace to be-come a ser-vant of the
3. share this heav-en - ly feast. We be-come one bod - y in the
4. see God's bound - less love. We are saints and sin-ners who are

1. Lord of Life, who was bro - ken to make us whole. There is
2. great and small, that all peo - ple may know God's face. Though his
3. blood of Christ, from the great to the ver - y least. When we
4. joined by faith here on earth and in heav'n a - bove. Nei - ther

1. no great-er love, as bless-ed as this: to lay down one's
2. birth was di - vine, he knelt as a slave, to wash com-mon
3. eat of this bread, and drink of this cup, we hon - or the
4. wom - an nor man, not ser-vant or free, but one in the

1. life for a friend.
2. dust from our feet.
3. death of the Lord.
4. eyes of the Lord.
} Let us ev - er glo-ry in the cross of Christ and the

Fine

|1, 2| **2** |3|

1-4. tri-umph of God's great love.

Good Friday

1. Let us ever glory in the cross of Christ
   who redeems us with his blood.
   Let us tell the story of the cross of Christ
   and the pow'r of his saving love.
   Like a lamb he was slain;
   he carried our shame,
   to show us the mercy of God.
   Let us ever glory in the cross of Christ
   and the triumph of God's great love.

2. Let us bring our burdens
   to the cross of Christ
   who has known our sorrow and tears.
   In the great compassion of
   the heart of Christ,
   God has walked in our hopes and fears.
   He was mocked and betrayed,
   deserted by friends, and banished
   to die among thieves.
   Let us ever glory in the cross of Christ
   and the triumph of God's great love.

3. Let us kneel in homage at
   the cross of Christ
   where we see God's human face.
   We behold the Maker of the sun and stars
   as he hangs on the throne of grace.
   As we share in his pain,
   his sorrow and shame,
   our hearts will be tested in fire.
   Let us ever glory in the cross of Christ
   and the triumph of God's great love.

Easter

1. Let us ever glory in the cross of Christ,
   our salvation and our hope.
   Let us bow in homage to the Lord of Life,
   who was broken to make us whole.
   There is no greater love, as blessed as this:
   to lay down one's life for a friend.
   Let us ever glory in the cross of Christ
   and the triumph of God's great love.

2. Let us ever glory in the cross of Christ
   who is risen from the grave.
   He will come in glory to receive our hearts
   at the dawn of the lasting day.
   For the trumpet will sound,
   the dead shall be raised,
   and death shall defeat us no more.
   Let us ever glory in the cross of Christ
   and the triumph of God's great love.

3. Let us raise our voices to the cross of Christ
   where the earth and heaven unite.
   God has wed creation on the tree of hope
   where the darkness becomes our light.
   Let us join in the dance of heaven and earth,
   give thanks for the goodness of God.
   Let us ever glory in the cross of Christ
   and the triumph of God's great love.

Text and music: Dan Schutte, b. 1947, © 2000, Daniel L. Schutte. Published by OCP. All rights reserved.

WHEN JESUS WEPT 376

When Jesus wept the fall - ing tear In mer - cy
flow'd be - yond all bound, When Je - sus groan'd, a trem-bling
fear Seiz'd all the guil - ty world a - round.

Text: LM; *The New England Psalm Singer*, 1770.
Music: WHEN JESUS WEPT; William Billings, 1746–1800.

377   Pange, Lingua, Gloriosi/Sing of Glory

*Verses 1-4

1. Pan - ge,   lin - gua,   glo - ri - ó - si   Cór - po - ris
2. No - bis   da - tus,   no - bis   na - tus   Ex   in - tá -
3. In   su - pré-mae   no - cte   coe - nae,   Ré - cum - bens
4. Ver - bum   ca - ro,   pa - nem   ve - rum   Ver - bo   car-

1. *Sing   of   glo - ry   and   his   bod - y,   Won - drous mys-*
2. *Gift   for   us and   gift   for - ev - er,   From   the   vir-*
3. *At   the   last, the   pas - chal   sup - per,   With   his   friends*
4. *Word made flesh, by   word made pres - ent,   Bod - y   bro -*

1. my - sté - ri - um   San - gui - nís - que pre - ti - ó - si,
2. cta   Vír - gi - ne,   Et   in   mún - do con - ver - sá - tus,
3. cum   frá - tri - bus,   Ob - ser - vá - ta   le - ge ple - ne
4. nem   éf - fi - cit: Fit - que san - guis Chri - sti me - rum,

1. *t'ry   to   be - hold,   Blood poured out   in death and dy - ing,*
2. *gin's womb was born,   Flesh   of   flesh and one   a - mong us,*
3. *be - fore   they fled,   First   he   ate   the meal   of pas-sage,*
4. *ken   for   the Feast,   And   his blood, the cup   of bless- ing,*

1. Quem   in   mún - di   pré - ti - um   Fru - ctus   ven - tris
2. Spar - so   ver - bi   sé - mi - ne,   Su - i   mo - ras
3. Ci - bis   in   le - gá - li - bus,   Ci - bum   tur - bae
4. Et   si   sen - sus   dé - fi - cit,   Ad   fir - mán - dum

1. *Roy - al   gift   so cheap - ly   sold.   First   a   moth - er's*
2. *Cru - ci - fied   and   put   to scorn,   That   the   Gos - pel*
3. *Pas - chal lamb   and   pas - chal bread;   Then   him - self   as*
4. *Shed   for   all   by   Christ the Priest: Though the   sens - es*

1. ge - ne - ró - si   Rex   ef - fú - dit   gén - ti - um.
2. in - co - lá - tus   Mi - ro   clau - sit   ór - di - ne.
3. du - o - dé - nae   Se   dat   su - is   má - ni - bus.
4. cor   sin - cé - rum   So - la   fi - des   súf - fi - cit.

1. *self - less   off - 'ring   Ran-som   now   for   sins   un - told.*
2. *seed might scat - ter   As   of   old   the   Lord   had sworn.*
3. *food   he   of - fered   That the   man - y   might   be   fed.*
4. *fail   and   fal - ter,   Faith con - firms true   hearts   in   peace.*

**Verses 5-6

5. Tan-tum er - go Sa - cra-mén - tum Ve - ne - ré -
6. Ge - ni - tó - ri, Ge - ni - tó - que Laus et ju -

5. *Ho - ly sac - ra - ment, most ho - ly, Let us bow*
6. *God Be - get - ter and Be - got - ten, Yours be praise*

5. mur cér - nu - i: Et an - tí - quum do - cu - mén-tum
6. bi - lá - ti - o, Sa - lus, ho - nor, vir - tus quo - que

5. *on bend-ed knee: Vi-sions of the an - cient prom-ise*
6. *and maj - es - ty, Hon- or, glo - ry and sal - va-tion,*

5. No - vo ce-dat rí - tu - i: Prae-stet fi - des sup - ple -
6. Sit et be - ne - dí - cti - o: Pro - ce - dén - ti ab u -

5. *Now ful- filled in mys-te - ry. Faith de-clares what none dare*
6. *Bless- ing for e - ter - ni - ty, With the One pro - ceed-ing*

5. mén-tum Sén - su - um de - fé - ctu - i.
6. tró - que Com-par sit lau - dá - ti - o. A - men.

5. *fath- om; Faith re-veals what none may see.*
6. *al - ways, E - qual-ly in u - ni - ty. A - men.*

*Verses 1–4 are repeated as necessary until the procession reaches the place of repose.
**Verses 5–6 are sung while the priest, kneeling, incenses the Blessed Sacrament.
    Then the Blessed Sacrament is placed in the tabernacle of repose.

Text: 87 87 87; *Pange lingua gloriosi*; St. Thomas Aquinas, 1227–1274; tr. by Harry Hagan, OSB, b. 1947,
    © 1990, St. Meinrad Archabbey. Published by OCP. All rights reserved.
Music: PANGE LINGUA GLORIOSI; Chant, Mode III.

378 PANGE, LINGUA, GLORIOSI/SING OF GLORY

1. Pan - ge, lin - gua, glo - ri - ó - si Cór - po - ris my - sté - ri - um
2. No - bis da - tus, no - bis na - tus Ex in - tá - cta Vír - gi - ne,
3. In su - pré - mae no - cte coe - nae, Ré - cum - bens cum frá - tri - bus,
4. Ver - bum ca - ro, pa - nem ve - rum Ver - bo car - nem éf - fi - cit:

5. Tan - tum er - go Sa - cra - mén - tum Ve - ne - ré - mur cér - nu - i:
6. Ge - ni - tó - ri, Ge - ni - tó - que Laus et ju - bi - lá - ti - o,

1. San - gui - nís - que pre - ti - ó - si, Quem in mun - di pré - ti - um
2. Et in mun - do con - ver - sá - tus, Spar - so ver - bi sé - mi - ne,
3. Ob - ser - vá - ta le - ge ple - ne Ci - bis in le - gá - li - bus,
4. Fit - que san - guis Chri - sti me - rum, Et si sen - sus dé - fi - cit,

5. Et an - tí - quum do - cu - mén - tum No - vo ce - dat rí - tu - i:
6. Sa - lus, ho - nor, vir - tus quo - que Sit et be - ne - dí - cti - o:

1. Fru - ctus ven - tris ge - ne - ró - si Rex ef - fú - dit gén - ti - um.
2. Su - i mo - ras in - co - lá - tus Mi - ro clau - sit ór - di - ne.
3. Ci - bum tur - bae du - o - dé - nae Se dat su - is má - ni - bus.
4. Ad fir - mán - dum cor sin - cé - rum So - la fi - des súf - fi - cit.

5. Prae - stet fi - des sup - ple - mén - tum Sén - su - um de - fé - ctu - i.
6. Pro - ce - dén - ti ab u - tró - que Com - par sit lau - dá - ti - o.

*1. Sing of glory and his body,
Wondrous myst'ry to behold,
Blood poured out in death and dying,
Royal gift so cheaply sold.
First a mother's selfless off'ring
Ransom now for sins untold.

2. Gift for us and gift forever,
From the virgin's womb was born,
Flesh of flesh and one among us,
Crucified and put to scorn,
That the Gospel seed might scatter
As of old the Lord had sworn.

3. At the last, the paschal supper,
With his friends before they fled,
First he ate the meal of passage:
Paschal lamb and paschal bread;
Then himself as food he offered
That the many might be fed.

4. Word made flesh, by word made present,
Body broken for the Feast,
And his blood, the cup of blessing,
Shed for all by Christ the Priest:
Though the senses fail and falter,
Faith confirms true hearts in peace.

**5. Holy sacrament, most holy,
Let us bow on bended knee:
Visions of the ancient promise
Now fulfilled in mystery.
Faith declares what none dare fathom;
Faith reveals what none may see.

6. God Begetter and Begotten,
Yours be praise and majesty,
Honor, glory and salvation,
Blessing for eternity,
With the One proceeding always,
Equally in unity.

*Verses 1–4 are repeated as necessary until the procession reaches the place of repose.
**Verses 5–6 are sung while the priest, kneeling, incenses the Blessed Sacrament.
Then the Blessed Sacrament is placed in the tabernacle of repose.

Text: 87 87 87; *Pange lingua gloriosi*; St. Thomas Aquinas, 1227–1274; tr. by Harry Hagan, OSB, b. 1947,
© 1990, St. Meinrad Archabbey. Published by OCP. All rights reserved.
Music: ST. THOMAS (TANTUM ERGO); John F. Wade, 1711–1786.

NO GREATER LOVE 379

There can be no great-er love than to lay down your life for a friend.

*Verses available in accompaniment books.

Text: Refrain, John 15:13; adapt. by Tim Schoenbachler, b. 1952, © 1986, OCP. All rights reserved.
Music: Tim Schoenbachler, © 1986, OCP. All rights reserved.

WOOD OF THE CROSS 380

Refrain

Be-hold the wood of the cross, on which hung the Sav-ior of the world. O come, O come, let us wor-ship, let us a-dore.

Verses
1. O God, my God, _____ why have you a-ban-doned me? _
2. I am de-spised, _ re-ject-ed by my peo-ple. _____
3. My bones are bro-ken. They pierce my hands and feet. _____
4. The jaws of death _ are clos-ing in up-on me. _____ The
5. You are en-throned _____ in the ho-ly place. _____ In

to Refrain
1. Why have you for-sak-en me? An-swer me, O God!
2. How could they for-get me? _ An-swer me, O God!
3. Why have you a-ban-doned me? An-swer me, O God!
4. wick-ed laugh and taunt me. _ An-swer me, O God!
5. you our fa-thers trust-ed. _ An-swer me, O God!

Text: Based on *Good Friday Liturgy*; Psalm 22; Owen Alstott, b. 1947.
Music: Owen Alstott.
Text and music © 1982, OCP. All rights reserved.

381 **BEHOLD THE CROSS**

Verses 1-3, 5

1, 5. Be - hold the cross on which was hung life's ver - y Lord, _____
2. Nails in his hands, nails in his feet, a trai - tor kiss __ up-
3. Eyes that won't see, ears that won't hear, lips that de - ny __ the

1, 5. God's on - ly Son; Ma - ry's own babe, so cold and so
2. on __ his cheek; and his pierced heart, now bro - ken in
3. friend once so dear; slow - ly he turns and cap - tures your

1, 5. still, help - less be - fore her on Cal - va - ry hill. (to Vs 2)
2. two, love cru - ci - fied __ for me and for you. (to Vs 3)
3. eye, then pass - es on __ to Cal - v'ry to die. (to Vs 4)

 Verse 4

4. Be - hold the cross of Christ in our midst: all those who bear his

4. wounds in their flesh. Suf - f'ring for crimes of mer - cy and peace,

to Vs. 5

4. signs of the king - dom on Cal - va - ry street.

Text: Based on the *Liturgy for Good Friday*; Bob Hurd, b. 1950.
Music: Bob Hurd.

382 **LORD, WE ADORE YOU**

Ostinato Refrain

Lord, we a - dore you, kneel - ing be - fore you; bring - ing our sor - rows,

leav - ing our bur - dens for you, our Re - deem - er, here at your cross.

O Sacred Head, Surrounded

1a. O Sa-cred Head, sur-round-ed By crown of pierc-ing thorn!
2a. In this, your bit-ter pas-sion, Good Shep-herd, think of me
3a. What lan-guage shall I bor-row To thank you, dear-est friend,
*1b. O Sa-cred Head, sur-round-ed By crown of pierc-ing thorn!
2b. O Love, all love tran-scend-ing, O Wis-dom from on high!
3b. O Je-sus, we a-dore thee, Up-on the cross our King!

1a. O bleed-ing Head, so wound-ed, Re-viled and put to scorn!
2a. With your most kind com-pas-sion, Un-worth-y though I be:
3a. For this, your dy-ing sor-row, Your mer-cy with-out end?
1b. O bleed-ing Head, so wound-ed, Re-viled and put to scorn!
2b. O Truth, un-changed, un-chang-ing, Sur-ren-dered up to die!
3b. We hum-bly bow be-fore thee, And of thy vic-t'ry sing!

1a. The pow'r of death comes o'er you, The glow of life de-cays,
2a. Be-neath your cross a-bid-ing, For-ev-er would I rest,
3a. Lord, make me yours for-ev-er, A loy-al ser-vant true,
1b. No come-li-ness or beau-ty Thy wound-ed face be-trays,
2b. Was e'er a love so won-drous! That from his heav'n-ly throne
3b. Thy cross is our sal-va-tion, Our hope from day to day,

1a. Yet an-gel hosts a-dore you, And trem-ble as they gaze.
2a. In your dear love con-fid-ing, And with your pres-ence blest.
3a. And let me nev-er, nev-er Out-live my love for you.
1b. Yet an-gel hosts a-dore thee And trem-ble as they gaze.
2b. God should de-scend a-mong us To suf-fer for his own.
3b. Our peace and con-so-la-tion When life shall fade a-way.

*Alternate verses.

Text: 76 76 D; *Salve caput cruentatum*; ascr. to Bernard of Clairvaux, 1091–1153.
 Verses 1, 2 tr. by Henry W. Baker, 1821–1877, alt.; verse 3 tr. by James W. Alexander, 1804–1859, alt.
 Alternate verses: verse 1 tr. by Henry W. Baker, alt.; verse 2, Owen Alstott, b. 1947;
 verse 3, Owen Alstott, composite. Alternate verses 2, 3 © 1977, OCP. All rights reserved.
Music: PASSION CHORALE; Hans Leo Hassler, 1564–1612; adapt. by Johann Sebastian Bach, 1685–1750.

384   SING, MY TONGUE, THE SAVIOR'S GLORY

1. Sing, my tongue, the Sav-ior's glo - ry: Tell his tri - umph
2. Faith-ful cross, O tree all beau - teous! Tree all peer-less
3. Eat - ing of the tree for - bid - den, Hu - mans sank in
4. Such the or - der God ap-point - ed When for sin he

1. far and wide; Tell a - loud the fa - mous sto - ry
2. and di - vine, Not a grove on earth can show us
3. Sa - tan's snare, When our pit - y - ing Cre - a - tor
4. would a - tone; To the ser - pent thus op - pos - ing

1. Of his bod - y cru - ci - fied; How up - on the cross a
2. Such a flow'r and leaf as thine. Sweet the nails, and sweet the
3. Did this sec - ond tree pre-pare; Des - tined, man - y ag - es
4. Schemes yet deep - er than his own; Thence the rem - e - dy pro -

(last verse only)

1. vic-tim, Van-quish-ing in death, he died.
2. wood, _ Lad - en with so sweet a load!
3. lat - er, That first e - vil to re - pair.
4. cur-ing, When the fa - tal wound had come. A - men.

5. So when now at length the fullness
Of the sacred time drew nigh,
Then the Son, the world's Creator,
Left his Father's throne on high;
From a virgin's womb appearing,
Clothed in our mortality.

6. Thus did Christ to perfect manhood
In our mortal flesh attain:
Then of his free choice he goes on
To a death of bitter pain;
And as lamb upon the altar
Of the cross, for us is slain.

7. Lofty tree, bend down your branches,
To embrace your sacred load;
Oh, relax the native tension
Of that all too rigid wood;
Gently, gently bear the members
Of your dying King and God.

8. Blessing, honor everlasting,
To the immortal Deity;
To the Father, Son, and Spirit,
Equal praises ever be;
Glory through the earth and heaven,
Trinity in Unity. Amen.

Text: 87 87 87; Venantius Honorius Fortunatus, 530–609; tr. by John M. Neale, 1818–1866.
Music: PANGE LINGUA GLORIOSI; Chant, Mode III; *Liber Hymnarius*, 1983.

WERE YOU THERE

1. Were you there when they cru - ci - fied my Lord?
2. Were you there when they nailed him to the tree?
3. Were you there when they pierced him in the side?
4. Were you there when the sun re - fused to shine?
5. Were you there when they laid him in the tomb?
6. Were you there when he rose up from the grave?

1. Were you there when they cru - ci - fied my Lord?
2. Were you there when they nailed him to the tree?
3. Were you there when they pierced him in the side?
4. Were you there when the sun re - fused to shine?
5. Were you there when they laid him in the tomb?
6. Were you there when he rose up from the grave?

1-6. Oh! Some - times it caus - es

1-6. me to trem - ble, trem - ble, trem - ble,

1. Were you there when they cru - ci - fied my Lord?
2. Were you there when they nailed him to the tree?
3. Were you there when they pierced him in the side?
4. Were you there when the sun re - fused to shine?
5. Were you there when they laid him in the tomb?
6. Were you there when he rose up from the grave?

Text: 10 10 14 10; Spiritual; *Old Plantation Hymns*, Boston, 1899.
Music: WERE YOU THERE; Spiritual; *Old Plantation Hymns*, Boston, 1899.

386

BEHOLD THE LAMB OF GOD

Verse 1

1. Be-hold the Lamb of God, be-hold the

1. Lamb of God who car-ries our bur-den, who

1. knows our pain, who bears the sins of the world.

Refrain

Be-hold the Lamb of God, be-hold the

Lamb of God; Je - sus,

to Verses 2-4
Fine

Je - sus is the Lamb of God.

Verse 2

2. Sure-ly he has borne our grief and car-ried the

2. sor-rows of us all. Struck down in our stead, re-

to Refrain

2. ject-ed and scorned, and by his wounds we are healed.

Verse 3

3. Fa - ther, for-give them, they do not un-der-stand,

3. they do not un-der-stand what they do.

Verse 4

4. The king-dom of this world has be-come the

4. king-dom of Christ, and he shall reign for

to Refrain

4. end-less days. Worth-y is the Lamb.

Text: Based on John 1:29; Isaiah 53:4–5; Luke 23:34; Revelation 11:15; Bob Dufford, b. 1943.
Music: Bob Dufford.

WHEN I SURVEY THE WONDROUS CROSS 387

1. When I sur-vey the won-drous cross On which the
2. For-bid it, Lord, that I should boast Save in the
3. See, from his head, his hands, his feet, The pain and
4. Were ev-'ry realm of na-ture mine, My gift would

1. Prince of glo-ry died, My rich-est gain I
2. death of Christ, my Lord; The vain things that now
3. love flow min-gled down; Did e'er such love and
4. still be far too small: Love so a-maz-ing,

1. count but loss, And pour con-tempt on all my pride.
2. tempt me most, I sac-ri-fice them to his blood.
3. sor-row meet, Or thorns com-pose so rich a crown?
4. so di-vine, De-mands my soul, my life, my all.

Text: LM; Isaac Watts, 1674–1748, alt.
Music: HAMBURG; Lowell Mason, 1792–1872.

388   Behold the Wood

Be - hold, be - hold the wood of the cross, on which is
hung our sal - va - tion. O come, let us a - dore.

Verses

1. Un - less a grain of wheat shall fall up - on the ground and die, it
2. And when my hour of glo - ry comes as all was meant to be,
3. For there can be no great - er love __ shown up - on this land than
4. My Fa - ther, if it be your plan, this cup might pass me by; yet
5. For sure - ly he has borne our tears, is wound - ed by our sin, and
6. My bod - y now is torn with pain, my friends have left and gone. O

to Refrain

1. shall re - main but a sin - gle grain and not give life.
2. you shall see me lift - ed up up - on a tree.
3. in the one who came to die that we might live.
4. let it hap - pen as you will if I must die.
5. yet he o - pens not his mouth that we might live.
6. lov - ing Fa - ther, take my life in - to your hands.

Text: Based on John 12:24, 32; 15:13; Good Friday Liturgy; Dan Schutte, b. 1947.
Music: Dan Schutte.

389   Ours Were the Griefs He Bore

Ours were the griefs he bore, ours were the pains he
car - ried. Ours were the sins he took on him,
and by his wounds we are healed.

Text: Based on Isaiah 53:4–5; 1 Peter 2:24; Stephen Dean, b. 1948.
Music: Stephen Dean.

My Song Is Love Unknown

390

1. My song is love un - known, My Sav - ior's love to
2. He came from his blest throne Sal - va - tion to be -
3. Some - times they strew his way, And his sweet prais - es
4. Why, what hath my Lord done? What makes this rage and
5. They rise and needs will have My dear Lord made a -
6. In life no house, no home My Lord on earth might
7. Here might I stay and sing, No sto - ry so di -

1. me, Love to the love - less shown That they might
2. stow, But all made strange, and none The longed - for
3. sing, Re - sound - ing all the day Ho - san - nas
4. spite? He made the lame to run, He gave the
5. way; A mur - der - er they save, The Prince of
6. have; In death no friend - ly tomb But what a
7. vine! Nev - er was love, dear King, Nev - er was

1. love - ly be. O who am I That
2. Christ would know. But O my friend, My
3. to their King. Then "Cru - ci - fy!" Is
4. blind their sight. Sweet in - ju - ries! Yet
5. Life they slay. Yet stead - fast he To
6. strang - er gave. What may I say? Heav'n
7. grief like thine. This is my friend, In

1. for my sake The Lord should take Frail flesh, and die?
2. friend in - deed, Who at my need His life did spend!
3. all their breath, And for his death They thirst and cry.
4. they at these Them - selves dis - please, And 'gainst him rise.
5. suf - f'ring goes, That he his foes From thence might free.
6. was his home; But mine the tomb Where - in he lay.
7. whose sweet praise I all my days Could glad - ly spend!

Text: 66 66 44 44; Samuel Crossman, ca. 1624–1683.
Music: LOVE UNKNOWN; John Ireland, 1879–1962, © 1924, 1995, John Ireland. All rights reserved.
Administered by the John Ireland Trust, London. Used with permission.

391

YOUR ONLY SON

Verses

1. Your on-ly Son, no sin to hide, but you have
2. Your gift of love they cru-ci-fied, they laughed and
3. I was so lost I should have died, but you have

1. sent him from your side to walk up-on this guilt-y
2. scorned him as he died; the hum-ble King they named a
3. brought me to your side to be led by your staff and

1. sod, and to be-come the Lamb of God.
2. fraud, and sac-ri-ficed the Lamb of God.
3. rod, and to be called a lamb of God.

Refrain

O Lamb of God, sweet Lamb of God; I love the

ho-ly Lamb of God. O wash me in his pre-cious

blood. My Je-sus Christ, the Lamb of God.

392 ## THE SEVEN LAST WORDS FROM THE CROSS

*Refrain

O vos o-mnes qui tran-si-tis per vi-am at-

ten-di-te et vi-de-te si est do-lor si-cut do-lor me-us.

Translation: O all you who pass this way, look and see is any sorrow like the sorrow that afflicts me.

*Verses available in accompaniment books.

Text: Refrain based on Lamentations 1:12.

O Sacred Head

Verses 1, 2, 4

1. O Sa - cred Head, sur - round - ed by
2. No come - li - ness or beau - ty your
4. Life - giv - ing love, em - pow'r us with

1. crown of pierc - ing thorn! O bleed - ing Head, so
2. wound - ed face be - trays. Yet an - gel hosts a -
4. cour - age bold and true to walk the road of

1. wound - ed, re - viled and put to scorn!
2. dore you and trem - ble as they
4. jus - tice, and bear the cross with

2. gaze. 4. you, and bear the cross with you.

Verse 3

3. My sis - ter ren - dered voice - less, de - meaned and

3. still in chains, my broth - er still ex -

to Verse 4

3. ploit - ed, im - ag - es of your pain.

Text: Verses 1 & 2 ascr. to Bernard of Clairvaux, 1091–1153, alt.; verses 3 & 4, Bob Hurd, b. 1950, © 1990, Bob Hurd.
Published by OCP. All rights reserved.
Music: Bob Hurd, © 1990, Bob Hurd. Published by OCP. All rights reserved.

394

LITANY OF THE SAINTS

Lord, have mer-cy. **Lord, have mer-cy.**
Christ, have mer-cy. **Christ, have mer-cy.**
Lord, have mer-cy. **Lord, have mer-cy.**

Holy Mary, Mother of God, **pray for us.**
Saint Mích - ael,

Holy Angels of Gód,	Saint Grégory,
Saint John the Báptist,	Saint Augústine,
Saint Jóseph,	Saint Athanásius,
Saint Peter and Saint Pául,	Saint Básil,
Saint Ándrew,	Saint Mártin,
Saint Jóhn,	Saint Bénedict,
Saint Mary Mágdalene,	Saint Francis and Saint Dóminic,
Saint Stéphen,	Saint Francis Xávier,
Saint Ignatius of Ántioch,	Saint John Viánney,
Saint Láwrence,	Saint Catherine of Siéna,
Saint Perpetua and Saint Felícity,	Saint Teresa of Jésus,
Saint Ágnes,	All holy men and women, Saints of Gód,

Lord, be mer-ci-ful, **Lord, de-liv-er us, we pray.**

From àll é-vil, **Lord, de-liv-er us, we pray.**

From èverý sin,	By your Death and Rèsurréction,
From everlàsting déath,	By the outpouring of the
By your Ìncarnátion,	Hòly Spírit,

Be merciful to us sin-ners, **Lord, we ask you, hear our prayer.**

If there are candidates to be baptized

Bring these chosen ones to new birth through the grace of Bap - tism,

Lord, we ask you, hear our prayer.

If there is no one to be baptized

Cantors

Make this font holy by your grace for the new birth of your chil - dren,

All

Lord, we ask you, hear our prayer.

Cantors   All

Jesus, Son of the liv - ing God, **Lord, we ask you, hear our prayer.**

Cantors, All repeat   Cantors, All repeat

Christ, hear us.   Christ, gra-cious-ly hear us.

OUT OF DARKNESS   395

Refrain

Out of dark-ness the light of Christ will shine, as the
dawn of day breaks through the night. Then the poor and oppressed will cry out and be heard by the light that ris - es from the night.

Verses

1. Let the darkness flee from here.
   Put an end to sadness and fear.
   The hungry will eat, the sick will dance,
   the dead will live again.

2. This is the night, O holy of nights,
   the chains of death are destroyed.

This is the light;
the glory of God is raised to life again.

3. A single flame,
   a flicker of hope spreads like a sea of fire.
   Open the door, shout to the night:
   We will live again.

*Last time repeat final phrase.

396 **CHRISTIANS, TO THE PASCHAL VICTIM**

1. Chris-tians, to the Pas-chal Vic-tim Of-fer your thank-ful prais-es!
1. *Ví - cti-mae pa-schá - li lau-des im-mo-lent Chri-sti - á - ni.*

2. A Lamb the sheep re-deems; — Christ, who on - ly is sin - less,
3. Death and life have con-tend-ed in that com-bat stu-pen-dous:
2. *A - gnus re - dé-mit o - ves: Chri-stus ín - no-cens Pa - tri*
3. *Mors et vi - ta du - él - lo con - fli - xé - re mi-rán - do:*

2. Rec - on - ciles sin - ners to the Fa - ther.
3. The Prince of life, who died, reigns im - mor - tal.
2. *re - con - ci - li - á - vit pec - ca - tó - res.*
3. *dux vi - tae mór - tu - us, re - gnat vi - vus.*

4. Speak, Ma - ry, de - clar-ing What you saw, — way-far-ing.
6. Bright an-gels, at - test-ing, The shroud and nap-kin rest-ing.
4. *Dic no - bis Ma - rí - a, quid vi - dí - sti in vi - a?*
6. *An - gé - li - cos te-stes, su - dá - ri - um, et ve-stes.*

5. "The tomb of Christ, who is liv - ing,
7. Yes, Christ my hope is a - ris - en;
5. *Se - púl - crum Chri - sti vi - vén - tis,*
7. *Sur - ré - xit Chri - stus spes me - a:*

5. The glo - ry of Je - sus' res - ur - rec - tion;
7. To Gal - i - lee he goes be - fore you."
5. *et gló - ri - am vi - di re - sur - gén - tis:*
7. *prae - cé - det su - os in Ga - li - laé - am.*

8. Christ in-deed from death is ris - en, our new life ob-tain-ing.
8. *Sci-mus Chrí-stum sur - re - xís - se a mór-tu - is ve - re:*

8. Have mer - cy, vic - tor King, ev - er reign - ing!
8. *tu no - bis vi - ctor Rex, mi - se - ré - re.*

A – men. Al – le – lú – ia.

Text: Irregular; Poetic Sequence for Easter, *Victimae paschali laudes*; fr. *The Roman Missal*,
English text © 1964, The National Catholic Welfare Conference, Inc. (now US Conference of Catholic Bishops).
All rights reserved. Used with permission.
Music: VICTIMAE PASCHALI LAUDES; Chant, Mode I; *Graduale Romanum*, 1974.

CHRIST, THE LORD, IS RISEN TODAY   397

1. Christ, the Lord, is ris'n to - day; Chris-tians, haste your
2. Christ, the Vic - tim un - de - filed, God and sin - ners
3. Say, O won-d'ring Ma - ry, say What you saw a -
4. Christ, who once for sin - ners bled, Now the first - born

1. vows to pay; Make your joy and prais - es known At the
2. re - con-ciled; When in strange and awe-some strife Met to -
3. long the way. "I be - held two an - gels bright, Emp - ty
4. from the dead, Throned in end - less might and pow'r, Lives and

1. Pas - chal Vic - tim's throne; For the sheep the Lamb has bled,
2. geth - er death and life; Chris-tians, on this hap - py day
3. tomb and wrap-pings white; I be - held the glo - ry bright
4. reigns for - ev - er - more. Hail, e - ter - nal Hope on high!

1. Sin - less in the sin - ner's stead; Christ, the Lord, is
2. Haste with joy your vows to pay; Christ, the Lord, is
3. Of the ris - en Lord of light; Christ, my hope, is
4. Hail, our King of Vic - to - ry! Hail, our Prince of

1. ris'n on high; Now he lives, no more to die!
2. ris'n on high; Now he lives, no more to die!
3. ris'n a - gain; Now he lives, and lives to reign!"
4. Life a - dored! Help and save us, gra - cious Lord!

Text: 77 77 D; *Victimae Paschali laudes*; ascr. to Wipo of Burgundy, ca. 1000–1050; tr. by Jane E. Leeson, 1808–1881, alt.
Music: VICTIMAE PASCHALI; Würth's *Katholisches Gesangbuch*, 1859.

398   CHRIST IS ARISEN

Verses

1. To the Pas-chal Vic-tim Give thank-ful praise!
2. Ma-ry, speak, con-fess-ing What you have seen.
3. Chris-tians, sing his glo-ry With ev-'ry breath;

1. Christ, ev-er sin-less, his sheep now he saves.
2. "Christ's tomb lies emp-ty where once he had been;
3. Sing of his king-dom, vic-to-rious o'er death!

1. Death and life con-tend-ed In dread-ful strife;
2. An-gels bright, con-firm-ing; Shroud laid a-side;
3. Je-sus, grant us mer-cy: New life from heav'n!

1. Death did not hold __ him, im-mor-tal his life.
2. He goes to Gal-i-lee, he lives though he died."
3. Christ ev-er reigns! __ Al-le-lu-ia! A-men!

Refrain

Al-le-lu-ia, his tri-umph we sing!

Christ is a-ris-en, the Vic-tor, the King!

Text: 64 10 D with refrain; based on the Sequence for Easter (*Victimae paschali laudes*); Randall DeBruyn, b. 1947.
Music: RISEN KING; Randall DeBruyn.
Text and music © 1993, OCP. All rights reserved.

399   SPRINGS OF WATER, BLESS THE LORD

*Refrain

Springs of wa-ter, bless the Lord! Give him glo-ry and praise for-ev-er.

to Verses
last time: to Coda

Springs of wa-ter, bless the Lord! Give him glo-ry and praise for-ev-er.

*Verses available in accompaniment books.

Coda

Give him glo-ry and praise for-ev-er. Give him glo-ry and praise for-ev-er.

Give him glo-ry and praise for-ev-er. Al-le-lu-ia! Al-le-lu-ia!

THE DAY OF RESURRECTION   **400**

1. The day of res-ur-rec - tion! Earth, spread the news a-broad;
2. Our hearts be free from e - vil That we may see a-right
3. His love is ev-er-last - ing; His mer-cies nev-er cease;
4. Now let the heav'ns be joy - ful, And earth her song be-gin;

1. The Pas-chal feast of glad - ness, The Pas-chal feast of God.
2. The Sav-ior res-ur-rect - ed In his e-ter-nal light,
3. The res-ur-rect-ed Sav - ior, Will all our joys in-crease.
4. The whole world keep high tri - umph And all that is there-in;

1. From death to life e - ter - nal, From earth to heav-en's height
2. And hear his mes-sage plain - ly, De - liv-ered calm and clear:
3. He'll keep us in his fa - vor, Sup - ply-ing ho-ly grace,
4. Let all things in cre-a - tion Their notes of glad-ness blend,

1. Our Sav-ior Christ has brought us, The glo-rious Lord of Light.
2. "Re-joice with me in tri-umph, Be glad and do not fear."
3. To all his pil-grim peo - ple Who seek his heav'n-ly place.
4. For Christ the Lord is ris - en, Our joy that has no end.

401   JESUS CHRIST IS RISEN TODAY

1. Je - sus Christ is ris'n to - day,
2. Hymns of praise then let us sing,
3. But the pains which he en-dured,
4. Sing we to our God a - bove,

Al - le - lu - ia!

1. Our tri - um-phant ho - ly day,
2. Un - to Christ, our heav'n-ly King,
3. Our sal - va - tion have pro-cured;
4. Praise e - ter - nal as his love,

Al - le - lu - ia!

1. Who did once up - on the cross,
2. Who en-dured the cross and grave,
3. Now a - bove the sky he's King,
4. One true God by all con-fessed,

Al - le - lu - ia!

1. Suf - fer to re-deem our loss.
2. Sin - ners to re-deem and save.
3. Where the an-gels ev - er sing.
4. Fa - ther, Son, and Spir - it blest.

Al - le - lu - ia!

Text: 77 77 with alleluias; verse 1, Latin, 14th cent., para. in *Lyra Davidica*, 1708, alt.;
   verses 2–3, *The Compleat Psalmodist*, ca. 1750, alt.; verse 4, Charles Wesley, 1707–1788, alt.
Music: EASTER HYMN; later form of melody fr. *Lyra Davidica*, 1708.

402   COME, YE FAITHFUL, RAISE THE STRAIN

1. Come, ye faith - ful, raise the strain Of tri - um - phant glad-ness;
2. 'Tis the spring of souls to - day; Christ has burst his pris - on,
3. Now the queen of sea-sons bright With the day of splen-dor,
4. Nei - ther could the gates of death, Nor the tomb's dark por - tal,
5. "Al - le - lu - ia!" now we cry To our King im - mor - tal,

1. God has brought his Is - ra - el In - to joy from sad-ness;
2. And from three days' sleep in death As a sun has ris - en;
3. With the roy - al feast of feasts Comes its joy to ren - der;
4. Nor the watch - ers, nor the seal Hold him as a mor - tal;
5. Who, tri - um - phant, burst the bars Of the tomb's dark por - tal;

1. Loosed from Pha-roah's bit-ter yoke Ja-cob's sons and daugh-ters;
2. All the win-ter of our sins, Long and dark is fly-ing
3. Comes to glad-den faith-ful hearts Who with true af-fec-tion
4. But to-day a-mong the twelve Christ ap-peared, be-stow-ing
5. "Al - le - lu - ia!" with the Son, God the Fa-ther prais-ing;

1. Led them with un-moist-ened foot Through the Red Sea wa-ters.
2. From his light, to whom we give Laud and praise un - dy - ing.
3. Wel-come in un - wea-ried strains Je - sus' res-ur-rec-tion.
4. Last-ing peace which ev - er-more Pass-es hu-man know-ing.
5. "Al - le - lu - ia!" yet a - gain To the Spir-it rais-ing.

Text: 76 76 D; based on Exodus 15; St. John of Damascus, 8th cent.; tr. by John M. Neale, 1818–1866, alt.
Music: GAUDEAMUS PARITER; Johann Horn, ca. 1495–1547.

CHRIST, THE LORD, IS RISEN TODAY 403

1. Christ, the Lord, is ris'n to - day:
2. Lives a - gain our glo-rious King;
3. Love's re-deem-ing work is done;
4. Soar we now where Christ has led,
Al - le - lu - ia!

1. All on earth with an - gels say:
2. Where, O death, is now your sting?
3. Fought the fight, the bat-tle won;
4. Fol-l'wing our ex - alt-ed Head;
Al - le - lu - ia!

1. Raise your joys and tri - umphs high:
2. Once he died our souls to save;
3. Death in vain for-bids him rise;
4. Made like him, like him we rise:
Al - le - lu - ia!

1. Sing, O heav'ns, and earth re - ply:
2. Where your vic - to - ry, O grave?
3. Christ has o - pened par - a - dise.
4. Ours the cross, the grave, the skies.
Al - le - lu - ia!

Text: 77 77 with alleluias; Charles Wesley, 1707–1788, alt.
Music: LLANFAIR; Robert Williams, 1781–1821.

404

RESUCITÓ/HE IS RISEN

Refrain

Re - su - ci - tó,   re - su - ci - tó,   re - su - ci -
A - le - lu - ya,   a - le - lu - ya,   a - le - lu -

1, 2   2nd time: to Verses   Final

tó,   a - le - lu - ya.
ya,   re - su - ci - tó.   tó.   A - le - lu - ya.

Verses

1. La ___ muer - te   ¿dón - de es - tá la
2. Gra - cias se - an   da - das al
3. A - le - grí - a,   a - le - grí - a her -
4. Si con Él mo - ri - mos,   y con Él vi -
1. And ___ death now,   van - ished is the
2. The ___ king - dom,   praise to God, the
3. Our ___ glad - ness,   bless - ful in our
4. With ___ him then,   die and live with

1. muer - te?   ¿Dón - de es - tá mi muer - te?
2. Pa - dre   que nos pa - só a su rei - no
3. ma - nos,   que si hoy nos que - re - mos
4. vi - mos,   y con Él can - ta - mos.
1. fear now,   ban - ished are my tears now,
2. king - dom!   Raised up to the king - dom,
3. glad - ness,   this will be our glad - ness,
4. him then,   rise and sing our hymn then,

to Refrain

1. ¿Dón - de su vic - to - ria? _____
2. don - de se vi - ve de a - mor. _____
3. y es que re - su - ci - tó. _____
4. y ¡A - le - lu - ya! _____
1. death has passed a - way. _____
2. we shall live in love. _____
3. that he is a - live. _____
4. sing al - le - lu - ia. _____

Text: Spanish, Kiko Argüello; English tr., OCP.
Music: Kiko Argüello.

O SONS AND DAUGHTERS

Refrain

Al - le - lu - ia! Al - le - lu - ia! Al - le - lu - ia!

Verses

1. O sons and daugh - ters, let us sing! The King of
2. That Eas - ter morn, at break of day, The faith - ful
3. An an - gel clad in white they see, Who sat, and
4. That night the a - pos - tles met in fear; A - mid them
5. When Thom - as first the tid - ings heard, How they had
6. "My wound - ed side, O Thom - as, see; Be - hold my
7. No long - er Thom - as then de - nied; He saw the
8. How blest are they who have not seen, And yet whose
9. On this most ho - ly day of days, To God your

1. heav'n, the glo - rious King, O'er death to - day rose
2. wom - en went their way To seek the tomb where
3. spoke un - to the three: "Your Lord has gone to
4. came their Lord most dear, And said, "My peace be
5. seen the ris - en Lord, He doubt - ed the dis -
6. hands, my feet," said he. "Not faith - less, but be -
7. feet, the hands, the side; "You are my Lord and
8. faith has con - stant been, For they e - ter - nal
9. hearts and voic - es raise, In laud, and ju - bi -

to Refrain

1. tri - um - phing. Al - le - lu - ia!
2. Je - sus lay. Al - le - lu - ia!
3. Gal - i - lee." Al - le - lu - ia!
4. on all here." Al - le - lu - ia!
5. ci - ples' word. Al - le - lu - ia!
6. liev - ing be." Al - le - lu - ia!
7. God," he cried. Al - le - lu - ia!
8. life shall win. Al - le - lu - ia!
9. lee and praise. Al - le - lu - ia!

Text: 888 with alleluias; attr. to Jean Tisserand, d. 1494; tr. by John M. Neale, 1818–1866, alt.
Music: O FILII ET FILIAE; Chant, Mode II; *Airs sur les hymnes sacrez, odes et noëls*, 1623.

406

THREE DAYS

1. Three days our world was bro - ken; the
2. Three days— and on the third day, the
3. Three days our world was bro - ken and

1. Lord of life lay dead. "Take up your cross," he
2. wom - en came at dawn. His tomb, they said, was
3. in an in - stant healed, God's cov - e - nant of

1. told us who fol - lowed where he led. Would
2. emp - ty, his bro - ken bod - y gone. Who
3. mer - cy in mys - ter - y re - vealed. Two

1. we now hang in tor - ment with thieves on ev - 'ry side,
2. could be - lieve their sto - ry? The dead do not a - rise,
3. thou - sand years are one day in God's e - ter - nal sight,

1. our Pass - o - ver shat - tered, our hope cru - ci - fied?
2. yet he walks a - mong us, and with our own eyes
3. and yes - ter - day's sor - rows are this day's de - light.

1. Three days we hid in si - lence, in
2. we've seen him at this ta - ble; we've
3. Though still Christ's bod - y suf - fers, pierced

1. bit - ter fear and grief. Three days we clung to -
2. shared his bread and wine. Hearts burn - ing bright with -
3. dai - ly by the sword, yet death has no do -

1. geth - er where he had washed our feet.
2. in us, we've seen his glo - ry shine.
3. min - ion: the ris - en Christ is Lord!

Text: 13 13 13 11 13 13; M.D. Ridge, © 1999, M.D. Ridge. Published by OCP. All rights reserved.
Music: THAXTED; Gustav T. Holst, 1874–1932, alt.

At the Lamb's High Feast 407

1. At the Lamb's high feast we sing Praise to our vic -
2. Where the Pas - chal blood is poured, Death's dark an - gel
3. Might - y vic - tim from the sky, Hell's fierce pow'rs be -
4. Eas - ter tri - umph, Eas - ter joy, This a - lone can

1. to - rious King, Who has washed us in the tide
2. sheathes his sword; Is - rael's hosts tri - um - phant go
3. neath you lie; You have con - quered in the fight,
4. sin de - stroy; From sin's pow'r, Lord, set us free,

1. Flow - ing from his wound - ed side; Praise we him, whose
2. Through the wave that drowns the foe. Praise we Christ whose
3. You have brought us life and light: Now no more can
4. New - born souls in you to be. Hymns of glo - ry,

1. love di - vine Gives his sa - cred blood for wine, Gives his
2. blood was shed, Pas - chal vic - tim, Pas - chal bread! With sin -
3. death ap - pall, Now no more the grave en - thrall; You have
4. songs of praise, Fa - ther, un - to you we raise: And to

1. bod - y for the feast, Christ the vic - tim, Christ the priest.
2. cer - i - ty and love Eat we man - na from a - bove.
3. o - pened Par - a - dise, And in you the saints shall rise.
4. you, our ris - en King, With the Spir - it, praise we sing.

Text: 77 77 D; Ad regias Agni dapes; Latin, 4th cent.; tr. by Robert Campbell, 1814–1868, alt.
Music: SALZBURG; Jakob Hintze, 1622–1702; adapt. by Johann Sebastian Bach, 1685–1750.

408 THE STRIFE IS O'ER

Refrain

Al - le - lu - ia! Al - le - lu - ia! Al - le - lu - ia!

Verses

1. The strife is o'er, the bat - tle done;
2. The pow'rs of death have done their worst,
3. On the third morn he rose a - gain,
4. He closed the yawn - ing gates of hell;
5. O Ris - en Lord, all praise to thee,

1. Now is the Vic - tor's tri - umph won; O let the
2. But Christ their le - gions has dis - persed; Let shouts of
3. Glo - rious in maj - es - ty to reign; O let us
4. The bars from heav'n's high por - tals fell; Let hymns of
5. Who from our sin has set us free, That we may

to Refrain

1. song of praise be sung: Al - le - lu - ia!
2. praise and joy out - burst: Al - le - lu - ia!
3. swell the joy - ful strain: Al - le - lu - ia!
4. praise his tri - umph tell: Al - le - lu - ia!
5. live e - ter - nal - ly! Al - le - lu - ia!

Text: 888 with alleluias; *Finita iam sunt praelia*; Latin, 12th cent.; tr. by Francis Pott, 1832–1909, alt.
Music: VICTORY; Giovanni Pierluigi da Palestrina, 1525–1594; adapt. by Willam H. Monk, 1823–1889.

409 BE JOYFUL, MARY, HEAVENLY QUEEN

1. Be joy - ful, Ma - ry, heav'n-ly Queen, Be joy - ful, Ma -
2. The Son you bore by heav-en's grace, Be joy - ful, Ma -
3. The Lord has ris - en from the dead, Be joy - ful, Ma -
4. Now pray to God, O Vir - gin fair, Be joy - ful, Ma -

1. ry! Your Son who died was liv - ing seen,
2. ry! Did all our guilt and sin ef - face,
3. ry! He rose with might as he had said,
4. ry! That he our souls to heav - en bear,

Al -

1-4. le - lu - ia, Re - joice, re - joice, O Ma - ry!

Text: 85 84 7; *Regina Caeli, jubila*; Latin, 17th cent.; tr. anon. in *Psallite*, 1901, alt.
Music: REGINA CAELI; Johann Leisentritt's *Catholicum Hymnologium*, 1584.

JOIN IN THE DANCE   410

Refrain

Join in the dance of the earth's ju - bi - la - tion! This is the feast of the

love of God. Shout from the heights to the ends of cre - a - tion:

Je - sus the Sav - ior is ris - en from the grave!

Verses

1. Wake, O peo - ple; sleep no long - er: greet the
2. All cre - a - tion, like a moth - er, la - bors
3. Now our shame be - comes our glo - ry on this
4. None on earth, no prince or pow - er, nei - ther
5. Love's tri - um - phant day of vic - t'ry heav - en
6. Christ for - ev - er, Lord of a - ges, Love be -

1. break - ing day! Christ, Re - deem - er,
2. to give birth. Soon the pain will
3. ho - ly tree. Now the reign of
4. death nor life, noth - ing now can
5. o - pens wide. On the tree of
6. yond our dreams: Christ, our hope of

to Refrain

1. Lamb and Li - on, turns the night a - way!
2. be for - got - ten, joy for all the earth!
3. death is end - ed; now we are set free!
4. ev - er part us from the love of Christ!
5. hope and glo - ry death it - self has died!
6. heav - en's glo - ry, all that yet will be!

411   ALLELUIA! ALLELUIA! LET THE HOLY ANTHEM RISE

1. Al - le - lu - ia! Al - le - lu - ia! Let the ho - ly an-them
2. Al - le - lu - ia! Al - le - lu - ia! Like the sun from out the
3. Al - le - lu - ia! Al - le - lu - ia! He has burst our pris - on
4. Al - le - lu - ia! Al - le - lu - ia! Bless - ed Je - sus, make us

1. rise, And the choirs of heav-en chant it In the
2. wave, He has ris - en up in tri - umph From the
3. bars; He has lift - ed up the por - tals Of our
4. rise From the life of this cor - rup - tion To the

1. tem - ple of the skies; Let the moun - tains skip with
2. dark - ness of the grave. He's the splen - dor of the
3. home be-yond the stars: He has won for us our
4. life that nev - er dies. May your glo - ry be our

1. glad - ness, And the joy - ful val - leys ring With ho -
2. na - tions, He's the lamp of end-less day; He's the
3. free - dom, 'Neath his feet our foes are trod; He has
4. por - tion, When the days of time are past, And the

1. san - nas in the high - est To our Sav - ior and our King!
2. ver - y Lord of glo - ry Who is ris - en up to - day!
3. pur - chased back our birth-right To the king - dom of our God!
4. dead shall be a - wak - ened By the trum - pet's might-y blast!

Text: 87 87 D; Edward Caswall, 1814–1878.
Music: HOLY ANTHEM; *St. Basil's Hymnal*, 1889.

412   LET HEAVEN REJOICE

Refrain

Let heav-en re-joice and earth be glad; let all cre-a-tion sing. Let

chil-dren pro-claim through ev - 'ry land: "Ho - san - na to our King."

Verses 1-3

1. Sound the trum - pet in - to the night; the day of the Lord is
2. Rise in splen-dor; shake off your sleep; put on your robes of
3. Raise your voic - es, be not a - fraid. Pro-claim it in ev - 'ry

to Refrain

1. near. Wake your peo - ple, lift your voice, pro-claim it to the world.
2. joy. And in the morn-ing you shall see the glo - ry of the Lord.
3. land. Christ has died, but he has ris - en; he will come a - gain.

Verse 4

4. Sing a new song un-to the Lord, whose la-bor has led us to life. With

to Refrain

4. grate-ful hearts and joy-ful danc-ing, play be-fore the Lord.

ALLELUIA NO. 1   **413**

Refrain

Al - le - lu - ia, al - le - lu - ia! Give thanks to the ris-en Lord. Al - le-

Verses

lu-ia, al-le-lu-ia! Give praise to his name. 1. Je - sus is Lord of
2. Spread the good news o'er
3. We have been cru - ci-
4. Come, let us praise the

to Refrain

1. all the earth; He is the king of cre - a - tion.
2. all the earth: Je - sus has died and has ris - en.
3. fied with Christ; Now we shall live ___ for - ev - er.
4. liv - ing God; Joy - ful - ly sing to our Sav - ior.

414

THIS JOYFUL EASTERTIDE

1. This joy-ful Eas-ter-tide, A-way with sin and
2. Death's flood has lost its chill, Since Je-sus crossed the
3. My flesh in hope shall rest, And for a sea-son

1. sor - row! My Love, the Cru-ci-
2. riv - er: Lord of all life, from
3. slum - ber, Till trump from east to

1. fied, Has sprung to life this mor - row.
2. ill My pass-ing life de-liv - er.
3. west Shall wake the dead in num - ber.

Refrain

Had Christ, that once was slain, Ne'er burst his three-day pris-

on, Our faith had been in vain; But now is Christ a-ris-en, a-

ris-en, a-ris-en, a-ris - en.

Text: 67 67 with refrain; George R. Woodward, 1848–1934.
Music: VREUCHTEN; Oudaen's *David's Psalmen*, 1685, alt.

415

ALLELUIA! ALLELUIA

1. Al - le - lu - ia! Al - le - lu - ia! Hearts and voic - es
2. Now the i - ron bars are bro - ken, Christ from death to
3. Christ is ris - en, we are ris - en! Shed up - on us
4. Al - le - lu - ia! Al - le - lu - ia! Glo - ry be to

1. heav'n - ward raise: Sing to God a hymn of glad - ness,
2. life is born, Glo - rious life and life im - mor - tal,
3. heav'n - ly grace, Rain and dew and gleams of glo - ry
4. God on high; Al - le - lu - ia to the Sav - ior

1. Sing to God a hymn of praise. Christ, who on the
2. On that ho - ly Eas - ter morn. Christ has tri-umphed,
3. From your ho - ly ra - diant face; That, with hearts in
4. Who has won the vic - to - ry; Al - le - lu - ia

1. cross a vic - tim, For the world's sal - va - tion bled, Je - sus
2. and we con - quer By this might - y en - ter - prise, We with
3. heav - en dwell-ing, We on earth, your ser-vants true, Will by
4. to the Spir - it, Fount of love and sanc - ti - ty; Al - le -

1. Christ, the King of glo - ry, Now is ris - en from the dead.
2. Christ to life e - ter - nal By his res - ur - rec - tion rise.
3. an - gel hands be gath-ered, And be ev - er, Lord, with you.
4. lu - ia! Al - le - lu - ia! To the Tri - une Maj - es - ty.

Text: 87 87 D; Christopher Wordsworth, 1807–1885.
Music: HYMN TO JOY; Ludwig van Beethoven, 1770–1827; adapt. by Edward Hodges, 1796–1867.

Regina Caeli/O Queen of Heaven 416

Re - gí - na cae - li, lae - tá - re, al - le - lú - ia,
O Queen of heav - en, be joy - ful, al - le - lu - ia,

qui - a quem me - ru - í - sti por - tá - re, al - le - lú - ia,
For he whom you have hum - bly borne for us, al - le - lu - ia,

re - sur - ré - xit si - cut di - xit, al - le - lú - ia,
Has a - ris - en, as he prom-ised, al - le - lu - ia,

O - ra pro no - bis De - um, al - le - lú - ia.
Of - fer now our prayer to God, al - le - lu - ia.

Text: Irregular; Latin, 12th cent.; tr. by C. Winfred Douglas, 1867–1944, alt.
Music: REGINA CAELI LAETARE; Chant, Mode VI; *Liber Cantualis*, 1983.

417 TWO WERE BOUND FOR EMMAUS

1, 5. Two were bound for Em - ma - us, dis - heart - ened
2. On the Sea of Ti - ber - ius, when the night was
3. Then they knew it was Je - sus and they has - tened
4. When the road makes us wea - ry, when our la - bor

1, 5. and ___ lost; all their hope for the fu - ture had been
2. near - ly gone and their toil seemed so use - less, not one
3. in to shore; bread and fish for their break - fast from the
4. seems but loss, when the fire of faith weak - ens and too

1, 5. nailed to a cross. Love un - known then walked be - side ___ them,
2. fish had they caught, from the shore the strang - er called to them:
3. hands of their Lord. "O ___ Pe - ter, if you love ___ me
4. high seems the cost, let the Church turn to its ris - en Lord,

1, 5. come ___ back from the dead, and they knew he was
2. "Cast your net, friends, once more." And they filled it to
3. you must care for my sheep; if you fol - low your
4. who for us bore the cross, and we'll find our hearts

1, 5. ris - en in the break - ing of bread.
2. burst - ing, but the net was not torn.
3. Shep - herd, then a shep - herd you'll be."
4. burn - ing at the sound of his voice.

Text: 11 13 13 13; based on Luke 24:13–35; John 21:1–19; Bob Hurd, b. 1950.
Music: KENMARE; Bob Hurd.
Text and music © 2000, Bob Hurd. Published by OCP. All rights reserved.

418 CHRIST IS ALIVE

1. Christ is a - live! Let Chris - tians sing. The cross stands
2. Christ is a - live! No long - er bound To dis - tant
3. In ev - 'ry in - sult, rift, and war, Where col - or,
4. Wom - en and men, in age and youth, Can feel the
5. Christ is a - live, and comes to bring Good news to

1. emp - ty to the sky. Let streets and homes with prais - es
2. years in Pal - es - tine, But sav - ing, heal - ing here and
3. scorn or wealth di - vide, Christ suf - fers still, yet loves the
4. Spir - it, hear the call, And find the way, the life, the
5. this and ev - 'ry age, Till earth and sky and o - cean

1. ring. Love, drowned in death, shall nev - er die.
2. now, And touch - ing ev - 'ry place and time.
3. more, And lives, where e - ven hope has died.
4. truth, Re - vealed in Je - sus, freed for all.
5. ring With joy, with jus - tice, love and praise.

Text: LM; Romans 6:5–11; Brian Wren, b. 1936, © 1975, revised 1995, Hope Publishing Co.
All rights reserved. Used with permission.
Music: TRURO; Williams' *Psalmodia Evangelica, Part II*, 1789.

THIS DAY WAS MADE BY THE LORD 419

Refrain
This day was made by the Lord, let us re-joice, let us be glad.

let us re-joice in sal - va - tion!

Verses
Cantor
1. I thank you, your love is e -
2. Your hand raised me up ___ in
3. The stone which the build - ers re -
4. You o - pened the gates ___ of
5. ℣ You are my strength and my

All
1. ter - nal, you have giv - en me life. You have giv - en me life.
2. tri - umph, you have giv - en me life. You have giv - en me life.
3. ject - ed is the cor - ner-stone, _ is the cor - ner-stone. _
4. heav - en, you have giv - en me life. You have giv - en me life.
5. Sav - ior, you have giv - en me life. You have giv - en me life.

to Refrain
1-5. I will pro - claim the won - ders you do!

Text: Based on Psalm 118; Christopher Walker, b. 1947.
Music: Christopher Walker.
Text and music © 1988, 1989, Christopher Walker. Published by OCP. All rights reserved.

420   CHRIST, THE LORD, IS RISEN AGAIN

1. Christ, the Lord, is ris'n a - gain, Christ has bro - ken ev - 'ry chain! Hark, the an - gels shout for joy, Sing - ing ev - er - more on high:
2. Christ who gave for us his life, Who for us en - dured the strife, Is our Pas - chal Lamb to - day. We, too, sing for joy and say:
3. Christ who bore all pain and loss Com - fort - less up - on the cross, Lives in glo - ry now on high, Pleads for us and hears our cry:
4. He who slum - bered in the grave Is ex - alt - ed now to save; Now through - out the world it rings That the Lamb is King of kings.
5. Now he bids us tell a - broad How the lost may be re - stored, How the pen - i - tent for - giv'n, How we, too, may en - ter heav'n.
6. You, our Pas - chal Lamb in - deed, Christ, to - day your peo - ple feed; Take our sins and guilt a - way, That we all may sing for joy:

1-6. Al - le - lu - ia! Al - le - lu - ia!

1-6. Al - le - lu - ia! Al - le - lu - ia!

Text: 77 77 with alleluias; Michael Weisse, ca. 1480–1534; tr. by Catherine Winkworth, 1827–1878, alt.
Music: CHRIST IST ERSTANDEN; German Melody, 12th cent.

421   THIS IS THE DAY

Refrain: 1st time: Cantor, All repeat; thereafter: All

This is the day! This is the day! This is the day that the Lord has made! Let us re-joice!

(to Verses)

Let us re-joice! Let us re-joice and be glad!

Final time only

Let us re-joice and be glad!

Verses: Cantor

1. This is the day that the Lord has made.
   Let us rejoice and be glad.

2. Give thanks to the Lord!
   Our God is good.
   Whose love endures forever.
   Let all the children of Israel say:
   God's love endures forever.

3. The right hand of God has struck with power.
   The right hand of God is exalted.
   I shall not die, but I shall live
   and proclaim the works of the Lord!

4. The stone which the builders rejected
   has become the foundation of our house!
   By the Lord has this been done.
   How wonderful to behold!

NOW THE GREEN BLADE RISES

422

1. Now the green blade ris-es from the bur-ied grain,
2. In the grave they laid him, love by ha-tred slain,
3. Forth he came at Eas-ter, like the ris-en grain,
4. When our hearts are win-try, griev-ing, or in pain,

1. Wheat that in dark earth man-y days has lain;
2. Think-ing that he would nev-er wake a-gain,
3. He that for three days in the grave had lain;
4. Your touch can call us back to life a-gain,

1. Love lives a-gain, that with the dead has been:
2. Laid in the earth like grain that sleeps un-seen:
3. Raised from the dead, my liv-ing Lord is seen:
4. Fields of our hearts that dead and bare have been:

1-4. Love is come a-gain like wheat a-ris-ing green.

423   HOLY, HOLY, HOLY CRY

Verses

1. The Lamb of God stands on the height
2. In bit - ter sac - ri - fice once slain,
3. To him now let our prayers a - rise
4. While heav - ens' prais - es hail his worth,

1. a - mong the glo - rious clouds of light,
2. he lives in tri - umph there to reign
3. in clouds of in - cense to the skies,
4. he catch - es up the prayers of earth

1. a - bove the cit - y paved in gold
2. a - mong the saints clad all in white
3. from cen - ser borne by an - gel hands,
4. in wound - ed hands, till, count - less throng,

1   to Verse 2

1. where death and dark - ness have no hold.
2. in realms where day yields not to night.
3. bright tongues of fire from far - flung lands.
4. the sing - ers come to join the song.

2-4   Refrain

And, "Ho - ly, ho - ly, ho - ly" cry to you,

our Lord Most High. "Ho - ly, ho - ly, ho - ly" cry

1, 2, Final   to Verses 3, 4
3   (Fine)

to you, our God Most High.

3 Bridge

Soloist: To Fa - ther, Son, and Spir - it, Three High.

Choir/All: To Fa - ther, Son, and Spir - it, Three in One all - ho - ly Mys - ter - y.

To Fa - ther, Son, in One all - ho - ly Mys - ter - y.

and Spir - it, Three in One all - ho - ly Mys - ter - y.

to Refrain
All: And,

424   FESTIVAL CANTICLE: WORTHY IS CHRIST

This is the feast of vic-to-ry for our God. Al-le-
lu - ia, al-le - lu - ia, al - le - lu - ia. lu - ia.

Verses

1. Wor-thy is Christ, the __ Lamb who was slain, whose
2. Pow - er, rich - es, __ wis - dom, and strength, and
3. Sing with all the __ peo - ple of God, and
4. Bless - ing, hon - or, __ glo - ry, and might be to
5. For the Lamb _____ who was slain has be -

to Refrain

1. blood set us free ___ to be peo - ple of God.
2. hon - or, ___ bless - ing, and glo - ry are his.
3. join in the hymn of all cre - a - tion.
4. God and the Lamb for ev - er. A - men.
5. gun his ___ reign. ___ Al - le - lu - ia.

Text: Based on Revelation 5:12–14; Richard Hillert, 1923–2010, © 1978, *Lutheran Book of Worship.*
  All rights reserved. Reprinted by permission of Augsburg Fortress.
Music: Richard Hillert, © 1975, 1988, Richard Hillert. All rights reserved. Used with permission.

425   JESUS IS RISEN

1. Je - sus is ris-en! Let us sing! Praise to the ev - er - liv-ing
2. On this most ho - ly day of days, Let us to-geth-er sing his
3. To God the Fa-ther let us sing, To God the Son, our ris - en

1. King! Al - le - lu - ia! Al - le - lu - ia! Praise him in song, ye Ser - a -
2. praise! Al - le - lu - ia! Al - le - lu - ia! Raise joy-ful voic - es to the
3. King! Al - le - lu - ia! Al - le - lu - ia! And e-qual-ly let us a -

1. phim! Praise him with joy, ye Cher-u - bim!)
2. sky! Sing out, ye heav-ens, in re - ply: } Al - le - lu - ia! Al - le -
3. dore The Ho - ly Spir - it ev - er - more!)

1-3. lu - ia! Al - le - lu - ia! Al - le - lu - ia! Al - le - lu - ia!

Text: LM with alleluias; Compilers, 1978.
Music: LASST UNS ERFREUEN; *Auserlesene Catholische Geistliche Kirchengesänge,* Cologne, 1623.

SING WE TRIUMPHANT HYMNS OF PRAISE 426

1. Sing we triumphant hymns of praise
To greet our Lord these festive days,
Alleluia, alleluia!
Who by a road before untrod
Ascended to the throne of God,
Alleluia, alleluia, alleluia,
alleluia, alleluia!

2. In wond'ring awe his faithful band
Upon the Mount of Olives stand.
Alleluia, alleluia!
And with the Virgin Mother see
Their Lord ascend in majesty.
Alleluia, alleluia, alleluia,
alleluia, alleluia!

3. O risen Christ, ascended Lord,
All praise to you let earth accord,
Alleluia, alleluia!
Who are, while endless ages run,
With Father and with Spirit, One.
Alleluia, alleluia, alleluia,
alleluia, alleluia!

4. To God the Father let us sing,
To God the Son, our risen King,
Alleluia, alleluia!
And equally let us adore
The Holy Spirit evermore,
Alleluia, alleluia, alleluia,
alleluia, alleluia!

Text: LM with alleluias; St. Bede the Venerable, 673–735; verses 1, 2, 4 tr. by John D. Chambers, 1805–1893;
verse 3 tr. by Benjamin Webb, 1819–1885.
Music: LASST UNS ERFREUEN; *Auserlesene Catholische Geistliche Kirchengesänge,* Cologne, 1623.

CREATOR SPIRIT, BY WHOSE AID 427

1. Creator Spirit, by whose aid
The world's foundations first were laid!
Alleluia! Alleluia!
Give us thyself that we may see
The Father and the Son by thee.
Alleluia! Alleluia! Alleluia!
Alleluia! Alleluia!

2. O Source of uncreated light,
The Father's promised Paraclete;
Alleluia! Alleluia!

Thrice holy Font, Thrice holy Fire,
Our hearts with heav'nly love inspire.
Alleluia! Alleluia! Alleluia!
Alleluia! Alleluia!

3. All adoration ever be,
Eternal Paraclete to thee.
Alleluia! Alleluia!
From sin and sorrow set us free
That we may live eternally.
Alleluia! Alleluia! Alleluia!
Alleluia! Alleluia!

Text: LM with alleluias; *Veni, Creator Spiritus;* attr. to Rabanus Maurus, 776–856;
para. by John Dryden, 1631–1700; alt. Compilers, 1977.
Music: LASST UNS ERFREUEN; *Auserlesene Catholische Geistliche Kirchengesänge,* Cologne, 1623.

428   HAIL THEE, FESTIVAL DAY

Refrain

Hail thee, fes-ti-val day! Blest day to be hal-lowed for ev - er;

Day when our Lord was raised, Break-ing the king - dom of death.

Verses 1, 3, 5

Easter   1. All the fair beau - ty of earth   From
Ascension   3. He who was nailed to the cross   Is
Pentecost   5. Bright in the like - ness of fire,   On

1. death of the win - ter a - ris - ing! Ev - 'ry good
3. Rul - er and Lord of all peo - ple. All things cre -
5. those who a - wait his ap - pear - ing, He whom the

1. gift of the year Now with its Mas-ter re - turns:
3. a - ted on earth Sing to the glo - ry of God:
5. Lord had fore-told, Sud - den-ly, swift-ly de-scends:

to Refrain

Verses 2, 4, 6

Easter   2. Rise from the grave now, O Lord, The Au - thor of
Ascension   4. Dai - ly the love - li - ness grows, A - dorned with the
Pentecost   6. Forth from the Fa - ther he comes With sev - en - fold

2. life and cre - a - tion. Tread-ing the path-way of
4. glo - ry of blos - som; Heav - en her gates un -
6. mys - ti - cal of - f'ring, Pour-ing on all hu - man

2. death, New life you give to us all:
4. bars, Fling - ing her in - crease of light:
6. souls In - fi - nite rich - es of God:

to Refrain

Text: 79 77 with refrain; Venantius Honorius Fortunatus, ca. 530–609; tr. composite.
Music: SALVE FESTA DIES; Ralph Vaughan Williams, 1872–1958.

Hail the Day That Sees Him Rise

1. Hail the day that sees him rise
2. There for him high tri - umph waits:
3. See! the heav'n its Lord re - ceives,
4. See! he lifts his hands a - bove.
5. Lord, though part - ed from our sight
6. There with you we shall re - main,

Al - le - lu - ia!

1. To his throne be - yond the skies,
2. Lift your heads, e - ter - nal gates,
3. Yet he loves the earth he leaves;
4. See! he shows the wounds of love.
5. Far be - yond the star - ry height,
6. Share the glo - ry of your reign,

Al - le - lu - ia!

1. Christ, the Lamb for sin - ners giv'n,
2. He has con - quered death and sin,
3. Though re - turn - ing to his throne,
4. Hark! his gra - cious lips be - stow,
5. Lift our hearts that we may rise
6. There your face un - cloud - ed view,

Al - le - lu - ia!

1. En - ters now the high - est heav'n!
2. Take the King of glo - ry in.
3. Still he calls the world his own.
4. Bless - ings on his church be - low.
5. One with you be - yond the skies:
6. Find our heav'n of heav'ns in you.

Al - le - lu - ia!

Text: 77 77 with alleluias; Charles Wesley, 1707–1788, and Thomas Cotterill, 1779–1823, alt.
Music: LLANFAIR; Robert Williams, 1781–1821.

430   GO MAKE OF ALL DISCIPLES

1. "Go make of all dis - ci - ples:" We hear the
2. "Go make of all dis - ci - ples:" Bap - tiz - ing
3. "Go make of all dis - ci - ples:" We at your
4. "Go make of all dis - ci - ples:" We wel - come

1. call, O Lord, That comes from you, our Fa - ther, In
2. in the name Of Fa - ther, Son, and Spir - it— From
3. feet would stay Un - til each life's vo - ca - tion Ac -
4. your com-mand; "Lo, I am with you al - ways:" We

1. your e - ter - nal Word. In - spire our ways of
2. age to age the same. We call each new dis -
3. cents your ho - ly way. We cul - ti - vate the
4. take your guid - ing hand. The task looms large be -

1. learn - ing Through earn-est, fer-vent prayer, And let our
2. ci - ple To fol - low you, O Lord, Re - deem - ing
3. na - ture God plants in ev - 'ry heart, Re - veal - ing
4. fore us— We fol - low with-out fear. In heav'n and

1. dai - ly liv - ing Re - veal you ev - 'ry - where.
2. soul and bod - y By wa - ter and the Word.
3. in our wit - ness The Mas - ter Teach-er's art.
4. earth your pow - er Shall bring God's king - dom here.

Text: 76 76 D; Matthew 12:19–20; "Go Make of All Disciples" words by Leon M. Adkins, 1896–1986, alt.
© 1964, Abingdon Press (Administered by The Copyright Company, Nashville, TN). All rights reserved.
International copyright secured. Used with permission.
Music: ELLACOMBE; *Gesangbuch der Herzogl, Wirtembergischen Katholischen Hofkapelle*, 1784, alt.;
adapt. fr. Würth's *Katholisches Gesangbuch*, 1863.

LORD, YOU GIVE THE GREAT COMMISSION

431

1. Lord, you give the great com-mis-sion: "Heal the sick and
2. Lord, you call us to your ser-vice: "In my name bap-
3. Lord, you make the com-mon ho-ly: "This my bod-y,
4. Lord, you show us love's true mea-sure: "Fa-ther, what they
5. Lord, you bless with words as-sur-ing: "I am with you

1. preach the word." Lest the church ne-glect its mis-sion
2. tize and teach." That the world may trust your prom-ise,
3. this my blood." Let us all, for earth's true glo-ry,
4. do, for-give." Yet we hoard as pri-vate trea-sure
5. to the end." Faith and hope and love re-stor-ing,

1. And the gos-pel go un-heard, Help us wit-ness to your
2. Life a-bun-dant meant for each, Give us all new fer-vor,
3. Dai-ly lift life heav-en-ward, Ask-ing that the world a-
4. All that you so free-ly give. May your care and mer-cy
5. May we serve as you in-tend And, a-mid the cares that

1. pur-pose With re-newed in-teg-ri-ty:
2. draw us Clos-er in com-mu-ni-ty:
3. round us Share your chil-dren's lib-er-ty: With the Spir-it's
4. lead us To a just so-ci-e-ty:
5. claim us, Hold in mind e-ter-ni-ty:

1-5. gifts em-pow'r us For the work of min-is-try.

Text: 87 87 D; Jeffery Rowthorn, b. 1934, © 1978, Hope Publishing Co. All rights reserved. Used with permission.
Music: ABBOT'S LEIGH; Cyril Vincent Taylor, 1907–1991, © 1942, renewed 1970, Hope Publishing Co.
    All rights reserved. Used with permission.

432 COME, O HOLY SPIRIT, COME/VENI SANCTE SPIRITUS

1. Come, O Ho - ly Spir - it, come! And from your ce -
2. Come, O Fa - ther of the poor! Come, ___ source of
1. *Ve - ni San - cte Spí - ri - tus, Et e - mít - te*
2. *Ve - ni pa - ter páu - pe - rum, Ve - ni da - tor*

1. les - tial home Shed a ray of light di - vine!
2. all our store! Come, with - in our bos - oms shine!
1. *caé - li - tus Lu - cis tu - ae rá - di - um.*
2. *mú - ne - rum, Ve - ni lu - men cór - di - um.*

3. You, of com - fort - ers the best; You, the soul's most
4. In our la - bor, rest most sweet; Grate - ful cool - ness
3. *Con - so - lá - tor ó - pti - me, Dul - cis ho - spes*
4. *In la - bó - re ré - qui - es, In ae - stu tem -*

3. wel - come guest; Sweet re - fresh - ment here be - low;
4. in the heat; Sol - ace in the midst of woe.
3. *á - ni - mae, Dul - ce re - fri - gé - ri - um.*
4. *pé - ri - es, In fle - tu so - lá - ti - um.*

5. O most bless - ed Light di - vine, Shine with - in
6. Where you are not, we have naught, Noth - ing good
5. *O lux be - a - tís - si - ma, Re - ple cor -*
6. *Si - ne tu - o nú - mi - ne, Ni - hil est*

5. these hearts of yours, And our in - most be - ing fill!
6. in deed or thought, Noth - ing free from taint of ill.
5. *dis ín - ti - ma Tu - ó - rum fi - dé - li - um.*
6. *in hó - mi - ne, Ni - hil est in - nó - xi - um.*

7. Heal our wounds, our strength re - new; On our dry - ness
8. Bend the stub - born heart and will; Melt the fro - zen,
7. *La - va quod est sór - di - dum, Ri - ga quod est*
8. *Fle - cte quod est rí - gi - dum, Fo - ve quod est*

7. pour your dew; Wash the stains of guilt a - way;
8. warm the chill; Guide the steps that go a - stray.
7. *á - ri - dum, Sa - na quod est sáu - ci - um.*
8. *frí - gi - dum, Re - ge quod est dé - vi - um.*

9. On the faith - ful, who a - dore And con - fess you, ev - er - more
10. Give them vir - tue's sure re - ward; Give them your sal - va - tion, Lord;
9. *Da tu - is fi - dé - li - bus, In te con - fi - den - ti - bus,*
10. *Da vir - tú - tis mé - ri - tum, Da sa - lú - tis éx - i - tum,*

9. In your sev'n - fold gift de - scend;
10. Give them joys that nev - er end. A - men. Al - le - lu - ia.
9. *Sa - crum sep - te - ná - ri - um.*
10. *Da per - én - ne gáu - di - um.* A - men. Al - le - lú - ia.

Text: Poetic Sequence for Pentecost, *Veni, Sancte Spiritus*; English text fr. *The Roman Missal* © 1964,
  National Catholic Welfare Conference, Inc. (now US Conference of Catholic Bishops).
  All rights reserved. Used with permission.
Music: Chant, Mode I.

SEND US YOUR SPIRIT 433

1. Send us your spir - it, O Lord. Eve - ning en - folds us and
2. Hold us with mer - cy, O Lord. Sor - row has spo - ken, has
3. Teach us your wis - dom, O Lord. Shad - ows have cloud - ed, have
4. Send us good sum - mer, O Lord. Win - ters have chilled us, and

1. holds us too near. Wake the morn - ing light. Make our liv - ing
2. bro - ken our hearts. Clothe us in your care. Be the life we
3. crowd - ed our sight. Give us hearts that see. Set our lov - ing
4. stilled us too long. Give us love's own fire. Be our true de-

1. bright. Shine on our dark - ness, O Lord.
2. bear. Feed us and fill us, O Lord.
3. free. Hear us and help us, O Lord.
4. sire. Send us your spir - it, O Lord.

Text: Inspired by *Veni, Sancte Spiritus*; Dan Schutte, b. 1947.
Music: Dan Schutte.
Text and music © 1985, OCP. All rights reserved.

434

COME, O HOLY SPIRIT

1. Come, O Ho-ly Spir-it, come! And from your ce-
2. You, of com-fort-ers the best; You, the soul's most
3. O most bless-ed Light di-vine, May that Light with-
4. Heal our wounds, our strength re-new; On our dry-ness
5. On the faith-ful who a-dore And con-fess you

1. les-tial home Shed a ray of light di-vine!
2. wel-come guest; Sweet re-fresh-ment here be-low;
3. in us shine, And our in-most be-ing fill!
4. pour your dew; Wash the stains of guilt a-way:
5. ev-er more, In your sev'n-fold gift de-scend;

1. Come, O Ho-ly Spir-it, come! Come, O Fa-ther of the
2. Come, O Ho-ly Spir-it, come! In our la-bor, rest most
3. Come, O Ho-ly Spir-it, come! In your ab-sence, we have
4. Come, O Ho-ly Spir-it, come! Bend the stub-born heart and
5. Come, O Ho-ly Spir-it, come! Give them vir-tue's sure re-

1. poor! Come, O Source of all our store! Come, with-
2. sweet; Grate-ful cool-ness in the heat; Sol-ace
3. naught, Noth-ing good in deed or thought, Noth-ing
4. will; Melt the fro-zen, warm the chill; Guide the
5. ward; Give them your sal-va-tion, Lord; Give them

1. in our bos-oms shine! Come, O Ho-ly Spir-it, come!
2. in the midst of woe. Come, O Ho-ly Spir-it, come!
3. free from taint of ill. Come, O Ho-ly Spir-it, come!
4. steps that go a-stray. Come, O Ho-ly Spir-it, come!
5. joys that nev-er end. Come, O Ho-ly Spir-it, come!

Text: 77 77 D; fr. the Pentecost Sequence, *Veni, Sancte Spiritus*, alt.; adapt. by Owen Alstott, b. 1947,
© 1980, OCP. All rights reserved.
Music: HYMN TO JOY; Ludwig van Beethoven, 1770–1827; adapt. by Edward Hodges, 1796–1867.

Come, O Holy Spirit, Come

Verses 1-2, 5-6, 9-10

1. Come, O Ho-ly Spir-it, come! And from your ce-
2. Come, O Fa-ther of the poor! Come, O source of
5. O most bless-ed Light di-vine, Shine with-in these
6. Where you are not, we have naught, Noth-ing good in
9. On the faith-ful, who a-dore And con-fess you,
10. Give them vir-tue's sure re-ward; Give them your sal-

1. les - tial home Shed a ray__ of light di-vine! (to Vs 2)
2. all our store! Come, with-in__ our bos-oms shine. (to Vs 3)
5. hearts of yours, And our in-most be-ing fill! (to Vs 6)
6. deed or thought, Noth-ing free__ from taint of ill. (to Vs 7)
9. ev - er-more In your sev-en-fold gift de-scend; (to Vs 10)
10. va - tion, Lord; Give them joys__ that nev-er end. (to Final)

Final

10. A - men. Al - le - lu - ia!

Verses 3-4, 7-8

3. You, of com-fort-ers the best; You, the soul's most
4. In our la-bor, rest most sweet; Grate-ful cool-ness
7. Heal our wounds, our strength re-new; On our dry-ness
8. Bend the stub-born heart and will; Melt the fro-zen,

3. wel-come guest; Sweet re-fresh-ment here be-low; (to Vs 4)
4. in the heat; So-lace in the midst of woe. (to Vs 5)
7. pour your dew; Wash the stains of guilt a-way: (to Vs 8)
8. warm the chill; Guide the steps that go a-stray. (to Vs 9)

Text: Poetic Sequence for Pentecost, *Veni, Sancte Spiritus*; English text fr. *The Roman Missal*,

436   HOLY SPIRIT, COME NOW

Refrain

Ho - ly Spir - it, come,   Ho - ly Spir - it, come now,

come now.   **Verses**

1. Oh, the sweet -
2. In the faith
3. With the rev -

1. - ness of your mer - cy and grace!   Bring us true wis -
2. we share,___ flow - ing from truth,   bring us the knowl -
3. - 'rence of the Lord,_ love is shown.   Serv - ing each oth -

1. - dom right here in this place.   Bring a glim -
2. - edge that brings us to you.   Through the dark -
3. - er, God's pres - ence is known.   Oh, the good -

1. - mer of the depth of God's will.   Bring un - der - stand -
2. - ness of de - spair and of fear,   give us the cour -
3. - ness and the glo - ry of God!   Hearts o - ver - flow -

to Refrain

1. - ing; God's plan be ful - filled.
2. - age to know you are here.
3. - ing with won - der and awe.

Text and music: Jesse Manibusan, b. 1958, © 2006, Jesse Manibusan.
Published by spiritandsong.com®, a division of OCP. All rights reserved.

437   COME, HOLY SPIRIT

Ostinato Refrain

Come, Ho - ly Spir - it; come, Ho - ly Spir - it;

come, Ho - ly Spir - it; set our hearts on fire.

Verses

1. Come, Spirit, Lord of Light,
   come from your heav'nly height,
   come and restore our sight.
   Come, O Spirit.

2. Consoler, Spirit blest,
   the soul's most welcome guest,
   our ease in toil and stress;
   come, O Spirit.

3. Blest Spirit, guide our way;
   without your help we stray.
   Come to our hearts today;
   come, O Spirit.

4. Come set our hearts on fire,
   make goodness our desire,
   our weak'ning souls inspire;
   come, O Spirit.

5. Come to us from above
   and fill our hearts with love,
   descend, O Heav'nly Dove.
   Come, O Spirit.

6. Give comfort when we die,
   give life with you on high,
   unending joys supply;
   come, O Spirit.

Text: Based on *Veni, Sancte Spiritus*, 12th cent.; Stephen Dean, b. 1948.
Music: Stephen Dean.
Text and music © 2001, Stephen Dean. Published by OCP. All rights reserved.

COME DOWN, O LOVE DIVINE 438

1. Come down, O Love di - vine, Seek thou this soul of
2. O let it free - ly burn, Till earth - ly pas - sions
3. And so the yearn - ing strong, With which the soul will

1. mine, And vis - it it with thine own ar - dor glow - ing;
2. turn To dust and ash - es in its heat con - sum - ing;
3. long, Shall far out-pass the pow'r of hu - man tell - ing;

1. O Com - fort - er, draw near, With - in my heart ap -
2. And let thy glo - rious light Shine ev - er on my
3. For none can guess its grace, Till we be - come the

1. pear, And kin - dle it, thy ho - ly flame be - stow - ing.
2. sight, And clothe me round, the while my path il - lum - ing.
3. place Where - in the Ho - ly Spir - it makes a dwell - ing.

Text: 66 11 D; Bianco da Siena, d. 1434; tr. by Richard F. Littledale, 1833–1890.
Music: DOWN AMPNEY; Ralph Vaughan Williams, 1872–1958.

439 ## By the Waking of Our Hearts

By the wak-ing of our hearts, by the stir-ring of our souls,

may the Spir-it of God a-bide and bring us to-geth-er in Christ.

Verses

1. Come, O Spir - it, from a - bove, come from your ce - les - tial heights.
2. Come, O Sav - ior of the poor, come, O source of gifts en - sured.
3. In our la - bor, rest most sweet; grate - ful cool-ness in the heat.
4. Bend the stub-born heart and will, melt the fro - zen, warm the chill.
5. Grant us vir-tue's sure re - ward, may your gra-cious love be sent.

to Refrain

1. Come with your bless - ed light so _____ ra - diant bright.
2. Come with your gen - tle hope, so _____ won-drous and pure.
3. Con - sole our rest - less lives, by your com - fort, we seek.
4. Come guide our search-ing minds toward your prom - ise ful - filled.
5. Come with your peace and joy that shall nev - er end.

Text: Verses based on the Pentecost Sequence, *Veni, Sancte Spiritus*; Ricky Manalo, CSP, b. 1965.
Music: Ricky Manalo, CSP.

440 ## Envía Tu Espíritu

Refrain

*En - ví-a tu Es-pí-ri-tu, en - ví-a tu Es-pí-ri-tu, en-

ví-a tu Es-pí-ri-tu, se-a re-no-va-da la faz de la tie-

- rra. Se-a re-no-va-da la faz de la tie - rra.

*Refrain translation: "Send out your Spirit, and renew the face of the earth."

1. Spir - it of the liv - ing God, burn in our hearts,
2. Wind of prom - ise, wind of change, friend of the poor,
3. Breath of life and ho - li - ness, heal ev - 'ry wound,

to Refrain

1. and make us a peo - ple of hope and com-pas - sion.
2. em - pow - er your peo - ple to make peace and jus - tice.
3. and lead us be-yond ev - 'ry sin that di-vides us.

Text: Based on Psalm 104:30 and *Veni, Sancte Spiritus*; Latin, 12th cent.; adapt. by Bob Hurd, b. 1950.
Music: Bob Hurd.
Text and music © 1988, Bob Hurd. Published by OCP. All rights reserved.

Veni, Sancte Spiritus   441

Ve - ni San - cte Spi - ri - tus; Ve - ni San - cte Spi - ri - tus;
Ve - ni, ve - ni San - cte Spi - ri - tus; Ve - ni San - cte Spi - ri - tus.

Verses: Cantor

1. Holy Spirit, Lord of Light,
   radiance give from celestial height.
   Come, O Spirit of the poor,
   come now with treasures that endure:
   Light of all who live.

2. You of all consolers the best.
   You the soul's delightful guest;
   refreshing peace bestow.
   You in toil my comfort sweet.
   You coolness in the heat.
   You my solace in time of woe.

3. Light immortal, light divine;
   fire of love our hearts refine,
   our inmost being fill.

Take your grace away
and nothing pure in us will stay,
all our good is turned to ill.

4. Heal our wounds, our strength renew,
   on our dryness pour your dew;
   wash guilt away,
   bend the stubborn heart,
   melt the frozen,
   warm the chill
   and guide the steps that go astray.

5. Seven-fold gifts on us be pleased to pour,
   who you confess and you adore;
   bring us your comfort when we die;
   give us life with you on high;
   give us joys, give us joys that never end.

Text: Refrain, Latin, 12th cent. Verses based on the Pentecost Sequence, *Veni, Sancte Spiritus*;
   adapt. by Christopher Walker, b. 1947, © 1981, 1982, Christopher Walker. Published by OCP. All rights reserved.
Music: Christopher Walker, © 1981, 1982, Christopher Walker. Published by OCP. All rights reserved.

442

HOLY SPIRIT

Ostinato Refrain: All

Ho - ly Spir - it, come in - to our lives.

Verses: Cantor

1. Give us a spir - it of wis - dom, an un - der - stand - ing heart. _____ Give us a spir - it of knowl - edge, and lead us to the truth. _____
2. Give us a spir - it of cour - age, and judg - ment that is wise. _____ Give us a spir - it of rev - 'rence, of won - der and of awe. _____
3. Spir - it of love and com - pas - sion, give hope to all the poor. _____ Spir - it of jus - tice and mer - cy, come o - pen ev - 'ry door. _____
4. Spir - it of all con - so - la - tion, O lift our hearts this day. _____ Spir - it of all un - der - stand - ing, O help us know your way. _____
5. Spir - it of light and of wis - dom, O lift us from our sor - row. _ Spir - it of peace and for - give - ness, O help us face to - mor - row. _
6. Spir - it of strength and of heal - ing, bend stub - born heart and will. _____ Spir - it of trust and of car - ing, O melt us, warm our chill. _____

Ho - ly Spir - it, make us tru - ly wise.

to Refrain

Text: Verses 1 & 2 based on Isaiah 11:2; verses 3–6 based on the Pentecost Sequence; Ken Canedo, b. 1953.
Music: Ken Canedo.

COME, HOLY GHOST

1. Come, Ho - ly Ghost, Cre - a - tor blest,
2. O Com - fort - er, to thee we cry,
3. To ev - 'ry sense thy light im - part
4. O grant that we through thee may come
5. Praise be to thee, Fa - ther and Son

1. And in our hearts take up thy rest;
2. Thou heav'n - ly gift of God most high;
3. And shed thy love in ev - 'ry heart.
4. To know the Fa - ther and the Son,
5. And Ho - ly Spir - it, with them one;

1. Come with thy grace and heav'n - ly aid
2. Thou font of life, and fire of love,
3. To our weak flesh, thy strength sup - ply;
4. And hold with firm, un - chang - ing faith,
5. And may the Son on us be - stow

1. To fill the hearts which thou hast made,
2. And sweet a - noint - ing from a - bove,
3. Un - fail - ing cour - age from on high,
4. That thou art Spir - it of them both,
5. The gifts that from the Spir - it flow,

1. To fill the hearts which thou hast made.
2. And sweet a - noint - ing from a - bove.
3. Un - fail - ing cour - age from on high.
4. That thou art Spir - it of them both.
5. The gifts that from the Spir - it flow.

Text: LM with repeat; *Veni, Creator Spiritus*; attr. to Rabanus Maurus, 776–856; tr. by Edward Caswall, 1814–1878, alt.
Music: LAMBILLOTTE; Louis Lambillotte, SJ, 1796–1855.

444

VENI, CREATOR SPIRITUS/
CREATOR SPIRIT, LORD OF GRACE

1. Ve - ni Cre - á - tor Spí - ri - tus, Men - tes tu - ó -
2. Qui dí - ce - ris Pa - rá - cli - tus, ¹Do - num De - i
3. Tu se - pti - fór - mis mú - ne - re, ²De - xtrae De - i
4. Ac - cén - de lu - men sén - si - bus, In - fún - de a - mó -

1. *Cre - a - tor Spir - it, Lord of grace, Come make in us*
2. *O Spir - it, hear your peo - ple's cry! Come down, O Gift*
3. *As once on Christ the Ser - vant's head The oil of sev'n-*
4. *Of ev - 'ry gift the liv - ing source, Of might - y deeds*

1. rum ví - si - ta, Im - ple su - pér - na grá - ti -
2. al - tís - si - mi, Fons vi - vus, i - gnis, cá - ri -
3. tu dí - gi - tus, Tu ri - te pro - mís - sum Pa -
4. rem cór - di - bus, In - fír - ma nó - stri cór - po -

1. *your dwell - ing place! O pur - est Light, in dark - ness*
2. *of God most high! De - scend in peace, O heav'n - ly*
3. *fold grace you shed, So now a - noint from love's deep*
4. *the un - seen force, The Fa - ther sends his Prom - ised*

1. a Quae tu cre - á - sti pé - cto - ra.
2. tas, Et spi - ri - tá - lis ún - cti - o.
3. tris, Ser - mó - ne di - tans gút - tu - ra.
4. ris Vir - tú - te fir - mans pér - pe - ti. (A - men.)

1. *shine; Fill love - less hearts, O Love di - vine!*
2. *Dove; Come, fount of life; come, flame of love!*
3. *springs Your cho - sen proph - ets, priests, and kings!*
4. *One To speak for all who serve his Son! (A - men.)*

5. Hostem repéllas lóngius
   Pacémque dones prótinus;
   Ductóre sic te práevio
   Vitémus omne nóxium.

5. *Keep far all those who wish us ill!*
   O Dove of peace, be with us still!
   In every danger at our side,
   O Friend, befriend us; be our guide!

6. Per te sciámus da Patrem,
   Noscámus atque Fílium,
   ³Te utriúsque Spíritum
   Credámus omni témpore.

6. *Reveal to us the Father's love,*
   Reveal his Son, who reigns above!
   To truth, O Truth, make all souls true;
   In love, O Love, make all things new!

⁴7. Deo Patri sit glória,
   Et Fílio, quia mórtuis
   Surréxit, ac Paráclito,
   In saeculórum sáecula. Amen.

7. *To God the Father glory be,*
   And to the Son from death set free;
   And to the Holy Spirit raise
   Our praise to God for endless days. Amen.

Note: The Latin text above is reproduced from the *Graduale Romanum*, 1974. Textual variants are noted below:
1) formerly *Altíssimi donum Dei,*
2) formerly *Dígitus patérnae déxterae,*
3) formerly *Teque utriúsque Spíritum.*
4) Verse 7 does not appear in the *Graduale Romanum*, 1974.

Text: LM; *Veni, Creator Spiritus*; attr. to Rabanus Maurus, 776–856; *Graduale Romanum*, 1974. Verses 1–6 tr. by James D. Quinn, SJ, b. 1919, © James D. Quinn, SJ. All rights reserved. Used with permission of Selah Publishing Co., Inc., North American agent. Verse 7 tr. by Glenn CJ Byer, b. 1961, © 2002, OCP. All rights reserved.
Music: VENI CREATOR SPIRITUS; Chant, Mode VIII.

ALL PRAISE AND GLAD THANKSGIVING 445

1. All praise and glad thanks-giv-ing To God the Fa-ther
2. Christ Je-sus, we a-dore you, The Son of God most
3. O Ho-ly Spir-it, bless-ing To you who reign a-

1. be: The Font of all things liv-ing, Who reigns e-
2. high; With thanks we sing be-fore you, Who came for
3. bove! Your won-drous gifts con-fess-ing, The Church sings

1. ter-nal-ly.
2. us to die. } Praise to God for-ev-er be,
3. forth your love!

1-3. One in life, in Per-sons three: Might-y God,

1-3. sav-ing God, God e-ter-nal Trin-i-ty!

Text: 76 76 77 67; based on *Trisagion*, Greek, 5th cent.; Melvin Farrell, SS, 1930–1986, © 1976, OCP. All rights reserved.
Music: GOTT VATER SEI GEPRIESEN; *Limburg Gesangbuch*, 1838.

ALL HAIL, ADORED TRINITY 446

1. All hail, a-dor-ed Trin-i-ty! All hail, e-
2. Three per-sons praise we ev-er-more, One on-ly
3. O Trin-i-ty! O U-ni-ty! Be pres-ent

1. ter-nal U-ni-ty! O God the Fa-ther,
2. God our hearts a-dore: In thy sure mer-cy,
3. as we wor-ship thee; And with the songs that

1. God the Son, And God the Spir-it, ev-er One.
2. ev-er kind, May we your strong pro-tec-tion find.
3. an-gels sing U-nite the hymns of praise we bring.

Text: LM; *Ave colenda Trinitas*, ca. 11th cent.; tr. by John D. Chambers, 1805–1893, alt.
Music: OLD HUNDREDTH; *Genevan Psalter*, 1551; attr. to Louis Bourgeois, ca. 1510–1561, alt.

447   ON THIS DAY, THE FIRST OF DAYS

1. On this day, the first of days, God the
2. On this day th'e - ter - nal Son O - ver
3. O that fer - vent love to - day May in
4. Fa - ther, who cre - at - ed me Im - age
5. Ho - ly Word, all prais - es be! You, from
6. Ho - ly Spir - it, you im - part Gifts to
7. God, the bless - ed Three in One, Fa - ther,

1. Fa - ther's name we praise; Who, cre - a - tion's
2. death his tri - umph won; On this day the
3. ev - 'ry heart have sway, Teach - ing us to
4. of your - self to be, May your grace be
5. sin have set me free; And, up - on love's
6. shine in ev - 'ry heart; Best of gifts, your -
7. Spir - it, with the Son; One in you with

1. Font and Spring, Did the world from dark - ness bring.
2. Spir - it came With the gifts of liv - ing flame.
3. praise a - right God the source of life and light.
4. ev - er mine, Fill me with your love di - vine.
5. flame, a - rise Un - to you a sac - ri - fice.
6. self be - stow; Dwell in me your love to know.
7. all a - bove, We send forth our hearts of love.

Text: 77 77; *Die parente temporum*; Le Mans Breviary, 1748; tr. by Henry W. Baker, 1821–1877, alt.;
    Hymns Ancient and Modern, 1861.
Music: LÜBECK; Freylinghausen's *Geistreiches Gesangbuch*, 1704; adapt. by William H. Havergal, 1793–1870.

448   HOLY, HOLY, HOLY

1. Ho - ly, Ho - ly, Ho - ly! Lord ____ God Al - might - y!
2. Ho - ly, Ho - ly, Ho - ly! All the saints a - dore thee,
3. Ho - ly, Ho - ly, Ho - ly! Though the dark - ness hide thee,
4. Ho - ly, Ho - ly, Ho - ly! Lord ____ God Al - might - y!

1. Ear - ly in the morn - ing our song shall rise to thee:
2. Cast - ing down their gold - en crowns a - round the glass - y sea;
3. Though the eye made blind by sin thy glo - ry may not see,
4. All thy works shall praise thy Name, in earth, and sky, and sea;

1. Ho - ly, Ho - ly, Ho - ly! Mer - ci - ful and might - y,
2. Cher - u - bim and ser - a - phim fall - ing down be - fore thee,
3. On - ly thou art ho - ly; there is none be - side thee,
4. Ho - ly, Ho - ly, Ho - ly! Mer - ci - ful and might - y,

1. God in three Per - sons, bless - ed Trin - i - ty.
2. Which wert, and art, and ev - er - more shalt be.
3. Per - fect in pow'r, in love, and pur - i - ty.
4. God in three Per - sons, bless - ed Trin - i - ty.

Text: 11 12 12 10; Reginald Heber, 1783–1826, alt.
Music: NICAEA; John B. Dykes, 1823–1876.

HOW WONDERFUL THE THREE-IN-ONE 449

1. How won - der - ful the Three - in - One,
2. Be - fore the flow of dawn and dark,
3. The Lov - er's own Be - lov'd, in time,
4. Their E - qual Friend all life sus - tains
5. How won - der - ful the Liv - ing God:

1. Whose en - er - gies of danc - ing light
2. Cre - a - tion's Lov - er dreamed of earth,
3. Be - tween a cra - dle and a cross,
4. With green - ing pow'r and lov - ing care,
5. Di - vine Be - lov'd, Em - pow'r - ing Friend,

1. Are un - di - vid - ed, pure and good,
2. And with a car - ing deep and wise,
3. At home in flesh, gave love and life
4. And calls us, born a - gain by grace,
5. E - ter - nal Lov - er, Three - in - One,

1. Com - mun - ing love in shared de - light.
2. All things con - ceived and brought to birth.
3. To heal our bro - ken - ness and loss.
4. In Love's com - mun - ing life to share.
5. Our hope's be - gin - ning, way and end.

450   COME NOW, ALMIGHTY KING

1. Come now, Al-might-y King,   Help us your name to sing,
2. Come now, In-car-nate Word,   Our just and might-y Lord,
3. Come, Ho-ly Com-fort-er,   Your sa-cred wit-ness bear
4. To the great One in Three,   E-ter-nal prais-es be

1. Help us to praise: Fa-ther, all glo-ri-ous, Ev-er vic-
2. Our prayer at-tend: Come, and your peo-ple bless, And give your
3. In this glad hour: To us your grace im-part, And rule in
4. For-ev-er-more!   Your sov-'reign maj-es-ty May we in

1. to-ri-ous, Come, and reign o-ver us, An-cient of Days.
2. word suc-cess; Strength-en your righ-teous-ness, Sav-ior and Friend.
3. ev-'ry heart! Nev-er from us de-part, Spir-it of pow'r.
4. glo-ry see, And to e-ter-ni-ty Love and a-dore!

Text: 66 4 666 4; anon., ca. 1757, alt.
Music: ITALIAN HYMN; Felice de Giardini, 1716–1796, alt.

451   O GOD, ALMIGHTY FATHER

1. O God, al-might-y Fa-ther, Cre-a-tor of all
2. O Je-sus, Word in-car-nate, Re-deem-er most a-
3. O God, the Ho-ly Spir-it, Who lives with-in our

1. things, The heav-ens stand in won-der, While earth your
2. dored, All glo-ry, praise, and hon-or Be yours, O
3. soul, Send forth your light and lead us To our e-

1. glo-ry sings.
2. sov-'reign Lord.   O most ho-ly Trin-i-ty,
3. ter-nal goal.

1-3. Un-di-vid-ed u-ni-ty, Ho-ly God,

1-3. might - y God, God im - mor - tal be a - dored!

Text: 76 76 77 67; anon.; tr. by Irvin Udulutsch, OFM, Cap., 1920–2010, alt., © 1959, 1977, Order of St. Benedict.
All rights reseved. Administered by The Liturgical Press, Collegeville, MN. Used with permission.
Music: GOTT VATER SEI GEPRIESEN; *Limburg Gesangbuch*, 1838.

HOLY, HOLY, HOLY 452

1. Ho - ly, Ho - ly, Ho - ly! Lord God Al -
2. Ho - ly, Ho - ly, Ho - ly! All the saints a -
3. Ho - ly, Ho - ly, Ho - ly! Though the dark - ness
4. Ho - ly, Ho - ly, Ho - ly! Lord God Al -

1. might - y! Ear - ly in the morn - ing our
2. dore thee, Cast - ing down their gol - den crowns a -
3. hide thee, Though the eye of sin - ners thy
4. might - y! All thy works shall praise thy Name, in

1. song shall rise to thee: Ho - ly, Ho - ly,
2. round the glass - y sea; Cher - u - bim and
3. glo - ry may not see, On - ly thou art
4. earth and sky and sea; Ho - ly, Ho - ly,

1. Ho - ly! Mer - ci - ful and might - y,
2. ser - a - phim fall - ing down be - fore thee.
3. ho - ly; there is none be - side thee,
4. Ho - ly! Mer - ci - ful and might - y,

1. God in three Per - sons, bless - ed Trin - i - ty.
2. With songs of praise for all e - ter - ni - ty.
3. Per - fect in Pow'r, in love, and pu - ri - ty.
4. God in three Per - sons, bless - ed Trin - i - ty!

Text: Reginald Heber, 1783–1826, alt.
Music: Timothy R. Smith, b. 1960, © 1999, Timothy R. Smith. Published by spiritandsong.com®, a division of OCP.
All rights reserved.

453

LAUD, O ZION

Verses 1, 2

*1. Lo! the an - gel's food is giv - en To the
2. Truth the an - cient types ful - fill - ing, I - saac

1. pil - grim who has striv - en; See the chil-dren's bread from
2. bound, a vic - tim will - ing, Pas - chal lamb, its life - blood

1. heav - en, which on dogs may not be spent.
2. spill - ing, man - na to the fa-thers sent.

Verses 3, 4

3. Ver - y bread, good shep-herd, tend us,
4. You who all things can and know,

3. Je - su, of your love be - friend us,
4. Who on earth such food be - stow,

3. You re-fresh us, you de - fend us, Your e - ter - nal
4. Grant us with your saints, though low - est, Where the heav'n - ly

1

3. good-ness send us In the land of life to see.
4. feast you show,

2

3.
4. Fel - low heirs and guests to

4. be. A - men. Al - le - lu - ia.

*The shorter form of this sequence is given here. The long form is available in the octavo, *Laud, O Zion*,
edition 11500, by Randall DeBruyn.

Text: Sequence for the Solemnity of the Most Holy Body and Blood of Christ (*Lauda Sion*);
English text fr. *The Roman Missal*, © 1964, National Catholic Welfare Conference, Inc.
(now US Conference of Catholic Bishops). All rights reserved. Used with permission.
Music: Randall DeBruyn, b. 1947, © 2000, 2001, Randall DeBruyn. Published by OCP. All rights reserved.

Draw Near and Take the Body of the Lord 454

1. Draw near and take the bod - y of the Lord, Re - ceive the
2. Our lov - ing Sav - ior, Christ, the on - ly Son, Who by his
3. Let us ap-proach with thank - ful hearts sin - cere, And gain the
4. With heav'n-ly bread he makes the hun-gry whole, Gives liv - ing

1. ho - ly blood for you out-poured, Saved by that pre-cious bod - y
2. cross and blood the vic-t'ry won, Gave his own life for great-est
3. safe-guard of sal - va - tion here. God, who all faith - ful ser-vants
4. wa - ters to the thirst-y soul. The one e - ter - nal God, to

1. and that blood, Where - by re-freshed, we of - fer thanks to God.
2. and for least: Him - self the Vic - tim and him - self the Priest.
3. rules and shields, To all be - liev - ers life e - ter - nal yields.
4. whom shall bow All on the last day; he is with us now.

Text: 10 10 10 10; *Sancti, venite, Christi corpus sumite*; Antiphonary of Bennchar, 7th cent.;
 tr. by John M. Neale, 1818–1866, alt.
Music: ANIMA CHRISTI; William J. Maher, SJ, 1823–1877, alt.

Jesus, the Very Thought of You 455

1. Je - sus, the ver - y thought of you
2. No voice can sing, no heart can frame,
3. O hope of ev - 'ry hum - ble soul,
4. O Je - sus, be our joy to - day;

1. Fills us with sweet de - light; But sweet-er far your
2. Nor can the mind re - call A sweet-er sound than
3. O joy of all the meek, How kind you are to
4. Help us to prize your love; Grant us at last to

1. face to view And rest with - in your light.
2. your blest name, O Sav - ior of us all!
3. those who fall, How good to those who seek!
4. hear you say: "Come, share my home a - bove."

Text: CM; *Jesu dulcis memoria*, ca. 12th cent.; attr. to Bernard of Clairvaux, 1091–1153;
 tr. by Edward Caswall, 1814–1878, alt.
Music: ST. AGNES; John B. Dykes, 1823–1876.

456

Heart of Jesus

1. Heart of Je - sus, ho - ly mys - t'ry, beat with - in our hearts, we
2. Heart of Je - sus, giv - en for us, may we love as we are
3. Heart of Je - sus, no __ strang - er to our dark - ness and our
4. Heart of Je - sus, ho - ly wis - dom, ev - er an - cient, ev - er

1. pray. May we mir - ror your com - pas - sion, let your
2. loved. May your Church be a good shep - herd, seek - ing
3. grief, how you wept for poor __ Laz - 'rus and a -
4. new, may your king - dom grow a - mong us in each

1. mind be ours to - day. Make us ves - sels of your glo - ry,
2. out those who are lost, break - ing bread with all who hun - ger,
3. woke him from his sleep. How you bore for us the spear - wound,
4. thing we say and do. May we fight the good fight glad - ly,

1. in our weak - ness show your strength. Make this Church a bold
2. giv - ing voice to the op - pressed: win - ning jus - tice and
3. great - er love there can - not be than to lay down one's
4. run the race our whole lives through, till at last with the

1. sign of your pow - er - ful grace.
2. peace for all those in dis - tress.
3. life to __ set oth - ers free.
4. saints we shall find rest in you.

Text and music: Bob Hurd, b. 1950, © 2000, Bob Hurd. Published by OCP. All rights reserved.

Sacred Heart of Jesus

Verses

1. Sa-cred Heart of Je-sus, meek and mild. Look on us and
2. Sa-cred Heart of Je-sus, our des-ire. May your name be

1. keep us by your side. We give you thanks and praise your name.
2. praised and glo-ri-fied. Re-new our spir-its once a-gain.

1. Set our hearts a-flame that we may love you more and more ev-'ry
2. Make us know your love and in the morn-ing we will seek your ho-ly

1. day. Show us how to live the ho-ly way. So that wher-
2. face. Lead us to the prom-ise of your grace. And as we

1. ev-er we may go, the riv-er of your love through us may flow.
2. face the set-ting sun, make us see the glo-ry of your land.

Refrain

Sa-cred Heart of Je-sus draw us clo-ser to your love. Stir our

hearts with fire from a-bove. Sa-cred Heart of Je-sus ev-er

1.

faith-ful, ev-er true. Touch our lives, and make us more like

to Verse 2   Final

you.   lives,   and make us more like you.

458   **ALLELUIA! SING TO JESUS**

1. Al - le - lu - ia! sing to Je - sus! His the
2. Al - le - lu - ia! not as or - phans Are we
3. Al - le - lu - ia! Bread of An - gels, Here on
4. Al - le - lu - ia! King e - ter - nal, You the
5. Al - le - lu - ia! Al - le - lu - ia! Glo - ry

1. scep - ter, his the throne; Al - le - lu - ia!
2. left in sor - row now; Al - le - lu - ia!
3. earth our food, our stay! Al - le - lu - ia!
4. Lord of lords we own; Al - le - lu - ia!
5. be to God on high; Al - le - lu - ia

1. his the tri - umph, His the vic - to - ry a - lone;
2. he is near us, Faith be - lieves, nor ques - tions how:
3. here the sin - ful Flee to you from day to day:
4. born of Ma - ry, Earth your foot - stool, heav'n your throne:
5. to the Sav - ior Who has won the vic - to - ry;

1. Hark! the songs of peace - ful Zi - on Thun - der
2. Though the cloud from sight re - ceived him, When the
3. In - ter - ces - sor, friend of sin - ners, Earth's re -
4. You with - in the veil have en - tered, Robed in
5. Al - le - lu - ia to the Spir - it, Font of

1. like a might - y flood; Je - sus out of ev - 'ry
2. for - ty days were o'er, Shall our hearts for - get his
3. deem - er, plead for me, Where the songs of all the
4. flesh, our great high priest; Here on earth both priest and
5. love and sanc - ti - ty; Al - le - lu - ia! Al - le -

1. na - tion Has re - deemed us by his blood.
2. prom - ise? "I am with you ev - er - more!"
3. sin - less Sweep a - cross the crys - tal sea.
4. vic - tim In the Eu - cha - ris - tic feast.
5. lu - ia! To the tri - une maj - es - ty.

Text: 87 87 D; William C. Dix, 1837–1898, alt.
Music: HYFRYDOL; Rowland H. Prichard, 1811–1887.

REJOICE, THE LORD IS KING 459

1. Re-joice, the Lord is King: Your Lord and King a-dore! Re-
2. Our Lord and Sav-ior reigns, The God of truth and love; When
3. His king-dom can-not fail, He rules o'er earth and heav'n; The
4. Re-joice in glo-rious hope! Our Lord and judge shall come And

1. joice, give thanks and sing, And tri-umph ev-er-more:
2. he had purged our stains, He took his seat a-bove:
3. keys of death and hell Are to our Je-sus giv'n:
4. take his ser-vants up To their e-ter-nal home:
Lift up your

1-4. heart, lift up your voice! Re-joice, a-gain I say, re-joice!

Text: 66 66 88; *Hymns for Our Lord's Resurrection*, 1746; Charles Wesley, 1707–1788, alt.
Music: DARWALL'S 148TH; John Darwall, 1731–1789.

JESUS SHALL REIGN 460

1. Je-sus shall reign wher-e'er the sun Does its suc-
2. To him shall end-less prayer be made, And prais-es
3. Peo-ple and realms of ev-'ry tongue Dwell on his
4. Bless-ings a-bound wher-e'er he reigns, The pris-'ners
5. Let ev-'ry crea-ture rise and bring Their joy-ful

1. ces-sive jour-neys run; His king-dom stretch from
2. throng to crown his head; His name like sweet per-
3. love with sweet-est song, And chil-dren's voic-es
4. leap to lose their chains; The wea-ry find e-
5. prais-es to our King; An-gels de-scend with

1. shore to shore, Till moons shall wax and wane no more.
2. fume shall rise With ev-'ry morn-ing sac-ri-fice.
3. shall pro-claim Their ear-ly bless-ings on his name.
4. ter-nal rest, And all who suf-fer want are blest.
5. songs a-gain, And earth re-peat the loud a-men!

Text: LM; based on Psalm 72; Isaac Watts, 1674–1748, alt.
Music: DUKE STREET; John Hatton, ca. 1710–1793.

461   CROWN HIM WITH MANY CROWNS

1. Crown him with man - y crowns, The Lamb up - on his
2. Crown him the Lord of life, Who tri - umphed o'er the
3. Crown him the Lord of love, Be - hold his hands and
4. Crown him the Lord of peace, Whose pow'r a scep - ter
5. Crown him the Lord of years, The ris - en Lord sub -

1. throne; Hark! how the heav'n - ly an - them drowns All
2. grave, And rose vic - to - rious in the strife For
3. side, Rich wounds yet vis - i - ble a - bove In
4. sways From pole to pole, that wars may cease, Ab -
5. lime, Cre - a - tor of the roll - ing spheres, The

1. mu - sic but its own. A - wake, my soul, and sing
2. those he came to save. His glo - ries now we sing,
3. beau - ty glo - ri - fied. No an - gel in the sky
4. sorbed in prayer and praise. His reign shall know no end,
5. Mas - ter of all time. All hail, Re - deem - er, hail!

1. Of him who set us free, And hail him as your
2. Who died and rose on high, Who died, e - ter - nal
3. Can ful - ly bear that sight, But down - ward bends his
4. And round his pierc - ed feet Fair flow'rs of Par - a -
5. For you have died for me; Your praise and glo - ry

1. heav'n - ly King Through all e - ter - ni - ty.
2. life to bring, And lives that death may die.
3. burn - ing eye At mys - ter - ies so bright.
4. dise ex - tend Their fra - grance ev - er sweet.
5. shall not fail Through - out e - ter - ni - ty.

Text: SMD; Revelation 19:12; verses 1, 3–5, Matthew Bridges, 1800–1894; verse 2, Godfrey Thring, 1823–1903, alt.
Music: DIADEMATA; George J. Elvey, 1816–1893.

All Hail the Power of Jesus' Name

1. All hail the pow'r of Je - sus' name! Let an - gels pros-trate
2. Crown him, you mar - tyrs of our God, Who from his al - tar
3. Hail him, you heirs of Da - vid's line Whom Da - vid Lord did
4. O that with ev - 'ry tribe and tongue We at his feet may

1. fall; Bring forth the roy - al di - a - dem And
2. call; Ex - tol him in whose path you trod, And
3. call, The God in - car - nate, Man di - vine, And
4. fall, Lift high the u - ni - ver - sal song And

1. crown him Lord of all; Bring forth the roy - al
2. crown him Lord of all; Ex - tol him in whose
3. crown him Lord of all; The God in - car - nate,
4. crown him Lord of all; Lift high the u - ni -

1. di - a - dem And crown him Lord of all.
2. path you trod, And crown him Lord of all.
3. Man di - vine, And crown him Lord of all.
4. ver - sal song And crown him Lord of all.

Text: 86 86 86; Edward Perronet, 1726–1792, alt.
Music: CORONATION; *Union Harmony*, 1793; Oliver Holden, 1765–1844.

463

HAIL, REDEEMER, KING DIVINE

Verses

1. Hail, re-deem-er, king di - vine! Priest and lamb, the throne is thine;
2. King of ev - er - last-ing might! Be to us e - ter - nal light,

1. King whose reign shall nev - er cease, Prince of ev - er - last-ing peace.
2. Till in peace each na - tion rings With thy prais-es, king of kings.

Refrain

An - gels, saints and na-tions sing: "Praised be Je - sus Christ, our king;

Lord of earth and sky and sea, King of love on Cal - va - ry."

Text: 77 77 with refrain; Patrick Brennen, 1877–1951, © Burns & Oates, Ltd. All rights reserved.
Reproduced by permission of Continuum International Publishing Group, Ltd.
Music: ST. GEORGE'S WINDSOR; George J. Elvey, 1816–1893.

464

JESUS CHRIST IS LORD

Refrain

Je - sus Christ is Lord.

Verses

1. He did not hold to his e - qual - i - ty with
2. He chose the will of God through death up - on a
3. And so God gave to him a name a - bove all

1. God, for he did emp - ty him - self to be as
2. cross, and God did raise___ him up, ex - alt - ing
3. names. May all in heav - en and earth pro - claim him

to Refrain

1. one of us, to be as one of us.
2. him on high, ex - alt - ing him on high.
3. now as Lord, pro-claim him now as Lord.

Text: Based on Philippians 2:6–11; Ken Canedo, b. 1953, © 1998, 2004, spiritandsong.com®, a division of OCP.
All rights reserved.
Music: Ken Canedo, © 2004, Ken Canedo. Published by spiritandsong.com®, a division of OCP. All rights reserved.

AT THE NAME OF JESUS

1. At the Name of Je - sus Ev - 'ry knee shall bow,
2. Hum-bled for a sea - son, To re - ceive a Name
3. Bore it up tri - um - phant, With its hu - man light,
4. In your hearts en - throne him; There let him sub - due
5. Je - sus, Lord and Sav - ior, Shall re - turn a - gain,

1. Ev - 'ry tongue con - fess him King of glo - ry now;
2. From the lips of sin - ners, Un - to whom he came,
3. Through all ranks of crea - tures, To the cen - tral height,
4. All that is not ho - ly, All that is not true:
5. With his Fa - ther's glo - ry O'er the earth to reign;

1. 'Tis the Fa - ther's plea - sure We should call him Lord,
2. Faith - ful - ly he bore it Spot - less to the last,
3. To the throne of God - head, To the Fa - ther's breast;
4. Crown him as your Cap - tain In temp - ta - tion's hour;
5. For all wreaths of em - pire Meet up - on his brow,

1. Who from the be - gin - ning Was the might - y Word.
2. Brought it back vic - to - rious, When through death he passed.
3. Filled it with the glo - ry Of that per - fect rest.
4. Let his will en - fold you In its light and power.
5. And our hearts con - fess him King of glo - ry now.

Text: 65 65 D; based on Philippians 2:5–7; Caroline Maria Noel, 1817–1877, alt.
Music: KING'S WESTON; Ralph Vaughan Williams, 1872–1958; fr. *Enlarged Songs of Praise*, 1931.

466

AT THE NAME OF JESUS

Refrain

At the name of Je-sus, ev-'ry knee shall bow, ev-'ry tongue con-
fess him: King of glo-ry now. Je-sus is Lord, King of glo-ry now!

last time only

Verses

1. He ___ emp-tied him - self, as a slave, yet free,
2. He ___ hum-bled him - self, and o-beyed God's will.
3. God ex-alt - ed him, raised him up on high
4. Christ ___ Je - sus will come at the end of time,

1. came in hu - man like-ness ___ for you and for me; in
2. On a cross he died ___ on Cal - va - ry's hill; for
3. so a-bove all oth - ers ___ his name will not die; that
4. come with ju - bi - la - tion ___ to call ___ us home. Un-

to Refrain

1. hu - man like - ness ___ for you and for me.
2. you and me he o-beyed ___ God's will.
3. name we hon - or ___ and glo - ri - fy.
4. til that day you and I will pro - claim:

Text: Refrain, Caroline Maria Noel, 1817–1877. Verses based on Philippians 2;
    Christopher Walker, b. 1947, © 1995, Christopher Walker. Published by OCP. All rights reserved.
Music: Christopher Walker, © 1995, Christopher Walker. Published by OCP. All rights reserved.

467

JESUS THE LORD

Refrain

2

Je - sus. Je - sus. Let all cre-

3

a - tion bend the knee to the Lord.

1. In him we live, we move and have our be-ing; In
1. him the Christ, in him the king! Je - sus, the Lord.

2. Though Son, he did not cling to god - li - ness; but
3. He lived o - be-dient - ly his Fa-ther's will ac -

2. emp-tied him - self, be-came a slave! } Je - sus, the Lord.
3. cept-ing his death, _ death on a tree! }

Text: Based on the Jesus Prayer; Philippians 2:5–11; Acts 17:28; Roc O'Connor, SJ, b. 1949.
Music: Roc O'Connor, SJ.
Text and music © 1981, Robert F. O'Connor, SJ, and OCP. All rights reserved.

To Jesus Christ, Our Sovereign King   468

1. To Je - sus Christ, our Sov - 'reign King, Who is the
2. Thy reign ex - tend, O King be - nign, To ev - 'ry
3. To thee and to thy Church, great King, We pledge our

1. world's sal - va - tion, All praise and hom - age do we bring And
2. land and na - tion; For in thy king - dom, Lord di - vine, A -
3. hearts' ob - la - tion Un - til be - fore thy throne we sing In

1. thanks and ad - o - ra - tion. }
2. lone we find sal - va - tion. } Christ Je - sus, vic - tor!
3. end - less ju - bi - la - tion. }

1-3. Christ Je-sus, rul - er! Christ Je-sus, Lord and re-deem - er!

Text: 87 87 55 8; refrain based on *Christus Vincit*, 8th cent.; Martin B. Hellriegel, 1891–1981,
   © 1941, assigned 1978 to Mrs. Irene C. Mueller. All rights reserved. Used with permission.
Music: ICH GLAUB AN GOTT; *Mainz Gesangbuch*, 1870.

469   THE KING OF KINGS, CHRIST JESUS REIGNS

1. The King of Kings, Christ Je-sus reigns The Lord of
2. E-ter-nal King, Christ is God's Word From end-less
3. O ris-en King, you light the way To heav-en's

1. ev-'ry na-tion; In lov-ing wis-dom he or-dains The
2. ag-es spo-ken; En-fleshed on earth, his voice was heard And
3. glo-rious por-tal; If in our hearts your truth has sway, We

1. course of all cre-a-tion! ⎫
2. Sa-tan's might was bro-ken! ⎬ Christ, we a-dore you! Christ,
3. too have life im-mor-tal! ⎭

1-3. we im-plore you: Christ, keep us ev-er be-fore you!

Text: 87 87 55 8; Melvin Farrell, SS, 1930–1986, © 1977, OCP. All rights reserved.
Music: ICH GLAUB AN GOTT; *Mainz Gesangbuch*, 1870.

470   THE KING OF GLORY

Refrain

The King of glo-ry comes, the na-tion re-joic-es. O-pen the gates be-fore him,

lift up your voic-es.
Verses
1. Who is the King of glo-ry; how shall we
2. In all of Gal-i-lee, in cit-y or
3. Sing then of Da-vid's Son, our Sav-ior and
4. He gave his life for us, the pledge of sal-
5. He con-quered sin and death; he tru-ly has

to Refrain

1. call him? He is Em-man-u-el, the prom-ised of a-ges.
2. vil-lage, He goes a-mong his peo-ple cur-ing their ill-ness.
3. broth-er; In all of Gal-i-lee was nev-er an-oth-er.
4. va-tion, He took up-on him-self the sins of the na-tion.
5. ris-en, And he will share with us his heav-en-ly vi-sion.

Text: 12 12 with refrain; Willard F. Jabusch, b. 1930, © 1967, Willard F. Jabusch. All rights reserved. Administered by OCP.
Music: KING OF GLORY; trad. Israeli Folk Song.

ALMA REDEMPTORIS MATER

Al - ma Red - em - ptó - ris Ma - ter,
Lov - *ing Moth - er of our Sav - ior;*

quae pér - vi - a cae - li por - ta ma - nes,
thou o - pen gate lead - ing us to heav - en,

Et stel - la ma - ris, suc - cúr - re ca - dén - ti
and Star of the Sea, help thy fall - en peo - ple,

súr - ge - re qui cu - rat pó - pu - lo:
help all those who seek to rise a - gain.

Tu quae ge - nu - í - sti, na - tú - ra mi - rán - te,
Maid - en who didst give birth, all na - ture won - der - ing,

tu - um san - ctum Ge - ni - tó - rem:
to thy ho - ly Lord Cre - a - tor:

Vir - go pri - us ac po - sté - ri - us,
Vir - gin be - fore and vir - gin al - ways

Ga - bri - é - lis ab o - re su - mens il - lud A - ve,
who re - ceived from Ga - briel's mouth this mes - sage from heav - en,

pec - ca - tó - rum mi - se - ré - re.
take pit - y on us poor sin - ners.

Text: Ascr. to Hermannus Contractus, 1013–1054; adapt. by Theodore N. Marier, 1912–2001, © 1953, Theodore N. Marier.
Music: Chant, Mode V.

472   SING OF MARY

1. Sing of Ma-ry, pure and low-ly, Vir-gin Moth-er un-de-
2. Sing of Je-sus, son of Ma-ry, In the home at Naz-a-
3. Glo-ry be to God the Fa-ther; Glo-ry be to God the

1. filed. Sing of God's own Son most ho-ly, Who be-came her
2. reth. Toil and la-bor can-not wea-ry Love en-dur-ing
3. Son; Glo-ry be to God the Spir-it; Glo-ry to the

1. lit-tle child. Fair-est child of fair-est moth-er,
2. un-to death. Con-stant was the love he gave her,
3. Three in One. From the heart of bless-ed Ma-ry,

1. God the Lord who came to earth, Word made flesh, our
2. Though he went forth from her side, Forth to preach and
3. From all saints the song as-cends, And the Church the

1. ver-y broth-er, Takes our na-ture by his birth.
2. heal and suf-fer, Till on Cal-va-ry he died.
3. strain re-ech-oes Un-to earth's re-mot-est ends.

Text: 87 87 D; Roland F. Palmer, SSJE, 1891–1985, © Estate of Roland F. Palmer. All rights reserved. Used with permission.
Music: PLEADING SAVIOR; *Christian Lyre*, 1830.

473   LET IT BE DONE TO US

Verses

1, 5. Let it be done to us ac-cord-ing to your word.
2. And in the reign of God the hun-gry have their fill.
3. And in the reign of God the might-y be-come least.
4. In her own be-ing she be-came your dwell-ing place.

1, 5. Through us be spo-ken the Gos-pel to the world.
2. Let us break bread with all those who hun-ger still,
3. The poor are raised up to join the Prince of Peace.
4. And from her own flesh you took a hu-man face.

1, 5. Make us true dis - ci - ples with Ma - ry who pro - claims:
2. trust - ing that God's prom - ise will one day be ful - filled:
3. Let our work for jus - tice pre - pare this ho - ly feast:
4. Make your church, like Ma - ry, a sac - ra - ment of grace:

Refrain

Ma - gní - fi - cat, ma - gní - fi - cat, á - ni - ma me - a

Dó - mi - num, á - ni - ma me - a Dó - mi - num.

Text: Based on Luke 1:46–55; Bob Hurd, b. 1950.
Music: Bob Hurd.

MARY'S SONG 474

1. My soul pro - claims the Lord my God. My spir - it
2. All na - tions now will share my joy; For gifts God
3. For those who fear the Ho - ly One, God's mer - cy
4. God fills the hun - gry with good things, And sends the
5. Then let all na - tions praise our God, The Fa - ther

1. sings God's praise, Who looks on me, and
2. has out - poured. This low - ly one has
3. will not die. Whose strong right arm puts
4. rich a - way; The prom - ise made to
5. and the Son, The Spir - it blest, who

1. lifts me up, That glad - ness fills my days.
2. been made great. I mag - ni - fy the Lord.
3. down the proud, And lifts the low - ly high.
4. A - bra - ham Is filled to end - less day.
5. lives in us, While end - less a - ges run.

Text: CM; based on Luke 1:46–55; Anne Carter, 1944–1993, © 1988, Society of the Sacred Heart.
Music: NEW BRITAIN; *Columbian Harmony*, 1829.

475   SING WE OF THE BLESSED MOTHER

1. Sing we of the bless-ed Moth-er Who re-ceived the
2. Sing we, too, of Ma-ry's sor-rows, Of the sword that
3. Sing a-gain the joys of Ma-ry When she saw the
4. Sing the great-est joy of Ma-ry When on earth her

1. an-gel's word, And o-be-dient to the sum-mons
2. pierced her through, When be-neath the cross of Je-sus
3. ris-en Lord, And in prayer with Christ's a-pos-tles,
4. work was done, And the Lord of all cre-a-tion

1. Bore in love the in-fant Lord; Sing we of the joys of
2. She his weight of suf-f'ring knew, Looked up-on her Son and
3. Wait-ed on his prom-ised word: From on high the blaz-ing
4. Brought her to his heav'n-ly home: Vir-gin Moth-er, Ma-ry

1. Ma-ry At whose breast that child was fed Who is Son
2. Sav-ior Reign-ing from the aw-ful tree, Saw the price
3. glo-ry Of the Spir-it's pres-ence came, Heav'n-ly breath
4. bless-ed, Raised on high and crowned with grace, May your Son,

1. of God e-ter-nal And the ev-er-last-ing Bread.
2. of our re-demp-tion Paid to set the sin-ner free.
3. of God's own be-ing, To-kened in the wind and flame.
4. the world's re-deem-er, Grant us all to see his face.

Text: 87 87 D; 'Sing we of the Blessed Mother' by George B. Timms, 1910–1997.
Reproduced by permission of Oxford University Press. All rights reserved.
Music: OMNI DIE DIC MARIAE; *Trier Gesängbuch*, 1695.

476   PILGRIM PRAYER

Refrain

Hail Ma-ry, full of grace, bless the jour-ney,

bless the place we go to and we leave.

Verses

1. We give praise for the won - der of our God,
2. We give praise for the wis - dom of our God,
3. We give praise for the mer - cy of our God,
4. We give praise for the kind-ness of our God,
5. We give praise for the pa - tience of our God,
6. We give praise for the good-ness of our God,

to Refrain

1. who sends us com - pan - ions on our way.
2. who gives us the free - dom to be - lieve.
3. who lives in the doubt and in the dream.
4. who teach - es us gent - ly to for - give.
5. who heals us in ways we can - not know.
6. who smiles on the pil - grim com - ing home.

Text and music: Pia Moriarty, b. 1948, © 2003, Pia Moriarty. Published by OCP. All rights reserved.

MARY, WOMAN OF THE PROMISE 477

1. Ma - ry, wom - an of the prom - ise; Ves - sel of your
2. Ma - ry, song of ho - ly wis - dom, Sung be - fore the
3. Ma - ry, morn - ing star of jus - tice; Mir - ror of the
4. Ma - ry, mod - el of com - pas - sion; Wound-ed by your
5. Ma - ry, wom - an of the Gos - pel; Hum - ble home for

1. peo - ple's dreams, Through your o - pen, will - ing
2. world be - gan, Faith - ful to the Word with -
3. ra - diant light, In the shad - ows of life's
4. off - spring's pain, When our hearts are torn by
5. trea - sured seed, Help us to be true dis -

1. spir - it Wa - ters of God's good - ness streamed.
2. in, you Car - ried out God's won - drous plan.
3. jour - ney, Be a bea - con for our sight.
4. sor - row, Teach us how to love a - gain.
5. ci - ples Bear - ing fruit in word and deed.

Text: 87 87; Mary Frances Fleischaker, © 1988, Mary Frances Fleischaker. All rights reserved.
    Used with permission of Selah Publishing Co., Inc., exclusive agent.
Music: DRAKES BROUGHTON; Edward Elgar, 1857–1934.

478

THERE IS NOTHING TOLD

Verses

1-6. There is noth-ing told a-bout this wom-an, but that

1. she had once be-come en-gaged, and an an-gel ad-
2. she had brought in-to the world, in the land of Ju-
3. she had searched for three long days for her child who was
4. she at Ca-na was a guest, and that Je-sus changed
5. she was stand-ing by the cross when her son stretched his
6. she was one in prayer with those up-on whom tongues of

1. dressed her and said: "You are bless-ed a-mong all your kind."
2. de-a, her son; for some shep-herds have passed on this tale.
3. bus-y else-where, and her heart then did not un-der-stand.
4. wa-ter to wine, so that all might be-lieve who he was.
5. arms out on high, and met death with a thief on each side.
6. fire did de-scend, and the Spir-it bap-tized them with flame.

Refrain

On this day all earth and all par-a-dise join in nam-ing you

hap-py and blessed; Vir-gin Ma-ry, bless-ed are you.

479

ON THIS DAY, O BEAUTIFUL MOTHER

Refrain

On this day, O beau-ti-ful Moth-er, On this

day we give thee our love. Near thee, Ma-don-na,

fond-ly we hov-er, Trust-ing thy gen-tle care to prove.

1. On this day we ask to share, Dear-est Moth-er,
2. Queen of an-gels, deign to hear Lisp-ing chil-dren's

1. thy sweet care; Aid us ere our feet a-
2. hum-ble pray'r; Young hearts gain, O Vir-gin

to Refrain

1. stray Wan-der from thy guid-ing way.
2. pure, Sweet-ly to thy-self al-lure.

Text: 77 77 with refrain; Rohr's *Favorite Catholic Melodies*, 1857.
Music: BEAUTIFUL MOTHER; Louis Lambillotte, SJ, 1796–1855.

MARY'S SONG   480

1. My soul doth glo-ry in your love, O Lord.
2. Great are you, God, and ho-ly is your name.
3. Ah, how you fill the hun-gry with your love.
4. My soul doth glo-ry in your love, O Lord.

1. My soul doth glo-ry in your love, O Lord. For you
2. Your mer-cy reach-es to the end of time. Ah, the
3. With emp-ty hands the rich are sent a-way. You will
4. My soul doth glo-ry in your love, O Lord. For you

1. gazed on your ser-vant with com-pas-sion, And you
2. low-ly you raise__ to the heav-ens, And the
3. al-ways be mind-ful of your mer-cy, As you
4. smiled on your ser-vant with com-pas-sion, And you

1. reached out and took me by the hand.
2. proud-heart-ed have no part with you.
3. prom-ised your peo-ple long a-go.
4. reached out and took me by the hand.

Text: Based on Luke 1:46–55; Millie Rieth, 1940–2003.
Music: Millie Rieth.

481   HAIL MARY: GENTLE WOMAN

Intro: Cantor

Hail Mary, full of grace, the Lord is with you.
Blessed are you among women and
blest is the fruit of your womb, Jesus.

Holy Mary, Mother of God,
pray for us sinners now
and at the hour of death. Amen.

Refrain: All

Gen-tle wom-an, qui-et light, morn-ing star, so strong and bright, gen-tle Moth-er, peace-ful dove, teach us wis-dom; teach us love.

Verses: All

1. You were cho - sen by the Fa-ther;
2. Bless-ed are you a-mong wom-en,

1. you were cho - sen for the Son. You were
2. blest in turn all wom-en, too. Bless-ed

1. cho - sen ⁊ from all wom-en and for
2. they ⁊ with peace - ful spir-its. Bless-ed

to Refrain

1. wom-an, shin-ing one.
2. they with gen - tle hearts.

Text: Based on Luke 1:28, 42; Carey Landry, b. 1944.
Music: Carey Landry
Text and music © 1975, 1978, Carey Landry and OCP. All rights reserved.

SONG OF MARY

1. Let us sing the prais-es of Ma-ry, daugh-ter of Da-vid's
2. Let us sing the prais-es of Ma-ry, cho-sen as bless-ed
3. Let us sing the prais-es of Ma-ry, wom-an of strong and
4. Let us sing the prais-es of Ma-ry, pierced by the sword of
5. Let us sing the prais-es of Ma-ry, friend of the poor in

1. ho-ly line, she who heard the voice of an an-gel
2. from the least, she who heard the song of the an-gels
3. stead-fast love. She who raised the Sav-ior of na-tions
4. sor-row's pain, she who saw the child of her lov-ing
5. ev-'ry age, she who saw her Son and her Sav-ior

1. tell-ing the plan of God's de-sign, how in wis-dom's
2. fill-ing the night with heav-en's peace. When the prom-ised
3. held in her arms the Son of God. She who knew the
4. nailed on a cross to die in shame. Though his friends would
5. ris-en in glo-ry from the grave. Sin and death shall

1. ho-ly sight she would moth-er heav-en's Christ.
2. time had come she gave birth to God's own Son.
3. Fa-ther's grace taught her Son to know God's face.
4. flee in fear she re-mained for-ev-er near.
5. reign no more; Christ has o-pened heav-en's door.

1–5. Bless-ed be the name of Ma-ry, she who trust-ed the

2

1–5. love of God.

Text: 98 98 77 88; Dan Schutte, b. 1947.
Music: SONG OF MARY; Dan Schutte.

483

AVE MARIA

1. A - ve Ma - ri - a, gra - ti - a ple - na,
2. Be - ne - dic - ta, blest a - mong wom - en,
3. Sanc - ta Ma - ri - a, Ho - ly Ma - ry,

1. O ho - ly Ma - ry, _____ full _____ of grace;
2. be - ne - dic - tus, the child that you bore:
3. Ma - ter _____ De - i, _____ Moth - er of God:

1. Do - mi - nus te - cum, with you the Ho - ly One.
2. Je - sus the Sav - ior, God's love in - car - nate,
3. O - ra pro no - bis, pray for our faith - ful - ness

1. Such is your gift _____ to know _____ God in your
2. be - ne - dic - ta, deep wom - an of
3. all through the sea - sons of life with hope and with

1 to Verse 2 ‖ **2**

1. heart. 2. faith. A - ve Ma - ri -

to Verse 3

2. a, A - ve, A - ve Ma - ri - a.

Final

3. love. O - ra pro no - bis, pray for our faith - ful - ness

3. all through the sea - sons of life with hope and with love.

Text and music: Gregory Norbet, b. 1940, © 1994, Gregory Norbet. Published by OCP. All rights reserved.

O Sanctissima/O Most Holy One

484

1. O san - ctís - si - ma, O pi - ís - si - ma,
2. Tu so - lá - ti - um Et re - fú - gi - um,
3. Ec - ce dé - bi - les, Per - quam flé - bi - les,
4. Vir - go ré - spi - ce, Ma - ter, ád - spi - ce,

1. O San - ctís - si - ma, Ho - ly Queen of Love,
2. O most beau - ti - ful, And most mer - ci - ful,
3. Ma - ry, Mys - tic Rose, Font that o - ver-flows,
4. Ma - ry, plead for us; In - ter - cede for us.

1. Dul - cis vir - go Ma - rí - a!
2. Vir - go ma - ter Ma - rí - a!
3. Sal - va nos, _____ Ma - rí - a!
4. Au - di nos, _____ Ma - rí - a!

1. Dear - est Vir - gin and Moth - er.
2. Gate of Heav - en, we hail you.
3. Seat of Wis - dom, we greet you.
4. Come and lead us to Je - sus.

1. Ma - ter a - má - ta, In - te - me - rá - ta,
2. Quid - quid op - tá - mus, Per _____ te spe - rá - mus,
3. Tol - le lan - guó - res, Sa - na do - ló - res,
4. Tu _____ me - di - cí - nam, Por - tas di - ví - nam;

1. Blest by ev - 'ry na - tion, Ev - 'ry gen - er - a - tion:
2. Star of our sal - va - tion, Crown of all cre - a - tion:
3. Moth - er of our Sav - ior, Full of grace and fa - vor:
4. Moth - er in our sad - ness, Moth - er in our glad - ness:

1-4. O - ra, o - ra pro no - bis!
1-4. O - ra, o - ra pro no - bis!

Text: 55 7 D; Latin verse 1 fr. Herder's *Stimmen der Völker in Liedern*, 1807; verses 2–4 fr. *Arundel Hymnal*, 1905.
English tr. by Harry Hagan, OSB, b. 1947, © 2003, St. Meinrad Archabbey. Published by OCP. All rights reserved.
Music: O DU FRÖHLICHE; Tattersall's *Improved Psalmody*, 1794.

485

SALVE, REGINA/HAIL, MARY

Sal - ve, Re - gí - na, ma - ter mi - se - ri - cór - di - ae: Vi - ta dul-
Hail, Ma - ry, moth - er and queen of ten - der mer - cy, our life, our

cé - do et spes no - stra, sal - ve. Ad te cla - má - mus,
com - fort, and our hope, we hail you. From this for - eign land

éx - su - les, fí - li - i He - vae. Ad te sus - pi - rá - mus,
Eve's sons and daugh - ters cry to you. So lost, so full of fear,

ge - mén - tes et flen - tes in hac la - cri - má - rum val - le.
we mourn, we grieve, we sigh from this tear - ful vale of ex - ile.

E - ia er - go, Ad - vo - cá - ta no - stra, il - los tu - os mi-
Ah, then, our help, our ad - vo - cate and guide, turn now to us the

se - ri - cór - des ó - cu - los ad nos con - vér - te.
gaze of your all - lov - ing eyes, so full of mer - cy.

Et Je - sum, be - ne - dí - ctum fruc - tum ven - tris tu - i,
And Je - sus— your Son, and Lord, your womb's most bless - ed fruit—

no - bis post hoc ex - sí - li - um os - tén - de.
show him to us when we com - plete our so - journ.

O cle - mens, O pi - a,
O gen - tle, O lov - ing,

O _____ dul - cis Vir - go Ma - rí - a.
O _____ be - lov - ed, O Vir - gin Ma - ry.

Text: Latin, attr. to Hermanus Contractus, 1013–1054; English, Paul F. Ford, b. 1947, © 1995, Paul F. Ford.
    Published by OCP. All rights reserved.
Music: Chant, Mode V.

AVE MARIA   486

A - ve, Ma - rí - a,   grá - ti - a   ple - na,
A - ve, Ma - rí - a: Hail, Ma - ry,   full   of   grace,

Dó - mi - nus te - cum,   be - ne - dí - cta   tu
the   Lord   is   with   you.   O   how   blest   are   you

in   mu - li - é - ri - bus,   et   be - ne - dí -
a - mong   all   earth's   wom - en.   And   how   tru - ly

ctus   fruc - tus   ven - tris   tu - i,   Je - sus.
blest   is   the   fruit   of   your   womb,   Je - sus.

San - cta   Ma - rí - a,   Ma - ter   De - i,
O   ho - ly   Ma - ry,   God's   own   moth - er,

o - ra   pro   no - bis   pec - ca - tó - ri - bus,
pray __ for   us,   your   chil - dren   who   stray   from   the   way,

nunc   et   in __ ho - ra   mor - tis   no - strae.   A - men.
now   and   in   that   fin - al   hour   when   we   come   to   die.   A - men.

Text: Part one, Latin, based on Luke 1:28, 42; part two, Latin, 16th cent. English © 1995, Paul F. Ford.
    Published by OCP. All rights reserved.
Music: Chant, Mode I.

487   HOLY IS HIS NAME

Verses

1. My soul proclaims the great-ness of the Lord,
2. He has mer-cy in ev-'ry gen-er-a-tion.   He

1. and my spir-it ex-ults in God my Sav-ior.   For he has
2. has re-vealed his pow-er and his glo-ry.   He has cast

1. looked with mer-cy on my low-li-ness,   and my name will be for-
2. down the might-y in their ar-ro-gance,   and has lift-ed up the

1. ev-er ex-alt-ed.   For the might-y God has done great
2. meek and the low-ly.   He has come to help his ser-vant

1. things for me,   and his mer-cy will reach from age to
2. Is-ra-el;   he re-mem-bers his prom-ise to our

Refrain

1. age.   And ho-ly, ho-ly, ho-ly is his name.
2. fa-thers.

Text: Based on Luke 1:46–55; John Michael Talbot, b. 1954.
Music: John Michael Talbot.
Text and music © 1980, Birdwing Music/BMG Songs, Inc. All rights reserved.
    Administered by EMI CMG Publishing. Used with permission.

488   IN HIS TEMPLE NOW BEHOLD HIM

1. In his tem-ple now be-hold him,   See the long ex-
2. In the arms of her who bore him,   Vir-gin pure, be-
3. Je-sus, by your pres-en-ta-tion,   When they blest you,
4. Prince and au-thor of sal-va-tion,   Be your bound-less

1. pect-ed Lord;   An-cient proph-ets had fore-told him;
2. hold him lie,   While his a-ged saints a-dore him
3. weak and poor,   Make us see our great sal-va-tion,
4. love our theme!   Je-sus, praise to you be giv-en,

1. God has now ful-filled his word, Now, to praise him,
2. Ere in faith and hope they die. Al - le - lu - ia!
3. Seal us with your prom-ise sure, And pre-sent us
4. By the world you did re-deem, With the Fa - ther

1. his re-deem-ed shall break forth with one ac - cord.
2. Al - le - lu - ia! Lo, th'in-car-nate God most high.
3. in your glo - ry to your Fa - ther, cleansed and pure.
4. and the Spir - it, Lord of maj-es - ty su - preme.

Text: 87 87 87; Luke 2:22–24; verses 1–3, Henry J. Pyle, 1825–1903; verse 4, William Cooke, 1821–1894.
Music: ST. THOMAS (TANTUM ERGO); John F. Wade, 1711–1786.

HOLY PATRON, THEE SALUTING 489

Verses

1. Ho - ly pa-tron, thee sa-lut-ing Here we meet, with
2. Thou who faith-ful - ly at-tend-ed Him whom heav'n and
3. May our fer-vent pray'rs as-cend-ing, Move thee for our
4. Through this life, O watch a-round us! Fill with love our

1. hearts sin - cere; Blest Saint Jo - seph, all u - nit - ing,
2. earth a - dore; Who with pi - ous care de - fend - ed
3. souls to plead; May thy smile of peace de - scend-ing,
4. ev - 'ry breath, And, when part - ing fear sur-rounds us,

Refrain

1. Call on thee to hear our prayer. Hap - py saint, in
2. Ma - ry, Vir - gin ev - er pure.
3. Ben - e - dic - tions on us shed.
4. Guide us through the toils of death.

bliss a - dor-ing Je - sus, Sav - ior of hu-man-kind, Hear thy

chil-dren thee im-plor-ing, May we thy pro - tec-tion find.

Text: 87 87 with refrain; American, ca. 1843; Anon.
Music: PLEADING SAVIOR; Christian Lyre, 1830.

490   COME NOW, AND PRAISE THE HUMBLE SAINT

1. Come now, and praise the hum - ble saint Of
2. The Ar - chi - tect's high mir - a - cles He
3. For him there was no glo - ry here, No
4. But now with - in the Fa - ther's grace Where

1. Da - vid's house and line, The car - pen - ter whose
2. saw, and what was done; The Vir - gin's spouse, the
3. crown or mar - tyr's fame; For him there was the
4. saints and an - gels throng, Be - side his spouse, be -

1. life ful - filled Our gra - cious God's de - sign.
2. guard - ian of Great Da - vid's great - er Son.
3. pa - tient life Of faith and hum - ble name.
4. fore the Son, He joins the heav'n - ly song.

Text: CM; George W. Williams, b. 1922, © 1979, The Hymn Society. All rights reserved.
Administered by Hope Publishing Co. Used with permission.
Music: LAND OF REST; Trad. American Melody.

491   A JUST MAN HONORED FROM ABOVE

1. A just man hon - ored from a - bove, A si - lent
2. A man who act - ed on the word, He car - ried
3. A man of faith, a man of trust, He bore what -
4. We praise you, God of maj - es - ty, One ho - ly

1. man, a man of love, Saint Jo - seph served the
2. out what he had heard: He took the Moth - er
3. ev - er loss he must To keep the Moth - er
4. three - fold Mys - ter - y; Be Fa - ther, Son and

1. Lord a - lone On ex - ile's road, in fam - 'ly home.
2. and her Child From scorn - er's stone and ty - rant wild.
3. and her Son Un - til his life's great work was done.
4. Spir - it blest By all who share in eve - ning's rest.

Text: LM; Genevieve Glen, OSB, b. 1945, © 1998, The Benedictine Nuns of the Abbey of St. Walburga.
Published by OCP. All rights reserved.
Music: JESU DULCIS MEMORIA; Chant, Mode I.

PRAISE WE THE LORD THIS DAY

492

1. Praise we the Lord this day, This day so long fore - told, Whose prom - ise shone with cheer - ing ray On wait - ing saints of old.
2. The Proph - et gave the sign For faith - ful folk to read: A vir - gin, born of Da - vid's line, Shall bear the prom - ised Seed.
3. Ask not how this should be, But wor - ship and a - dore Like her whom God's own maj - es - ty Came down to shad - ow o'er.
4. She meek - ly bowed her head To hear the gra - cious word, Ma - ry, the pure and low - ly maid, The fa - vored of the Lord.
5. Bless - ed shall be her name In all the Church on earth Through whom that won - drous mer - cy came, The in - car - nate Sav - ior's birth.
6. O Christ, the Vir - gin's Son, We praise you and a - dore, You are with God the Fa - ther One And Spir - it ev - er - more.

Text: SM; Matthew 1:23; *Hymns for the Festivals and Saints' Days*, 1846.
Music: SWABIA; Johann M. Speiss, 1715–1772; adapt. by William H. Havergal, 1793–1870.

THE GOD WHOM EARTH AND SEA AND SKY

493

1. The God whom earth and sea and sky A - dore and praise and mag - ni - fy, Whose might they claim, whose love they tell, In Ma - ry's bod - y comes to dwell.
2. O Moth - er blest! the cho - sen shrine Where - in the ar - chi - tect di - vine, Whose hand con - tains the earth and sky, Has come in hu - man form to lie.
3. Blest in the mes - sage Ga - briel brought; Blest in the work the Spir - it wrought; Most blest, to bring to hu - man birth The long de - sired of all the earth.
4. O Lord, the Vir - gin - born, to you E - ter - nal praise and laud are due, Whom with the Fa - ther we a - dore And Spir - it blest for ev - er - more.

Text: LM; *Quem terra, pontus, aethera*; Venantius Honorius Fortunatus, ca. 530–609; tr. by John M. Neale, 1818–1866, alt.
Music: EISENACH; melody fr. *Das ander Theil des andern newen Operis Geistlicher Deutscher Lieder*, 1605;
    adapt. by Johann Hermann Schein, 1586–1630.

494 THE GREAT FORERUNNER OF THE MORN

1. The great fore - run - ner of the morn, The
2. With heav'n - ly mes - sage Ga - briel came, That
3. His might - y deeds ex - alt his fame To

1. her - ald of the Word, is born; And faith - ful hearts shall
2. John should be that her - ald's name, And with pro - phet - ic
3. great - er than a proph - et's name; Of wom - an - born shall

1. nev - er fail With thanks and praise his light to hail.
2. ut - t'rance told His ac - tions great and man - i - fold.
3. nev - er be A great - er proph - et than was he.

Text: LM; *Praecursor altus luminis*; St. Bede the Venerable, 673–735; tr. by John M. Neale, 1818–1866, alt.
Music: WINCHESTER NEW; Georg Wittwe's *Musikalisches Hand-Buch*, Hamburg, 1690;
    adapt. by William H. Havergal, 1793–1870.

495 TWO NOBLE SAINTS

1. Two no - ble saints both root - ed In faith and ho - ly love,
2. The words of Paul as - sure us Of Christ's re - deem - ing word;

1. By hope of God u - nit - ed They reach to heav'n a - bove.
2. The works of Pe - ter show us How we may serve the Lord.

1. One on a cross is mar - tyred, One by the sword is slain;
2. So praise we the Cre - a - tor, And praise we Christ the Son,

1. Both tri - umph in their dy - ing, Both glo - rious saint-hood gain.
2. Who with the Ho - ly Spir - it, Now reign, blest Three in One.

Text: 76 76 D; based on *Decora lux aeternitatis auream*; Anne K. LeCroy, b. 1930, © Anne K. LeCroy.
    All rights reserved. Used with permission.
Music: ELLACOMBE; *Gesangbuch der Herzogl, Wirtembergischen Katholischen Hofkapelle*, 1784, alt.;
    adapt. fr. Würth's *Katholisches Gesangbuch*, 1863.

TRANSFIGURATION

1. Je - sus, on the moun - tain peak, stands a - lone in glo - ry
2. Trem - bling at his feet we saw Mo - ses and E - li - jah
3. Swift the cloud of glo - ry came, God, pro - claim - ing in its
4. Je - sus is the cho - sen one, liv - ing hope of ev - 'ry

1. blaz - ing. Let us, if we dare to speak, join the
2. speak - ing. All the proph - ets and the law shout through
3. thun - der, Je - sus as the Son by name! Na - tions,
4. na - tion, hear and heed him, ev - 'ry - one; sing, with

1. saints and an - gels prais - ing.
2. them their joy - ful greet - ing: Praise and glo - ry,
3. cry a - loud in won - der: *Al - le - lu - ia,
4. earth and all cre - a - tion:

1-4. praise and glo - ry, praise and glo - ry to our Lord!
1-4. *al - le - lu - ia, al - le - lu - ia!*

1. Let us, if we dare to speak, join the saints and an - gels
2. All the pro - phets and the law shout through them their joy - ful
3. Je - sus as the Son by name: na - tions, cry a - loud in
4. Hear and heed him, ev - 'ry - one; sing with earth and all cre-

(Fine) Interlude **6**

1. prais - ing.
2. greet - ing.
3. won - der.
4. a - tion.

*Outside the season of Lent

497 'Tis Good, Lord, to Be Here

1. 'Tis good, Lord, to be here! Your
2. 'Tis good, Lord, to be here, Your
3. Ful - fill - er of the past! Prom -
4. Be - fore we taste of death, We
5. 'Tis good, Lord, to be here! Yet

1. glo - ry fills the night; Your face and gar - ments,
2. beau - ty to be - hold, Where Mo - ses and E -
3. ise of things to be! We hail your bod - y
4. see your king - dom come; We long to hold the
5. we may not re - main; But since you bid us

1. like the sun, Shine with un - bor - rowed light.
2. li - jah stand, Your mes - sen - gers of old.
3. glo - ri - fied, And our re - demp - tion see.
4. vi - sion bright, And make this hill our home.
5. leave the mount, Come with us to the plain.

Text: SM; based on Luke 9:32–33; Joseph A. Robinson, 1858–1933, alt., Esmé D. E. Bird.
Music: SWABIA; Johann M. Speiss, 1715–1772; adapt. by William H. Havergal, 1793–1870.

498 Hail, Holy Queen

Verses

1. Hail, ho - ly Queen en - throned a - bove, O Ma - ri - a!
2. Our life, our sweet - ness here be - low, O Ma - ri - a!
3. As ex - iles all to you we cry, O Ma - ri - a!
4. Turn then, most gra - cious ad - vo - cate, O Ma - ri - a!
5. O gen - tle, lov - ing, ho - ly one, O Ma - ri - a!
6. And when from death to life we've passed, O Ma - ri - a!

1. Hail, Queen of mer - cy and of love, O Ma - ri - a!
2. Our hope in sor - row and in woe, O Ma - ri - a!
3. Come, soothe with hope our mis - er - y, O Ma - ri - a!
4. Toward us your eyes com - pas - sion - ate, O Ma - ri - a!
5. Make us each day more like your Son, O Ma - ri - a!
6. Show us your Son, our Lord, at last, O Ma - ri - a!

Refrain

Tri-umph, all ye cher-u-bim, Sing with us, ye
ser-a-phim! Heav'n and earth re-sound the hymn:
Sal - ve, sal - ve, sal - ve, Re-gi-na!

Text: 84 84 with refrain; *Salve, Regina, mater misericordiae*, ca. 1080;
verses 1, 2, 5 and refrain tr. anon. in *Roman Hymnal*, 1884; verses 3, 4, 6, para.
Music: SALVE REGINA COELITUM; Melchior Ludwig Herold, 1753–1810; *Choralmelodien zum Heiligen Gesänge*, 1808.

BRIGHT AS THE SUN, FAIR AS THE MOON 499

1. Bright as the sun, fair as the moon, She reigns, who
2. Night is not dark where she stands bright, The wom-an
3. O God, we read by her love's flame The Word in

1. held with - in her womb The Word made flesh, God's
2. robed in liv - ing light, Crowned with the stars, who
3. whom we sing your name: We bow be - fore your

1. Son made hers, To whom the an - gel host de - fers.
2. served on earth The Word to whom her faith gave birth.
3. maj - es - ty, One ho - ly, three - fold Mys - ter - y.

Text: LM; Genevieve Glen, OSB, b. 1945, © 1998, The Benedictine Nuns of the Abbey of St. Walburga.
Published by OCP. All rights reserved.
Music: TRURO; William's *Psalmodia Evangelica*, Part II, 1789.

500   LIFT HIGH THE CROSS

Refrain

Lift high the cross, the love of Christ pro-claim till all the world a-dore his sa-cred name.

Verses

1. Come, Chris-tians, fol - low where our cap-tain trod, Our King vic - to - rious, Christ, the Son of God.
2. Led on their way by this tri - um-phant sign, The hosts of God in con-quering ranks com-bine.
3. Each new-born ser - vant of the Cru - ci - fied Bears on the brow the seal of him who died.
4. O Lord, once lift - ed on the glo-rious tree, As thou hast prom-ised, draw the world to thee.
5. So shall our song of tri-umph ev - er be: Praise to the Cru - ci - fied for vic - to - ry!

to Refrain

Text: 10 10 with refrain; based on 1 Corinthians 1:18; George W. Kitchin, 1827–1912;
   alt. by Michael R. Newbolt, 1874–1956.
Music: CRUCIFER; Sydney H. Nicholson, 1875–1947.
Text and music © 1974, Hope Publishing Co. All rights reserved. Used with permission.

501   TAKE UP YOUR CROSS

1. Take up your cross, the Sav - ior said, If you would my dis - ci - ple be; De - ny your - self, the world for - sake, And hum - bly fol - low af - ter me.
2. Take up your cross, be not a - shamed! Let not dis - grace your spir - it fill! For God him - self en - dured to die Up - on a cross, on Cal - vary's hill.
3. Take up your cross, which gives you strength, Which makes your trem-bling spir - it brave: 'Twill guide you to a bet - ter home And lead to vic - t'ry o'er the grave.
4. Take up your cross, and fol - low Christ, Nor think till death to lay it down; For on - ly they who bear the cross May hope to wear the glo - rious crown.

Text: LM; Charles W. Everest, 1814–1877, alt.
Music: ERHALT UNS, HERR; J. Klug's *Geistliche Lieder*, Wittenberg, 1543;
   adapt. by Johann Sebastian Bach, 1685–1750, alt.

Take Up Our Cross

502

Verse 1

1. Behold the wood that bears our name;   The tree from which salvation blooms;
behold the nails that hold our sin.   the death by which we're born again.

Refrain

We take up our cross and fol - low him; we lay down our lives that we might live. We car-ry the hope of Christ with - in; we take up our cross and fol - low him.

Verse 2

2. We embrace the sacrifice,   The burdens of this world made light;
and walk the path we cannot see.   by blood and thorn we are redeemed.

Litany of the Saints

503

Repeat each invocation immediately after the Priest or Cantor:

Lord, have mer-cy.   Christ, have mer-cy.   Lord, have mer-cy.

Invocations

Responses: Sing 1-5 four times; 6 two times

(Saint Invocation)   1-4. pray____ for____ us.
("Lord, be merciful,")   5. Lord, de - liv - er us, we pray.
("Be merciful to us sinners.")   6. Lord, we ask you, hear our prayer.

1-4. pray____ for____ us.
5. Lord, de - liv - er us, we pray.
6. Lord, we ask you, hear our prayer.

to Responses

1-5. All you ho - ly men and wom-en, pray for us.
6. Christ,__ hear us. Christ,__ gra-cious - ly hear us.

504

For All the Saints

1. For all the saints who from their la-bors
2. You were their rock, their for-tress and their
3. O may your sol - diers, faith-ful, true, and
4. O blest com - mun - ion, fam - i - ly di -
5. And when the strife is fierce, the war - fare
6. The gold - en eve - ning bright-ens in the
7. But then there breaks a yet more glo - rious
8. From earth's wide bounds, from o - cean's far - thest

1. rest, All who _____ by faith be - fore the
2. might; _____ You, Lord, their cap - tain in the
3. bold, _____ Fight as the saints who no - bly
4. vine! _____ We fee - bly strug - gle, they in
5. long, _____ Steals on the ear the dis - tant
6. west; _____ Soon, soon to faith - ful war - riors
7. day: The saints _____ tri - um - phant rise in
8. coast, Through gates _____ of pearl streams in the

1. world con - fessed, Your name, O _____
2. well - fought fight; _____ You, in the
3. fought of old, And win, with _____
4. glo - ry shine; Yet all are _____
5. tri - umph song, And hearts are _____
6. comes their rest; _____ Sweet is the
7. bright ar - ray; The king of _____
8. count - less host, _____ Sing - ing to

1. Je - sus, be for - ev - er blest.
2. dark - ness drear, their one true light.
3. them, the vic - tor's crown of gold.
4. one with - in your great de - sign.
5. brave a - gain, and arms are strong.
6. calm of par - a - dise the blest.
7. glo - ry pass - es on his way.
8. Fa - ther, Son, and Ho - ly Ghost:

1-8. Al - le - lu - ia! Al - le - lu - ia!

Text: 10 10 10 with alleluias; William W. How, 1823–1897, alt.
Music: SINE NOMINE; *English Hymnal*, 1906; Ralph Vaughan Williams, 1872–1958.

YE WATCHERS AND YE HOLY ONES

505

1. Ye watch-ers and ye ho - ly ones, Bright ser-aphs, cher - u - bim, and thrones, Raise the glad strain, Al - le - lu - ia! Cry out, do - min - ions, prince-doms, powers, Vir - tues, arch-an - gels, an - gels' choirs,
2. O high - er than the cher - u - bim, More glo - rious than the ser - a - phim, Lead their prais - es, Al - le - lu - ia! O bear - er of the e - ter - nal Word, Most gra - cious, mag - ni - fy the Lord,
3. Re - spond, ye souls in end - less rest, Ye pa - tri - archs and proph-ets blest, Al - le - lu - ia, Al - le - lu - ia! Ye ho - ly Twelve, ye mar - tyrs strong, All saints tri - um-phant, raise in song,
4. O friends, in glad-ness let us sing, Ce - les - tial an - thems ech - o - ing, Al - le - lu - ia, Al - le - lu - ia! To God the Fa - ther, God the Son, And God the Spir - it, Three-in - One,

Al - le - lu - ia, Al - le - lu - ia,

1-4. Al - le - lu - ia, Al - le - lu - ia, Al - le - lu - ia!

Text: LM with alleluias; *English Hymnal*, 1906; John A. Riley, 1858–1945.
Music: LASST UNS ERFREUEN; *Auserlesene Catholische Geistliche Kirchengesänge*, Cologne, 1623.

506   LITANY

1-3. (Saint N.,)   Pray for us. (Saint N.,)

1-3. Pray for us. (Saint N.,)   Pray for us. (Saint N.,)

1-3. Pray for us. (O - ra pro no-bis.) O - ra pro no - bis. 2, 3. (Saint N.,)

3. O - ra pro no-bis. (O - ra pro no -) O - ra pro no - bis.

507   LUX AETERNA LITANY

Refrain
Cantor: *Lux ae - tér - na.*   Cantor: *Do - na e - is ré - qui -*

All: Lux ae-tér - na.

em.   1...   to Litany

All: Do - na e - is ré - qui - em.

Final
Cantor: *A - men.*

- em.   All: A - men.

Litany of Remembrance
(Cantor sings names from the Book of Remembrance)
to Refrain

All: We re-mem - ber.

CHURCH OF GOD, ELECT AND GLORIOUS 508

1. Church of God, e - lect and glo - rious, ho - ly na - tion,
2. God has called you out of dark - ness in - to his most
3. Once you were an al - ien peo - ple, strang-ers to God's
4. Church of God, e - lect and ho - ly, be the peo - ple

1. cho - sen race; called as God's own spe - cial
2. mar - v'lous light, brought his truth to life with -
3. heart of love; but he brought you home in
4. he in - tends; strong in faith and swift to

1. peo - ple, roy - al priests and heirs of grace: know the
2. in you, turned your blind - ness in - to sight. Let your
3. mer - cy, cit - i - zens of heav'n a - bove. Let his
4. an - swer each com - mand your mas - ter sends: roy - al

1. pur - pose of your call - ing, show to all God's
2. light so shine a - round you that God's name is
3. love flow out to oth - ers, let them feel a
4. priests, ful - fill your call - ing through your sac - ri -

1. might - y deeds; tell of love which knows no
2. glo - ri - fied; and all find fresh hope and
3. Fa - ther's care; that they too may know his
4. fice and prayer; give your lives in joy - ful

1. lim - its, grace which meets all hu - man needs.
2. pur - pose in Christ Je - sus cru - ci - fied.
3. wel - come and his count - less bless - ings share.
4. ser - vice, sing his praise, his love de - clare.

509   I SAW WATER FLOWING

Refrain

I saw wa-ter flow-ing, flow-ing from the side of the tem-ple; and where the wa-ter flowed there was new life.

Verses

1. When your hour had come and they pierced you, Lord,
2. Come to Christ the Lord, the ___ liv - ing stone, re -
3. Not to us, O Lord, but to you all praise,
4. May this house of prayer be a home to all.
5. May this church em - bod - y your pres - ence, Lord:

1. blood and wa - ter flowed forth ___ from your side.
2. ject - ed once but now ___ the cor - ner - stone.
3. for a - part from you ___ we build in vain.
4. May the love of Christ reign with - in these walls,
5. help for the op-pressed, Good News for the poor.

1. With great love you gave your - self for
2. Joined to him, we are God's dwell - ing
3. Help us live this ho - ly mys - ter -
4. so the ones who knock find wel - come
5. Use our hands to build your reign of

1. us! Who can tell the great love by which you
2. place, priest - ly peo - ple and in - stru - ments of
3. y: "It is no long - er I who live, but
4. here and all those who are thirst - ing re - ceive
5. peace; give us vi - sion to fash - ion a more

to Refrain

1. brought your Church to birth!
2. God's re - deem - ing grace.
3. Christ who lives in me."
4. liv - ing wa - ter here.
5. just so - ci - e - ty.

Text: Refrain based on Ezekiel 47:1–2, 9; verses based on John 16:21; 17:1; 19:34; 1 Peter 2:4–9; Psalm 127:1; Galatians 2:20; Bob Hurd, b. 1950.
Music: Bob Hurd.

HOLY IS THE TEMPLE

Refrain

Ho - ly is the tem-ple of the LORD, it is the
hand-i-work, the dwell-ing place of God.

Verses

1. How love - ly your dwell-ing place, LORD of hosts.
2. ℣ Spar-rows and swal-lows build their nests
3. How bless - ed are those who live in your house.
4. Our God is a ram - part and a shield;

1. I long and I yearn for the courts of the
2. with - in your house where they shel - ter their
3. In un - ceas - ing song they of - fer you
4. be-stow - er of grace, hold - ing back no good

1. LORD, my whole be - ing cries out to God,
2. young, ℣ be - side your al - tars, LORD,
3. praise. Hap - py those who find strength in you,
4. thing ℣ from those who walk righ - teous - ly;

to Refrain

1. ℣ I sing out with joy to the liv - ing God.
2. ℣ your al - tars, my king and my God.
3. ℣ who hold in their hearts the way to Zi - on.
4. hap-py those, O LORD, who trust in you.

Text: Based on Psalm 84:2–6, 12–13; Bob Hurd, b. 1950.
Music: Bob Hurd.

511

O HOLY MARY

Refrain

O ho - ly Dwell-ing Place of God.   O ho - ly Tem-ple of the

Word.   O ho - ly Ma - ry,   ho-ly Moth-er of God.

Verses

1. O ra - diant star of heav - en, il - lum - in - ing the night;
2. O blest be - yond all oth - ers, of ev - 'ry land and race,
3. From heav'n the an - gel Ga - bri - el an-nounced the an - cient plan
4. With joy be - yond all meas - ure you cared for God's own son
5. Ex - qui - site was your sor - row, un - e-qualed was the loss
6. All praise and ad - o - ra - tion we sing now to your son

to Refrain

1. re - flec - tion of the Son,__ our source of life and light.
2. pos - sess - ing in your soul __ the full-ness of God's grace.
3. and hum - bly you ac - cept-ed to bear the God-made - man.
4. and pon-dered in your heart __ the new age now be - gun.
5. you suf - fered when your son __ was raised up - on the cross.
6. who reigns in high - est heav-en and has the vic - t'ry won.

512

IMMACULATE MARY

Verses

1. Im - mac - u - late Ma - ry, your prais - es we sing;
2. In heav - en the bless - ed your glo - ry pro - claim;
3. Your name is our pow - er, your vir - tues our light;
4. We pray for the Church, our true moth - er on earth,

1. You reign now with Je - sus, our Sav - ior and King.
2. On earth we, your chil - dren, in - voke your fair name.
3. Your love is our com - fort, your pray'rs are our might.
4. And ask you to watch o'er the land of our birth.

Refrain

A - ve, a - ve, a - ve, Ma - ri - a!

A - ve, a - ve, Ma - ri - a!

Text: 11 11 with refrain; anon. in *Parochial Hymn Book*, Boston, 1897;
  rev. of *Hail Virgin of virgins* by Jeremiah Cummings, 1814–1866, alt.
Music: LOURDES HYMN; trad. Pyrenean Melody; pub. Grenoble, 1882; alt. by Augustus Edmonds Tozer, 1857–1910.

RITUAL MUSIC

SIGNING OF THE SENSES   513

Verse 1: Priest

1. Receive the cross on your forehead. It is Christ himself who now strengthens
   you with this sign of his love. Learn to know and follow him.

Response

By this sign may you re-ceive Christ's love and al-ways fol-low him.

Verses 2-6: Priest

2. Receive the sign of the cross on your ears, that you may hear the voice of the Lord.

3. Receive the sign of the cross on your eyes, that you may see the glory of God.

4. Receive the sign of the cross on your lips, that you may respond
   to the word of God.

5. Receive the sign of the cross over your heart, that Christ may dwell there by faith.

6. Receive the sign of the cross on your shoulders that you may bear
   the gentle yoke of Christ.

Blessing: Priest

7. I sign you with the sign of eternal life in the name of the Father,
   and of the Son, and of the Holy Spirit.

Final Response

A - men. A - men. A - men.

Text © 1985, ICEL. All rights reserved. Used with permission.
Music: Randall DeBruyn, b. 1947, © 1987, OCP. All rights reserved.

514   YOU HAVE CALLED US

Refrain: 1st time: Cantor, All repeat; thereafter: All

You have called us by our name. We be-long to you.

You have called us by our name and we are yours.

Verses

1. You have cho - sen us to be mem - bers
2. You will lead us to your light, walk be -
3. You will hold us when we fall, give new
4. You will nour - ish, you will lead, giv - ing
5. Through our shar - ing here to - day may our

1. of your fam - i - ly. In your love you have cre -
2. fore us through the night. You will guide us on our
3. strength to hear your call. You will nev - er be be -
4. ev - 'ry gift we need, for your reign will be es -
5. faith and life con - vey Christ our light and Christ our

to Refrain

1. at - ed us to live in u - ni - ty.
2. jour - ney. You will keep our vi - sion bright.
3. yond us, for your love is all in all.
4. tab - lished from the small - est of all seeds.
5. vi - sion, Christ our pur - pose, Christ our way.

515   FLOW RIVER FLOW

Refrain

Flow riv - er flow, flow o - ver me. O liv - ing wa - ter,

poured out for free; O liv - ing wa - ter, flow o - ver me.

Verses

1. You will be mine and I will be your God,
2. The blind shall see, the mute shall find a voice,
3. Who-ev-er drinks the wa-ter I will give

1. for I will wash you clean. And a new
2. the lame shall leap for joy. Riv-ers will
3. will nev-er thirst a-gain. The drink I

1. heart, a heart of flesh and feel-ing, I will
2. flow in-to dry and bar-ren des-ert, flow-ers
3. give is an ev-er-flow-ing riv-er, well-ing

to Refrain

1. place with-in you for your heart of stone.
2. bloom in splen-dor, glo-ry fill the land.
3. up with-in you to give e-ter-nal life.

Text: Based on Ezekiel 11:19, 20; Isaiah 35:1–6; John 4:7–15; Bob Hurd, b. 1950.
Music: Bob Hurd.

BAPTIZED IN WATER 516

1. Bap-tized in wa-ter, Sealed by the Spir-it, Cleansed by the
2. Bap-tized in wa-ter, Sealed by the Spir-it, Dead in the
3. Bap-tized in wa-ter, Sealed by the Spir-it, Marked with the

1. blood of Christ our King: Heirs of sal-va-tion, Trust-ing his
2. tomb with Christ our King: One with his ris-ing, Freed and for-
3. sign of Christ our King: Born of one Fa-ther, We are his

1. prom-ise, Faith-ful-ly now God's praise we sing.
2. giv-en, Thank-ful-ly now God's praise we sing.
3. chil-dren, Joy-ful-ly now God's praise we sing.

Text: 55 8 D; Michael Saward, b. 1932, © 1982, The Jubilate Group. All rights reserved.
Music: BUNESSAN; Trad. Gaelic Melody.

517   **RIVER OF GLORY**

Refrain

River of glory, springs of our birth, flood of God's
rich-es poured on the earth. We are born from the dark-ness
and clothed in the light! We are bathed in the glo-ry of

1-4 (to Verses) God!
Final God, bathed in the glo-ry of God!

Verses

1. Foun-tain of mer-cy, grace flow-ing free, streams of sal-
2. Here there is ha-ven, heal-ing and health, joy for the
3. Bread for our jour-ney God will pro-vide. Hope for all
4. Dark-ness is ban-ished, night turned a-way. Christ is our

(to Refrain)

1. va-tion, spill-ing with love from a tree!
2. ask-ing, love in a-bun-dance of wealth!
3. a-ges, Je-sus, com-pan-ion and guide!
4. sun-light, lift-ing and lead-ing our way!

518   **YOU HAVE PUT ON CHRIST**

You have put on Christ, al-le-lu-ia!

Bap-tized in Christ, al-le-lu-ia!

WADE IN THE WATER

519

Refrain

Wade in the wa-ter, wade in the wa-ter chil-dren,

Wade in the wa-ter, God's a-goin' to trou-ble the wa-ter.

Verses
Cantor   All

1. See ___ that ___ host all dressed in white,
2. See ___ that ___ band all dressed in red,   God's a-goin' to
3. If you don't be-lieve I've been re-deemed,

Cantor

1-3. trou-ble the wa - ter.
1. The lead - er ___ looks like the
2. Looks like the ___ band that ___
3. Just fol - low me down to ___

All   to Refrain

1. Is - rael - ite,
2. Mo - ses led,   God's a-goin' to trou-ble the wa - ter.
3. Jor - dan's stream.

Text: Traditional.
Music: Spiritual.

MAY THE WORD OF GOD STRENGTHEN YOU

520

May the word of God strength-en you. May the word of God

nour-ish you. May the word of God com-fort you all your life.

Text and music: *Celtic Mass*; Christopher Walker, b. 1947, © 1996, Christopher Walker.
Published by OCP. All rights reserved.

521   O BREATHE ON ME, O BREATH OF GOD

1. O breathe on me, O Breath of God, Fill
2. O breathe on me, O Breath of God, Un -
3. O breathe on me, O Breath of God, My
4. O breathe on me, O Breath of God, So

1. me with life a - new, That I may love the
2. til my heart is pure; Un - til my will is
3. will to yours in - cline, Un - til this self - ish
4. I shall nev - er die, But live with you the

1. things you love, And do what you would do.
2. one with yours, To do and to en - dure.
3. part of me Glows with your fire di - vine.
4. per - fect life For all e - ter - ni - ty.

Text: CM; Edwin Hatch, 1835–1889, alt.
Music: ST. COLUMBA; trad. Irish Melody.

522   YOU HAVE PUT ON CHRIST

Refrain: 1st time: Cantor; thereafter: All

You have put on Christ; in him you have been bap-tized. Al - le -

lu - ia, al-le - lu - ia, al-le - lu - ia! ia! ia!

Verses: Cantor/Choir

1. We who were dead are now reborn.
   We who were buried now are raised.
   We who were dwelling in the dark
      now see light.

2. For though in Adam all have sinned,
   in Jesus Christ are all made clean.
   The grace abounding of his death
      sets us free.

3. One Lord we serve, who died for us;
   one faith we hold in life to come;
   one God and Father of us all
      we proclaim.

4. And this we know, that nothing ill,
   no prince nor pow'r, nor death nor sin,
   can separate us from God's love,
      shown in Christ.

We Belong to You

Refrain

We be-long to you, O Lord of our long-ing, We be-long to you. In our dai-ly liv-ing, dy-ing and ris-ing We be-long to you.

to Verses | *Final*

We be-long to you. We be-long to you.

Verses

1. In the wa-ters of your mer-cy, ⁊ When the
2. Filled with gifts and filled with good-ness, ⁊ Spir-it
3. When we share the bread you've bro-ken, ⁊ With the
4. We are called to share your word, Lord, In all we

1. old be-comes the new, Souls u-nit-ed in the
2. breath-ing life in-to All who seek to find their
3. man-y and the few, We are blessed and we are
4. say and all we do. As our jour-ney moves us

to Refrain

1. mys - t'ry:
2. pur - pose:
3. bro - ken;
4. on - ward,

We be-long to you.

524   NOW IN THE HOUSEHOLD OF CHRIST/ AHORA EN LA CASA DE CRISTO

Now in the house-hold of Christ, we bless you, we bless you. A - ho-ra en la ca - sa de Cris - to, los ben - de - ci - mos, los ben - de - ci - mos.

525   GIVE ME EARS TO LISTEN

Verses

1, 4. Let me be your ser - vant; let me walk your way.
2. In si - lence, when you call me, let me hear your voice.
3. Last night, when I a - woke I heard you call my name.

1, 4. Guide me on your path; give night the light of day.
2. Je - sus, walk be - side me; let my soul re - joice. When
3. You re-freshed my soul; I felt your burn - ing flame. Oh,

1, 4. Let me be a sure foun - da - tion, pure and strong.
2. winds and cur - rents bat - ter me, help me be sure.
3. strength - en me to bear my cross and walk your way.

1, 4. Let me tell of your sal - va - tion all life long.
2. Give me cour - age from the storms when they oc - cur.
3. Give me grace to com - fort those with all I say.

Give me ears to lis-ten. Give me eyes to see. Give me words to

1, 3, Final
to Vss. 2, 4
(Fine)

2

2

to Verse 3

speak and show your face to me. me.

Text and music: Timothy R. Smith, b. 1960, © 2005, Timothy R. Smith.
Published by spiritandsong.com®, a division of OCP. All rights reserved.

HEALING WATERS 526

Refrain

Heal-ing wa-ters, flow o-ver me. Mer-cy's wa-ter, re-

new-ing me. Mer-cy's o-cean, trans-form-ing me. Heal-ing

Verses

wa-ter, re-new me. 1. Re-new my heart, O God,____
2. Wash me in wa-ters of love;_

1. __ come change my hard-ened heart, come fill my hard-ened heart with
2. __cleanse me and pur-i-fy me, for on-ly you can cleanse me,

1. mer-cy.__ You are the wa-ter of life.__ You are the
2. Lord.____ Wash o-ver me, O Lord.____ Re-fresh my

to Refrain

1. breath of heav-en, come fill my hard-ened heart with mer-cy, Lord.
2. thirst-y soul for you a-lone can make me ho-ly, Lord.

Text and music: Trevor Thomson, b. 1971, © 2000, Trevor Thomson.
Published by spiritandsong.com®, a division of OCP. All rights reserved.

527

SHOW US YOUR MERCY

Refrain: 1st time: Cantor/All; thereafter: All

In times of trou-ble, God, come to our aid.

Show us your mer-cy, come save! In times of trou-ble, God, come to our aid. Show us your mer-cy, come save!

1-3 to Verses | **Final** save! Show us your mer-cy, come save!

Verses

1. We live se-cure in the shel-ter of God, safe in the fold of God's wings. We will pro-claim the great-ness of God, the rock of sal-va-tion God brings.
2. Lost and a-fraid, we're nev-er a-lone, God watch-es o-ver our lives. Walk-ing our path and light-ing our way, guard-ing us day and by night.
3. All of our lives we look to our God. We will lie safe in God's care. God is our rock. In God we can trust all of our trou-bles to bear.

to Refrain

Text: Based on Psalm 91; Mark Friedman, b. 1952.
Music: Mark Friedman.
Text and music © 1996, 1998, Mark Friedman. Published by OCP. All rights reserved.

Save Us, O Lord

528

Refrain

Save us, O Lord; car-ry us back. Rouse your pow-er and come.

Res-cue your peo-ple; show us your face. Bring us back.

Verse 1

1. O Shep-herd of Is-ra-el, hear us. Re-turn and we shall be

to Refrain

1. saved. A-rise, O Lord; hear our cries, O Lord: bring us back!

Verse 2

2. How long will you hide from your peo-ple? We long to

to Refrain

2. see your face. Give ear to us. Draw near to us, Lord God of hosts!

Verse 3

3. Turn a-gain; care for your vine; pro-tect what your

3. right hand has plant-ed. Your vine-yards are tram-pled, up-

to Refrain

3. root-ed, and burned. Come to us, Fa-ther of might!

Text: Based on Psalm 80; Bob Dufford, SJ, b. 1943.
Music: Bob Dufford, SJ.

529   HOSEA

Verses

1. Come back to me with all your heart. Don't let
   ⁜ Trees do bend, though straight and tall; so must
2. The wil - der - ness will lead ____ you to your
   In - teg - ri - ty and jus - tice with ten-der-
3. ⁜ You shall sleep se - cure with peace; faith-ful -

Refrain

1. fear keep us a - part. Long have I wait-ed for your
   we to oth - ers' call.
2. heart where I will speak.
   ness ⁜ you shall know.
3. ness will be your joy.

com-ing home to me and liv - ing deep-ly our new life.

Text: Based on Hosea; Weston Priory, Gregory Norbet, OSB, b. 1940.
Music: Weston Priory, Gregory Norbet, OSB.
Text and music © 1972, The Benedictine Foundation of the State of Vermont, Inc.

530   SOFTLY AND TENDERLY JESUS IS CALLING

Verses

1. Soft - ly and ten-der - ly Je - sus is call - ing, call - ing for
2. Why should we tar - ry when Je - sus is plead-ing, plead-ing for
3. O for the won-der - ful love he has prom-ised, prom-ised for

1. you and for me; see, on the por - tals he's
2. you and for me? Why should we lin - ger and
3. you and for me! Though we have sinned, he has

1. wait - ing and watch-ing, watch-ing for you and for me.
2. heed not his mer - cies, mer-cies for you and for me?
3. mer - cy and par - don, par-don for you and for me.

Come home, come home, you who are
wea-ry, come home; ear-nest-ly, ten-der-ly,
Je-sus is call-ing, call-ing for you to come home!

Text: 11 7 11 7 with refrain; Will L. Thompson, 1847–1909, alt.
Music: THOMPSON; Will L. Thompson.

SEEK THE LORD 531

Seek the Lord while he may be found;
call to him while he is still near.

Verses 1-3
1. To-day is the day ___ and now the prop-er hour to for-
2. As high as the sky _____ is a-bove the earth, so
3. Find-ing the Lord, _____ let us cling to him. His

1. sake our sin-ful lives ___ and turn to the Lord.
2. high a-bove our ways, ___ the ways of the Lord.
3. words, his ways _____ lead us to life.

Verse 4
4. Some-day we'll live in the house of God;

4. gaze on his face and praise his name.

Text: Based on Isaiah 55:6–9; Roc O'Connor, SJ, b. 1949.
Music: Roc O'Connor, SJ.

532   LOVING AND FORGIVING

Refrain: 1st time: Cantor, All repeat; thereafter: All

Lov-ing and for-giv-ing are you, O Lord; slow to an-ger,

rich in kind-ness, lov-ing and for-giv-ing are you.

Verses: Cantor/Choir

1. All my be-ing, bless the Lord,___ bless the ho-ly
2. God for-gives us all our sins,___ heal-ing those who
3. Good and gra-cious is the Lord,___ slow to an-ger,
4. As heav-en soars a-bove the earth, so great the love of

1. name of God.___ All my be-ing, bless the Lord, re-
2. live in pain,___ sav-ing us from fi-nal death. God
3. rich in love.___ God re-mem-bers not our sins; for-
4. God for us. As far as east is from the west, the

to Refrain

1. mem-b'ring the good-ness of God.
2. fills us with good-ness and love.
3. giv-ing and lov-ing is God.
4. Lord takes our sins___ from us.

Text: Based on Psalm 103:8, 1–2, 3–4, 8–10, 11–12; Scott Soper, b. 1961.
Music: Scott Soper.
Text and music © 1992, OCP. All rights reserved.

533   REMEMBER YOUR LOVE

Refrain

Re-mem-ber your love and your faith-ful-ness, O Lord. Re-

mem-ber your peo-ple and have mer-cy on us, Lord.

Verses

1. The Lord is my light and my sal - va - tion,
2. If you dwelt, O Lord, up - on our sin - ful - ness,
3. O Lord, hear the sound of my call
4. As sen - ti - nels wait up - on the day - light,
5. Be - fore all the moun-tains were be - got - ten

1. whom should I fear? The Lord is my
2. then who could stand? But with you there is
3. and an - swer me. My heart cries
4. wait for the Lord. I trust in your
5. and earth took shape, e - ven then, O

to Refrain

1. life and my ref - uge, when I call God hears.
2. mer - cy and for-give-ness and a guid - ing hand.
3. out for your pres-ence; it is you I seek.
4. kind-ness and re - demp-tion; and your faith - ful word.
5. Lord, you were our ref - uge through-out ev - 'ry age.

Text: Based on Psalms 25, 27, 90, 130; Mike Balhoff, b. 1946.
Music: Darryl Ducote, b. 1945, and Gary Daigle, b. 1957.

CREATE IN ME 534

Refrain — Fine

Cre - ate in me a clean heart.

Verses

1. Have mer - cy on me, God, in your com - pas - sion.
2. O pu - ri - fy my heart and teach me wis-dom;
3. O give me back the joy of your sal - va - tion;

to Refrain

1. Re-move my sin. Wash me from my guilt.
2. then I shall be clean - er than the snow.
3. a will - ing spir - it sus-tain in me.

Text: Based on Psalm 51:12, 3–4, 8–9, 14; Bob Hurd, b. 1950.
Music: Bob Hurd.

535   CHANGE OUR HEARTS

Refrain

Change our hearts this time, your word says it can be. Change our

minds this time, your life could make us free. We are the peo-

-ple your call set a-part, Lord, this time change our

1-3 to Verses | Final

hearts. hearts. This time change our hearts. This time

change our minds. This time change our hearts, change our hearts.

Verse 1

1. Brought by your hand to the edge of our dreams, one foot in

1. par-a-dise, one in the waste; drawn by your prom-is-es,

to Refrain

1. still we are lured by the shad-ows and the chains we leave be-hind. But

Verses 2, 3

2. Now as we watch you stretch out your hands, of-f'ring a - bun - dan-
3. Show us the way that leads to your side, o - ver the moun-tains __

2. ces, __ full - ness of joy. Your milk and hon-ey seem dis-tant, un-
3. __ and sands of the soul. Be for us man-na,__ wa-ter from

2. real,   when we have bread and wa-ter in our hands. But
3. stone, _____ light which says we nev-er walk a-lone. And

Text and music: Rory Cooney, b. 1952, © 1984, spiritandsong.com®, a division of OCP. All rights reserved.

WHERE THERE IS LOVE   536

Refrain

Where there is love,   there is God. _____   The love of

God has gath-ered us to - geth-er; Al-le-lu - ia.

Verses 1, 3

1. Love is pa - tient, love is kind,   nev - er jeal-ous, nev - er proud,
3. Man-y things will pass a - way. There are but three things that last:

1. nev-er seek-ing for one's self. _____ Love nev-er leads to an-ger. _____
3. Faith, Hope, and Love; _ the great-est of these is Love. _____

Verse 2

2. Love is gra-cious and for-giv - ing,   tak-ing no de-light in wrong;

2. Love re-joic - es in the truth; Love will en - dure.

Text: Based on 1 John 4:16; 1 Corinthians 13:4–7, 10, 13; David Haas, b. 1957.
Music: David Haas.
Text and music © 1985, David Haas. Published by OCP. All rights reserved.

537   WHERE LOVE IS FOUND

Refrain

Where char-i-ty and love are found, there will the face of God be seen. The love of Christ will bind our hearts; as one bod-y we will be.

Verses

1. Love is pa-tient, love is kind,
2. Love is stead-fast to the end,
3. Though I speak with an-gel's tongue,
4. There are three things that will last:

1. nev-er boast-ful, nev-er proud. Love is hope-ful in its
2. ev-er read-y to en-dure. Love is gra-cious in its
3. I am noth-ing more than sound. I am but a cym-bal
4. there is faith, hope and ___ love. But the great-est of all

to Refrain

1. wait-ing, ev-er trust-ing in God's light.
2. kind-ness, ev-er read-y to for-give.
3. clang-ing if I sing with-out God's love.
4. bless-ings is the faith-ful-ness of love.

Text: Based on the Latin chant *Ubi Caritas*, 9th cent.; 1 Corinthians 13:1–7, 13; Dan Schutte, b. 1947.
Music: Dan Schutte.
Text and music © 2001, Daniel L. Schutte. Published by OCP. All rights reserved.

538   MAY GOD BLESS YOU

Refrain

May God bless you with his love, al-ways fill you with his love; may he hold you in the hol-low of his hand. For the Lord is with you in good-ness and love; may his light shine out in your heart.

Verses

1. Hap-py are they who re-flect his faith, seek-ing a depth with-out bound.
2. Bless-ed are they who re-flect his hope, find-ing a strength with-out bound.
3. Joy-ful are they who re-flect his love, liv-ing a gift with-out bound.
4. Ra-diant are they who re-flect his life, bond-ing their love with the Word.

to Refrain

1. Lord, it is good that we are here to see that faith which oth-ers have found.
2. Lord, it is good that we are here to see that hope which oth-ers have found.
3. Lord, it is good that we are here to see that love which oth-ers have found.
4. Lord, it is good that we are here to share that life with one __ ac-cord.

Text and music: George Van Grieken, FSC, b. 1952, © 1984, OCP. All rights reserved.

HEAR US NOW, OUR GOD AND FATHER   539

1. Hear us now, our God and Fa-ther, Send your Spir-it from a-
2. Give them joy to light-en sor-row! Give them hope to bright-en
3. May the grace of Christ, our Sav-ior, And the Fa-ther's bound-less

1. bove On this Chris-tian man and wom-an Who here
2. life! Go with them to face the mor-row, Stay with
3. love, With the Ho-ly Spir-it's fa-vor Rest up-

1. make their vows of love! Bind their hearts in true de-vo-tion
2. them in ev-'ry strife. As your Word has prom-ised, ev-er
3. on them from a-bove. Thus may they a-bide in un-ion

1. End-less as the sea-shore's sands, Bound-less as the
2. Fill them with your strength and grace, So that each may
3. With each oth-er and the Lord, And pos-sess in

1. deep-est o-ceans, Blest and sealed by your own hands.
2. serve the oth-er Till they see you face to face.
3. sweet com-mu-nion Joys which earth can-not af-ford.

Text: 87 87 D; verses 1–2, Harry N. Huxhold, 1922–2006, © 1978, *Lutheran Book of Worship*. All rights reserved.
Used with permission of Augsburg Fortress. Verse 3, John Newton, 1725–1807, alt.
Music: HYFRYDOL; Rowland H. Prichard, 1811–1887.

540   Si Yo No Tengo Amor/If I Do Not Have Love

Si yo no ten-go a-mor, yo na - da soy, Se - ñor. Si
If I do not have love, then I am noth-ing, Lord. If

yo no ten-go a - mor, yo na - da soy, Se - ñor.
I do not have love, then I am noth-ing, Lord.

Estrofas

1. El amor es comprensivo.
   El amor es servicial.
   El amor no tiene envidia.
   El amor no busca el mal.

2. El amor nunca se irrita.
   El amor no es descortés.
   El amor no es egoísta.
   El amor nunca es doblez.

3. El amor disculpa todo.
   El amor es caridad.
   No se alegra de lo injusto.
   Sólo goza en la verdad.

4. El amor soporta todo.
   El amor todo lo cree.
   El amor todo lo espera.
   El amor es siempre fiel.

5. Nuestra fe, nuestra esperanza,
   frente a Dios terminará.
   El amor es algo eterno.
   Nunca, nunca pasará.

Verses

1. *For the love of God is understanding,*
   helpful to the end.
   Love refuses to do evil
   and is faithful, like a friend.

2. *For the love of God will always*
   keep a neighbor's care in mind,
   never jealous or suspicious,
   never hateful or unkind.

3. *For the love of God is all forgiveness,*
   charity unbound.
   It rejoices not in suff'ring
   but in peace and justice found.

4. *For the love of God is patient,*
   always open, always free.
   Love gives sight to those in darkness
   and true hope to those in need.

5. *In the end our faith may leave us*
   and all hope may disappear.
   Only love will never pass away
   for Christ is always here.

541   Wherever You Go

1. Wher-ev-er you go   I shall go.   Wher-ev-er you live

1. so shall I live.   Your peo-ple will be my peo -

1. ple, and your God will be my God too.

Verse 2

2. Wher-ev-er you die   I shall die,   and there shall

2. I   be bur-ied be-side you.   We will be to-geth-er for-

2. ev - er, and our love   will be the gift of our   life.

GOD, WHO CREATED HEARTS TO LOVE 542

1. God who cre - at - ed hearts to love, Show-'ring all bless-ings
2. Je - sus at Ca - na gave a sign, Turn - ing the wa - ter
3. Spir - it of God, be at their side: Wis - dom and com - fort,
4. Sing, friends and fam-'ly gath-ered here, Voic - es in wit - ness
5. God, let our joy-ful sing - ing be Sign of our faith com -

1. from a - bove, Al-le-lu - ia! Al-le-lu - ia! Give these, who come to
2. in - to wine: Al-le-lu - ia! Al-le-lu - ia! Sign that con - tin - ues
3. guard-ian, guide. Al-le-lu - ia! Al-le-lu - ia! Make of their hearts a
4. ring - ing clear; Al-le-lu - ia! Al-le-lu - ia! Here is the mys-ter -
5. mu - ni - ty. Al-le-lu - ia! Al-le-lu - ia! Bap - tized in wa - ter,

1. you with praise, Peace, love and laugh-ter all their days. ⎫
2. as he said— Love, liv - ing, ris - en from the dead. ⎪
3. rest-ing place; In ev - 'ry tri - al, gen - tle grace. ⎬ Al-le - lu-ia!
4. y be - gun: Wom - an and man be-com-ing one. ⎪
5. we are fed, Shar-ing the liv - ing wine and bread. ⎭

1-5. Al-le - lu - ia! Al-le - lu - ia! Al-le - lu - ia! Al-le - lu - ia!

543   **WHEN LOVE IS FOUND**

1. When love is found and hope comes home, Sing and be glad
2. When love has flow'red in trust and care, Build both each day,
3. When love is tried as loved-ones change, Hold still to hope
4. When love is torn and trust be-trayed, Pray strength to love
5. Praise God for love, praise God for life, In age or youth,

1. that two are one. When love ex-plodes and fills the
2. that love may dare To reach be-yond home's warmth and
3. though all seems strange, Till ease re-turns and love grows
4. till tor-ments fade, Till lov-ers keep no score of
5. in hus-band, wife. Lift up your hearts, let love be

1. sky, Praise God and share our Mak-er's joy.
2. light, To serve and strive for truth and right.
3. wise Through lis-t'ning ears and o-pened eyes.
4. wrong, But hear through pain love's Eas-ter song.
5. fed Through death and life in bro-ken bread.

Text: LM; Brian Wren, b. 1936, © 1983, Hope Publishing Co. All rights reserved. Used with permission.
Music: O WALY WALY; trad. English Melody.

544   **O FATHER, ALL-CREATING**

1. O Fa-ther, all-cre-at-ing, Whose wis-dom, love, and pow'r
2. O Sav-ior, guest in Ca-na Of old in Gal-i-lee,
3. O Spir-it of the Fa-ther, Breathe on them from a-bove,
4. Un-less you build it, Fa-ther, The house is built in vain;

1. First bound two lives to-geth-er In E-den's pri-mal hour,
2. May these who ask your bless-ing Your lov-ing pres-ence see.
3. So might-y in your pure-ness, So ten-der in your love;
4. Un-less you bless it, Sav-ior, The joy will turn to pain;

1. To these who come be-fore you, Your ear-liest gifts re-new:
2. Their store of earth-ly glad-ness Trans-form to heav'n-ly wine,
3. That, guard-ed by your pres-ence, From sin and strife kept free,
4. But none can break the un-ion Of hearts in you made one;

1. A home by you made hap-py, A love by you kept true.
2. And teach them, in the tast-ing, To know your gift di-vine.
3. Their hearts may seek your guid-ance, And love you faith-ful-ly.
4. The love your Spir-it bless-es Is end-less love be-gun.

Text: 76 76 D; John Ellerton, 1826–1893, alt.
Music: AURELIA; Samuel S. Wesley, 1810–1876.

HEALING RIVER OF THE SPIRIT 545

1. Heal-ing riv-er of the Spir-it, Bathe the wounds that liv-ing brings. Plunge our pain, our sin, our sad-ness Deep be-neath your sa-cred springs. Wea-ry from the rest-less search-ing That has lured us from your side, We dis-cov-er in your pres-ence Peace the world can-not pro-vide.

2. Well-spring of the heal-ing Spir-it, Stream that flows to bring re-lease, As we gain our selves, our sen-ses, May our lives re-flect your peace. Grate-ful for the flood that heals us, May your church en-act your grace. As we meet both friend and strang-er, May we see our Sav-ior's face.

3. Liv-ing stream that heals the na-tions, Make us chan-nels of your pow'r. All the world is torn by con-flict; Wars are rag-ing at this hour. Sav-ing Spir-it, move a-mong us, Guide our wind-ing hu-man course, Till we find our way to-geth-er, Flow-ing home-ward to our Source.

Text: 87 87 D; Ruth C. Duck, b. 1947, © 1996, The Pilgrim Press. From *Circles of Care* by Ruth C. Duck,
   © 1998, The Pilgrim Press. All rights reserved. Used with permission.
Music: BEACH SPRING; *The Sacred Harp*, 1844.

546   O CHRIST, THE HEALER

1. O Christ, the heal - er, we have come To
2. From ev - 'ry ail - ment flesh en - dures Our
3. How strong, O Lord, are our de - sires, How
4. In con - flicts that de - stroy our health We
5. Grant that we all, made one in faith, In

1. pray for health, to plead for friends. How can we fail to
2. bod - ies clam - or to be freed; Yet in our hearts we
3. weak our knowl - edge of our - selves! Re - lease in us those
4. rec - og - nize the world's dis - ease; Our com - mon life de -
5. your com - mun - i - ty may find The whole - ness that, en -

1. be re - stored, When reached by love that nev - er ends?
2. would con - fess That whole - ness is our deep - est need.
3. heal - ing truths Un - con - scious pride re - sists or shelves.
4. clares our ills: Is there no cure, O Christ, for these?
5. rich - ing us, Shall reach the whole of hu - man - kind.

Text: LM; Fred Pratt Green, 1903–2000, © 1969, Hope Publishing Co. All rights reserved. Used with permission.
Music: ERHALT UNS, HERR; J. Klug's *Geistliche Lieder*, Wittenberg, 1543;
   adapt. by Johann Sebastian Bach, 1685–1750, alt.

547   BE STILL, MY SOUL

1. Be still, my soul— the Lord is on thy side!
2. Be still, my soul— thy God doth un - der - take
3. Be still, my soul— the hour is has - t'ning on

1. Bear pa - tient - ly the cross of grief or pain;
2. To guide the fu - ture as he has the past;
3. When we shall be for - ev - er with the Lord,

1. Leave to thy God to or - der and pro - vide—
2. Thy hope, thy con - fi - dence let noth - ing shake—
3. When dis - ap - point - ment, grief, and fear are gone,

1. In ev-'ry change he faith-ful will re-main.
2. All now mys-te-rious shall be bright at last.
3. Sor-row for-got, love's pur-est joys re-stored.

1. Be still, my soul— thy best, thy heav'n-ly friend
2. Be still, my soul— the waves and winds still know
3. Be still, my soul— when change and tears are past,

1. Through thorn-y ways leads to a joy-ful end.
2. His voice who ruled them while he dwelt be-low.
3. All safe and bless-ed we shall meet at last.

Text: 10 10 10 10 10 10; Katharina von Schlegel; in *Neue Sammlung Geistlicher Lieder*, 1752;
tr. by Jane Borthwick, 1813–1897.
Music: FINLANDIA; Jean Sibelius, 1865–1957.

PRECIOUS LORD, TAKE MY HAND   548

1. Pre-cious Lord, take my hand, Lead me on, let me
2. When my way grows drear, Pre-cious Lord, lin-ger
3. When the dark-ness ap-pears And the night draws

1. stand; I am tired, I am weak, I am worn;
2. near, When my life is al-most gone;
3. near, And the day is past and gone,

1. Through the storm, through the night, Lead me on to the light:
2. Hear my cry, hear my call, Hold my hand lest I fall:
3. At the riv-er I stand, Guide my feet, hold my hand:

1-3. Take my hand, pre-cious Lord, lead me home.

Text: Irregular; Thomas A. Dorsey, 1899–1993.
Music: PRECIOUS LORD; Thomas A. Dorsey.

549　　　　　　　　HOLY DARKNESS

Refrain

Ho-ly dark-ness, bless-ed night, heav-en's an-swer hid-den from our sight. As we a-wait you, O God of si-lence, we em-brace your ho-ly night.

Verses 1-3

1. I have tried you in fires of af-flic-tion; I have taught your soul to grieve. In the bar-ren soil of your lone-li-ness, there I will plant my seed.
2. I have taught you the price of com-pas-sion; you have stood be-fore the grave. Though my love can seem like a rag-ing storm, this is the love that saves.
3. Were you there when I raised up the moun-tains? Can you guide the morn-ing star? Does the hawk take flight when you give com-mand? Why do you doubt my pow'r?

Verses 4, 5

4. In your deep-est hour of dark-ness I will give you wealth un-told. When the si-lence stills your spir-it, will my rich-es fill your soul.
5. As the watch-man waits for morn-ing, and the bride a-waits her groom, so we wait to hear your foot-steps as we rest be-neath your moon.

O Loving God

Verses

1. O lov-ing God, we send your daugh-ter home to you,
   (son) ___
2. O lov-ing God, have mer-cy and for-give - ness

1. home to a place of ev - er - last-ing love, to join there
2. up - on your ser - vant's now de-part-ed soul, and may your

1. with the an - gel choirs and bless-ed saints, and to be -
2. grace and love en - fold her/him ev - er-more, so she/he may

Refrain

1. hold your glo-rious ho - ly face. Re-ceive her/his soul and
2. dwell in par - a - dise at last.

let e - ter-nal light shine, e - ter-nal light for-ev - er on her/his

soul, so she/he may be for - ev - er in your dwell-ing place,

and be at rest in peace un - til we meet her/him there.

Text: 12 10 12 10 with refrain; Paulette M. McCoy, b. 1953, © 2004, Paulette M. McCoy.
   Published by OCP. All rights reserved.
Music: LONDONDERRY AIR; fr. *The Ancient Music of Ireland*, 1855.

551   **HOW LOVELY IS YOUR DWELLING PLACE**

Refrain

O how love-ly is your dwell-ing place, dwell-ing of the Lord of hosts! How we long for your house, O Lord, sing-ing out a song of joy to the liv - ing God!

Verses

1. E - ven spar - rows find a home with you, and swal-lows lay their young to rest. Bless-ed are ____ those who dwell in you and sing your praise, O God!
2. Bless'd are those who find their strength in you, whose hearts are high-ways for your will. Bring-ing joy to those a - round ____ them, they go from strength to strength.
3. Hear our prayer, O Lord ____ God of hosts; re - ceive our lives in - to your hands! Look in - to the hearts of those you love and grant us all we need!
4. For one day with - in your house ex - ceeds a thou-sand spent a - way from you. We would rath - er serve with - in your house than wealth and pow'r re - ceive.
5. For our God pro - tects us from all harm; he gives his fa - vor and his love. All good things will come to those who love the Lord, and walk with him.

to Refrain

I, THE LORD

Refrain

I, the Lord, am with you, al-ways by your side.

Come and take my hand, for I will lead you home. Fol-low

1, 2 me, fol-low me. **2 to Verses**

Final Fol-low me, fol-low me.

Verse 1

1. I am the res-ur-rec-tion, and I am the life; if

to Refrain

1. you be-lieve in me, you shall live for-ev-er.

Verse 2

2. You shall have new life and live it to the full.

to Refrain

2. Turn your sor-row in-to joy, for life has just be-gun.

553 SONG OF FAREWELL

Refrain: 1st time: Cantor, All repeat; thereafter: All

May the choirs of an-gels come to greet you. May they speed you to par-a-dise. May the Lord en-fold you in his mer-cy. May you find e-ter-nal life.

Verses

1. The __ Lord is my light and my help; _____ it is
2. There is one thing I ask of the Lord; _____ that he
3. O __ Lord, hear my voice when I cry; _____ have __
4. I am sure I shall see the Lord's good-ness; __ I shall

1. he who pro-tects me from harm. _____ The __ Lord is the strength
2. grant me my heart-felt de-sire. _____ To __ dwell in the courts
3. mer-cy on me and give an-swer. __ Do not cast me a-way
4. dwell in the land of the liv-ing. __ Hope in God, __ stand firm

to Refrain

1. of my days; _____ be-fore whom should I trem-ble with fear? _____
2. of our God _____ ev-'ry day of my life in his pres-ence. __
3. in your an-ger, __ for __ you are the God of my help. _____
4. and take heart, _____ place all your trust in the Lord. _____

Text: Refrain based on *In Paradisum*; verses based on Psalm 27; Ernest Sands, b. 1949.
Music: Ernest Sands.
Text and music © 1990, Ernest Sands. Published by OCP. All rights reserved.

554 GIVE ME JESUS

Verses

1. In the morn-ing when I rise, in the morn-ing when I rise,
2. Now the jour-ney has be-gun, now the jour-ney has be-gun,
3. When the prize is sure-ly won, when the prize is sure-ly won,
4. I _____ heard my moth-er say, I _____ heard my moth-er say,
5. Dark __ mid-night was my cry, dark __ mid-night was my cry,
6. Oh, __ when I come to die, oh, __ when I come to die,

1. in the morn-ing when I rise, give me Je - sus. Give me Je -
2. now the jour-ney has be - gun, give me Je - sus.
3. when the prize is sure - ly won, give me Je - sus.
4. I ___ heard my moth-er say, give me Je - sus.
5. dark ___ mid-night was my cry, give me Je - sus.
6. oh, ___ when I come to die, give me Je - sus.

sus, give me Je - sus. You may have all this world. Give me Je - sus.

Text: Verses 1, 4–6 and refrain, Spiritual. Verses 2–3, James Hansen, b. 1937, © 1992, James Hansen.
Published by OCP. All rights reserved.
Music: Spiritual.

MAY THE ANGELS BE YOUR GUIDE 555

Refrain

May the an - gels be your guide, may they lead you in - to par - a -

dise, and take you home to the new Je - ru - sa - lem.

Verses

1. There is one thing I ask of God; for this I
2. When I cry out, ___ hear my voice. Have mer - cy,
3. I shall see God's ___ good - ness, for - ev - er

1. long, ___ for this I hope: to dwell in the house of
2. Lord, ___ and an-swer me. Do not cast me a - way in
3. dwell with the liv - ing. Hope in God, ___ and take

to Refrain

1. God ev - 'ry day of my life.
2. an - ger, for ___ you are my help.
3. heart; place your trust in the Lord.

Text: Based on In Paradisum and Psalm 27:4, 7, 9, 13–14; Michele MacAller and Kathy McGrath.
Music: Michele MacAller and Kathy McGrath.
Text and music © 1998, Michele MacAller and Kathleen McGrath. Published by OCP. All rights reserved.

556   I KNOW THAT MY REDEEMER LIVES

1. I know that my Re-deem-er lives, the One who
2. I know that I shall one day see the good-ness
3. The last day I shall rise a-gain, shall be re-

1. calls me home. I long to see God face-to-face, to
2. of the Lord, when God will wipe a-way our tears, and
3. made like God. My home shall be by God's own side, the

Refrain

1. see with my own eyes. I know that my Re-
2. death will be no more.
3. dy-ing, ris-ing Lord.

deem-er lives, that I shall rise a-gain. gain.

Text: Based on Job 19; Psalm 27; Isaiah 25; Scott Soper, b. 1961.
Music: Scott Soper.

557   THE LORD IS MY LIGHT

1. The ___ Lord is my light, my ___ help, my sal-
2. There is one thing I ask of the Lord that I
3. I ___ know I will live to ___ see the Lord's

1. va-tion. Why should I fear? With God I fear
2. long for: all of my days with God to be
3. good-ness; now, in this life, I'm sure I will

1. no one. God pro-tects me ___ all my ___
2. dwell-ing, gaz-ing with awe at the beau-ty of
3. see it. Trust in the Lord, be ___ strong and be

1. life. With the Lord what should I ___ dread? ___
2. God, and in won-der look on God's house. ___
3. brave; wait in hope for God, our sal-va-tion.

The Lord is my light, the Lord is my help, the Lord is my sal - va - tion.

Text: Based on Psalm 27; Christopher Walker, b. 1947.
Music: Christopher Walker.

PARABLE 558

Refrain

1-4. To ev-'ry thing there is a sea-son; a time to be born

1-4. and a time to die.
1, 4. A time to plant and a time for har-vest;
2. A time to speak and a time for si - lence;
3. A time for joy and a time for griev-ing;

1, 4. a time to meet and a time to part. 4. part.
2. a time to wound and a time to heal.
3. a time to seek and a time to lose.

1. A sow - er went
2. Noth - ing can
3. God's word is

1. out to sow the seed. Some of it fell up - on the path, some fell on
2. grow in bar - ren soil; bri - ars and ra - vens take their toll; still there is
3. like the far-mer's seed, root-ed in joy - ful, lov-ing hearts, grow-ing like

to Refrain

1. shal - low, rock - y soil, and some a - mong chok-ing thorns.
2. grain a hun-dred - fold, from seed that took root and grew.
3. grain in fer - tile ground, a har-vest that o - ver - flows.

Text: Based on Ecclesiastes 3:1–9; Matthew 13:4–8; M.D. Ridge.
Music: M.D. Ridge.

559   KEEP IN MIND

Refrain

Keep in mind that Je-sus Christ has died for us and is ris-en from the dead. He is our sav-ing Lord, he is joy for all ag - es.

Verse 1   (to Refrain)

1. If we die with the Lord, we shall live with the Lord.
If we en - dure with the Lord, we shall reign with the Lord.

Verses 2, 3   (to Refrain)

2. In him all our sor - row, in him all our joy.
In him hope of glo - ry, in him all our love.
3. In him our re - demp - tion, in him all our grace.
In him our sal - va - tion, in him all our peace.

Text: Based on 2 Timothy 2:8–12; Lucien Deiss, CSSp, 1921–2007.
Music: Lucien Deiss, CSSp.
Text and music © 1965, World Library Publications. All rights reserved. Used with permission.

560   SONG OF FAREWELL

1. May the an - gels car - ry you to par - a - dise.
2. May the choirs of an - gels come to wel - come you home
3. Fa - ther, wel-come them in - to your king - dom.

1. May the saints and mar - tyrs come to greet you.
2. and lead you joy - ful - ly to heav - en.
3. Please grant them life ev - er - last - ing.

1. May you rest in the arms of A - bra - ham
2. And may those who loved you who have gone be - fore
3. As they live now in the New Je - ru - sa - lem,

1. and know peace in heav - en for - ev - er.
2. be___ there with arms out-stretched to greet you.
3. may your Spir - it fill their souls with free - dom.

Text: Based on *In Paradisum*; Grayson Warren Brown, b. 1948.
Music: Grayson Warren Brown.
Text and music © 2006, Grayson Warren Brown. Published by OCP. All rights reserved.

GO IN PEACE

561

Verses

1. There will be no more dark - ness. There is no more night,
2. See the Fa-ther is wait - ing with a robe of white,

1. no more night. There will be no more sad - ness, on - ly joy and
2. pur - est white. Go and feast at his ta - ble with the bread of

1. light, joy and light. Lift your eyes be-yond the hills and
2. life, bread of life. Lift your heart, re-joice and sing for

1. see the dawn. There is beau - ti - ful mer - cy in the arms
2. you are home; home at last and for-ev - er in the arms

Refrain

1. of the ho - ly one. Go in peace, God be with you.
2. of the ho - ly one.

Go in peace, be at rest with the saints and the an - gels.

Now you are free. Go in peace.

Text and music: Sarah Hart, b. 1968, and Dwight Liles, b. 1957, © 2004, Sarah Hart and Dwight Liles.
Published by spiritandsong.com®, a division of OCP. All rights reserved.

562   YES, I SHALL ARISE

Refrain

Yes, I shall a-rise! I shall gaze up-on the love-li-ness of God for-ev-er-more.

Verses

1. One thing I ask ___ of the Lord, this I seek: to
2. Day af - ter day I seek the house of the Lord.
3. Yearn - ing and pin - ing for the courts of the Lord, my
4. Thus will I go in - to the al - tar of God, the
5. Hap - py are they who place their trust in the Lord, for

to Refrain

1. dwell in the house of the Lord all the days of my life.
2. When shall I en - ter and see, see the face of my God?
3. flesh and my spir - it cry out for the God of my life.
4. God of my glad-ness and joy, giv - ing thanks on the harp.
5. they shall in - her - it the prize; theirs is life with-out end!

Text: Based on Psalms 27 and 43; Owen Alstott, b. 1947, © 1988, OCP. All rights reserved.
Music: Owen Alstott, © 1988, OCP. All rights reserved.

563   O JESUS, JOY OF LOVING HEARTS

1. O Je - sus, joy of lov - ing hearts, The fount of
2. Your truth un-changed has ev - er stood; You save all
3. We taste you, Lord, our liv - ing bread, And long to
4. For you our rest - less spir - its yearn Wher - e'er our
5. O Je - sus, ev - er with us stay; Make all our

1. life and our true light, We seek the peace your love im -
2. those who heed your call; To those who seek you, you are
3. feast up - on you still; We drink of you, the foun - tain -
4. chang-ing lot is cast; Glad, when your pres - ence we dis -
5. mo-ments calm and bright; Oh, chase the night of sin a -

1. parts   And stand re - joic - ing   in   your sight.
2. good,   To those who find you— all   in   all.
3. head,   Our thirst - ing souls to quench and fill.
4. cern,   Blest, when our faith can   hold you fast.
5. way,   Shed o'er the world your   ho - ly light.

Text: LM; attr. to Bernard of Clairvaux, ca. 1090–1153; tr. by Ray Palmer, 1808–1887, alt.
Music: JESU DULCIS MEMORIA; Chant, Mode I.

O Saving Victim/O Salutaris Hostia 564

1. O   sav - ing   Vic - tim,   o - p'ning wide   The gate of
2. All praise and thanks to   thee as - cend   For - ev - er -
1. O   sa - lu - tá - ris   hó - sti - a,   Quae cae - li
2. U - ni tri - nó - que   Dó - mi - no   Sit sem - pi -

1. heav'n to   us   be - low,   Our foes press on   from
2. more, blest One   in   Three;   O grant us   life   that
1. pan - dis ós - ti - um: Bel - la pre - munt ho -
2. tér - na   gló - ri - a,   Qui vi - tam si - ne

1. ev - ery side;   Thine aid sup - ply,   thy strength be - stow.
2. shall not end   In our true na - tive land with thee.
1. stí - li - a,   Da ro - bur, fer au - xí - li - um.
2. tér - mi - no   No - bis do - net in pá - tri - a.

Text: LM; Latin, St. Thomas Aquinas, 1227–1274; tr. by Edward Caswall, 1814–1878.
Music: WERNER; Anthony Werner, fl. 1863.

565 O SAVING VICTIM/O SAVING LAMB

1. O Sav-ing Vic-tim, o-pen wide The gate of heav'n to
2. To your great name be end-less praise, Im-mor-tal God-head,

1. us be-low, Our foes press on from ev-'ry side;
2. One in Three; O grant us end-less length of days

1. Your aid sup-ply, your strength be-stow.
2. In our true na-tive land with thee.

Refrain

O Sav-ing Lamb, please take my hand. O Love Di-vine, be

1, 3 | *2, Final* *(Fine)* | *to Verse 2*

all of mine. mine, for all of time.

Text: Verses, LM, *O Salutaris*, St. Thomas Aquinas, 1227–1274; tr. by Edward Caswall, 1814–1878, alt.
Refrain, Tom Booth, b. 1961, © 2008, Tom Booth.
Published by spiritandsong.com®, a division of OCP. All rights reserved.
Music: Verses, DUGUET; attr. to Abbé Dieudonne Duguet, 1794–1849.
Refrain, Tom Booth, © 2008, Tom Booth. Published by spiritandsong.com®, a division of OCP. All rights reserved.

HOLY GOD, WE PRAISE THY NAME

566

1. Ho - ly God, we praise thy name; Lord of all, we
2. Hark! the loud ce - les - tial hymn An - gel choirs a -
3. Lo! the ap - os - tol - ic train Join, the sa - cred
4. Ho - ly Fa - ther, Ho - ly Son, Ho - ly Spir - it,

1. bow be - fore thee! All on earth thy scep - tre claim,
2. bove are rais - ing; Cher - u - bim and Ser - a - phim,
3. Name to hal - low; Proph - ets swell the loud re - frain,
4. Three we name thee; While in es - sence on - ly One,

1. All in heav'n a - bove a - dore thee; In - fi -
2. In un - ceas - ing cho - rus prais - ing; Fill the
3. And the white - robed mar - tyrs fol - low; And from
4. Un - di - vid - ed God we claim thee; And a -

1. nite, thy vast do - main, Ev - er - last - ing
2. heav'ns with sweet ac - cord: "Ho - ly, ho - ly,
3. morn to set of sun, Through the Church the
4. dor - ing, bend the knee, While we own the

1. is thy reign. In - fi - nite, thy vast do -
2. ho - ly Lord!" Fill the heav'ns with sweet ac -
3. song goes on. And from morn to set of
4. mys - ter - y. And a - dor - ing, bend the

1. main, Ev - er - last - ing is thy reign.
2. cord: "Ho - ly, ho - ly, ho - ly Lord!"
3. sun, Through the Church the song goes on.
4. knee, While we own the mys - ter - y.

Text: 78 78 77 with repeat; *Te Deum laudamus*; attr. to St. Nicetas, ca. 335–414; *Grosser Gott, wir loben dich*;
tr. ascr. to Ignaz Franz, 1719–1790; tr. by Clarence A. Walworth, 1820–1900.
Music: GROSSER GOTT; *Allgemeines Katholisches Gesangbuch*, Vienna, ca. 1774.

567 GOD, WE PRAISE YOU

1. God, we praise you! God, we bless you! God, we
2. True a - pos - tles, faith - ful proph - ets, Saints who
3. Je - sus Christ, the King of glo - ry, Ev - er -
4. Christ, at God's right hand vic - to - rious, You will

1. name you sov-'reign Lord! Might - y King whom an - gels
2. set their world a - blaze, Mar - tyrs, once un - known, un -
3. last - ing Son of God, Hum - ble was your vir - gin
4. judge the world you made; Lord, in mer - cy help your

1. wor - ship, Fa - ther, by your Church a - dored:
2. heed - ed, Join one grow - ing song of praise,
3. moth - er, Hard the lone - ly path you trod:
4. ser - vants For whose free - dom you have paid:

1. All cre - a - tion shows your glo - ry, Heav'n and
2. While your Church on earth con - fess - es One ma -
3. By your cross is sin de - feat - ed, Hell con -
4. Raise us up from dust to glo - ry, Guard us

1. earth draw near your throne, Sing - ing "Ho - ly, ho - ly,
2. jes - tic Trin - i - ty: Fa - ther, Son, and Ho - ly
3. front - ed face to face, Heav - en o - pened to be -
4. from all sin to - day; King en - throned a - bove all

1. ho - ly," Lord of hosts and God a - lone!
2. Spir - it, God, our hope e - ter - nal - ly.
3. liev - ers, Sin - ners jus - ti - fied by grace.
4. prais - es, Save your peo - ple, God, we pray.

Text: 87 87 D; *Te Deum laudamus*; attr. to St. Nicetas, ca. 335–414; tr. by Christopher Idle, b. 1938,
© 1982, The Jubilate Group. All rights reserved. Administered by Hope Publishing Co. Used with permission.
Music: NETTLETON; J. Wyeth's *Repository of Sacred Music, Part II*, 1813.

O Bless the Lord

568

Refrain

O bless the Lord, the God of our sal - va-tion, Rock of strength and a ref-uge sure! O bless the Lord, the God of ev-'ry na-tion, o - ver all the earth!

Verses

1. O bless the Lord,
2. Let all the earth
3. Let all the na -
4. Let all the peo-

1. high-est heav - ens a-bove! Bless the Lord!
2. sing with joy to the Lord, all the seas,
3. - tions on earth bless the Lord, for the Lord
4. - ple on earth bless the Lord! Young and old,

1. Glo - ri - fy his name! Sun in the day, moon and
2. crea-tures of the deep! Moun-tains and hills, birds and
3. gov-erns all the world! Let all the rul - ers on
4. glo - ri - fy his name! Let ev - 'ry voice sing with

to Refrain

1. stars in the night, wor - ship and praise!
2. beasts in the fields, wor - ship and praise!
3. earth bless the Lord! Wor - ship and praise!
4. joy to the Lord: "Glo - ry and praise!"

569

FROM ALL THAT DWELL BELOW THE SKIES/
PRAISE GOD FROM WHOM ALL BLESSINGS FLOW

1. From all that dwell be - low the skies,
2. E - ter - nal are your mer - cies, Lord;
3. Your loft - y themes, all mor - tals, bring;
4. In ev - 'ry land be - gin the song;

Doxology Praise God, from whom all bless - ings flow;

1. Let the Cre - a - tor's praise a - rise;
2. E - ter - nal truth at - tends your word:
3. In songs of praise di - vine - ly sing;
4. To ev - 'ry land the strains be - long;

Praise him, all crea - tures here be - low;

1. Let the Re - deem - er's name be sung,
2. Your praise shall sound from shore to shore,
3. The great sal - va - tion loud pro - claim,
4. In cheer - ful sounds all voic - es raise,

Praise him a - bove, you heav'n - ly host:

1. Through ev - 'ry land by ev - 'ry tongue.
2. Till suns shall rise and set no more.
3. And shout for joy the Sav - ior's name.
4. And fill the world with loud - est praise.

Praise Fa - ther, Son and Ho - ly Ghost.

Text: LM; based on Psalm 117; verses 1–2, Isaac Watts, 1674–1748, alt; verses 3–4, anon., ca. 1781;
Doxology, Thomas Ken, 1637–1711.
Music: OLD HUNDREDTH; *Genevan Psalter*, 1551; attr. to Louis Bourgeois, ca. 1510–1561, alt.

570

ALL PEOPLE THAT ON EARTH DO DWELL

1. All people that on earth do dwell,
   Sing to the Lord with cheerful voice;
   Him serve with mirth, his praise forth tell,
   Come we before him, and rejoice.

2. Know that the Lord is God indeed;
   Without our aid he did us make;
   We are his folk, he does us feed,
   And for his sheep he does us take.

3. O enter then his gates with praise;
   Approach with joy his courts unto;

Praise, laud, and bless his Name always,
For it is seemly so to do.

4. For why? the Lord our God is good:
   His mercy is for ever sure;
   His truth at all times firmly stood,
   And shall from age to age endure.

5. To Father, Son, and Holy Ghost,
   The God whom heav'n and earth adore,
   From us and from the angel host
   Be praise and glory evermore.

Text: LM; based on Psalm 100; William Kethe, d. ca. 1594, alt.
Music: OLD HUNDREDTH; *Genevan Psalter*, 1551; attr. to Louis Bourgeois, ca. 1510–1561, alt.

COME, CHRISTIANS, JOIN TO SING

1. Come, Chris-tians, join to sing
2. Come, lift your hearts on high;
3. Praise yet our Christ a-gain; } Al - le - lu - ia! A - men!

1. Loud praise to Christ our King;
2. Let prais-es fill the sky;
3. Life shall not end the strain; } Al - le - lu - ia! A - men!

1. Let all, with heart and voice, Be - fore his throne re-joice;
2. He is our guide and friend; Our cry he will at-tend;
3. On heav-en's joy-ful shore His good-ness we'll a-dore,

1. Praise is his gra-cious choice:
2. His love shall nev-er end:
3. Sing - ing for - ev - er - more: } Al - le - lu - ia! A - men!

Text: 66 66 D; Christian Henry Bateman, 1813–1889, alt.
Music: MADRID; anon. melody, Philadelphia, 1826.

BLESSED BY YOUR SACRIFICE

1. Blessed by your sac - ri - fice, Strong in your love, O Christ,
2. O Splen-dor, Glo - ry bright, Brought forth as Light from Light!
3. Come, raise the an-them high! Let prais-es fill the sky!

1. Our grate-ful voic - es to you we raise. True ad - o - ra - tion
2. O Day, all days en - light-en - ing! An-gels with one ac - cord
3. Sing out a new song un - to the Lord! Let all, with heart and voice,

1. Through-out cre - a - tion Rings out in joy - ful songs of praise.
2. Cry "Ho - ly, Ho - ly Lord!" To you, our ev - er - last - ing King.
3. Be - fore the throne re-joice Of him whom heav'n and earth a - dore.

Text: Irregular; Owen Alstott, b. 1947, and Jeanne Frolick, SFCC, © 1979, 1982, OCP. All rights reserved.
Music: ST. ELIZABETH; Trad. Silesian Melody; Hoffman and Richter's *Schlesische Volkslieder*, Leipzig, 1842.

573   ALL THE ENDS OF THE EARTH

Refrain

All the ends of the earth, all you crea-tures of the sea, lift up your eyes to the won-ders of the Lord. For the Lord of the earth, the mas-ter of the sea, has come with jus-tice for the world.

Verse 1

1. Break in-to song at the deeds of the Lord, the won-ders God has done in ev-'ry age. *to Refrain*

Verse 2

2. Heav-en and earth shall re-joice in his might; ev-'ry heart ev-'ry na-tion call him Lord. *to Refrain*

Verse 3

3. The Lord has made sal-va-tion known, faith-ful to the prom-is-es of old. Let the ends of the earth, let the sea and all it holds make mu-sic be-fore our King! *to Refrain*

Text: Based on Psalm 98; Bob Dufford, SJ, b. 1943.
Music: Bob Dufford, SJ.

GLORY AND PRAISE TO OUR GOD

Refrain

Glo-ry and praise to our God, who a-lone gives light to our days.

Man-y are the bless-ings he bears to those who trust in his ways.

Verses 1-3

1. We, the daugh-ters and sons of him who
2. In his wis-dom he strength-ens us, like
3. Ev-'ry mo-ment of ev-'ry day our

1. built the val-leys and plains, praise the won-ders our
2. gold that's test-ed in fire. Though the pow-er of
3. God is wait-ing to save, al-ways read-y to

to Refrain

1. God has done in ev-'ry heart that sings.
2. sin pre-vails, our God is there to save.
3. seek the lost, to an-swer those who pray.

Verse 4

4. God has wa-tered our bar-ren land and spent his mer-ci-ful rain.

to Refrain

4. Now the riv-ers of life run full for an-y-one to drink.

Text: Based on Psalms 65 and 66; Dan Schutte, b. 1947.
Music: Dan Schutte.

575   JOYFUL, JOYFUL, WE ADORE YOU

1. Joy - ful, joy - ful, we a - dore you, God of glo - ry,
2. All your works with joy sur - round you, Earth and heav'n re -
3. Al - ways giv - ing and for - giv - ing, Ev - er bless - ing,
4. Mor - tals, join the might - y cho - rus Which the morn - ing

1. Lord of love; Hearts un - fold like flow'rs be - fore you,
2. flect your rays, Stars and an - gels sing a - round you,
3. ev - er blest, Well-spring of the joy of liv - ing,
4. stars be - gan; Love di - vine is reign - ing o'er us,

1. O - p'ning to the sun a - bove. Melt the clouds of
2. Cen - ter of un - bro - ken praise; Field and for - est,
3. O - cean depth of hap - py rest! Lov - ing Fa - ther,
4. Bind - ing all with - in its span. Ev - er sing - ing,

1. sin and sad - ness; Drive the dark of doubt a - way;
2. vale and moun - tain, Flow - 'ry mead - ow, flash - ing sea,
3. Christ our broth - er, Let your light up - on us shine;
4. march we on - ward, Vic - tors in the midst of strife;

1. Giv - er of im - mor - tal glad-ness, Fill us with the light of day!
2. Chant-ing bird and flow-ing foun-tain, Prais-ing you e - ter - nal-ly!
3. Teach us how to love each oth - er, Lift us to the joy di-vine.
4. Joy - ful mu - sic leads us sun-ward, In the tri-umph song of life.

Text: 87 87 D; Henry van Dyke, 1852–1933, alt.
Music: HYMN TO JOY; Ludwig van Beethoven, 1770–1827; adapt. by Edward Hodges, 1796–1867.

576   O BLESS THE LORD, MY SOUL

1. O bless the Lord, my soul! His grace to thee pro - claim!
2. O bless the Lord, my soul! His mer - cies bear in mind!
3. He clothes us with his love; Up - holds us with his truth;
4. Then bless his ho - ly name, Whose grace hath made us whole,

1. And all that is with-in me join To bless his ho-ly name!
2. For-get not all his ben-e-fits! The Lord to thee is kind.
3. He heals all our in-fir-mi-ties And ran-soms us from death.
4. Whose lov-ing kind-ness crowns our days! O bless the Lord, my soul!

Text: SM; para. of Psalm 103:1–5; James Montgomery, 1771–1854, alt.
Music: ST. THOMAS (WILLIAMS); *New Universal Psalmodist*, 1770; Aaron Williams, 1731–1776, alt.

We Praise You, O God   577

1. We praise you, O God; ___ ac-claim you as Lord.
2. A-pos-tles and proph-ets, the mar-tyrs for Christ,
3. Lord Je-sus the Christ, ___ your death brings us life.
4. Lord, grant us sal-va-tion, pro-tect us from harm.

1. All of cre-a-tion re-sounds to the voice of the
2. sing of your good-ness while bathed in the beams of your
3. Come with your judg-ment and grant us a place in the
4. Free us from e-vil and bless us with mer-cy as

1. heav-en-ly host u-nit-ed in song,
2. in-fi-nite love, your splen-dor and light,
3. King-dom of God, at one with your saints,
4. dai-ly in you we trust and we hope,
praising your

1-4. maj-es-ty, prais-ing your glo-ry. Al-le-lu-ia, al-le-

1-4. lu-ia. Ho-ly is God, ho-ly and strong. Al-le-lu-

1-4. ia, al-le-lu-ia. Ho-ly Im-mor-tal One.

Text: Based on the *Te Deum laudamus*; attr. to St. Nicetas, ca. 335–414; Peter Jones, b. 1951.
Music: Peter Jones.
Text and music © 1993, Peter Jones. Published by OCP. All rights reserved.

578   ALL CREATURES OF OUR GOD AND KING

1. All crea-tures of our God and King, Lift
2. Great rush-ing winds that are so strong, White
3. Swift flow-ing wa-ter, pure and clear, Make
4. Dear moth-er earth, who day by day Un-
5. All you that are of ten-der heart, For-
6. And you, most kind and gen-tle death, Wait-
7. Let all things their Cre-a-tor bless And

1. up your voice and let us sing; Al - le - lu - ia!
2. clouds a - bove that sail a - long, O ___ praise him!
3. mu - sic for your Lord to hear, Al - le - lu - ia!
4. folds rich bless-ings on our way, O ___ praise him!
5. giv - ing oth - ers, take your part. Sing his prais - es!
6. ing to hush our fi - nal breath, O ___ praise him!
7. wor - ship him in hum - ble - ness! O ___ praise him!

1. Al - le - lu - ia! Bright burn - ing sun with gold - en
2. Al - le - lu - ia! Fair ris - ing morn, in praise re-
3. Al - le - lu - ia! Fierce fire so mas - ter - ful and
4. Al - le - lu - ia! The flow'rs and fruits that in you
5. Al - le - lu - ia! All you that pain and sor - row
6. Al - le - lu - ia! You lead back home the child of
7. Al - le - lu - ia! Praise God the Fa - ther, praise the

1. beam, Pale sil - ver moon with soft - er gleam,
2. joice; O stars of eve - ning, find a voice!
3. bright, Pro - vid - ing us both warmth and light,
4. grow, Let them his glo - ry al - so show!
5. bear, Praise God, and on him cast your care!
6. God, Where Christ our Lord the way has trod:
7. Son, And praise the Spir - it, Three - in - One:

1-7. O praise him! O praise him! Al - le - lu - ia!

1-7. Al - le - lu - ia! Al - le - lu - ia!

Text: LM with additions; St. Francis of Assisi, 1182–1226; *Laudato sia Deo mio Signore*; tr. by William H. Draper, 1855–1933, alt. © 1927, J. Curwen & Sons, Ltd. for the USA, France and Mexico. All rights reserved. International copyright secured. Reprinted by permission of G. Schirmer, Inc., as agents for J. Curwen & Sons, Ltd. Music: LASST UNS ERFREUEN; *Auserlesene Catholische Geistliche Kirchengesänge*, Cologne, 1623.

WE PRAISE YOU

Refrain

We praise you, O Lord, for all your works are won-der-ful. We praise
you, O Lord, for ev-er is your love.

Verses

1. Your wis-dom made the
2. ⅞ You have cho-sen
3. You led us out of
4. The na-tions fash-ioned
5. O house of Is - ra-
*6. ⅞ Hap - py is the
*7. ⅞ May the Lord give

1. heav-ens and the earth, O Lord;   you formed the land, then
2. Ja-cob for your-self, O Lord;   so ten-der-ly you
3. E-gypt with a guid-ing hand.   You raised your arm to
4. sil - ver i - dols, gol-den gods;   but none have hear-ing,
5. el, now come to bless the Lord,   O house of Aar - on,
6. home of you that fear the Lord;   so fruit - ful shall your
7. you his bless-ings all your days.   ⅞ May you see him

1. set the lights;   and like your love the sun will
2. spoke his name;   then called a ho - ly na - tion,
3. set us free.   And like a ten - der vine you
4. speech or sight.   Their mak - ers shall be like their
5. bless his name.   O bless the Lord, all you who
6. love be - come.   Your chil-dren flour-ish like the
7. fill your land   un - til your chil-dren bring their

to Refrain

1. rule the day,   and stars will grace the night.
2. Is - ra - el,   to make them yours, you came.
3. plant-ed us   to grow un - to the sea.
4. emp-ty gods,   the Lord a - lone brings life.
5. hon - or him,   and praise his ho - ly name.
6. ol - ive plants,   for ev - er are you one.
7. chil-dren home   to show his love a - gain.

*Wedding verses.

Text: Verses 1–5 based on Psalms 80:9–12; 135:15–18; 136:5–9; verses 6, 7 based on Psalm 128:1, 3, 5–6;
   Mike Balhoff, b. 1946.
Music: Darryl Ducote, b. 1945, and Gary Daigle, b. 1957.

580   SING TO THE MOUNTAINS

Refrain

Sing to the moun-tains, sing to the sea. Raise your voic - es,

lift your hearts. This is the day the Lord has made. Let all the

to Verses | Last time

earth re - joice. Let all the earth re - joice.

Verse 1

1. I will give thanks to you, my Lord. You have

1. an - swered my plea. You have saved my

to Refrain

1. soul from death. You are my strength and my song.

Verse 2

2. Ho - ly, ho - ly, ho - ly Lord. Heav -

to Refrain

2. en and earth are full of your glo - ry.

Verse 3

3. This is the day that the Lord has made. Let us be glad and re-joice.

to Refrain

3. Death has lost and all is life. Sing of the glo-ry of God.

Text: Based on Psalm 118:24; Isaiah 6:3; Bob Dufford, SJ, b. 1943.
Music: Bob Dufford, SJ.
Text and music © 1975, Robert J. Dufford, SJ, and OCP. All rights reserved.

You Alone

Refrain

You a-lone are ho - ly, you a-lone are Lord.
You a-lone are wor - thy to be hon-ored and a -
dored. Mer-cy you have giv - en, kind-ness you have
shown. Love is you a - lone.

Verses

1. Who of us is sin - less in this place?
2. What is there to do but thank you, then,

1. Who of us de - serves your sav - ing grace?
2. for the gift that we might call you friend?

1. Who of us is good at all with-out your bless-
2. Great - er love has not been known than that for which

1. - ed love that falls up - on our hearts to
2. you gave your on - ly son, that you might

2 to Refrain

1. heal our bro - ken - ness?
2. see us, pure and blessed.

582   SING OF THE LORD'S GOODNESS

Verses

1. Sing of the Lord's good-ness, Fa - ther of all wis - dom,
2. Pow - er he has wield - ed, hon - or is his gar - ment,
3. Cour-age in our dark - ness, com - fort in our sor - row,
4. Praise him with your sing - ing, praise him with the trum - pet,

1. come to him and bless his name. Mer - cy he has shown us,
2. ris - en from the snares of death. His word he has spo - ken,
3. Spir - it of our God most high; so - lace for the wear - y,
4. praise God with the lute and harp; praise him with the cym-bals,

1. his love is for - ev - er, faith - ful to the end of days.
2. one bread he has bro-ken, new life he now gives to all.
3. par - don for the sin - ner, splen-dor of the liv - ing God.
4. praise him with your danc-ing, praise God till the end of days.

Refrain

Come, then, all you na-tions, sing of your Lord's good-ness, mel-o-dies
of praise and thanks to God. Ring out the Lord's glo-ry, praise him with
your mu - sic, wor-ship him and bless his name.

583   HE IS THE LORD

Refrain

Sing to the Lord with shouts of joy, let all cre -
a - tion re - joice! Come join the song of praise to our
God! He is the Lord! He is the Lord!

1. Cry out with joy to the Lord, __ all you na - tions! __
2. Give thanks to God __ our Fa - ther for his love. __
3. Great is the King of cre - a - tion; he is faith - ful. __

1. _____ Serve the Lord. Serve the Lord. __
2. _____ Bless our God. Bless our God. __
3. _____ Praise his name. Praise his name. __

to Refrain

1. __ Come be - fore him sing-ing for joy! __
2. _____ His mer - cy is for - ev - er! __
3. _____ Sing of his sal - va - tion! __

PRAISE THE LORD, YE HEAVENS   584

1. Praise the Lord! ye heav'ns a - dore him; Praise him an - gels, in the height;
2. Praise the Lord! for he is glo - rious; Nev - er shall his prom-ise fail;
3. Wor-ship, hon - or, glo - ry, bless-ing, Lord, we of - fer un - to thee;

1. Sun and moon, re - joice be - fore him; Praise him, all ye stars of light.
2. God has made his saints vic - to - rious; Sin and death shall not pre - vail.
3. Young and old, thy praise ex-press-ing, In glad hom - age bend the knee.

1. Praise the Lord! for he has spo - ken; Worlds his might-y voice o - beyed;
2. Praise the God of our sal - va - tion! Hosts on high his pow'r pro-claim;
3. All the saints in heav'n a - dore thee, We would bow be - fore thy throne;

1. Laws which nev - er shall be bro - ken For their guid-ance he has made.
2. Heav'n, and earth, and all cre - a - tion, Laud and mag - ni - fy his name.
3. As thine an - gels serve be-fore thee, So on earth thy will be done.

585   PRAISE TO THE LORD

1. Praise to the Lord, the Al - might - y, the King of cre -
2. Praise to the Lord, a - bove all things so won - drous - ly
3. Praise to the Lord, who will pros - per your work and de -
4. Praise to the Lord! O let all that is in me a -

1. a - tion! O my soul, praise him, for
2. reign - ing, Shel - t'ring you un - der his
3. fend you; Sure - ly his good - ness and
4. dore him! All that has life and breath,

1. he is your health and sal - va - tion!
2. wings, and so gent - ly sus - tain - ing.
3. mer - cy shall dai - ly at - tend you.
4. come now with prais - es be - fore him!

1. Come, all who hear: Now to his al - tar draw
2. Have you not seen All that is need - ful has
3. Pon - der a - new What the Al - might - y can
4. Let the "A - men!" Sound from his peo - ple a -

1. near, Join - ing in glad ad - o - ra - tion!
2. been Sent by his gra - cious or - dain - ing?
3. do As with his love he be - friends you.
4. gain, Glad - ly with praise we a - dore him!

Text: 14 14 47 8; Joachim Neander, 1650–1680; tr. by Catherine Winkworth, 1827–1878, alt.
Music: LOBE DEN HERREN; *Ernewerten Gesangbuch*, Stralsund, 1665.

586   PRAISE, MY SOUL, THE KING OF HEAVEN

1. Praise, my soul, the King of heav - en;
2. Praise him for his grace and fa - vor
3. Fa - ther - like he tends and spares us;
4. Frail as sum - mer's flow'r we flour - ish,
5. An - gels, help us to a - dore him;

1. To his feet thy trib - ute bring; Ran - somed,
2. To his peo - ple in dis - tress; Praise him
3. Well our fee - ble frame he knows; In his
4. Blows the wind and it is gone; But while
5. You be - hold him face to face; Sun and

1. healed, re - stored, for - giv - en, Ev - er - more his
2. still the same as ev - er, Slow to chide, and
3. hands he gent - ly bears us, Res - cues us from
4. mor - tals rise and per - ish, God en - dures un-
5. moon, bow down be - fore him, All who dwell in

1. prais - es sing:
2. swift to bless:
3. all our foes. Al - le - lu - ia! Al - le -
4. chang - ing on:
5. time and space:

1-5. lu - ia!
Praise the ev - er - last - ing King.
Glo - rious in his faith - ful - ness.
Wide - ly yet his mer - cy flows.
Praise the high e - ter - nal one!
Praise with us the God of grace.

Text: 87 87 87; based on Psalm 103; Henry F. Lyte, 1793–1847, alt.
Music: LAUDA ANIMA; John Goss, 1800–1880.

GOD, WHOSE LOVE IS REIGNING O'ER US   587

1. God, whose love is reigning o'er us,
   Source of all, the ending true;
   Hear the universal chorus
   Raised in joyful praise to you:
   Alleluia, Alleluia,
   Worship ancient, worship new.

2. Word of God from nature bringing
   Springtime green and autumn gold;
   Mountain streams like children singing,
   Ocean waves like thunder bold:
   Alleluia, Alleluia,
   As creation's tale is told.

3. Holy God of ancient glory,
   Choosing man and woman, too;
   Abr'am's faith and Sarah's story

Formed a people bound to you.
Alleluia, Alleluia,
To your cov'nant keep us true.

4. Cov'nant, new again in Jesus,
   Starchild born to set us free;
   Sent to heal us, sent to teach us
   How love's children we might be.
   Alleluia, Alleluia,
   Risen Christ, our Savior he!

5. Lift we then our human voices
   In the songs that faith would bring;
   Live we then in human choices
   Lives that, like our music, sing:
   Alleluia, Alleluia,
   Joined in love our praises ring!

Text: 87 87 87; William Boyd Grove, © 1980, William Boyd Grove. All rights reserved. Used with permission.
Music: LAUDA ANIMA; John Goss, 1800–1880.

588   SHOUT TO THE LORD

My Je-sus, my Sav-ior; Lord, there is none like you.

All of my days I want to praise the won-ders of your

might-y love. My com-fort, my shel-ter,

tow-er of ref - uge and strength; let ev-ery breath,

all that I am, nev-er cease to wor-ship you.

Refrain

Shout to the Lord, all the earth; let us sing

es-ty, praise to the king. Moun-tains bow down and the seas

will roar at the sound of your name.

I sing for joy at the work of your hands. For -

ev - er I'll love you, for - ev - er I'll stand.

Noth-ing com-pares to the prom - ise I have in you.

O GOD BEYOND ALL PRAISING   589

1. O God be-yond all prais - ing, We wor-ship you to - day
2. Then hear, O gra-cious Sav - ior, Ac - cept the love we bring,

1. And sing the love a - maz - ing That songs can - not re - pay;
2. That we who know your fa - vor May serve you as our King;

1. For we can on - ly won-der At ev - 'ry gift you send,
2. And wheth - er our to - mor-rows Be filled with good or ill,

1. At bless-ings with - out num - ber And mer-cies with - out end:
2. We'll tri - umph through our sor - rows And rise to bless you still:

1. We lift our hearts be - fore you And wait up-on your word,
2. To mar - vel at your beau - ty And glo - ry in your ways,

1. We hon - or and a-dore you, Our great and might-y Lord.
2. And make a joy-ful du - ty Our sac - ri - fice of praise.

590   SING PRAISE TO GOD WHO REIGNS ABOVE

1. Sing praise to God who reigns a-bove, The God of all
2. What God's al-might-y power has made, His gra-cious mer-
3. Then all my glad-some way a-long, I sing a-loud
4. Let all who name Christ's ho-ly name, Give God all praise

1. cre - a-tion, The God of power, the God of love, The
2. cy keep-ing; By morn-ing glow or eve-ning shade His
3. your prais-es, That all may hear the grate-ful song My
4. and glo-ry; All you who own his power, pro-claim A -

1. God of our sal - va-tion; With heal-ing balm my
2. watch-ful eye ne'er sleep-ing; With - in the king-dom
3. voice un-wea-ried rais-es; Be joy-ful in the
4. loud the won-drous sto-ry! Cast each false i-dol

1. soul he fills, And ev-'ry faith-less mur-mur stills:
2. of his might, Lo! all is just and all is right:
3. Lord, my heart, Both soul and bod-y sing your part:
4. from its throne, The Lord is God, and he a-lone:

1-4. To God all praise and glo - ry.

Text: 87 87 88 7; *Sei Lob und Ehr' dem höchsten Gut*; Johann J. Schütz, 1640–1690; tr. by Frances E. Cox, 1812–1897.
Music: MIT FREUDEN ZART; Bohemian Brethren's *Kirchengesänge*, 1566.

591   LET ALL MORTAL FLESH KEEP SILENCE

1. Let all mor-tal flesh keep si-lence, And with fear and
2. King of kings, yet born of Ma-ry, As of old on
3. Rank on rank the host of heav-en Spreads its van-guard
4. At his feet the six-winged ser-aph; Cher-u-bim with

1. trem-bling stand; Pon-der noth-ing earth-ly - mind-ed,
2. earth he stood, Lord of lords in hu-man ves-ture;
3. on the way, As the Light of Light de - scend-eth
4. sleep-less eye, Veil their fac-es to the Pres-ence,

1. For with bless-ing in his hand Christ our God to earth de -
2. In the Bod - y and the Blood He will give to all the
3. From the realms of end - less day, That the pow'rs of hell may
4. As with cease-less voice they cry, "Al - le - lu - ia, al - le -

1. scend - eth, Our full hom-age to de - mand.
2. faith - ful His own self for heav'n - ly food.
3. van - ish As the dark-ness clears a - way.
4. lu - ia! Al - le - lu - ia, Lord Most High!"

Text: 87 87 87; *Liturgy of St. James*, 4th cent.; para. by Gerard Moultrie, 1829–1885, alt.
Music: PICARDY; French, 17th cent.; *Chansons populaires des Provinces de France*, 1860.

SING A NEW SONG   592

Refrain

Sing a new song to the Lord. Praise him in the as - sem - bly
of his church. Sing a new song to the Lord. Praise him,

all you peo - ple of God.

Verses

1. Be glad, ___ O ___
2. ⁊ Praise his name with
3. ⁊ Let God's peo - ple

1. Is - ra - el, be - cause ___ of your cre - a - tor; re - joice, ___
2. danc - ing, play drums and harp ___ in praise, ___ for God de -
3. cel - e - brate the tri - umph of ___ their king. ___ Let them

to Refrain

1. O ___ Zi - on, be - cause ___ of ___ your king.
2. lights in his peo - ple, and lifts his chil-dren on high.
3. shout ___ and praise his name, while sing - ing all the night long.

593

LIFT UP YOUR HEARTS

Refrain

Lift up your hearts to the Lord, praise God's gra-cious mer-cy!

Sing out your joy to the Lord, whose love is en - dur - ing.

Verses

1. Shout with joy to the Lord, all the earth!
2. Let the earth wor-ship, sing - ing your praise.
3. God's right hand made a path through the night,
4. Lis - ten now, all you ser - vants of God,

1. Praise the name a - bove all names! Say to God, "How
2. Praise the glo - ry of your name! Come and see the
3. split the wa - ters of the sea. All cre - a - tion,
4. as I tell of these great works. Bless-ed be the

to Refrain

1. won - drous your works, how glo - rious your name!"
2. deeds of the Lord; bless God's ho - ly name!
3. lift up your voice: "Our God set us free!"
4. Lord of my life, whose love shall en - dure!

Text: Based on Psalm 66; Roc O'Connor, SJ, b. 1949.
Music: Roc O'Connor, SJ.
Text and music © 1981, 1993, Robert F. O'Connor, SJ, and OCP. All rights reserved.

594

IMMORTAL, INVISIBLE, GOD ONLY WISE

1. Im - mor - tal, in - vis - i - ble, God on - ly wise,
2. Un - rest - ing, un - hast - ing, and si - lent as light,
3. Life - giv - ing Cre - a - tor, of both great and small;
4. Great Fa - ther of glo - ry, pure Fa - ther of light,

1. In light in - ac - ces - si - ble hid from our eyes,
2. Nor want-ing, nor wast-ing, you rule day and night;
3. Of all life the mak - er, the true life of all;
4. Your an - gels a - dor - ing, all veil - ing their sight;

1. Most bless-ed, most glo-rious, the An-cient of Days,
2. Your jus-tice like moun-tains high soar-ing a - bove
3. We blos-som, then with - er, as leaves on a tree,
4. We too, God in - vis - i - ble, of - fer our praise;

1. Al - might - y, vic - to - rious, your great name we praise.
2. Your clouds, which are foun-tains of good-ness and love.
3. But you live for ev - er, who is and will be.
4. O light in - ac - ces - si - ble, An - cient of Days!

Text: 11 11 11 11; 1 Timothy 1:17; Walter C. Smith, 1824–1908, alt.
Music: ST. DENIO; Roberts' *Canaidau y Cyssegr*, 1839.

Sing a Joyful Song 595

Refrain

Sing a joy-ful song to the Lord! Al-le-lu - ia!

Let the heav-ens and earth re - joice! Al-le-lu - ia!

Al-le-lu - ia!

Verses

1. The heav-ens pro-
2. Our God is a
3. Sing praise, O Je -
4. Sing praise to the

1. claim God's name, and earth in re - ply ech-oes
2. might - y God, un - e-qualled in pow'r, yet with
3. ru - sa - lem! Sing praise to your King, rul - ing
4. God of gods, the An-cient of Days! Ho - ly,

to Refrain

1. back with joy - ful songs __ of praise!
2. gen - tle mer - cy cov-ers the earth.
3. earth with jus - tice age af - ter age.
4. ho - ly, ho - ly Lord __ of all!

Text: Based on Psalm 145; Jim Farrell, b. 1947, © 1984, OCP. All rights reserved.
Music: Jim Farrell, © 1984, OCP. All rights reserved.

596   ALLE, ALLE, ALLELUIA

Refrain   *Al - le,   al - le,   al - le - lu - ia,*
Verses 1. Fa - ther,   Fa - ther,   mak - er   of   the   world.
    2. Je - sus,   Je - sus,   Je - sus   is   the   way.
    3. Spir - it,   Spir - it,   come down   on   us,   Lord.

al - le,   al - le,   al - le - lu - ia.
1. Fa - ther,   Fa - ther,   cre - a - tor   of   the   earth.
2. Je - sus,   Je - sus,   Je - sus   is   the   truth.
3. Spir - it,   Spir - it,   rain down   on   us,   Lord.

Al - le,   al - le,   al - le - lu - ia.
1. Fa - ther,   Fa - ther,   speak - er   of   the   word.
2. Je - sus,   Je - sus,   Je - sus   is   the   life.
3. Spir - it,   Spir - it,   flood us   with   your   pow'r.

Al - le, al - le,   al - le, al - le - lu - ia.
1. Make us, Fa - ther, break us, Fa - ther, mold us   in   your ways.
2. Je - sus is the way, he is the truth, he is the   life.
3. Fill us with the light of God, oh,   fill   us with your pow'r.

1-6
Al - le, al - le,   al - le, al - le - lu - ia. (to Verses)
1. Make us, Fa - ther, break us, Fa - ther, mold us   in   your ways. (to Refrain)
2. Je - sus is the way, he is the truth, he is the   life. (to Refrain)
3. Fill us with the light of God, oh,   fill   us with your pow'r. (to Refrain)

Final
ia.   Al - le,   al - le, al - le - lu - ia.

Al - le,   al - le,   al - le - lu - ia.   Al - le!

LAUDATE, LAUDATE DOMINUM

Refrain

Lau - da - te, lau - da - te Do - mi - num, om - nes gen - tes, lau -
We praise you, we praise your ho - ly name, God of jus - tice, e -

da - te Do - mi - num. Ex - sul - ta - te, ju - bi - la - te per
ter - nal - ly the same. May our liv - ing be thanks - giv - ing, re -

1. an - nos Do - mi - ni, om - nes gen - tes. gen - tes.
joic - ing in your name now and al - ways. al - ways.

*Verses

1. In the faith of Christ we walk hand in hand,
2. In the name of Christ we will spread the seed;
3. In the pow'r of Christ we pro - claim one Lord.

1. light be - fore our path as the Lord has planned;
2. share the Word of God with all those in need,
3. All who put on Christ are by faith re - stored;

1. shin - ing the torch of faith in our land:
2. faith - ful in thought and word and deed:
3. shar - ing new life, sal - va - tion's re - ward:

to Refrain

1-3. in the name of Christ Je - sus.

*Additional verses available in accompaniment books.

598   SING A NEW SONG

Refrain

Sing a new song un-to the Lord; let your song be sung from
moun-tains high. Sing a new song un-to the Lord, sing-ing
al - le - lu - ia.

Verses

1. Shout with glad-ness! Dance for joy!
2. Rise, O chil-dren, from your sleep;
3. Glad my soul for I have seen

1. O come be - fore the Lord. And play for God on
2. your Sav - ior now has come. He has turned your
3. the glo - ry of the Lord. The trum - pet sounds; the

to Refrain

1. glad tam - bou-rines, and let your trum - pet sound.
2. sor - row to joy, and filled your soul with song.
3. dead shall be raised. I know my Sav - ior lives.

Text: Based on Psalm 98:1, 4–6; Dan Schutte, b. 1947.
Music: Dan Schutte.

599   HALLELUYA! WE SING YOUR PRAISES

Refrain

Hal - le - lu - ya! We sing your prais-es, all our
hearts are filled with glad - ness. Hal - le - lu - ya! We sing your
prais - es, all our hearts are filled with glad - ness.

1. Christ the Lord to us said: I am wine, I am bread,
2. Now he sends us all out, strong in faith, free of doubt,

to Refrain

1. I am wine, I am bread, give to all who thirst and hun - ger.
2. strong in faith, free of doubt, to pro-claim the joy - ful Gos - pel.

ABBA, FATHER 600

Refrain Ab - ba, Ab - ba, Fa -
Verses 1. Mold us, mold us and fash - ion
2. Fa - ther, may we be one in
3. Glo - ry, glo - ry and praise to

ther. You are the pot - ter;
1. us in - to the im - age of
2. you. May we be one in you as
3. you. Glo - ry and praise to you for-

we are the clay, the work of your
1. Je - sus, your Son, of Je - sus, your
2. he is in you, and you are in
3. ev - er, a - men, for - ev - er, a -

| 1-6 | Final |
| 2 | 2 |

hands. (to Verses) Ab - ba!
1. Son. (to Refrain)
2. him. (to Refrain)
3. men. (to Refrain)

601   When in Our Music

1. When in our mu - sic God is glo - ri - fied, And a - do-
2. How of - ten, mak - ing mu - sic, we have found A new di-
3. So has the Church, in lit - ur - gy and song, In faith and
4. And did not Je - sus sing a psalm that night When ut - most
5. Let ev - 'ry in - stru - ment be tuned for praise! Let all re-

1. ra - tion leaves no room for pride, It is as
2. men - sion in the world of sound, As wor - ship
3. love through cen - tu - ries of wrong, Borne wit - ness
4. e - vil strove a - gainst the light? Then let us
5. joice who have a voice to raise! And may God

1. though the whole cre - a - tion cried
2. moves us to a more pro - found
3. to the truth in ev - 'ry tongue,   }   Al - le - lu - ia!
4. sing, for whom he won the fight,
5. give us faith to sing al - ways

Text: 10 10 10 with alleluia; Fred Pratt Green, 1903–2000, © 1972, Hope Publishing Co.
 All rights reserved. Used with permission.
Music: ENGELBERG; Charles Villiers Stanford, 1852–1924, alt.

602   Grateful

Refrain

Grate - ful for the life you give us, thank - ful
Grate - ful for the Bread of Heav - en, thank - ful

for your Ho - ly Son, joy - ful in your
for your Ho - ly Word, joy - ful in your

1.
Spir - it flow - ing o - ver all, O God of Love.
mer - cy flow - ing,

1. You are more than we i-mag-ine, An-cient, Ho-ly, Liv-
2. May our lives pro-claim your jus-tice, may our voic-es sing

1. -ing Lord. E - ven when we doubt your pres-
2. your praise. May our hands work in your ser-

1. - ence you are faith - ful to your word.
2. - vice to the glo - ry of your name.

Text and music: Tom Tomaszek, b. 1950, © 2003, 2004, Thomas N. Tomaszek.
Published by spiritandsong.com®, a division of OCP. All rights reserved.

Now Thank We All Our God 603

1. Now thank we all our God With heart, and hands, and
2. O may this gra-cious God Through all our life be
3. All praise and thanks to God The Fa-ther now be

1. voic - es, Who won-drous things has done, In whom his world re-
2. near us, With ev - er joy-ful hearts And bless-ed peace to
3. giv - en, The Son, and Spir - it blest, Who reigns in high-est

1. joic - es; Who, from our moth-er's arms Has blessed us on our
2. cheer us; Pre-serve us in his grace, And guide us in dis-
3. heav - en, E - ter-nal, Tri - une God, Whom earth and heav'n a-

1. way With count-less gifts of love, And still is ours to - day.
2. tress, And free us from all sin, Till heav-en we pos-sess.
3. dore; For thus it was, is now, And shall be, ev - er-more.

Text: 67 67 66 66; Sirach 50:22–24; Martin Rinkart, 1586–1649; tr. by Catherine Winkworth, 1827–1878, alt.
Music: NUN DANKET; Johann Crüger, 1598–1662; adapt. by Felix Mendelssohn, 1809–1847, alt.

604 — ALL MY DAYS

Refrain

Till the end of my days, O Lord, I will bless your name, sing your praise, give you thanks, all my days.

Verses

1. You have made me lit-tle less than a god, _____
2. You have blessed _ me with good things and plen-ty ____
3. Your sun ___ and your moon give me light, _____
4. How great ___ is your love, O ____ Fa-ther, ___

1. and have lav-ished my heart with your love. With dig-ni-ty and
2. and sur-round-ed my ta - ble with friends. Their love _ and their
3. and your stars show the way through the night. Your riv - ers and
4. that you sent us your Sav - ior Son. His death _ and his

to Refrain

1. hon - or you've clothed me, giv-en me rule o-ver all.
2. laugh-ter en - rich me; to-geth-er we sing your_ praise.
3. streams have re - freshed me. I ___ will sing your_ praise.
4. ris - ing will heal us, and draw us ___ all un-to you.

Text: Based on Psalm 8; J-Glenn Murray, SJ.
Music: Dan Schutte, b. 1947.

605 — THANKS BE TO GOD

1. Thanks be to God whose love has gath-ered us this day;
2. Thanks be to God for all the gifts of life and light;
3. Thanks be to God who knows our se - cret joys and fears;
4. Thanks be to God who nev - er turns his face a - way;
5. Thanks be to God who made our world and all we see;

1. Thanks be to God who helps and guides us on our way.
2. Thanks be to God whose care pro-tects us day and night.
3. Thanks be to God who when we call him al - ways hears.
4. Thanks be to God who heals and par-dons all who stray.
5. Thanks be to God who gave his Son to set us free.

1. Thanks be to God who gives us voice that we may thank him:
2. Thanks be to God who keeps in mind us who for-get him:
3. Thanks be to God our rock and strength ev-er sus-tain-ing:
4. Thanks be to God who wel-comes us in-to the king-dom:
5. Thanks be to God whose Spir-it brings warmth and re-joic-ing:

1-5. De - o gra-ti-as, De - o gra-ti-as, Thanks be to God most high.

Text: 12 12 13 55 6; Stephen Dean, b. 1948.
Music: CHARIS; Stephen Dean.

COME, YE THANKFUL PEOPLE, COME 606

1. Come, ye thank-ful peo-ple, come, Raise the song of
2. All the world is God's own field, Fruit un-to his
3. For the Lord our God shall come, And shall take his
4. E - ven so, Lord, quick-ly come To your fi - nal

1. har - vest - home: All is safe-ly gath-ered in, Ere the
2. praise to yield; Wheat and tares to - geth - er sown, Un - to
3. har - vest home; From his field shall in that day All of -
4. har - vest - home; Gath - er all your peo - ple in, Free from

1. win - ter storms be - gin; God, our Mak - er, does pro - vide
2. joy or sor - row grown; First the blade, and then the ear,
3. fens - es purge a - way; Give his an - gels charge at last
4. sor - row, free from sin; There, for ev - er pu - ri - fied,

1. For our wants to be sup - plied; Come to God's own
2. Then the full corn shall ap - pear: Grant, O har - vest
3. In the fire the tares to cast, But the fruit - ful
4. In your pres - ence to a - bide: Come, with all your

1. tem - ple, come, Raise the song of har - vest - home.
2. Lord, that we Whole-some grain and pure may be.
3. ears to store In his gar - ner ev - er - more.
4. an - gels, come, Raise the glo - rious har - vest - home.

Text: 77 77 D; Henry Alford, 1810–1871, alt.
Music: ST. GEORGE'S WINDSOR; George J. Elvey, 1816–1893.

607   SING TO THE LORD OF HARVEST

1. Sing to the Lord of har-vest, Sing songs of love and
2. The clouds all drop God's boun-ty, The des-erts bloom and
3. Place at the sa-cred al-tar The gifts which good-ness

1. praise; With joy-ful hearts and voic-es Your
2. spring; The hills leap up in glad-ness, The
3. gave, The gold-en sheaves of har-vest, The

1. al-le-lu-ias raise! By God the roll-ing
2. val-leys laugh and sing. God gifts the earth in
3. souls Christ came to save; Your hearts lay down in

1. sea-sons In fruit-ful or-der move; Sing
2. full-ness, All things with large in-crease, And
3. hom-age, At ho-ly feet now fall, Through

1. to the Lord of har-vest A joy-ful song of love.
2. crowns the year with good-ness, With plen-ty and with peace.
3. all your life a-dor-ing The One who died for all.

Text: 76 76 D; John S.B. Monsell, 1811–1875, alt.
Music: WIE LIEBLICH IST DER MAIEN; Johann Steuerlein, 1546–1613.

608   LET ALL THINGS NOW LIVING

1. Let all things now liv-ing A song of thanks-giv-ing To
   Who fash-ioned and made us, Pro-tect-ed and stayed us, By
2. His law he en-forc-es, The stars in their cours-es, The
   The hills and the moun-tains, The riv-ers and foun-tains, The

1. God our Cre-a-tor tri-um-phant-ly raise;
   guid-ing us on to the end of our days. God's ban-ners are
2. sun in its or-bit o-be-dient-ly shine,
   depths of the o-cean pro-claim God di-vine. We, too, should be

1. o'er us, Pure light goes be - fore us, A pil - lar of fire shin-ing
2. voic-ing Our love and re - joic-ing With glad ad - o - ra-tion, a

1. forth in the night: Till shad-ows have van-ished And dark-ness is
2. song let us raise: Till all things now liv - ing U - nite in thanks-

1. ban-ished, As for-ward we trav - el from light in - to Light.
2. giv - ing, To God in the high - est, ho - san - na and praise.

Text: 66 11 66 11 D; Katherine K. Davis, 1892–1980, © 1939, 1966, E.C. Schirmer Music Co.,
a division of ECS Publishing, Boston, MA. All rights reserved. Used with permission.
Music: ASH GROVE; trad. Welsh Melody.

FOR THE BEAUTY OF THE EARTH   609

1. For the beau - ty of the earth, For the beau - ty
2. For the beau - ty of each hour Of the day and
3. For the joy of ear and eye, For the heart and
4. For the joy of hu - man love, Broth - er, sis - ter,
5. For the Church, who ev - er - more Lifts her ho - ly
6. For each per - fect gift di - vine To our world so

1. of the skies, For the love which from our birth
2. of the night, Hill and vale, and tree and flow'r,
3. mind's de - light, For the mys - tic har - mo - ny
4. par - ent, child, Friends on earth and friends a - bove;
5. hands a - bove, Of - f'ring up on ev - 'ry shore
6. free - ly giv'n, Joys be - stowed by love's de - sign,

1. O - ver and a - round us lies:
2. Sun and moon, and stars of light:
3. Link - ing sense to sound and sight:
4. For all gen - tle thoughts and mild:
5. Her pure sac - ri - fice of love:
6. Flow'rs of earth and fruits of heav'n:
Lord of all to

1-6. you we raise This our hymn of grate - ful praise.

Text: 77 77 77; *Lyra Eucharistica*, 1864; Folliot S. Pierpoint, 1835–1917, alt.
Music: DIX; Conrad Kocher, 1786–1872; adapt. by William H. Monk, 1823–1889.

610

GIVE THANKS TO THE LORD

Verses 1 & 2, 4 & 5, 7 & 8, 10

1. Give thanks to the Lord who does won - drous deeds, who
2. Give thanks to the God who has blessed our land, who
4. Give thanks to the God of the sum - mer rains, who
5. Give thanks to the Lord who is mer - ci - ful, whose
7. Give thanks to the Lord for the blaz - ing sun, for
8. Give thanks to the Lord for the crim - son skies, for
10. Give thanks to the God who has set us free, who

1. mas - ters the winds and the rag - ing seas,
2. guards ev - 'ry step with a might - y hand,
4. spreads out the hills and the gold - en plains,
5. kind - ness is wide and love boun - ti - ful,
7. great, roll - ing waves where the dol - phins run,
8. wild, wind - y heights where the ea - gle flies,
10. raised us to life on a bless - ed tree, whose

love is for ev - er, whose love is for ev - er, whose love is for

1, 4, 7, Final ev - er more!   *Fine* **2, 5, 8** more!

Verses 3, 6, 9

3. O, bless the Lord for ev - 'ry gift that comes to grace our way. And
6. O, bless the Lord with mu - sic, ev - 'ry crea - ture great and small. And
9. O, bless the Lord all peo - ple, for the mu - sic of the skies. And

3. praise the God of faith - ful - ness, who comes to light our day. (to Vss 4 & 5)
6. sing through all the a - ges of God's fa - vor to us all. (to Vss 7 & 8)
9. tell the won - drous sto - ry of a love that nev - er dies. (to Vs 10)

ALL GOOD GIFTS

1. We plow the fields and scat - ter the good seed on the
2. You on - ly are the mak - er of all things near and
3. We thank you, then, Cre - a - tor, for all things bright and

1. land, but it is fed and wa - tered by God's al - might - y
2. far, you paint the way-side flow - er, you light the eve - ning
3. good, the seed-time and the har - vest, our life, our health, our

1. hand. God sends the snow in win - ter, the warmth to swell the
2. star. The winds and waves o - bey you, by you the birds are
3. food. And all that we can of - fer, your bound-less love im-

1. grain, the breez-es and the sun-shine, and soft, re-fresh-ing rain.
2. fed; much more, to us, your chil - dren, you give our dai - ly bread.
3. parts; the gifts to you most pleas - ing are hum-ble, thank-ful hearts.

Refrain

All good gifts a-round us are sent from heav-en a-bove;

thank you, Lord, O thank you for all your love.

Text: 76 76 D with refrain; Matthias Claudius, 1740–1815; tr. by Jane M. Campbell, 1817–1878, alt.
Music: HEISLMAN; Kevin Keil, ASCAP, b. 1956, © 1993, Kevin Keil. Published by OCP. All rights reserved.

612

GOD'S LOVE IS EVERLASTING

God's love is ev-er-last-ing, faith-ful till the end of time. God's
love is ev-er-last-ing, God's love will nev-er end. end.

Verses

1. Give thanks to the Lord, for God is good. Give
2. Who cre-at-ed the earth, who di-vid-ed the seas, who
3. Who a-lone does great won-ders, who frees us from harm, who

1. thanks to the Lord of Lords. Give
2. set the heav'n - ly lights. The
3. nour-ish - es all liv - ing things. Give

1. thanks to the God a - bove oth - er gods.
2. sun to rule the day, the stars at night. God's
3. thanks to the God of heav - en and earth.

1-3. mer - cy en-dures for - ev - er.

Text: Based on Psalm 136:1–9; Tom Tomaszek, b. 1950.
Music: Tom Tomaszek.

613

JUBILATE DEO

① Ju - bi - lá - te! Ju - bi-lá - te De - o!

② Ju - bi-lá - te De - o! Ju - bi-lá - te De - o!

O - mnis ter - ra, ju - bi-lá - te De - o!

Translation: Shout with joy to God, all the earth.

Text: Based on Psalm 100:1.
Music: Barbara Bridge, b. 1950, © 1998, Barbara Bridge. Published by OCP. All rights reserved.

How Great Thou Art

614

Verses

1. O Lord my God! When I in awe-some won-der Con - si - der
2. When through the woods and for - est glades I wan - der, And hear the
3. And when I think that God, his Son not spar - ing, Sent him to
4. When Christ shall come with shout of ac - cla - ma - tion And take me

1. all the worlds thy hands have made, I see the stars, I
2. birds sing sweet - ly in the trees; When I look down from
3. die, I scarce can take it in, That on the cross, my
4. home, what joy shall fill my heart! Then I shall bow in

1. hear the roll - ing thun - der, Thy pow'r through-out the
2. lof - ty moun-tain gran - deur And hear the brook, and
3. bur - den glad - ly bear - ing, He bled and died to
4. hum - ble ad - o - ra - tion, And there pro - claim, my

Refrain

1. u - ni - verse dis-played; Then sings my soul, my Sav-ior God to
2. feel the gen - tle breeze;
3. take a - way my sin;
4. God, how great thou art!

thee; How great thou art, how great thou art! Then sings my soul, my

Sav-ior God to thee; How great thou art, how great thou art!

Words: Stuart K. Hine.
Music: Traditional Swedish folk tune/adapt. by Stuart K. Hine.
Words and music © 1949 and 1953 by The Stuart K. Hine Trust.
All rights in the USA except print rights administered by EMI CMG Publishing.
USA print rights administered by Hope Publishing Company. All rights reserved. Used with permission.

615   FOR THE FRUITS OF THIS CREATION

1. For the fruits of this cre-a-tion, Thanks be to God;
2. In the just re-ward of la-bor, God's will be done;
3. For the har-vests of the Spir-it, Thanks be to God;

1. For the gifts of ev-'ry na-tion, Thanks be to God;
2. In the help we give our neigh-bor, God's will be done;
3. For the good we all in-her-it, Thanks be to God;

1. For the plow-ing, sow-ing, reap-ing, Si-lent growth while we are
2. In the world-wide task of car-ing For the hun-gry and de-
3. For the won-ders that as-tound us, For the truths that will con-

1. sleep-ing, Fu-ture needs in earth's safe-keep-ing, Thanks be to God.
2. spair-ing, In the har-vests we are shar-ing, God's will be done.
3. found us, Most of all, that love has found us, Thanks be to God.

Text: 84 84 88 84; Fred Pratt Green, 1903–2000, © 1970, Hope Publishing Co. All rights reserved. Used with permission.
Music: AR HYD Y NOS; Trad. Welsh Melody.

616   OH, WHO CAN KNOW THE MIND OF GOD

1. Oh, who can know the mind of God, Or
2. Who else has cupped the seas in hand, Or
3. Who else sur-rounds in bound-less deeps The
4. Too high for us, O Lord, your ways, Too

1. who dare call his name, Whose glo-ry is the
2. set the skies a-light? Who else could carve from
3. is-land of the mind? Who else in clouds of
4. vast your works: to them We reach with trem-bling

1. ris-ing sun, Whose ev-'ry word is flame?
2. stone the land, Or sum-mon day from night?
3. si-lence keeps Long watch for all our kind?
4. words of praise To touch your gar-ment's hem.

Text: CM; Genevieve Glen, OSB, b. 1945, © 1998, The Benedictine Nuns of the Abbey of St. Walburga.
Published by OCP. All rights reserved.
Music: MORNING SONG; *Sixteen Tune Settings, Philadelphia*, 1812; *Kentucky Harmony*, 1816.

SACRED CREATION

Refrain

Sa-cred the land, sa - cred the wa - ter, sa-cred the sky,

ho - ly and true. Sa-cred all life, sa - cred each oth - er;

all re - flect God who is good.

Verses

1. All praise be yours through Broth - er Sun,
2. Broth - er Wind and Air that per - vades,
3. Through Broth - er Fire you bright - en the night,

1. bear - ing a like - ness of you, Most High One.
2. var - y their moods to sus - tain all you've made.
3. strong and ro - bust yet play - ful and bright.

1. Sis - ter Moon and Stars who are pre-cious, splen-did,
2. Sis - ter Wa - ter, use - ful and pure, low - ly,
3. Sis - ter Earth, our moth - er who nur-tures, feed-ing,

to Refrain

1. ride your glo - ri - ous sky.
2. free - ly shar - ing her life.
3. yield - ing flow - er and herb.

Text: Based on a text by St. Francis of Assisi, ca. 1182–1226, and the inspiration of Louis Vitale, OFM;
Rufino Zaragoza, OFM, b. 1957.
Music: Rufina Zaragoza, OFM.

618 I Sing the Mighty Power of God

1. I sing the might-y pow'r of God That made the
2. I sing the good-ness of the Lord That filled the
3. There's not a plant or flow'r be - low, But makes thy

1. moun-tains rise, That spread the flow-ing seas a - broad, And
2. earth with food; He formed the crea-tures with his word, And
3. glo - ries known; And clouds a - rise, and tem-pests blow By

1. built the loft - y skies. I sing the wis - dom
2. then pro-nounced them good. Lord, how thy won - ders
3. or - der from thy throne; While all that bor - rows

1. that or - dained The sun to rule the day; The moon shines
2. are dis - played Wher - e'er I turn my eye; If I sur -
3. life from thee Is ev - er in thy care, And ev - 'ry -

1. full at his com-mand, And all the stars o - bey.
2. vey the ground I tread, Or gaze up - on the sky!
3. where that I can be, Thou, God, are pres - ent there.

Text: CMD; Isaac Watts, 1674–1748, alt.
Music: ELLACOMBE; *Gesangbuch der Herzogl, Wirtembergischen Katholischen Hofkapelle*, 1784, alt.;
    adapt. fr. Würth's *Katholisches Gesangbuch*, 1863.

619 Word of God, You Spoke Creation

1. Word of God, you spoke cre - a - tion From the cha - os
2. Word of God, we all a - dore you, Flame that burns a -
3. Word of God, we sing and praise you, Mel - o - dy with

1. of the flood; Word made flesh, you wrought sal - va - tion
2. way the night, Word made flesh, we bow be - fore you,
3. love en - twined. Word made flesh, we glo - ri - fy you

1. By the spill-ing of your blood. Love of God re-vealed a-mong us,
2. Child who top-ples thrones of might: Splen-dor of God's hid-den glo - ry,
3. For the gift of love Di - vine. Spir - it of God's liv-ing pres-ence,

1. Life of God made light of earth, In - to be - ing
2. Full - ness of God's faith - ful love; Born with us to
3. Breath of God, re - ceived as gift; Sav - ing pow - er,

1. here you've sung us, In - to life brought us to birth.
2. death's dark sto - ry, Raised for us in light a - bove.
3. lov - ing es - sence, To you, God, our souls we lift.

Text: 87 87 D. Vss. 1 and 2, Jennifer Glen, CCVI, b. 1945, © 1987, 2001, The Sisters of Charity of the Incarnate Word.
   Published by OCP. All rights reserved. Vs. 3, Gael Berberick (ASCAP), © 2005, Gael Berberick.
   Published by OCP. All rights reserved.
Music: STEPHANIE; Gael Berberick (ASCAP) and Barney Walker (ASCAP), © 2005, Gael Berberick and Barney Walker.
   Published by OCP. All rights reserved.

ALL THE EARTH 620

Refrain

All the earth pro-claim the Lord; Sing your praise to God.

Verses

1. Serve you the Lord, heart filled with glad - ness.
2. Know that the Lord is our cre - a - tor.
3. We are the sheep of the green pas - ture;
4. Come to the gates bring-ing thanks-giv - ing;
5. Our Lord is good, with love en - dur - ing;
6. Hon - or and praise be to the Fa - ther,

to Refrain

1. Come in - to God's pres - ence sing-ing for joy!
2. Yes, God is our Fa - ther; we are his own.
3. For we are God's peo - ple, cho - sen by God.
4. O en - ter the court - yards sing-ing in praise.
5. God's word is a - bid - ing now with us all.
6. The Son and the Spir - it, world with - out end.

Text: Based on Psalm 100; Lucien Deiss, CSSp, 1921–2007.
Music: Lucien Deiss, CSSp.
Text and music © 1965, World Library Publications. All rights reserved. Used with permission.

621   I�f Gᴏᴅ Iꜱ ꜰᴏʀ Uꜱ

1. If God is for us, who can be a-gainst us?
2. If God is for us, who then can con-demn us?
3. If God is for us, who can stand a-gainst us?

1. If God is on our side, what can we be de-
2. Sure-ly not Christ our Lord, who a-rose from the
3. If Christ did set us free, who can make us a

1. nied? In all these things we are more than
2. dead. There's noth-ing in this world that can
3. slave? Can pain or suf - fer-ing keep us

1. con-quer-ors in Je - sus.
2. sep-a-rate us from his love.
3. from the love of Je - sus?

If God is

1-3. on our side, what can we be de-nied?

Text: Based on Romans 8:31–39; Grayson Warren Brown, b. 1948.
Music: Grayson Warren Brown.
Text and music © 1995, Grayson Warren Brown. Published by OCP. All rights reserved.

622   Lɪᴋᴇ ᴀ Sʜᴇᴘʜᴇʀᴅ

Refrain

Like a shep-herd he feeds his flock and gath-ers the lambs in his

arms, hold-ing them care-ful-ly close to his heart,

1-3
to Verses

Final

lead-ing them home. home, lead-ing them home.

1. Say to the cit-ies of Ju - dah: Pre-pare _ the
2. I _ my - self _ will shep-herd them, for oth-ers have

1. way of the Lord. Go to the moun-tain-top,
2. led them a - stray. The lost I will res - cue and

1. lift your voice: Je - ru - sa - lem, here is your God.
2. heal their wounds and pas-ture them, giv-ing them rest.

Verse 3

3. Come un-to me if you are heav-i-ly bur-dened, and

3. take my yoke up-on your shoul-ders. I will give you rest.

Text: Based on Isaiah 40:9ff; Ezekiel 34:11ff; Matthew 11:28ff; Bob Dufford, SJ, b. 1943.
Music: Bob Dufford, SJ.

I Have Loved You 623

Refrain

I have loved you with an ev-er-last-ing love, I have called you

and you are mine; I have loved you with an ev-er-last-ing love,

Verses

I have called you and you are mine. 1-3. Seek the face of the Lord and

to Refrain

1. long for him: he will bring you his light and his peace.
2. long for him: he will bring you his joy and his hope.
3. long for him: he will bring you his care and his love.

Text: Based on Jeremiah 31:3; Psalm 24:3; Michael Joncas, b. 1951.
Music: Michael Joncas.

624   YOUR GRACE IS ENOUGH

Verses

1. Great is your faith - ful-ness, O God   of Ja-cob;
2. Great is your love   and jus-tice, God   of Ja-cob;

1. you wres-tle with   the sin-ner's rest - less heart.
2. you use the weak   to lead the strong.

1. You lead me by   still wa-ters in - to mer-cy
2. You lead us in   the song of heav - en's vic-t'ry,

1. where noth - ing   can   keep us   a - part.
2. and   all your peo - ple sing a - long.

1, 2. So re - mem - ber   your peo - ple, re -

1, 2. mem - ber your   chil - dren, re - mem - ber your

1, 2. prom - ise, O God.   For your

Refrain

grace is e-nough,   yeah, your grace is e-nough,

yeah, your grace is e-nough,   yeah, your grace

is e-nough for me.

LORD OF GLORY

Refrain

Leap-ing the moun - tains, bound-ing the hills, see how our God has come to meet us. His voice is lift-ed; his face is joy. Now is the sea - son to sing our

1, 3 to Vss. 1, 3 | 2 to Vs. 2 | Final

song on high.

Verses 1, 2

1. Come, then, O Lord of glo - ry, show us your face. _____
2. He pas - tures his flock a - mong the wild _____ flow'rs ___ and

to Refrain

1. Speak, ___ for we know your words are life.
2. leads them to the moun-tain of his love.

Verse 3

3. All through the day, all through the night,

to Refrain

3. seek for the Lord and sing his love.

Text: Based on Song of Songs 2; Tim Manion, b. 1951.
Music: Tim Manion.

626　　　　　COME TO THE WATER

1. O let all who thirst, let them come to the
2. And let all who seek, let them come to the
3. And let all who toil, let them come to the
4. And let all the poor, let them come to the

1. wa - ter. And let all who have noth-ing,
2. wa - ter. And let all who have noth-ing,
3. wa - ter. And let all who are wea - ry,
4. wa - ter. Bring the ones who are lad - en,

1. let them come to the Lord: with-out
2. let them come to the Lord: with-out
3. let them come to the Lord: all who
4. bring them all to the Lord: bring the

1. mon-ey, with-out price. Why should you pay the
2. mon-ey, with-out strife. Why should you spend your
3. la - bor, with-out rest. How can your soul find
4. chil-dren, with-out might. Eas - y the load and

1. price, ex-cept for the Lord?
2. life, ex-cept for the Lord?
3. rest, ex-cept for the Lord?
4. light: come to the Lord.

Text: Based on Isaiah 55:1–2; Matthew 11:28–30; John Foley, S.J., b. 1939.
Music: John Foley, S.J.

627　　　　　RAIN DOWN

Refrain

Rain down, rain down, rain down your

1. love on your peo - ple. 2. love, God of life.

Verses

1. Faith-ful and true is the word of our God. All of God's
2. We who re-vere and find hope in our God live in the
3. God of cre-a-tion, we long for your truth; you are the

1. works are so wor-thy of trust. God's mer-cy falls on the
2. kind-ness and joy of God's wing. God will pro-tect us from
3. wa-ter of life that we thirst. Grant that your love and your

to Refrain

1. just and the right; full of God's love is the earth.
2. dark-ness and death; God will not leave us to starve.
3. peace touch our hearts, all of our hope lies in you.

Text: Based on Psalm 33; Jaime Cortez, b. 1963.
Music: Jaime Cortez.

ISAIAH 49   628

Verse 1

1. I will nev-er for-get you, my peo-ple; I have carved you

1. on the palm of my hand. I will nev-er for-get you; I will

1. not leave you or-phaned. I will nev-er for-get my own.

Verse 2

2. Does a moth-er for-get her ba-by? Or a

2. wom-an the child with-in her womb? Yet e-ven if these for-

(Repeat Vs 1)

2. get, yes, e-ven if these for-get, I will nev-er for-get my own.

Text: Based on Isaiah 49:15; Carey Landry, b. 1944.
Music: Carey Landry.

629   We Are the Light of the World

Verses

1. Bless - ed are they who are poor in spir - it,
2. Bless - ed are they who are meek and hum - ble,
3. Bless - ed are they who will mourn in sor - row,
4. Bless those who hun - ger and thirst for jus - tice,
5. Bless - ed are they who show oth - ers mer - cy,
6. Bless - ed are hearts that are clean and ho - ly,
7. Bless - ed are they who bring peace a - mong us,
8. Bless those who suf - fer from per - se - cu - tion,

1. Theirs is the king-dom of God. Bless us, O Lord, make us
2. They will in - her - it the earth. Bless us, O Lord, make us
3. They will be com - fort - ed. Bless us, O Lord, when we
4. They will be sat - is - fied. Bless us, O Lord, hear our
5. They will know mer - cy too. Bless us, O Lord, hear our
6. They will be - hold the Lord. Bless us, O Lord, make us
7. They are the chil - dren of God. Bless us, O Lord, may your
8. Theirs is the king-dom of God. Bless us, O Lord, when they

1. poor in spir - it; Bless us, O Lord, our God.
2. meek and hum - ble; Bless us, O Lord, our God.
3. share their sor - row; Bless us, O Lord, our God.
4. cry for jus - tice; Bless us, O Lord, our God.
5. cry for mer - cy; Bless us, O Lord, our God.
6. pure and ho - ly; Bless us, O Lord, our God.
7. peace be with us; Bless us, O Lord, our God.
8. per - se - cute us; Bless us, O Lord, our God.

Refrain

We are the light of the world, may our light shine be-fore all,

That they may see the good that we do, and give glo - ry to God.

Text: 10 6 10 6 with refrain; based on the Beatitudes; adapt. by Jean Anthony Greif, 1898–1981, alt.
Music: GREIF; Jean Anthony Greif.

I Am the Light of the World

Refrain

"I am the Light of the world," says the Lord,

"They who fol-low me will have the light of life."

Verses 1, 2

1. "A - rise," says the Lord, "Have no fear with -
2. "Walk in the light, there is no cause to

1. in you; for in my pres - ence there will be no
2. stum - ble; I have come to light the path be -

1. dark - ness. I am the Light of the world."
2. fore you. I am the Light of the world."

to Refrain

Verse 3

3. "Lis - ten to my words; they are from the One who

3. sent me: For you, my friends, are called to share God's

3. glo - ry. You are the Light of the world."

to Refrain

Text: Based on John 8:12; Ephesians 5:14; 1 John 2:10; Matthew 5:14; Greg Hayakawa, b. 1953.
Music: Greg Hayakawa.

631   YOUR LIGHT WILL COME, JERUSALEM

Refrain

Your light will come, Je - ru - sa - lem; for on you will dawn the glo - ry of the Lord, and all na - tions will walk in your light, al - le - lu - ia, al - le - lu - ia.

Verses

1. Christ is the light of the world, a light dis -
2. His light is mer - cy and peace, a peace sur -
3. His light is jus - tice and truth, and love which

1. pel - ling the dark - ness. May we, his
2. pass - ing all tell - ing. May we, his
3. casts out all ha - tred. May we, his

to Refrain

1. bod - y, re - flect that ho - ly light.
2. bod - y, be in - stru - ments of peace.
3. bod - y, pre - pare the reign of God.

I Want to Walk as a Child of the Light

Verses

1. I want to walk as a child of the light; I want to follow Jesus. God set the stars to give light to the world; the star of my life is Jesus.
2. I want to see the brightness of God; I want to look at Jesus. Clear Sun of righteousness, shine on my path, and show me the way to the Father.
3. I'm looking for the coming of Christ; I want to be with Jesus. When we have run with patience the race, we shall know the joy of Jesus.

Refrain

In him there is no darkness at all; the night and the day are both alike. The Lamb is the light of the city of God: Shine in my heart, Lord Jesus.

Text: Irregular; Kathleen Thomerson, b. 1934.
Music: HOUSTON; Kathleen Thomerson.

633   GOD IS LIGHT

Refrain

God is Light, in whom no dark-ness lives;
God is Love, in whom no hate can be;

walk as the chil - dren of light.
walk as God's chil - dren of love.

Verses

1. Hold in your heart Spir - it's a - noint - ing, em -
2. Walk in Christ's love with great thanks - giv - ing, __
3. Ra - diance be - hold, stand in the pres - ence of

to Refrain

1. pow - ered to bless and to heal __ with __ love.
2. choos - ing to serve oth - ers in his name.
3. mer - cy, for - give - ness, the faith - ful - ness of God.

Text and music: Gregory Norbet, b. 1940, © 2007, Gregory Norbet. Published by OCP. All rights reserved.

634   O RADIANT LIGHT

1. O ra - diant Light, O Sun di - vine Of God the
2. O Son of God, the source of life, Praise is your
3. Lord Je - sus Christ, as day - light fades, As shine the

1. Fa - ther's death - less face, O im - age of the Light sub -
2. due by night and day. Our hap - py lips must raise the
3. lights of e - ven - tide, We praise the Fa - ther with the

1. lime That fills the heav'n - ly dwell - ing place.
2. strain Of your es - teemed and splen - did name.
3. Son, The Spir - it blest, and with them one.

Text: LM; *Phos Hilaron*, Greek, ca. 200; tr. by William G. Storey, b. 1923, © William G. Storey.
All rights reserved. Used with permission.
Music: JESU DULCIS MEMORIA; Chant, Mode I.

We Are Marching/Siyahamba

Text and music: South African; collected and edited by Anders Nyberg, © 1984, Peace of Music Publishing, AB.
All rights reserved. Administered by Walton Music Corporation. Used with permission.

636 LORD OF THE DANCE

1. I danced in the morn-ing when the world was be-gun, And I
2. I danced for the scribe __ and the Phar - i - see, But they
3. I danced on the Sab-bath and I cured the __ lame, The __
4. I danced on a Fri - day when the sky turned _ black; It's __
5. They cut me __ down __ and I leapt up __ high, __

1. danced in the moon and the stars __ and the sun, And I
2. would not __ dance and they would-n't fol - low me; I __
3. ho - ly __ peo - ple, they said it was a shame; They __
4. hard to __ dance with the dev - il on your back; They __
5. I am the life that - 'll nev - er, nev - er die, I'll __

1. came down from heav-en and I danced on the earth, __ At
2. danced for the fish - er-men, for James and for John; __ They
3. whipped and they stripped _ and they hung me __ high, And they
4. bur - ied my bod-y and they thought I'd __ gone, __ But
5. live in __ you __ if you'll live in __ me; __

1. Beth - le - hem I __ had my birth. "Dance, then wher -
2. came with __ me and the dance went on.
3. left me __ there on a cross to die.
4. I am the dance and I still go on.
5. "I am the Lord of the Dance," said he.

ev - er you may be; I am the Lord of the Dance," said he. "I'll

lead you all wher-ev-er you may be, I will lead you all in the

Dance," said he.   Dance," said he.

Text: Sydney B. Carter, 1915–2004.
Music: Shaker Melody, 19th cent.; adapt. by Sydney B. Carter.

In Christ Alone

1. In Christ a - lone my hope is found, he is my light, my strength, my song; this cor - ner-stone, this sol - id ground, firm through the fierc - est drought and storm. What heights of love, what depths of peace, when fears are stilled, when striv-ings cease. My com - fort - er, my all in all, here in the love of Christ I stand.

2. In Christ a - lone, who took on flesh, full-ness of God in help - less babe! This gift of love and righ-teous - ness, scorned by the ones he came to save. Till on that cross as Je - sus died, the wrath of God was sat - is-fied. For ev - ery sin on him was laid; here in the death of Christ I live.

3. There in the ground his bod - y lay, light of the world, by dark - ness slain; then, burst - ing forth in glo - rious day, up from the grave he rose a - gain! And as he stands in vic - to - ry, sin's curse has lost its grip on me; for I am his and he is mine, bought with the pre - cious blood of Christ.

4. No guilt in life, no fear in death, this is the pow'r of Christ in me; from life's first cry to fi - nal breath, Je - sus com-mands my des - ti - ny. No pow'r of hell, no scheme of man, can ev - er pluck me from his hand; till he re-turns or calls me home, here in the pow'r of Christ I'll stand!

638   JESU, JOY OF OUR DESIRING

1. Je - su, joy of our de - sir - ing, Ho - ly wis - dom,
2. Through the way where hope is guid-ing, Hear what peace - ful

1. love most bright, Drawn by you, our souls as - pir-ing,
2. mu - sic rings; Where the flocks in you con - fid-ing,

1. Soar to un - cre - at - ed Light. Word of God, our flesh that
2. Drink of joy from death - less springs! Theirs is beau-ty's fair - est

1. fash-ioned With the fire of life im - pas-sioned, Striv - ing
2. plea-sure; Theirs is wis-dom's ho - liest trea-sure; You do

1. still to truth un - known, Soar-ing, dy - ing, 'round your throne.
2. ev - er lead your own, In the love of joys un - known.

Text: 87 87 88 77; *Christlich Herzens Andacht*, 1665; Martin Jahn, ca. 1620–1682; tr. by Robert S. Bridges, 1844–1930, rev.
Music: WERDE MUNTER; *Himmlische Lieder*, Vol. 3, Lüneberg, 1642; Johann P. Schop, ca. 1590–1664.

639   EARTHEN VESSELS

Refrain

We hold a trea-sure, not made of gold, in earth-en

ves-sels, wealth un-told; one trea-sure on - ly: the

Lord, the Christ, in earth-en ves - sels.

Verses

1. Light has shone in our dark-ness: God has shone in our heart
2. God has cho-sen the low - ly who are small in this world;

1. with the light of the glo-ry of Je - sus, the Lord.
2. in this weak-ness is glo-ry in Je - sus, the Lord.

Text: Based on 2 Corinthians 4:6–7; 1 Corinthians 1:27–29; John Foley, S.J., b. 1939.
Music: John Foley, S.J.
Text and music © 1975, 1978, 1991, John B. Foley, S.J., and OCP. All rights reserved.

CHRIST BEFORE US 640

1. Christ be - fore us, Christ be - side us, Christ to guide us
2. May we be for one an - oth - er all that you would
3. God be - fore us through the a - ges; Christ be - side us
4. O Re-deem - er, fill your ser-vants with your words of

1. all our days. He to car - ry all our sor - rows, he to
2. have us be. May we live your law of kind-ness, love, com-
3. here to - day. Spir - it, lead us forth for - ev - er; guide and
4. last - ing life. Give to those with hands of heal - ing love trans-

1. bear us per - fect grace. Je - sus, Sav - ior, Friend and Broth - er,
2. pas - sion, char - i - ty. May we climb your ho - ly moun-tain;
3. help us all our days. Christ the Sav - ior, God the Liv - ing,
4. cend - ing pain and strife. Make us lov - ing sons and daugh-ters;

1. In - ter - ces - sor, Son of God, save your peo - ple
2. may we see your ho - ly face! Vis - it now this
3. Great Cre - a - tor, Spir - it blest! Ho - ly Three-in -
4. make us ho - ly, kind and true, sent to la - bor

1. in your dy - ing, and in ris-ing, con - quer death.
2. hum - ble dwell-ing; dwell with-in this ho - ly place.
3. One Im - mor - tal, come and be our wel-come guest.
4. for your King-dom— rest - less till we rest in you.

Text: 87 87 D; Janèt Sullivan Whitaker, b. 1958; © 1990, Janèt Sullivan Whitaker. Published by OCP. All rights reserved.
Music: SUO GÂN; Trad. Welsh Melody.

641   O Christ, Our Teacher

1. O Christ, our Teach - er and our Way,
2. O Christ, our Teach - er and our Light,
3. O Christ, our Teach - er and our Life,
4. All praise to you, O Christ, our Way,

1. Teach us to fol - low you this day,
2. Il - lu - mine us with truth and right,
3. Teach us to rec - on - cile all strife,
4. Our Truth and Life, our on - ly Day!

1. And as our hearts with love ex - pand
2. That we may see but you a - lone,
3. To break down each di - vid - ing wall
4. All praise to you, O Christ, the Son

1. To run the way of your com - mands.
2. And by your light and truth be known.
3. And live this day in peace with all.
4. With Fa - ther and the Spir - it: One!

Text: LM; Harry Hagan, OSB, b. 1947, © 1999, St. Meinrad Archabbey. Published by OCP. All rights reserved.
Music: CONDITOR ALME SIDERUM; Chant, Mode IV.

642   Blessed Jesus, at Your Word

1. Bless - ed Je - sus, at your word we are gath - ered
2. All our knowl - edge, sense, and sight lie in deep - est
3. Glor - ious Lord, your - self im - part! Light of Light, from

1. all to hear you; let our hearts and minds be stirred
2. dark - ness shroud - ed, till your Spir - it breaks our night
3. God pro - ceed - ing, o - pen now each mind and heart,

1. now to seek and love and fear you; by your teach-ings
2. with the beams of truth un-cloud - ed; you a - lone to
3. help us by your Spir-it's plead - ing. Hear the cry your

1. true and ho - ly, drawn from earth to love you sole - ly.
2. God can win us; you must work all good with - in us.
3. Church now rais-es; Lord, ac - cept our prayers and prais - es.

Text: 78 78 88; Tobias Clausnitzer, 1619–1684; tr. by Catherine Winkworth, 1827–1878, alt.
Music: LIEBSTER JESU; Johann R. Ahle, 1625–1673, alt.; adapt. by Johann Sebastian Bach, 1685–1750.

PRAISE TO YOU, O CHRIST OUR SAVIOR 643

Refrain

Praise to you, O Christ, our Sav-ior, Word of the Fa-ther, call-ing us to life;

Son of God who leads us to free-dom: glo - ry to you, Lord Je-sus Christ!

Verses

1. You are the Word who calls us out of dark - ness; you are the
2. You are the one whom proph-ets hoped and longed for; you are the
3. You are the Word who calls us to be ser - vants; you are the
4. You are the Word who binds us and u - nites us; you are the

1. Word who leads us in - to light; you are the Word who
2. one who speaks to us to - day; you are the one who
3. Word whose on - ly law is love; you are the Word - made-
4. Word who calls us to be one; you are the Word who

to Refrain

1. brings us through the des - ert: glo - ry to you, Lord Je-sus Christ!
2. leads us to our fu - ture: glo - ry to you, Lord Je-sus Christ!
3. flesh who lives a-mong us: glo - ry to you, Lord Je-sus Christ!
4. teach - es us for-give-ness: glo - ry to you, Lord Je-sus Christ!

Text and music: Bernadette Farrell, b. 1957, © 1986, Bernadette Farrell. Published by OCP. All rights reserved.

644   YOUR WORDS ARE SPIRIT AND LIFE

Refrain

Your words are spir-it and life, O Lord: rich-er than gold, strong-er than death. Your words are spir-it and life, O Lord; life ev-er-last - ing.

Verses

1. God's law is per - fect, re-fresh-ing the soul, re-
2. God's pre-cepts keep us; their pur-pose is right. They
3. Liv - ing by God's truth is ho - ly and sure; God's
4. God's word is pre - cious, de-sired more than gold; worth

1. viv - ing the wea - ry spir - it. God's
2. glad-den the hearts of peo - ple. God's com-
3. pres-ence is ev - er - last-ing. God's
4. more than we dare i - mag-ine and,

1. rule can be trust-ed: bring-ing us wis-dom,
2. mand is so clear it brings us new vi - sion;
3. truth is e - ter-nal, bring-ing us jus-tice;
4. sweet-er than hon-ey, this word will feed us,

to Refrain

1. bring - ing God's wis - dom to birth.
2. bring - ing God's light to our eyes.
3. bring - ing God's jus - tice to earth.
4. bring - ing ful - fill - ment and joy.

Text: Based on Psalm 19:8–11; Bernadette Farrell, b. 1957.
Music: Bernadette Farrell.
Text and music © 1993, Bernadette Farrell. Published by OCP. All rights reserved.

O WORD OF GOD

645

*Ostinato Refrain

O Word of God, come in-to this space. O Word of God, come send us your grace. O-pen our minds; show us your truth. Trans-form our lives a-new.

*Verses available in accompaniment books.

BE THOU MY VISION

646

1. Be Thou my vi-sion, O Lord of my heart;
2. Be Thou my wis-dom, and Thou my true word;
3. Rich-es I heed not, or man's emp-ty praise,
4. High King of heav-en, my vic-to-ry won,

1. Naught be all else to me, save that Thou art:
2. I ev-er with Thee and Thou with me, Lord:
3. Thou mine in-her-i-tance, now and al-ways:
4. May I reach heav-en's joys, O bright heav'n's Sun!

1. Thou my best thought, __ by day or by night,
2. Thou my great Fa-ther, I Thy true son,
3. Thou and Thou on-ly, first in my heart,
4. Heart of my own heart, what-ev-er be-fall,

1. Wak-ing or sleep-ing, Thy pres-ence my light.
2. Thou in me dwell-ing, and I with Thee one.
3. High King of heav-en, my trea-sure Thou art.
4. Still be my vi-sion, O Rul-er of all.

Text: 10 10 10 10; Ancient Irish; tr. by Mary E. Byrne, 1905; fr. Eleanor Hull's *Poem Book of the Gael*, 1912, alt.
Music: SLANE; trad. Irish Melody; adapt. fr. *The Church Hymnary*, 1927.

647

LORD OF ALL HOPEFULNESS

1. Lord of all hope - ful - ness, Lord of all joy, Whose
2. Lord of all ea - ger - ness, Lord of all faith, Whose
3. Lord of all kind - li - ness, Lord of all grace, Your
4. Lord of all gen - tle - ness, Lord of all calm, Whose

1. trust, ev - er child - like, no cares can de - stroy, Be
2. strong hands were skilled at the plane and the lathe, Be
3. hands swift to wel - come, your arms to em - brace, Be
4. voice is con - tent - ment, whose pres - ence is balm, Be

1. there at our wak - ing, and give us, we pray, Your
2. there at our la - bors, and give us, we pray, Your
3. there at our hom - ing, and give us, we pray, Your
4. there at our sleep - ing, and give us, we pray, Your

1. bliss in our hearts, Lord, at the break of the day.
2. strength in our hearts, Lord, at the noon of the day.
3. love in our hearts, Lord, at the eve of the day.
4. peace in our hearts, Lord, at the end of the day.

Text: 10 11 11 12; 'Lord of all hopefulness,' words by Jan Struther, 1901–1953; fr. *Enlarged Songs of Praise*, 1931.
Reproduced by permission of Oxford University Press. All rights reserved.
Music: SLANE; trad. Irish Melody; adapt. fr. *The Church Hymnary*, 1927.

648

TO YOU, O GOD, I LIFT UP MY SOUL

Refrain: 1st time: Cantor, All repeat; thereafter: All

To you, O God, I lift up my soul; lift up my spir-it

| 1 | 2-4 to Vss. | Final |

to my Lord. To you I lift up my soul.

To you I lift up my soul. To you I lift up my soul.

1. Make me to know your ways, O God; teach me your
2. Good and up-right our gra - cious God, show-ing the
3. Stead-fast and kind your ways, O God; all who re-

1. paths, guide me. ⁔ You are my Sav - ior.
2. way, guid-ing the hum-ble to jus - tice.
3. vere your cov - e - nant ⁔ know your friend-ship.

Text: Based on Psalm 25:1, 4–5, 8–9, 10, 14; Bob Hurd, b. 1950.
Music: Bob Hurd.
Text and music © 1991, Bob Hurd. Published by OCP. All rights reserved.

THERE IS A LONGING 649

There is a long-ing in our hearts, O Lord, for you to reveal your - self to us. There is a long-ing in our hearts for
love we on - ly find in you, our God.

Verses

1. For jus - tice,
2. For wis - dom,
3. For heal - ing,
4. Lord save us,

1. for free - dom, for mer - cy: hear our prayer. In
2. for cour - age, for com-fort: hear our prayer. In
3. for whole-ness, for new life: hear our prayer. In
4. take pit - y, light in our dark - ness. We

1. sor - row, in grief:
2. weak-ness, in fear:
3. sick - ness, in death:
4. call you, we wait:
be near, hear our prayer, O God.

Text and music: Anne Quigley, © 1992, Anne Quigley. Published by OCP. All rights reserved.

650   CHRIST BE BESIDE ME

1. Christ be be - side me, Christ be be - fore me, Christ be be -
2. Christ on my right hand, Christ on my left hand, Christ all a -
3. Christ be in all hearts think - ing a - bout me; Christ be on

1. hind me, King of my heart. Christ be with - in me,
2. round me, shield in the strife. Christ in my sleep - ing,
3. all tongues tell - ing of me. Christ be the vi - sion

1. Christ be be - low me, Christ be a - bove me, nev - er to part.
2. Christ in my sit - ting, Christ in my ris - ing, light of my life.
3. in eyes that see me; In ears that hear me, Christ ev - er be.

651   GOD BE IN MY HEAD

1. God be in my head, God be in my heart,
2. God be in my work, God be in my play,

1. God be in my mind, God be in my soul,
2. God be in my home, God be in my prayer,

1. God be in my eyes, so that I may see your face;
2. God be in my song, so that I may sing your praise;

1. God be on my lips, God be in my life.
2. God be in my night, God be in my day.

THIS ALONE

Refrain

One thing I ask, this a-lone I seek, to dwell in the house of the Lord all my days. For one day with-in your tem-ple heals ev - 'ry day a - lone. O Lord, bring me to your dwell - ing.

Verses 1, 3

1. Hear, __ O __ Lord, __ the sound of my call - ing.
3. Wait on __ the Lord, and __ hope in his mer - cy.

1. Hear, __ O Lord, and show me your way.
3. Wait on ___ the Lord, and live in his love.

to Refrain

Verse 2

2. The Lord is my light and hope of sal - va - tion. The

2. Lord is my ref-uge; whom should I fear?

to Refrain

Text: Based on Psalm 27; Tim Manion, b. 1951.
Music: Tim Manion.

653   STAND BY ME

Verses

1. When the storms of life are rag-ing, Lord, stand by
2. In the midst of per - se - cu - tion, Lord, stand by

1. me. When the cur - rent pulls me un - der, Lord,
2. me. When my en - e - mies sur-round me, Lord,

1. stand by me. When the ris - ing wa - ters
2. stand by me. When the ty - rant wields his

1. toss me like a ship up - on the sea, You who
2. ter - ror and the ar - mies wage their might, When the

1. rule the wind and wa - ter, Lord, stand by me.
2. dark - ness o - ver-whelms me, Lord, stand by me.

Refrain

Stand by me, stand by me. Lift me up from the rest - less sea.

When I am lost, when love can't be found, when no one cares, Lord,

1 to Verse 2 ‖ Final Repeat twice

stand by me. stand by me.

Text: Inspired by "Stand by Me" by Charles A. Tindley, 1851–1933; Tom Kendzia, b. 1954.
Music: Tom Kendzia.

LEAD ME, GUIDE ME

Refrain

Lead me, guide me, a-long the way, for if you
lead me, I can-not stray. Lord, let me walk each
day with thee. Lead me, oh Lord, lead me.

Verses

1. I am weak and I need thy strength and
2. Help me tread in the paths of righ - teous -
3. I am lost if you take your hand from

1. pow'r to help me o - ver my weak - est
2. ness, be my aid when Sa - tan and sin op -
3. me, I am blind with - out thy Light to

1. hour. Help me through the dark - ness thy face to
2. press. I am put - ting all my trust in
3. see, Lord, just al - ways let me thy ser - vant

to Refrain

1. see, lead me, oh Lord, lead me.
2. thee. Lead me, oh Lord, lead me.
3. be. Lead me, oh Lord, lead me.

655   THESE ALONE ARE ENOUGH

1. Take my heart, O Lord, take my hopes and
2. Take my thoughts, O Lord, and my mem - o -
3. I sur - ren - der, Lord, all I have and
4. When the dark - ness falls on my fi - nal

1. dreams. Take my mind with all its plans and
2. ry. Take my tears, my joys, my lib - er -
3. hold. I re - turn to you your gifts un -
4. days, take the ver - y breath that sang your

1. schemes.
2. ty.
3. told.   Give me noth - ing more than your love and
4. praise.

1-4. grace. These a - lone, O God, are e - nough for me.

Text: Based on "Suscipe" Prayer of Ignatius of Loyola; Dan Schutte, b. 1947.
Music: Dan Schutte.

656   COME, LORD JESUS

Refrain
Come, Lord Je - sus, come.   Come and fill my heart

with your life.   Hold me close, Lord, hold me tight,

and come, Lord Je - sus, come.

1. Where there's de-spair in life, Lord, let me be your voice
2. Where there is sad-ness let me be your com-fort and

1. of hope. Where there's in-ju-ry, Lord,
2. your joy. When there's fear in our hearts

to Refrain

1. let me be your voice of peace.
2. let me be a sign of faith.

Text: Verses based on a prayer ascribed to St. Francis of Assisi, ca. 1182–1226;
    Steve Angrisano, b. 1965, and Tom Tomaszek, b. 1950.
Music: Steve Angrisano and Tom Tomaszek.
Text and music © 1997, Steve Angrisano and Thomas N. Tomaszek.
    Published by spiritandsong.com®, a division of OCP. All rights reserved.

SACRED SILENCE

657

Refrain Sa-cred si-lence, ho-ly o-cean, gen-tle wa-ter,
Verses 1. God my Fa-ther, Christ my broth-er, Ho-ly Spir-it,
       2. Ho-ly Ma-ry, gen-tle moth-er, God's pure ves-sel,

wash-ing o-ver me; help me lis-ten, Ho-ly
1. sanc-ti-fy-ing me; Lord, I'm sor-ry, please for-
2. pray-ing for me; saints and an-gels, all in

Spir-it. Come and speak to me. (to Verses)
1. give me. Come and set me free. (to Refrain)
2. heav-en, come and be with me. (to Refrain)

Final

Come and be with me. Come and speak to me.

Text: Tom Booth, b. 1961, Jenny Pixler and Anthony Kuner, © 2003, Tom Booth, Jenny Pixler and Anthony Kuner.
    Published by spiritandsong.com®, a division of OCP. All rights reserved.
Music: Tom Booth and Jenny Pixler, © 2003, Tom Booth and Jenny Pixler.
    Published by spiritandsong.com®, a division of OCP. All rights reserved.

658   FOR THE SAKE OF CHRIST

For the sake of Christ, I will-ing-ly ac-cept my weak-ness and my trials,

for when I am pow-er-less, then I am strong.   strong.

1. Al-though in God's __ love   my life   was blest,   my faith __ was
2. And   so when   I   am weak, then I   am free.   The pow - er of

1. giv - en to the test.   For mer-cy did I   pray, and then I   heard God say,
2. Christ will rest in   me. Through all that I   en-dure, the love of God   is sure.

1. "My   grace is e-nough for   you. My grace is e-nough for   you."
2. His   grace is e-nough for   me. His grace is e-nough for   me.

3. He   died for all, that those who live might live no long-er for them-selves.

3. Oh, live for Christ who gave his   life, and now is raised on   high.

Text: Based on 2 Corinthians 5:15; 12:7–10; Ken Canedo, b. 1953.
Music: Ken Canedo.
Text and music © 1995, 2005, Ken Canedo. Published by OCP. All rights reserved.

659   OPEN MY EYES

1. O-pen my eyes, Lord.   Help me to   see   your   face.
2. O-pen my ears, Lord.   Help me to   hear   your   voice.
3. O-pen my heart, Lord.   Help me to   love   like   you.
4. I live with - in   you.   Deep in your heart,   O   Love.

1. O-pen my eyes, Lord.   Help me to   see.
2. O-pen my ears, Lord.   Help me to   hear.
3. O-pen my heart, Lord.   Help me to   love.
4. I live with - in   you.   Rest now in   me.

Text: Based on Mark 8:22–25; Jesse Manibusan, b. 1958.
Music: Jesse Manibusan.
Text and music © 1988, Jesse Manibusan. Published by spiritandsong.com®, a division of OCP. All rights reserved.

JESUS, COME TO US   660

Refrain

Je - sus, come to us, lead us to your light. Je - sus, be with us,

for we need you.

Verses

1. Lord, we come be - fore you, _____ lis - ten
2. Lord, we come to praise you for your faith-ful -
3. Lord, you give us won-ders, _ your glo -

to Refrain

1. to   our   prayer. Fill us all with hope   and   your   love.
2. ness through night. You will be with us,   this   we   know.
3. ry   to   all.   We be-lieve in you,   come to   us.

Text and music: David Haas, b. 1957, © 1981, 1982, OCP. All rights reserved.

ST. PATRICK'S BREASTPLATE   661

Christ be be - hind me, Christ be be - fore me, Christ be be -

neath me, Christ be a - bove me, Christ in each heart that

thinks of me, Christ in each mouth that speaks of me.

Text: St. Patrick, 372–466; adapt. by Andrew Wright, b. 1955.
Music: Andrew Wright.
Text and music © 2001, Andrew Wright. Published by OCP. All rights reserved.

662   COME, MY WAY, MY TRUTH, MY LIFE

1. Come, my Way, my Truth, my Life: Such a
2. Come, my Light, my Feast, my Strength: Such a
3. Come, my Joy, my Love, my Heart: Such a

1. way as gives us breath; Such a truth as ends all
2. light as shows a feast; Such a feast as mends in
3. joy as none can move; Such a love as none can

1. strife; Such a life as kill - eth death.
2. length; Such a strength as makes his guest.
3. part; Such a heart as joys in love.

Text: 77 77; George Herbert, 1593–1632.
Music: THE CALL; *Five Mystical Songs*; Ralph Vaughan Williams, 1872–1958.

663   PSALM 42: AS THE DEER LONGS

1. As the deer longs for flow-ing streams, so longs my
2. My tears have fed me day and night, while some have
3. Why do I mourn and toil with - in, when it is

1. soul for you, O God. My soul does thirst
2. said "Where is your God?" But I re - call,
3. mine to hope in God? I shall a - gain

1. for the liv - ing God, when shall I come to see your
2. as my soul pours dry, the days of praise with-in your
3. sing __ praise to him, he is my help, he is my

| 1, 2 | 2 to Vss 2,3 | Final |

1. face? 3. God. He is my God.
2. house.

Text: Irregular; based on Psalm 42; Danna Harkin, © 1975, Word Music Group, LLC.
   All rights reserved. Used with permission.
Music: O WALY WALY, alt.; trad. English Melody.

DWELLING PLACE

Text: Based on Ephesians 3; John Foley, S.J., b. 1939.
Music: John Foley, S.J.

665

CENTER OF MY LIFE

Refrain: Repeat 1st time

O Lord, you are the cen-ter of my life: I will al-ways praise you,

1-5 (to Verses) | Final

I will al-ways serve you, I will al-ways keep you in my sight. 1. sight.
2.
3. And

Verses 1-3

1. Keep me safe, O God, ___ I take ref-uge in you. ___ I say to the
2. I will bless the Lord who gives me coun - sel, _____ who e - ven at
3. so my heart re-joic - es, my soul is glad; _____ e - ven in

1. Lord, "You are my God. My hap - pi - ness ____ lies in you a-
2. night di - rects my heart. I keep _ the Lord ____ ev - er in my
3. safe - ty shall my bod-y rest. For you will not leave my soul a-mong the

to Refrain

1. lone; my hap-pi-ness _____ lies in you a - lone." ___
2. sight: since he is at my right _ hand, _ I shall stand firm.
3. dead, nor let __ your be-lov-ed know de - cay. _____

Verse 4

4. You will show me the path of life, the full - ness of

4. joy in your pres-ence, at your right hand,

to Refrain

4. at your right hand hap-pi-ness for-ev - er.

We Walk by Faith/In Times of Trouble

Refrain

We walk by faith and not by sight, through joy and woe, through dark and light.

We jour-ney not a-lone, for-sak - en. You walk with us, our God and friend.

Verses

1. In times of trou - ble walk with us,
2. O faith - ful God, you dwell with us
3. We place our trust in you, O God.
4. O God of peace, re - main with us.
5. The storms of life shall bring us woe,

1. lov - ing God of mer - cy. Take our fear and sor - row;
2. in the depths of our souls; there, you speak your word of
3. You re - store hope in us. In the dark - est val - leys
4. Teach us your ways of truth. May we act with jus - tice,
5. yet we cling to your word: "Be - hold, I am with you

to Refrain

1. re - store___ our souls: make us peo - ple of hope.
2. com - pas - sion and truth. In your word we find life.
3. you light___ the way. In you is our cour - age.
4. com - pas - sion and love. This is all you ask of us.
5. un - til___ the end." In your word we find life.

Text: Barbara Bridge, b. 1950, © 1997, 2003, Barbara Bridge. Published by OCP. All rights reserved.
Music: Refrain, *Jesu dulcis memoria*; verses, *Ave maris stella*.

667 FAITH OF OUR FATHERS

1. Faith of our fa - thers! Liv - ing still
2. The mar - tyrs, chained in pris - ons dark,
3. Faith of our moth - ers! Ma - ry's pray'rs
4. Faith of our fa - thers! We will love

1. In spite of dun - geon, fire and sword:
2. Were still in heart and con - science free:
3. Shall win all na - tions un - to thee;
4. Both friend and foe in all our strife:

1. O how our hearts beat high with joy,
2. And tru - ly blest would be our fate,
3. And through the truth that comes from God,
4. And preach thee, too, as love knows how,

1. When - e'er we hear that glo - rious word:
2. If we, like them, should die for thee.
3. We all shall then in - deed be free.
4. By kind - ly words and vir - tuous life.

1. Faith of our fa - thers, ho - ly faith!
2. Faith of the mar - tyrs, ho - ly faith!
3. Faith of our moth - ers, ho - ly faith!
4. Faith of our fa - thers, ho - ly faith!

1-4. We will be true to thee till death.

Text: 88 88 88; Frederick W. Faber, 1814–1863, alt.
Music: ST. CATHERINE; Henri F. Hemy, 1818–1888; adapt. by James G. Walton, 1821–1905.

JESUS, LORD

668

Je - sus, Lord, strength-en us with faith in you.

Lift our hearts, fill us with new trust in your love.

Verses

1. God so loved the world he gave his on - ly Son,
2. God ___ sent his Son in - to a bro - ken world,
3. Je - sus is the light by which we see the truth;

to Refrain

1. With our faith in him we shall have e - ter - nal life.
2. Not ___ to con - demn, ___ but that we might be saved.
3. If we fol - low him we are blest in all we do.

*Opening Refrain is sung twice before proceeding to Verse 1.

Text: Based on John 3:16–21; Randall DeBruyn, b. 1947, © 1984, OCP. All rights reserved.
Music: Randall DeBruyn, © 1984, OCP. All rights reserved.

WE WALK BY FAITH

669

1, 5. We walk by faith, and not by sight: No gra-cious words we hear
2. We may not touch his hands and side, Nor fol - low where he trod;
3. Help then, O Lord, our un - be - lief, And may our faith a-bound;
4. That when our life of faith is done In realms of clear - er light

1, 5. Of him who spoke as none e'er spoke, But we be - lieve him near.
2. Yet in his prom-ise we re - joice And cry, "My Lord and God!"
3. To call on you when you are near, And seek where you are found:
4. We may be - hold you as you are In full and end-less sight.

Text: CM; Henry Alford, alt., 1810–1871.
Music: ST. ANNE; attr. to William Croft, 1678–1727.

670   AGE TO AGE

Refrain: 1st time: Cantor, All repeat; thereafter: All

Age to age we will love you. Dawn-ing light we will wake with you. In - to night we will fol-low you. We will love you age to age.

Verses

1. As the ea - gle flies __ to the heav'ns a - bove, __ on __ wings of faith God will bear you up.
2. As the lil - ies of the field __ nei-ther toil nor spin, what __ splen - dor we find in the love God gives.
3. Come, all you __ wea - ry, __ for you are blessed. God will light - en your bur - den and give you rest.
4. Lord, __ let my faith in you be re - vealed. __ On - ly say the word and I shall be healed.

2 to Refrain

Text: Based on Isaiah 40:31; Matthew 6:28; 11:28–30; Janet Vogt, b. 1953.
Music: Janet Vogt.

671   ON EAGLE'S WINGS

Verse 1

1. You who dwell in the shel-ter of the Lord, who a - bide in his

to Refrain

1. shad-ow for life, say to the Lord: "My ref-uge, my rock in whom I trust!"

Text: Based on Psalm 91; Michael Joncas, b. 1951.
Music: Michael Joncas.
Text and music © 1979, OCP. All rights reserved.

672 **O GOD, OUR HELP IN AGES PAST**

1. O God, our help in a - ges past, Our
2. Be - neath the shad - ow of your throne Your
3. Be - fore the hills in or - der stood, Or
4. A thou - sand a - ges in your sight Are
5. Time, like an ev - er - roll - ing stream, Bears
6. O God, our help in a - ges past, Our

1. hope for years to come, Our shel - ter from the
2. saints have dwelt se - cure; Suf - fi - cient is your
3. earth re - ceived her frame, From ev - er - last - ing
4. like an eve - ning gone; Short as the watch that
5. all our years a - way; They fly for - got - ten,
6. hope for years to come, Still be our guard while

1. storm - y blast, And our e - ter - nal home.
2. arm a - lone, And our de - fense is sure.
3. you are God, To end - less years the same.
4. ends the night Be - fore the ris - ing sun.
5. as a dream Dies at the o - p'ning day.
6. trou - bles last, And our e - ter - nal home.

Text: CM; based on Psalm 90; Isaac Watts, 1674–1748, alt.
Music: ST. ANNE; attr. to William Croft, 1678–1727.

673 **BE NOT AFRAID**

Verse 1
1. You shall cross the bar - ren des - ert, but you shall not die of

1. thirst. You shall wan - der far in safe - ty though you do not know the

1. way. You shall speak your words in for - eign lands and all will un - der-

to Refrain
1. stand. You shall see the face of God and live.

Refrain
Be not a-fraid. I go be-fore you al-ways. Come fol-low

1, 2   to Vss 2, 3   Final 2

me, and I will give you rest.

Verse 2
2. If you pass through rag-ing wa-ters in the sea, you shall not

2. drown. If you walk a-mid the burn-ing flames, you shall not be

2. harmed. If you stand be-fore the pow'r of hell and death is at your

to Refrain
2. side, know that I am with you through it all.

Verse 3
3. Bless-ed are your poor, for the king-dom shall be theirs. Blest are you that

3. weep and mourn, for one day you shall laugh. And if wick-ed tongues in-sult and

to Refrain
3. hate you all be-cause of me, bless-ed, bless-ed are you!

Text: Based on Isaiah 43:2–3; Luke 6:20ff; Bob Dufford, SJ, b. 1943.
Music: Bob Dufford, SJ.

674

A Mighty Fortress

1. A might-y for-tress is our God, A
2. No strength of ours can match his might! We
3. Though hordes of dev-ils fill the land All
4. God's Word for-ev-er shall a-bide, No

1. sword and shield vic-to-rious; He breaks the
2. would be lost, re-ject-ed. But now a
3. threat-'ning to de-vour us, We trem-ble
4. thanks to foes, who fear it; For God him-

1. cruel op-pres-sor's rod And wins sal-va-tion
2. cham-pion comes to fight, Whom God him-self e-
3. not, un-moved we stand; They can-not o-ver-
4. self fights by our side With weap-ons of the

1. glo-rious. The old sa-tan-ic foe
2. lect-ed. You ask who this may be?
3. pow'r us. Let this world's ty-rant rage;
4. Spir-it. Were they to take our house,

1. Has sworn to work us woe! With craft and
2. The Lord of hosts is he! Christ Je-sus,
3. In bat-tle we'll en-gage! His might is
4. Goods, hon-or, child, or spouse, Though life be

1. dread-ful might He arms him-self to fight.
2. might-y Lord, God's on-ly Son, a-dored.
3. doomed to fail! God's judg-ment must pre-vail!
4. wrenched a-way, They can-not win the day.

1. On earth he has no e - qual.
2. He holds the field vic - to - rious.
3. One lit - tle word sub - dues him.
4. The King - dom's ours for - ev - er!

FOR YOU ARE MY GOD 675

For you are my God; you a - lone are my joy. De-

fend me, O Lord.

Verses

1. You give mar - vel - ous
2. — You are my
3. — Glad are my
4. You show me the

1. com - rades __ to me: the faith - ful who dwell in your
2. por - tion __ and cup; it is you __ that I claim for my
3. heart __ and my soul; se - cure - ly my bod - y shall
4. path __ for my life; in your pres - ence __ the full - ness of

1. land. Those __ who choose a - li - en gods __
2. prize. Your her - i - tage __ is my de - light, __
3. rest. For you __ will not leave me __ for dead, __
4. joy. To be __ at your right hand __ for - ev - er __

to Refrain

1. __ have cho - sen an a - li - en band. __
2. __ the lot you have giv - en to me. __
3. __ nor lead your be - lov - ed a - stray. __
4. __ for me would be hap - pi - ness al - ways. __

676

ONLY A SHADOW

1. The love we have for you, O Lord, is
2. The bread we take and eat, O Lord, is
3. Our own be-lief in you, O Lord, is
4. The dreams we share to-day, O Lord, are
5. The joy we share to-day, O Lord, is

1. on - ly a shad-ow of your love for us;
2. your bod-y bro - ken and shared with us;
3. on - ly a shad-ow of your faith in us;
4. on - ly a shad-ow of your dreams for us;
5. on - ly a shad-ow of your joys for us;

1. on - ly a shad-ow of your love for us; your
2. your bod - y bro - ken and shared with us; the
3. on - ly a shad-ow of your faith in us; your
4. on - ly a shad-ow of your dreams for us; if
5. on - ly a shad-ow of your joys for us; when

1. deep a - bid - ing love. (to Verse 2)
2. gift of your great love. (to Refrain)
3. deep and last - ing faith. (to Verse 4)
4. we but fol - low you. (to Refrain)
5. we meet face to face. (to Refrain)

Refrain

Our lives are in your hands, our lives
are in your hands. Our love for you will
grow, O Lord; your light in us will shine.

Blest Be the Lord

Refrain

Blest be the Lord; blest be the Lord, the God of mer-cy, the God who saves. I shall not fear the dark of night, nor the ar-row that flies by day.

Verses

1. He will re-lease me from the nets of all my foes.
2. I need not shrink be-fore the ter-rors of the night,
3. Al-though a thou-sand strong have fall-en at my side,

1. He will pro-tect me from their wick-ed hands.
2. nor stand a-lone be-fore the light of day.
3. I'll not be shak-en with the Lord at hand.

1. Be-neath the shad-ow of his wings I
2. No harm shall come to me, no ar-row
3. His faith-ful love is all the ar-mor

to Refrain

1. will re-joice to find a dwell-ing place se-cure.
2. strike me down, no e-vil set-tle in my soul.
3. that I need to wage my bat-tle with the foe.

Text: Based on Psalm 91; Dan Schutte, b. 1947.
Music: Dan Schutte.

678　　　**O God, You Search Me**

1. O God, you search me and you know me.
2. You know my rest-ing and my ris-ing.
3. Be - fore a word is on my tongue, Lord,
4. Al - though your Spir - it is up - on me,
5. For you cre - at - ed me and shaped me,

1. All my thoughts lie o - pen to your gaze.
2. You dis - cern my pur - pose from a - far,
3. You have known its mean - ing through and through.
4. Still I search for shel - ter from your light.
5. Gave me life with - in my moth - er's womb.

1. When I walk or lie down you are be - fore me:
2. And with love ev - er - last - ing you be - siege me:
3. You are with me be - yond my un - der - stand - ing:
4. There is no - where on earth I can es - cape you:
5. For the won - der of who I am, I praise you:

1. Ev - er the mak - er and keep - er of my days.
2. In ev - 'ry mo - ment of life or death, you are.
3. God of my pres - ent, my past and fu - ture, too.
4. E - ven the dark - ness is ra - diant in your sight.
5. Safe in your hands, all cre - a - tion is made new.

679　　　**Only in God**

Verses

1. On - ly in God is my soul at_ rest, in___ him comes my sal -
2. On - ly in God is found safe - ty when my en - e - my pur -

1. va - tion. He, ___ on - ly, ___ is my_ rock, my strength_ and
2. sues me. On - ly in God is found glo - ry when I am found

1. my ___ sal - va - tion. My strong-hold, my Sav - ior,
2. meek and found low - ly.

I shall not be a - fraid at all. My strong-hold, my

Sav - ior, I shall not be moved. moved. On - ly in

God is my soul at rest, in him comes my sal - va - tion.

Text: Based on Psalm 62; John Michael Talbot, b. 1954.
Music: John Michael Talbot.
Text and music © 1980, Birdwing Music/BMG Songs. All rights reserved.
   Administered by EMI CMG Publishing. Used with permission.

AMAZING GRACE   680

1. A - maz - ing grace! How sweet the sound That saved a
2. 'Twas grace that taught my heart to fear, And grace my
3. The Lord has prom - ised good to me, His word my
4. Through man - y dan - gers, toils, and snares, I have al -
5. When we've been there ten thou - sand years, Bright shin - ing

1. wretch like me! I once was lost, but
2. fears re - lieved; How pre - cious did that
3. hope se - cures; He will my shield and
4. read - y come; 'Tis grace has brought me
5. as the sun, We've no less days to

1. now am found, Was blind but now I see.
2. grace ap - pear The hour I first be - lieved!
3. por - tion be As long as life en - dures.
4. safe thus far, And grace will lead me home.
5. sing God's praise Than when we'd first be - gun.

Text: CM; verses 1–4, John Newton, 1725–1807; verse 5, anon., fr. *A Collection of Sacred Ballads*, 1790.
Music: NEW BRITAIN; *Columbian Harmony*, 1829.

681

WE WILL RISE AGAIN

Verse 1
1. Like a shep-herd I will feed you; I will gath - er you with
1. care. I will lead you and hold you close to my heart.

Refrain
We will run and not grow wea - ry, for our God will be our
strength, and we will fly like the ea - gle, we will rise a - gain.

Verse 2
2. I am strength to the wea - ry; to the weak I am new life. Though the
2. young may grow wea - ry, I will be their hope.

Verse 3
3. Lift up your eyes, and see who made the stars. I
3. lead you, and I know you, I call you each by name.

Verse 4
4. Fear not, I am with you; I am your God. I will
4. strength-en you and help you; up - hold you with my hand.

Text: Based on Isaiah 40:11, 26, 29–30; 41:10; David Haas, b. 1957.
Music: David Haas.

THOUGH THE MOUNTAINS MAY FALL

Refrain

Though the moun - tains may fall and the hills turn to dust,
yet the love of the Lord will stand
as a shel - ter for all who will call on his name.
Sing the praise and the glo - ry of God.

Verses

1. Could the Lord ev - er leave you? Could the Lord for -
2. Should you turn and for - sake him, he will gent - ly
3. Go to him when you're wea - ry; he will give you
4. As he swore to your fa - thers, when the flood de -

1. get his love? Though a moth - er for -
2. call your name. Should you wan - der a -
3. ea - gle's wings. You will run, nev - er
4. stroyed the land, he will nev - er for -

to Refrain

1. sake her child, he will not a - ban - don you.
2. way from him, he will al - ways take you back.
3. tire, _____ for your God will be your strength.
4. sake you; _____ he will swear to you a - gain.

Text: Based on Isaiah 54:6–10; 49:15; 40:31–32; Dan Schutte, b. 1947.
Music: Dan Schutte.
Text and music © 1975, 1979, OCP. All rights reserved.

683 HOW FIRM A FOUNDATION

1. How firm a foun - da - tion, you saints of the Lord,
2. "Fear not, I am with you, O be not dis-mayed,
3. "When through the deep wa - ters I call you to go,
4. "The soul that on Je - sus still leans for re - pose,

1. Is laid for your faith in his ex - cel - lent Word!
2. For I am your God, and will still give you aid;
3. The riv - ers of woe shall not you o - ver - flow;
4. I will not, I will not de - sert to its foes;

1. What more can he say than to you he has said,
2. I'll strength - en you, help you, and cause you to stand,
3. For I will be with you, your trou - bles to bless,
4. That soul, though all hell should en - deav - or to shake,

1. To you who for ref - uge to Je - sus have fled?
2. Up - held by my righ - teous, om - nip - o - tent hand."
3. And sanc - ti - fy to you, your deep - est dis - tress."
4. I'll nev - er, no nev - er, no nev - er for - sake!"

Text: 11 11 11 11; "K" in Rippon's *A Selection of Hymns*, 1787.
Music: FOUNDATION; Funk's *A Compilation of Genuine Church Music*, Winchester, VA, 1832.

684 HERE I AM

Refrain

Here I am, stand-ing right be-side you. Here I am;

do not be a - fraid. Here I am, wait-ing like a lov - er.

1-3 to Vss. | Final

I am here; here I am. am. I am here; here I am.

1. Do not fear when the tempt-er calls you. Do not
1. fear e-ven though you fall. Do not fear, I have con-quered
1. e-vil. Do not fear, nev-er be a-fraid.

2. I am here in the face of ev-'ry child.
2. I am here in ev-'ry warm em-brace. I am here with
2. ten-der-ness and mer-cy. Here I am, I am here.

3. I am here in the midst of ev-'ry tri-al. I am
3. here in the face of de-spair. I am here when
3. par-don-ing your broth-er. Here I am, I am here.

685 SEEK YE FIRST

1. Seek ye___ first the king - dom of God and his
2. Ask and it shall be giv - en un - to you; seek, and
3. You do not live by bread ___ a - lone, but by

1. righ - teous - ness, And all these things shall be
2. ye shall ___ find; Knock, and it shall be ___
3. ev - 'ry ___ word That pro - ceeds from the

1. add - ed un - to you.
2. o - pened un - to you. } Al - le - lu, al - le - lu - ia.
3. mouth ___ of ___ God.

Text: Based on Matthew 6:33; Karen Lafferty, b. 1948.
Music: Karen Lafferty.

686 HOW CAN I KEEP FROM SINGING

Verses

1. My life flows on in end - less song; A -
2. Through all the tu - mult and the strife, I
3. What though the tem - pest 'round me roar, I
4. When ty - rants trem - ble, sick with fear, And
5. The peace of Christ makes fresh my heart, A

1. bove earth's lam - en - ta - tion. I hear the real though
2. hear that mu - sic ring - ing; It sounds and ech - oes
3. hear the truth it liv - eth. What though the dark - ness
4. hear their death knells ring - ing; When friends re - joice both
5. foun - tain ev - er spring - ing. All things are mine since

1. far - off hymn That hails a new cre - a - tion.
2. in my soul; How can I keep from sing - ing?
3. 'round me close, Songs in the night it giv - eth.
4. far and near, How can I keep from sing - ing?
5. I am his; How can I keep from sing - ing?

No storm can shake my in-most calm, While to that rock I'm cling-ing. Since Love is Lord of heav-en and earth, How can I keep from sing-ing?

Text: 87 87 with refrain; attr. to Robert Lowry, 1826–1899, alt.; verse 3, Doris Plenn.
Music: ENDLESS SONG; Quaker Hymn; attr. to Robert Lowry.

YOU ARE NEAR 687

Refrain

O Lord, I know you are near, stand-ing al-ways at my side. You guard me from the foe, and you lead me in ways ev-er-last-ing.

Verses

1. Lord, you have searched my heart, and you know when I
2. Where can I run from your love? If I climb to the
3. You know my heart and its ways, you who formed me be-
4. Mar-vel-ous to me are your works; how pro-found are your

1. sit and when I stand. Your hand is up-on me, pro-
2. heav-ens you are there; if I fly to the sun-rise or
3. fore I was born, in the se-cret of dark-ness be-
4. thoughts, my Lord. E-ven if I could count them, they

to Refrain

1. tect-ing me from death, keep-ing me from harm.
2. sail be-yond the sea, still I'd find you there.
3. fore I saw the sun, in my moth-er's womb.
4. num-ber as the stars, you would still be there.

Text: Based on Psalm 139; Dan Schutte, b. 1947.
Music: Dan Schutte.

688   THERE IS A BALM IN GILEAD

Refrain

There is a balm in Gil-e-ad to make the wound-ed whole,

there is a balm in Gil-e-ad to heal the sin-sick soul.

Verses

1. Some-times I feel dis-cour-aged, And __ think my work's in vain,
2. If you can-not preach like Pe-ter, If you can-not pray like Paul,
3. Don't __ ev-er feel dis-cour-aged, For __ Je-sus is your friend;

to Refrain

1. But __ then the Ho-ly Spir-it Re-vives my soul a-gain.
2. You can tell the love of Je-sus, And say, "He died for all."
3. And __ if you lack for knowl-edge, He'll ne'er re-fuse to lend.

Text: 76 76 with refrain; based on Jeremiah 8:22; Spiritual.
Music: BALM IN GILEAD; Spiritual.

689   SHELTER ME, O GOD

Refrain

Shel-ter me, O God; hide me in the shad-ow of your wings. You a-lone

Verses

are my hope.

1. When my foes sur-round me, set me
2. As a moth-er gath-ers her ____
3. Though I walk in dark-ness, through the

to Refrain

1. high a-bove their reach. Hear me when I call your name.
2. young be-neath her care, gath-er me in-to your arms.
3. nee-dle's eye of death, you will nev-er leave my side.

Text: Based on Psalm 16; Psalm 61; Luke 13:34; Bob Hurd, b. 1950.
Music: Bob Hurd.

THE KING OF LOVE MY SHEPHERD IS
690

1. The King of love my shep-herd is, Whose
2. Where streams of liv - ing wa - ter flow With
3. Per - verse and fool - ish I have strayed, But
4. In death's dark vale I fear no ill With
5. You spread a ta - ble in my sight, Your
6. And so through all the length of days Your

1. good - ness fails me nev - er; I noth - ing lack if
2. gen - tle care he leads me, And where the ver - dant
3. yet in love he sought me, And on his shoul - der
4. you, dear Lord, be - side me; Your rod and staff my
5. sav - ing grace be - stow - ing; And O what joy and
6. good - ness fails me nev - er: Good Shep - herd, may I

1. I am his, And he is mine for - ev - er.
2. pas - tures grow, With heav'n - ly food he feeds me.
3. gent - ly laid, And home, re - joic - ing, brought me.
4. com - fort still, Your cross be - fore to guide me.
5. true de - light From your pure chal - ice flow - ing!
6. sing your praise With - in your house for - ev - er.

Text: 87 87; based on Psalm 23; Matthew 18; John 10; Henry Williams Baker, 1821–1877, alt.
Music: ST. COLUMBA; trad. Irish Melody.

LIKE A CHILD RESTS
691

Refrain: 1st time: Cantor, All repeat; thereafter: All

Like a child rests in its moth-er's arms, so will I rest in

you. Like a so will I rest in you.

Verses   to Refrain

1. My God, I am not proud. I do not look for things too great.
2. My God, I trust in you. You care for me, you give me peace.
3. O Is - rael, trust in God, ___ now and al - ways trust in God.

Text: Based on Psalm 131; Christopher Walker, b. 1947.
Music: Christopher Walker.

692   I HEARD THE VOICE OF JESUS

1. I heard the voice of Je-sus say, "Come un-to me and
2. I heard the voice of Je-sus say, "Be - hold, I free - ly
3. I heard the voice of Je-sus say, "I am this dark world's

1. rest; Lay down, thou wea - ry one, lay down Thy head up -
2. give The liv - ing wa - ter; thirst - y one, Stoop down, and
3. light; Look un - to me, thy morn shall rise, And all thy

1. on my breast." I came to Je - sus as I was, So
2. drink, and live." I came to Je - sus, and I drank Of
3. day be bright." I looked to Je - sus, and I found In

1. wea - ry, worn and sad; I found in him a
2. that life - giv - ing stream; My thirst was quenched, my
3. him my star, my sun; And in that light of

1. rest - ing place, And he has made me glad.
2. soul re - vived, And now I live in him.
3. life I'll walk Till trav - 'ling days are done.

Text: CMD; Horatius Bonar, 1808–1889, alt.
Music: KINGSFOLD; trad. English Melody; *English Country Songs*, 1893; adapt. by Ralph Vaughan Williams, 1872–1958.

693   MY SOUL IS THIRSTING

Refrain

My soul is thirst-ing, my bod - y pines; for you my

heart is long-ing. Your love is bet - ter than

life it - self; you are the God who up - holds me.

You are the God whom I seek.

Verses

1. Like a dry wea-ry land with-out wa-ter, so my
2. I will bless you as long as I live; I will
3. In the watch-es of night I re-mem-ber; you, my

1. flesh pines for you; parched and life-less
2. sing songs of praise. In your pres-ence
3. God, you, my help. In the shad-ow

to Refrain

1. is my spir-it with-out you.
2. I will feast and be filled.
3. of your wings I re-joice.

Text: Based on Psalm 63:1–8; Bob Hurd, b. 1950.
Music: Bob Hurd.
Text and music © 1990, Bob Hurd. Published by OCP. All rights reserved.

BE STILL AND KNOW THAT I AM GOD   694

1-3. Be still and know that I am God. You are my

1. cho-sen one, to whom my love I give. My life is
2. cho-sen one, I came to set you free. Give me your
3. cho-sen one, to whom I show my ways. My love is

1. yours, in you I live.
2. cares and rest in me.   Be still, be still
3. with you all your days.

1-3. and know that I am God.

Text and music: Christopher Walker, b. 1947, and Paule Freeburg, DC, b. 1942,
© 2005, Christopher Walker and Paule Freeburg, DC. Published by OCP. All rights reserved.

695   **COME TO ME**

Refrain

Come to me, all who la-bor and are heav-y bur - dened, and

I shall give you rest. Take up my yoke and learn from

me, for I am meek and hum - ble of heart,

and you'll find rest for your souls. Yes, my

yoke is eas - y and my bur - den is

light.

Verses

1. You, God, are my shep-herd.
2. Be - side peace-ful wa - ters
3. Should I be sur-round-ed
4. Be - fore my deep hun - ger
5. Pur - sue me, O God, ___

1. I shall nev - er be in need. Fresh and green are the
2. you re - store ___ my true self; There you lead me to
3. by the shad - ows of death, I will not fear, for
4. you spread out ___ your ___ feast. My ___ skin you a -
5. with your fath - om - less love. In your tent let me

to Refrain

1. mead-ows where you give me ___ rest. ___
2. walk ___ in the path of new life.
3. you are stead - fast in your ___ love.
4. noint ___ with the rich - est of oil.
5. dwell ___ all the days of my life.

Text: Based on Matthew 11:28–30; Psalm 23; original text, Weston Priory, Gregory Norbet, OSB, b. 1940.
Music: Weston Priory, Gregory Norbet, OSB.
Text and music © 1971, 1994 (revised text), The Benedictine Foundation of the State of Vermont, Inc.
   All rights reserved. Used with permission.

IN EVERY AGE

Verses

1. Long be-fore the moun-tains came to be
2. Des-ti-ny is cast, and at your si-lent word
3. Teach us to make use of the time we have.

1. and the land and sea and stars of the night,
2. we re-turn to dust and scat-ter to the wind. A
3. Teach us to be pa - tient e - ven as we wait.

1. through the end-less sea - sons of all time, you have
2. thou-sand years are like a sin-gle mo-ment gone, as the
3. Teach us to em-brace our ev-'ry joy and pain. To sleep

1. al - ways been, you will al - ways be.
2. light that fades at the end of day.
3. peace - ful - ly, and to rise up strong.

Refrain

In ev-'ry age, O God, you have been our ref-uge.

1, 2 *to Verses 2, 3*

In ev-'ry age, O God, you have been our hope.

Final

God, you have been our hope,

you have been our ref - uge, you have been our hope.

Text: Based on Psalm 90:1–4, 12; Janèt Sullivan Whitaker, b. 1958.
Music: Janèt Sullivan Whitaker.

697 BECAUSE THE LORD IS MY SHEPHERD

Verses

1. Be - cause ___ the Lord is my shep - herd, I have
2. And when ___ the road leads to dark - ness, I shall
3. In love ___ you make me a ban - quet for my
4. Your good - ness ___ al - ways is with me and your

1. ev – 'ry thing ___ I need. He lets me rest in the
2. walk there ___ un - a - fraid. E - ven when death is close ___
3. en - e - mies ___ to see. You make me wel - come, ___
4. mer - cy ___ I know. Your lov - ing kind - ness ___

1. mead - ow and leads me to the qui - et streams. He re -
2. ___ I have cour - age, for your help is there. You are
3. pour - ing down hon - or from your might - y hand, and this
4. strength - ens me al - ways as I go through life. I shall

1. stores ___ my soul and he leads me in the paths that are right:
2. close ___ be - side me with com - fort, you are guid - ing my way:
3. joy ___ fills me with glad - ness; it is too much to bear:
4. dwell in your pres - ence for - ev - er, giv - ing praise to your name:

Refrain

Lord, you are my shep - herd, you are my friend.

I want to fol - low you al - ways, just to fol - low my friend.

Text: Based on Psalm 23; Christopher Walker, b. 1947.
Music: Christopher Walker.

FLY LIKE A BIRD

Refrain

Fly like a bird to the Lord, my soul. I want to soar like an ea-gle. Though I may jour-ney far a-way from home, I know I'll nev-er be a-lone.

Verses

1. O God, you know who I am.
2. Where can I run from your love?
3. When I am down and a-fraid,

1. You know my hopes and my dreams. In my
2. Where can I hide from my God? From the
3. when I am fall-ing a-way, you ex-

1. pon-der-ing and fears, in my joy and in my tears,
2. dawn of morn-ing's light to the dark-ness of the night,
3. tend a gen-tle hand, and I know you un-der-stand.

to Refrain

1-3. O God, your pres-ence is real.

699

MY SHEPHERD WILL SUPPLY MY NEED

1. My Shep-herd will sup-ply my need; The
2. When I walk through the shades of death, Your
3. The sure pro-vi-sions of my God At-

1. Lord God is his name. In pas-tures
2. pres-ence is my stay; One word of
3. tend me all my days; O may your

1. green he makes me feed, Be-side the liv-ing
2. your sup-port-ing breath Drives all my fears a-
3. house be my a-bode, And all my work be

1. stream. He brings my wan-d'ring
2. way. Your hand, in sight of
3. praise! There would I find a

1. spir-it back, When I for-sake his ways;
2. all my foes, Does still my ta-ble spread;
3. set-tled rest, While oth-ers go and come,

1. And leads me for his mer-cy's
2. My cup with bless-ings o-ver-
3. No more a stran-ger nor a

1. sake, In paths of truth and grace.
2. flows, Your oil a-noints my head.
3. guest; But like a child at home.

Text: 86 86 D; based on Psalm 23; Isaac Watts, 1674–1748, alt.
Music: RESIGNATION; William Walker's *The Southern Harmony*, 1835.

PEACE

Refrain

Peace I leave with you, my friends, peace the world can-not give.

(Repeat Final time)

Peace I leave with you, my friends, so that your joy be ev - er full.

Verses

1. The Fa - ther's love I came to give,
2. Take ____ his gift and be at peace;
3. By ____ this love which you should have,
4. Take ____ my words of life to heart,
5. All ____ I have I give to you;
6. I came so that you may have life,
7. If ____ you love me, keep my word,

to Refrain

1. to be the hope for all who live.
2. the Spir - it of our love I bring.
3. all ____ will know you are my friends.
4. and you will live with hope and joy.
5. I share with you the Fa - ther's love.
6. and have it to _____ the full.
7. and ____ our home we'll make with you.

Text: Based on John 14:27ff; Weston Priory, Gregory Norbet, OSB, b. 1940.
Music: Weston Priory, Gregory Norbet, OSB.
Text and music © 1971, The Benedictine Foundation of the State of Vermont, Inc.

DONA NOBIS PACEM

Do - na no - bis pa - cem, pa-cem. Do - na no - bis pa -

cem. Do - na no - bis pa-cem. Do-na no-bis pa - cem.

Do - na no - bis pa-cem. Do-na no-bis pa - cem.

Text and music: Traditional.

702

PRAYER OF ST. FRANCIS

Verses 1, 2, 4

1. Make me a chan-nel of your peace. Where there is ha-tred,
2. Make me a chan-nel of your peace. Where there's de-spair in
4. Make me a chan-nel of your peace. It is in par-don-

1. let me bring your love. _____ Where there is in - ju -
2. life, let me bring hope. _____ Where there is dark-ness _
4. ing that we are par-doned, _____ In giv-ing of our-

1. ry, your par-don, Lord, And where there's doubt, true
2. _____ on - ly light, And where there's sad - ness
4. selves that we re - ceive, And in dy - ing that we're

1, Final   1st time: to Verse 2   2
            (Fine)   to Verse 3

1. faith in you.
2. ev - er   2. joy.
4. born to e - ter - nal life.

Verse 3

3. O Mas-ter, grant that I may nev-er seek   So much to be con-

3. soled, as to con-sole,   To be un-der-stood, as to un-der-

to Verse 4

3. stand,   To be loved, as to love, with all my soul.

Text: Based on the prayer traditionally ascr. to St. Francis of Assisi, 1182–1226; Sebastian Temple, 1928–1997.
Music: Sebastian Temple.

Let There Be Peace on Earth

Let there be peace on earth and let it be-gin with me.

Let there be peace on earth, the peace that was meant to

be. With God as our Fa-ther, broth - ers
(optional text) we are

all are we; Let me walk with my broth-er in
fam - i - ly. Let us walk with each oth - er

per - fect har - mo - ny. Let peace be - gin with me, let

this be the mo-ment now. With ev - 'ry step I take, let

this be my sol - emn vow: To take each mo-ment and live each

mo-ment in peace e - ter - nal - ly. Let there be peace on earth and

1
let it be - gin with me.

Final
let it be - gin with me.

704   BEARERS OF PEACE

1. Peo - ple of Je - sus, trust - ed to be bear - ers of
2. Feel for the ones who have no more bread, feel for the
3. Feel for the ones whose homes are de - stroyed, feel for the
4. Stand with the ones who see a new way: peo - ple of
5. Pray for the day our chil - dren will see war strange and
6. Why spend your tears on what can - not heal? Why spend your
7. Chil - dren of peace, go forth through the earth, heal - ing our

1. peace from God's liv - ing tree, peace that the world it - self can-not
2. ones with chil - dren un - fed. Long - ing for food, they find in our
3. lives now shat-tered and void. Wait - ing for loved ones no - bod - y
4. faith who strug - gle and pray, giv - en the call to shape and re -
5. dis - tant as slav - er - y. Work for a world where new ways a -
6. rage on what you con-ceal? God's liv - ing Word cries out to re -
7. world and bring - ing to birth vi - sion to build and fash - ion a

1. know, the peace that is giv - en to plant and to grow.
2. hands a moun-tain of weap-ons more sa - cred than land.
3. saw: the in - no-cent peo - ple who suf - fer in war.
4. build our ac - tions, our con-scienc-es, our bro - ken world.
5. bound to meet and to di - a - logue till peace is found.
6. veal a love that will sat - is - fy, hope that is real.
7. way: the full - ness of life for God's peo - ple to - day.

Text: 9 9 9 11; Bernadette Farrell, b. 1957
Music: SOMERSTOWN; Bernadette Farrell.

705   DONA NOBIS PACEM

Do - na no - bis pa - cem. Do - na no -

bis pa - cem. cem. Do - na no -

- bis pa - cem. Do - na no - bis pa-cem.

1. Give us peace, God,___ peace for
2. God of near - ness,___ God of
3. Set us free, God, from mind - less
4. You re - new us___ with great
5. Be our breath, God,___ deep and
6. Ma - ra - na - tha:___ come to

1. all, like a riv - er run-ning free-ly. ____
2. life, you are with us; we re - joice. ____
3. ways; guide us in pur - su - ing good. ____
4. love; God a - mong us: this our joy! ____
5. pure; feed our hun - ger for your truth. ____
6. us with your heal - ing gift of peace. ____

PEACE IS FLOWING LIKE A RIVER   706

1, 5. Peace is flow-ing like a riv - er, flow - ing
2. Love is flow-ing like a riv - er, flow - ing
3. Heal - ing's flow-ing like a riv - er, flow - ing
4. Al - le - lu - ia, al - le - lu - ia. Al - le -

1, 5. out of you and me. ____ Flow - ing out in - to the
2. out of you and me. ____ Flow - ing out in - to the
3. out of you and me. ____ Flow - ing out in - to the
4. lu - ia, al - le - lu - ia. Al - le - lu - ia, al - le -

1, 5. des - ert, set - ting all the cap-tives free. ____
2. des - ert, set - ting all the cap-tives free. ____
3. des - ert, set - ting all the cap-tives free. ____
4. lu - ia. Al - le - lu - ia, al - le - lu - ia.

707   LITANY OF PEACE

Verses

1. God of love, your gift of peace is plant - ed
2. God of peace, wher - ev - er there is ha - tred,
3. May we bring your hope and glad - ness where de -
4. May we seek to un - der - stand an - oth - er
5. Faith - ful God, wher - ev - er there is dark - ness,
6. God of mer - cy, help us to for - give when
7. Gra - cious God, when - ev - er peo - ple hun - ger,
8. Set us free from all our fear and an - ger;

Refrain

1. deep with - in our hearts: Make me an in-stru-ment
2. may we bring your love:
3. spair and sad - ness are:
4. with a pa - tient heart:
5. may we bring your light:
6. there is in - jury done:
7. may we fill their need:
8. set us free to love:

of your peace. Make me an in - stru - ment of your peace.

Text: Based on the prayer traditionally ascr. to St. Francis of Assisi, 1182–1226; Barbara Bridge, b. 1950.
Music: Barbara Bridge.
Text and music © 2002, 2006, Barbara Bridge. Published by OCP. All rights reserved.

708   GIVE US YOUR PEACE

Refrain

Give us your peace, O God; give us your peace,

1. your peace.
2. your peace. *(Fine)*

Verses

1. When we're a - fraid, run - ning from truth,
2. When we are tired, wea - ry, and worn,
3. Lord, we be - long to you a - lone;

1. gath-er us back to you. ⁊ Take ev-ery fear
2. take us in-to your arms, where there is no need,
3. show us the way back home ⁊ in-to your light,

to Refrain

1. and fill our hearts. ⎫
2. there is no want. ⎬ Give us your peace, O God.
3. in-to your love. ⎭

LOVE DIVINE, ALL LOVES EXCELLING   709

1. Love di-vine, all loves ex-cel-ling, Joy of heav'n, to
2. Come, al-might-y to de-liv-er; Let us all your
3. Fin-ish then your new cre-a-tion, Pure and spot-less,

1. earth come down! Fix in us your hum-ble dwell-ing; All your
2. life re-ceive; Sud-den-ly re-turn and nev-er, Nev-er-
3. gra-cious Lord; Let us see your great sal-va-tion Per-fect-

1. faith-ful mer-cies crown. Je-sus, source of all com-pas-sion,
2. more your tem-ples leave. Lord, we would be al-ways bless-ing,
3. ly in you re-stored. Changed from glo-ry in-to glo-ry,

1. Love un-bound-ed, love all pure; Vis-it us with
2. Serve you as your hosts a-bove, Pray, and praise you
3. Till in heav'n we take our place, Till we sing be-

1. your sal-va-tion, Let your love in us en-dure.
2. with-out ceas-ing, Glo-ry in your pre-cious love.
3. fore the al-might-y, Lost in won-der, love and praise.

Text: 87 87 D; Charles Wesley, 1707–1788, alt.
Music: HYFRYDOL; Rowland H. Prichard, 1811–1887.

710

Ubi Caritas

Refrain

U - bi ca - ri - tas et a - mor, De - us i - bi

1 *2 to Verses (Fine)* Verses 1, 3

est. est.

1. We gath - er to - geth - er
   Our God is a - live, the
3. Then, joined with the bless - ed,
   Our joy none can mea - sure,

1. in the love of Christ;
   God of love is near;
3. filled with hope and grace,
   joy that knows no end,

let each one be
so love one an -
dear Lord, in great
re - sound - ing from

1. glad in him ____ and re - joice.
   oth - er with a heart sin - cere.   (to Refrain)
3. glo - ry may we see your face.
   end - less age to age. A - men.   (to Refrain)

Verse 2

2. We, the man - y, be - come one bod - y
   Let all quar - rels, all di - vi - sion,

2. as the Spir - it binds,
   all our con - flict cease;

and we seek to be
then will Christ tru - ly

2. one in Christ and one in heart and mind.
   dwell a - mong us as our Lord of Peace.   (to Refrain)

Text: Adapt. fr. Holy Thursday Liturgy; Laurence Rosania, b. 1957.
Music: Laurence Rosania.

Love Has Come

Verses

1. With one voice the an - gels sing songs that make cre -
2. God the Fa - ther, El - o - him, voice of thun - der,
3. God of Cov - e - nant, di - vine, lead us to the
4. Keep - er of the sac - ri - fice man - i - fest in
5. Now sal - va - tion has come in the New Je -

1. a - tion ring. Proph - ets hear and call us to
2. spir - it, wind: breathe on me your ver - y life;
3. end of time, be - yond sor - row, be - yond fear,
4. Je - sus Christ, born to die and wake the dead,
5. ru - sa - lem. Danc - ers dance and sing - ers roar; pro -

1. live in spir - it and in truth.
2. grace will make the dark - ness bright.
3. be - yond pride and earth - en tears.
4. as we hun - ger keep us fed.
5. claim - ing Je - sus Christ is Lord!

Refrain

Word of God, en - throned, dwell in us for - ev - er - more.

Love has come to show the way. Hal - le - lu -

jah, peace be with us. Love has come to show the way.

Text: Matt Maher, b. 1974.
Music: Matt Maher; arr. by Rick Modlin, b. 1966.

712 THERE'S A WIDENESS IN GOD'S MERCY

1. There's a wide-ness in God's mer - cy Like the wide-ness
2. For the love of God is broad-er Than the mea-sures
3. Trou-bled souls, why will you scat - ter Like a crowd of

1. of the sea; There's a kind - ness in his jus - tice
2. of our mind, And the heart of the E - ter - nal
3. fright - ened sheep? Fool - ish hearts, why will you wan - der

1. Which is more than lib - er - ty. There is plen - ti - ful re -
2. Is most won - der - ful - ly kind. If our love were but more
3. From a love so true and deep? There is wel-come for the

1. demp-tion In the blood that has been shed; There is
2. sim - ple We should take him at his word, And our
3. sin - ner And more grac - es for the good; There is

1. joy for all the mem-bers In the sor - rows of the Head.
2. lives would be thanks - giv - ing For the good-ness of our Lord.
3. mer - cy with the Sav - ior, There is heal - ing in his blood.

Text: 87 87 D; Frederick W. Faber, 1814–1863, alt.
Music: IN BABILONE; *Oude en Nieuwe Hollantse Boerenlities en Contradanseu*, ca. 1710.

713 ALL I ASK OF YOU

Refrain

All I ask of you is for-ev-er to re-mem-ber me as lov-ing

| 1-5 | to Verses | Final |

you. you, for - ev - er as lov-ing you.

Verses

1. Deep the joy of be - ing ___ to - geth - er in one
2. As we make our way ___ through all the joys and
3. Some - one will be call - ing you to be there for a -
4. Laugh - ter, joy and pres - ence: ___ the on - ly gifts you
5. Per - sons come in - to the fi - ber of our

to Refrain

1. heart ___ and for me that's just ___ where it is.
2. pain, ___ can we sense our young - er, tru - er selves?
3. while. ___ Can you hear their cry from deep with - in?
4. are! ___ Have you time? I'd like to be with you.
5. lives and then their shad - ows fade and dis - ap - pear. But

Text and music: Weston Priory, Gregory Norbet, OSB, b. 1940, © 1973, The Benedictine Foundation
of the State of Vermont, Inc. All rights reserved. Used with permission.

MAY LOVE BE OURS   714

Verses

1. Not for tongues of heav - en's an - gels, Not for wis - dom to
2. Love is hum - ble, love is gen - tle, Love is ten - der, true
3. Nev - er jeal - ous, nev - er self - ish, Love will not re - joice
4. In the day this world is fad - ing, Faith and hope will play

1. dis - cern, Not for faith that mas - ters moun - tains, For this bet - ter
2. and kind; Love is gra - cious, ev - er pa - tient, Gen - er - ous of
3. in wrong; Nev - er boast - ful nor re - sent - ful, Love be - lieves and
4. their part: But when Christ is seen in glo - ry, Love shall reign in

Refrain
*

1. gift we yearn: May love be ours, O Lord; may love be ours.
2. heart and mind.
3. suf - fers long.
4. ev - 'ry heart.

*Cue note is an alternate lower melody note.

Text: 87 87 with refrain; Timothy Dudley-Smith, b. 1926, © 1985, Hope Publishing Co.
All rights reserved. Used with permission.
Music: HEAVEN'S ANGELS; Stephen Dean, b. 1948, © 2002, Stephen Dean. Published by OCP. All rights reserved.

715 GOD IS LOVE

1. God is Love, let heav'n a-dore him; God is Love, let
2. God is Love; and love en-folds us, All the world in
3. God is Love; and though with blind-ness Sin af-flicts all

1. earth re-joice; Let cre-a-tion sing be-fore him And ex-
2. one em-brace: With un-fail-ing grasp God holds us, Ev-'ry
3. hu-man life, God's e-ter-nal lov-ing kind-ness Guides us

1. alt him with one voice. God who laid the earth's foun-da-tion,
2. child of ev-'ry race. And when hu-man hearts are break-ing
3. through our earth-ly strife. Sin and death and hell shall nev-er

1. God who spread the heav'ns a-bove, God who breathes through
2. Un-der sor-row's i-ron rod, Then we find that
3. O'er us fi-nal tri-umph gain; God is Love, so

1. all cre-a-tion: God is Love, e-ter-nal Love.
2. self-same ach-ing Deep with-in the heart of God.
3. Love for ev-er O'er the u-ni-verse must reign.

716 THE WILL OF YOUR LOVE/TU VOLUNTAD

*Ostinato Refrain: All

The will of your love, the will of your love be
Tu vo-lun-tad, tu com-pa-sión

done __ on __ earth __ as it is in heav-en.
se-a en la tie-rra co-mo en el cie-lo.

*Verses available in accompaniment books.

Christians, Let Us Love One Another 717

1. Chris-tians, let us love one an-oth-er, As we share the
2. We who break this bread are one bod-y, We who share this
3. We who eat and drink at this ta-ble Die and rise a-
4. On the path of life we may fal-ter, Earth-ly food a-
5. Wheat and grape in-car-nate a mys-t'ry: Je-sus is the
6. Je-sus is the vine, we the branch-es; We are grains of

1. true liv-ing bread. Je-sus is our God and our
2. cup are all one. Chil-dren of our Fa-ther in
3. gain with our Lord. Draw-ing from our Rock liv-ing
4. lone leaves us weak; Al-ways you in-vite from the
5. true liv-ing bread. Let us eat with joy and thanks-
6. wheat, Christ the bread. Those who eat this bread live for-

1. broth-er; With his flesh and blood we are fed.
2. heav-en, We are heirs with God's on-ly son.
3. wa-ter Giv'n to all who thirst for ac-cord.
4. al-tar, "Hun-gry souls their food here must seek." Ev-'ry-one who
5. giv-ing, Trust-ing in the word he has said.
6. ev-er, One with Christ, our Lord and our Head.

1-6. loves is born of God. Je-sus is our life. God is love.

Text: 98 98 98; Claudia Foltz, SNJM, and Armand Nigro, SJ, b. 1928, © 1973, Claudia Foltz, SNJM, and Armand Nigro, SJ.
Published by OCP. All rights reserved.
Music: PICARDY; French Carol, 17th cent.; *Chansons populaires des Provinces de France*, 1860.

Love One Another 718

*Refrain
Love one an-oth-er as I have loved you. Care for each
oth-er. I have cared for you. Bear each oth-er's bur-dens.
Bind each oth-er's wounds; and so you will know my re-turn.

*Verses available in accompaniment books.

Text: Based on John 14—16; 1 Corinthians 13; Bob Dufford, SJ, b. 1943.
Music: Bob Dufford, SJ.
Text and music © 1987, Robert J. Dufford, SJ. Published by OCP. All rights reserved.

719   **WHAT WONDROUS LOVE IS THIS**

1. What won-drous love is this, O my soul, O my soul? What won-drous love is this, O my soul? What won-drous love is this that caused the Lord of bliss To bear the dread-ful curse for my soul, for my soul, To bear the dread-ful curse for my soul?

2. What won-drous love is this, O my soul, O my soul? What won-drous love is this, O my soul? What won-drous love is this that caused the Lord of bliss To send this pre-cious peace to my soul, to my soul, To send this pre-cious peace to my soul?

3. To God and to the Lamb I will sing, I will sing; To God and to the Lamb, I will sing; To God and to the Lamb, who is the great I AM, While mil-lions join the theme, I will sing, I will sing; While mil-lions join the theme, I will sing.

4. And when from death I'm free, I'll sing on, I'll sing on; And when from death I'm free, I'll sing on; And when from death I'm free, I'll sing and joy-ful be, And through e-ter-ni-ty, I'll sing on, I'll sing on! And through e-ter-ni-ty, I'll sing on.

Text: 12 9 12 12 9; anon.; first appeared in *A General Selection of the Newest and Most Admired Hymns and Spiritual Songs*, 1811, adapt.
Music: WONDROUS LOVE; William Walker's *The Southern Harmony*, 1835.

720   **WHERE CHARITY AND LOVE PREVAIL**

1. Where char-i-ty and love pre-vail, There God is ev-er found;
2. With grate-ful joy and ho-ly fear God's char-i-ty we learn;
3. For-give we now each oth-er's faults As we our faults con-fess;
4. Let strife a-mong us be un-known, Let all con-ten-tion cease;
5. Let us re-call that in our midst Dwells God's be-got-ten Son;
6. No race nor creed can love ex-clude, If hon-ored be God's name;

1. Brought here to-geth-er by Christ's love, By love are we thus bound.
2. Let us with heart and mind and soul Now love God in re-turn.
3. And let us love each oth-er well In Chris-tian ho-li-ness.
4. Be God's the glo-ry that we seek, Be ours God's ho-ly peace.
5. As mem-bers of his bod-y joined, We are in Christ made one.
6. Our fam-i-ly em-brac-es all Whose Fa-ther is the same.

Text: CM; *Ubi Caritas*, 9th cent.; tr. by Omer Westendorf, 1916–1997.
Music: CHRISTIAN LOVE; Paul Benoit, OSB, 1893–1979.
Text and music © 1960, World Library Publications. All rights reserved. Used with permission.

In Perfect Charity   721

1. O most high and glo-rious God, cast your light in-to
2. O most high and glo-rious God, o-pen wide the door
3. Then most high and thank-ful praise I will sing un-to

1. the dark-ness of my heart. Give me right faith, and cer-tain
2. that leads me to your love. Give me your firm, yet gen-tle
3. the glo-ry of your name: To Fa-ther, Son, and Spir-it

1. hope, and per-fect, per-fect char-i-ty. Give me true
2. strength; may I live that per-fect char-i-ty. Lord, may your
3. bright, Liv-ing Pres-ence, Per-fect Char-i-ty. Praise to the

1. in-sight, Lord, and wis-dom, that I may al-ways live with-
2. peace be ev-er in me, that I may al-ways seek to
3. Love that shines in splen-dor, that lights the path-ways of my

1. in your ev-er ho-ly will. Lord, may your light with-
2. serve your chil-dren here on earth; that I may find my
3. heart, and brings me close to you. O Ho-ly One, in-

1. in me burn, shin-ing out in per-fect char-i-ty.
2. home with you, and live in per-fect char-i-ty.
3. vite me in, where you live in per-fect char-i-ty.

Text: Irregular; verse 1 based on a prayer of St. Francis of Assisi, 1182–1226; verses 2–3, Randall DeBruyn, b. 1947.
Music: PERFECT CHARITY; Randall DeBruyn.
Text and music © 1982, Randall DeBruyn. Published by OCP. All rights reserved.

722   ENDLESS IS YOUR LOVE

Refrain

You know my heart. You know my mind. You know my words long be-fore I speak them. There is no place that I can hide. End-less is your love for us. How vast the sum of all your deeds! End-less is your love for us.

Verses

1. Sure - ly there's a place e - ven you don't
2. Can't I hide at night, dark - ness be my
3. Won - der - ful your works, count - less as the

1. know. If I climb there, if I fly there,
2. light? Can you see the day in dark - ness,
3. sand. Earth and heav - en know your beau - ty,

to Refrain

1. can I hide from you?
2. can you find me there?
3. fash - ioned by your hand.

Text: Based on Psalm 139; Tom Kendzia, b. 1954.
Music: Tom Kendzia.

GOD IS LOVE

Refrain

God is love, and all who live in love a - bide in God, and

1 God a - bides in them.

2 (to Verses) (Fine) God a - bides in them.

Verses

1. The love of Christ has gath - ered us as one: In
2. There - fore, as now we gath - er in - to one, let
3. Then with the saints let us be - hold your face, a -

1. him let us re - joice; in him let us be glad.
2. dis - cord find no place, nor ha - tred rule our hearts.
3. light with glo - ry, Christ, our broth - er and our God.

1. Let us re - vere and love the liv - ing God. With
2. Let e - vil deeds and bit - ter words now cease, that
3. And may this joy, un - bound - ed and im - mense, ful -

to Refrain

1. heart and mind and soul now let us love sin - cere - ly.
2. Christ stay in our midst and dwell with us for - ev - er.
3. fill our hearts' de - sire through a - ges with - out end - ing.

Text: Based on 1 John 4:16b and *Ubi Caritas*; Michael Joncas, b. 1951.
Music: Michael Joncas.

724 **OUT OF DARKNESS**

Refrain

Out of dark-ness God has called us, claimed by Christ as God's own peo-ple. Ho-ly na-tion, roy-al priest-hood, walk-ing in God's

1. mar-v'lous light. *2-4* mar-v'lous light. *to Verses 2* *Final* mar-v'lous light. A - men.

Verses

1. Let us take   the words you give. Strong and faith-ful words   to live.
2. Let us take   the Christ you give. Bro - ken Bod - y, Christ   we live.
3. Let us take   the love you give,   that the way of love   we live.

1. Words   that in   our hearts are sown;   words   that bind us   as your own.
2. Christ   the ris - en   from the tomb;   Christ,   who calls us   as your own.
3. Love   to bring your peo - ple home;   love   to make us   all your own.

to Refrain

Text and music: Christopher Walker, b. 1947, © 1989, Christopher Walker. Published by OCP. All rights reserved.

725 **UNLESS A GRAIN OF WHEAT**

Refrain

Un-less a grain of wheat shall fall up-on the ground   and die, it re-mains   but a sin-gle grain   with no life.

Verses

1.   If   we   have   died with him,   then   we   shall   live with him;
2. If   an - y   one serves __ me,   then they must   fol - low me;
3.   Make your home   in   me   as   I   make mine in   you;
4. If   you   re - main   in   me   and   my word   lives in   you,
5.   Those who   love   me   are   loved   by   my   Fa - ther;
6.   Peace   I   leave with you,   my peace   I   give to   you;

1. if we hold firm, we shall reign with him. _____
2. wher - ev - er I am, my ser - vants will be.
3. those who re - main in me bear much fruit. _____
4. then you will be my dis - ci - ples. _____
5. we shall be with them and dwell in them. _____
6. peace which the world can - not give is my gift.

Text: Based on John 12:24–26; 14:23, 27; 15:4–5, 7–8; 2 Timothy 2:11–12; Bernadette Farrell, b. 1957.
Music: Bernadette Farrell.
Text and music © 1983, Bernadette Farrell. Published by OCP. All rights reserved.

TRANSFIGURE US, O LORD   726

Refrain

Trans - fig - ure us, O Lord, trans - fig - ure us, O Lord.

Break the chains that bind us; speak your heal - ing word, and

where you lead we'll fol - low. Trans - fig - ure us, O Lord.

Verses

1. Down from heights of glo - ry in - to the depths be - low, the
2. Light for those in dark - ness, the hun - gry have their fill, glad
3. Par - don for the sin - ner, a shep - herd for the sheep, a
4. To the ho - ly cit - y, Je - ru - sa - lem, you go; your

1. love of God self - emp - tied, the love of God to show. You
2. tid - ings for the hum - ble, the heal - ing of all ills; in
3. drink of liv - ing wa - ter for all who thirst and seek, and
4. face set toward the end - ing, the cross to be your throne.

1. light the path be - fore us, the way that we must go.
2. these we glimpse your glo - ry, God's prom - is - es ful - filled.
3. feast - ing at your ta - ble, the low - ly and the least.
4. Shall we jour - ney with you and share your pas - chal road?

Text: Based on Matthew 17:1–9; Mark 9:2–10; Luke 9:28b–36; Bob Hurd, b. 1950.
Music: Bob Hurd.
Text and music © 2002, Bob Hurd. Published by OCP. All rights reserved.

727

ANTHEM

Refrain

We are called, we are cho-sen. We are Christ for one an-oth-er. We are
prom-ised to to-mor-row, while we are for him to-day. We are
sign, we are won-der. We are sow-er, we are seed. We are
har-vest, we are hun-ger. We are ques-tion, we are creed.

Verses

1. Then where can we stand jus-ti-fied?_ In what can we be-lieve? In no one
2. Then how are we to stand at all,_ this world of bend-ed knee? In noth-ing
3. Then shall we not stand emp-ty_ at the al-tar of our dreams:_ When he

1. else but he who suf-fered, noth-ing more than he who rose.
2. more than bar-ren shad-ows. No one else but he could save us.
3. prom-ised us our-selves. _ Who mark time a-gainst to-mor-row.

1, 2. Who was jus-tice for the poor. Who was rage a-gainst the night.
3. Who are jus-tice for the poor. Who are rage a-gainst the night.

to Refrain

1, 2. Who was hope for peace-ful peo-ple. Who was light.
3. Who are hope for peace-ful peo-ple. Who are light.

All That Is Hidden

Text: Refrain based on Luke 12:2–3; Bernadette Farrell, b. 1957.
Music: Bernadette Farrell.

729   PESCADOR DE HOMBRES/LORD, YOU HAVE COME

Estrofas/Verses

1. Tú has ve - ni - do a la o - ri - lla, no has bus - ca - do
2. Tú sa - bes bien lo que ten - go; en mi bar - ca
3. Tú ne - ce - si - tas mis ma - nos, mi can - san - cio
4. Tú, pes - ca - dor de o - tros la - gos, an - sia e - ter - na

1. *Lord, you have come to the sea-shore, nei - ther search-ing for*
2. *Lord, see my goods, my pos - ses - sions; in my boat you find*
3. *Lord, take my hands and di - rect them. Help me spend my - self*
4. *Lord, as I drift on the wa - ters, be the rest - ing place*

1. ni a sa - bios ni a ri - cos; _____ tan só - lo quie - res
2. no hay o - ro ni es - pa - das, _____ tan só - lo re - des
3. que a o - tros des - can - se, _____ a - mor que quie - ra
4. de al - mas que es - pe - ran, _____ a - mi - go bue - no,

1. *the rich nor the wise, _____ de - sir - ing on - ly*
2. *no pow - er, no wealth. _____ Will you ac - cept, then,*
3. *in seek - ing the lost, _____ re - turn - ing love for*
4. *of my rest - less heart, _____ my life's com - pan - ion,*

Estribillo/Refrain

1. que yo te si - ga.
2. y mi tra - ba - jo.
3. se - guir a - man - do.
4. que a - sí me lla - mas.

1. *that I should fol - low.*
2. *my nets and la - bor?*
3. *the love you gave me.*
4. *my friend and ref - uge.*

Se - ñor, me has mi - ra - do a los

O Lord, with your eyes set up -

o - jos, son - ri - en - do _____ has di - cho mi
on me, gent - ly smil - ing, _____ you have spo - ken my

nom - bre, _____ en la a - re - na he de - ja - do mi bar - ca,
name; _____ all I longed for I have found by the wa - ter,

jun - to a ti bus - ca - ré o - tro mar.
at your side, I will seek oth - er shores.

Text: Spanish, Cesáreo Gabaráin, 1936–1991; English, OCP.
Music: Cesáreo Gabaráin.

GO MAKE A DIFFERENCE

Text: Based on Matthew 5:13–16; Steve Angrisano, b. 1965, and Tom Tomaszek, b. 1950.
Music: Steve Angrisano and Tom Tomaszek.
Text and music © 1997, Steve Angrisano and Thomas N. Tomaszek. Published by spiritandsong.com®, a division of OCP.
   All rights reserved.

731 JOURNEYSONG

*1. On this new day may we be gath-ered In the
2. Com - pan - ions on our pil - grim jour - ney, Spir - it -
3. Do not our hearts burn deep with - in us As we
4. From strength to strength, from cross to glo - ry, Lead us,

1. love of Christ. No pow'r of dark - ness
2. led we go; In friend and strang - er
3. hear his voice, And join to - geth - er
4. Lord of Light, Till jour - ney's end we

1. can es-trange us From the Lord ___ of Light.
2. Christ goes with us Speak - ing words ___ of hope.
3. at this ta - ble With the ris - en Lord?
4. come re - joic - ing To the ban-quet of life.

*Alternate text for use at Evening Prayer/Mass: "As evening falls may we be gathered...."(at Evening Prayer omit verse 3).

732 ONLY THIS I WANT

Refrain

On - ly this I want: but to know the Lord,

and to bear his cross, so to wear the crown he wore.

Verses

1. All but this is loss, worth-less ref - use to me,
2. I will run the race; I will fight the good fight,
3. Let your heart be glad, al - ways glad in the Lord,

to Refrain

1. for to gain the Lord is to gain ___ all I need.
2. so to win the prize of the king-dom of my Lord.
3. so to shine like stars in the dark-ness of the night.

LEAD ME, LORD

Verses

1. Bless-ed are the poor in spir-it, long-ing for their
2. Bless-ed are the mer-ci-ful, for mer-cy shall be
3. Blest are they who through their life-times sow the seeds of

1. Lord, for God's com-ing king-dom shall be theirs.
2. theirs, and the pure in heart shall see their God.
3. peace, all will call them chil-dren of the Lord.

1. Bless-ed are the sor-row-ing, for they shall be con-
2. Blest are they whose hun-ger on-ly ho-li-ness can
3. Blest are you, though per-se-cu-ted in your ho-ly

1. soled, and the meek shall come to rule the world.
2. fill, for I say they shall be sat-is-fied.
3. life, for in heav-en, great is your re-ward.

Refrain

Lead me, Lord, lead me, Lord, by the light of truth to

seek and to find the nar-row way. Be my way;

be my truth; be my life, my Lord, and lead me, Lord, to-

1-2 to Verses | **Final**

day. day. And lead me, Lord, to-day.

734 **WOMEN OF THE CHURCH**

Refrain

Wom-en of the Church, how rich is your leg-a-cy! Wom-en of the
Church, how great is your faith! Wom-en of the Church,
well-springs of in-teg-ri-ty, lead us in the ways of peace!

Verses 1, 2, 5

1. Wom-en at the foot of the cross, fear-less and
2. Com-pan-ions and dis-ci-ples of Je-sus, cho-sen and
5. Wom-en mar-tyred in our time, lay-ing down their

1. tru-ly faith-ful friends; first ones to see the
2. called by name, wit-ness-es of wis-dom,
5. lives for the poor, proph-ets of cour-age who

1. ris-en Lord of Life, and the first to tell good news!
2. weav-ers of the Word, lead us in the ways of truth!
5. stood with those op-pressed, help us all to walk your paths.

Verses 3, 4

3. Liv-ing signs of ser-vice and strength, hands of heal-ing,
4. Wom-en of com-pas-sion and care, bear-ers of God's

3. hearts of love, wom-en of vi-sion, voic-es for the
4. life-giv-ing light, cen-tered in prayer while work-ing for

3. voice-less, lead us in the ways of hope.
4. jus-tice, lead us in the ways of peace.

'TIS THE GIFT TO BE SIMPLE

1. 'Tis the gift to be sim-ple, 'tis the gift to be free, 'Tis the gift to
2. 'Tis the gift to be gen-tle, 'tis the gift to be fair, 'Tis the gift to
3. 'Tis the gift to be lov-ing, 'tis the gift best of all, Like a qui-et

1. come down where you ought to be, And when we find our-selves in the
2. wake and breathe the morn-ing air; And ev - 'ry day to walk in the
3. rain, it bless - es where it falls; And if we have the gift, we will

1. place just __ right __ 'Twill be in the val - ley of love and de-light.
2. path we __ choose, 'Tis the gift that we pray we may ne'er come to lose.
3. tru - ly be-lieve __ 'Tis bet - ter to give than it is to re-ceive.

Refrain

When true sim-plic - i - ty is gained, To bow and to bend we

shan't be a-shamed; To turn, turn will be our de-light, Till by

turn - ing, turn - ing we come 'round right.

Text: Irregular with refrain; Shaker Song, 18th cent. Verses 2–3, Joyce Merman, © 1975 (renewed), Shawnee Press, Inc.
   All rights reserved. Used with permission.
Music: SIMPLE GIFTS; Shaker Melody, 18th cent.

736   I WILL CHOOSE CHRIST

Refrain: 1st time: Cantor; thereafter: All

I will choose Christ, I will choose love, I choose to serve.

I give my heart, I give my life, I give my all

1-3 to Verses / Final

to you.   to you.   I give my all to you.

Verse 1

1. How man-y times must he call my name and show to

1. me that he is God? And as a ser-vant he

1. calls to me, you must serve too.

Verse 2

2. Christ, my teach - er and heal - er, teach my

2. heart and heal my soul. And as I walk this

2. road with you, teach me to love.

3. As I look up-on your cross, so too
3. must I die with you. And with the death of my
3. own de - sires, I'll rise with you.

GOD, WHOSE GLORY REIGNS ETERNAL 737

1. God, whose glo - ry reigns e - ter - nal, Span-ning space as
2. In Christ's heal - ing touch and teach - ing We see life as
3. Now we pon - der life's great mys - t'ry Suf-f'ring sav - ior,

1. well as time, Show us signs in seed and ker - nel, Life po -
2. you in - tend, Self-less love to oth - ers reach - ing, Pain and
3. cross en-throned, Past and fu - ture in one his - t'ry Our mor-

1. ten - tial, hope sub - lime. Grant us in - sight, all dis - cern - ing,
2. bro - ken - ness to end. And when hun - gry folk are nour-ished,
3. tal - i - ty Christ owned. And as res - ur - rec-tion's glo - ry

1. See - ing truth be - yond bare fact, Love trans - lat - ing
2. Filled by hope and word and bread, These are signs your
3. Shines in - to the emp - ty tomb, We, too, tell the

1. all our learn - ing In - to pow'r to be and act.
2. reign has flour - ished And from bond - age we are led.
3. an - cient sto - ry, Joy dis - pel - ling all the gloom.

738 THE EYES AND HANDS OF CHRIST

Refrain

Where two or three are gath-ered in my name,
love will be found, life will a - bound.
By name we are called, from wa-ter we are sent:
to be - come the eyes and hands of Christ.

Verses 1, 2

1. One we be-come, no long-er strang-ers. No long-er
2. One in the Spir-it, one in the Lord. One in the

1. emp-ty ___ or frail. Filled with the Spir-it, ev-'ry
2. break-ing of the bread. Life - giv - ing wit-ness of our

1. hun-ger sat-is-fied. Christ is the cen-ter of our lives.
2. dy-ing and new life. Held by the prom-ise in our hands.

to Refrain

Verse 3

3. Not what we are, but what we be - come. Not what we
3. say, but what we do. Liv - ing the chal-lenge as

to Refrain

3. bear-ers of light. We are the eyes and hands of Christ.

O Beauty, Ever Ancient

Verses

1. Oh, ___ late ___ have I loved you, oh, ___ late ___
2. My un-love-li-ness I ran from, turned to seek you
3. This cre-at-ed world is glo-rious, yet I could not
4. I had wan-dered far, per-ceiv-ing that I walked my
5. In your love-li-ness you made me, in your god-ly

1. have I turned; turned from seek-ing you in crea-tures, flee-ing
2. in all things, things you fash-ioned as a path-way; yet I
3. see with-in, see your love-li-ness be-hind all, find the
4. road a-lone. Yet you called, you shone, you sum-moned, and you
5. im-age true; by your grace you have re-newed me; let me

Refrain

1. grief and pain with-in. O Beau-ty, ev-er an-cient, O
2. lost my-self in them.
3. Giv-er in the gift.
4. drew my spir-it home.
5. live my life in you!

Beau-ty, ev-er new: you, the mir-ror of my life re-

newed, let me find my life in you!

Text: Based on a prayer from St. Augustine of Hippo's *Confessions,* ca. 400; Roc O'Connor, SJ, b. 1949.
Music: Roc O'Connor, SJ.

740   SENT FORTH BY GOD'S BLESSING

1. Sent forth by God's bless-ing, our true faith con - fess-ing, The
_ God's sac - ri - fice end - ed, O now be ex - tend-ed The
2. With praise and thanks - giv-ing, to God who is liv - ing, The
Our faith ev - er shar-ing, in love ev - er car-ing, We

1. peo-ple of God from his dwell-ing take leave.
_ fruits of this Mass in all hearts who be - lieve. The seed of Christ's
2. tasks of our ev - 'ry-day life we em - brace.
claim as our neigh-bor all those of each race. One bread that has

1. teach-ing, our in - ner souls reach-ing, Shall blos-som in ac -tion for
2. fed us, one light that has led us U - nite us as one in his

1. God and for all. His grace shall in - cite us, his love shall u -
2. life that we share. Then may all the liv-ing with praise and thanks -

1. nite us To fur-ther God's king-dom and an - swer his call.
2. giv - ing Give hon - or to Christ and his name that we bear.

Text: 12 11 12 11 D; Omer Westendorf, 1916–1997, alt., © 1964, World Library Publications.
All rights reserved. Used with permission.
Music: ASH GROVE; trad. Welsh Melody.

741   HOLY WISDOM, LAMP OF LEARNING

1. Ho - ly Wis-dom, lamp of learn - ing, Bless the light that
2. Vine of truth, in you we flour - ish; By your grace we
3. Ho - ly God, the hope of na - tions, Tune us toward your

1. rea - son lends. Teach us judg-ment as we kin - dle Sparks of
2. learn and grow. May the word of Christ a-mong us Shape our
3. righ-teous will, As the sym - pho - ny of a - ges Claims our

1. thought your Spir - it sends. Sanc - ti - fy our search for knowl-edge
2. life, our search to know. Joined to Christ in liv - ing, dy - ing,
3. best, our fin - est skill. Shape our search for peace and jus - tice

1. And the truth that sets us free. Come, il - lu - mine
2. May we help the church con - vey Wit - ness to the
3. Through pro - phet - ic deed and word. Christ, con - duct us,

1. mind and spir - it Joined in deep - est u - ni - ty.
2. sav - ing gos - pel, Bear - ing fruit of faith to - day.
3. set our rhy - thm, That God's praise be ev - er heard.

Text: 87 87 D; Ruth C. Duck, b. 1947; from *Circles of Care*, © 1996, The Pilgrim Press.
All rights reserved. Used with permission.
Music: BEACH SPRING; *The Sacred Harp*, 1844.

WORD OF GOD   742

1. Word of God, re - new your peo - ple,
2. Word of hope and word of heal - ing,
3. Word of peace and word of jus - tice,
4. With your cross of love up - on us,
5. God a - lone the pow'r we trust in,
6. By our name you call us on - ward,
7. Cross of Je - sus, free - ly cho - sen,
8. Cross of Je - sus, all - em - brac - ing,
9. By your cross re - stored, for - giv - en,
10. Through the cross of Christ our Sav - ior,
11. To the wa - ters lead your peo - ple,
12. Ris - en Sav - ior, with us al - ways,
13. Ho - ly Spir - it, raise your peo - ple,

1-13. make us now your liv - ing sign. Re - cre - ate us for your

1-13. pur - pose in this place and in this time.

Text and music: Bernadette Farrell, b. 1957, © 2000, 2001, Bernadette Farrell. Published by OCP. All rights reserved.

743   **VOICE OF CHRIST**

Verses 1, 2, 4

1. O ___ Lord, ___ you ___ bless us each day with
2. The ___ spar-row nei-ther sows nor ___ reaps, has
4. We a-wait ___ you with watch-ful ___ eyes, our

1. gifts from your hand. Now ___ as ___ our ___
2. store-house nor barn. And ___ flow-ers nei-ther
4. lamps burn-ing bright. Though we know ___ not when

1. cup o-ver-flows, may we too bring ___ forth.
2. spin nor ___ weave, yet they wear roy-al robes.
4. you will re-turn, we stand wake-ful through the night.

Refrain

We the hands, we the eyes, we the voice of Christ.

O faith-ful God, we en-trust our trea-sure to your heart.

Verse 3

3. The Lord hears the cry of the poor; the

3. lives of the weak he shall save. Bless-ed those who care for the

to Refrain

3. poor; hap-pi-ness is their re-ward.

Text: Based on Luke 12:22–40; Psalm 41:2–3; Psalm 72:12–13; Timothy R. Smith, b. 1960.
Music: Timothy R. Smith.
Text and music © 1993, Timothy R. Smith. Published by spiritandsong.com®, a division of OCP. All rights reserved.

With All the Saints

1. With all the saints, with proph - ets and mar - tyrs,
2. With all in need, the poor and for - sak - en
3. With ref - u - gees, and vic - tims of vio - lence,
4. With all who live com - pas - sion and mer - cy,
5. With all who dare to toil for that cit - y
6. So may this flock, this church once more gath - ered,

1. with ho - ly Ma - ry and Jo - seph, with
2. to whom the inn - keep - er shuts the door, with
3. with those made home - less by Her - od's sword, with
4. all who de - fend hu - man dig - ni - ty, with
5. whose light shall shine from the moun - tain - top, where
6. faith - ful - ly fol - low its Shep - herd's voice. To

1. those who came be - fore____ and those____ who will fol - low,
2. those who are the least,____ yet first____ in the king - dom,
3. all the dis - ap - peared____ and those____ who still mourn them,
4. peo - ple of good will____ from ev - ery faith and na - tion,
5. all may dwell in peace____ and know____ life's full mea - sure,
6. be a liv - ing sign of the love of God and neigh - bor,

1-6. we gath - er here to - day, one bod - y in the Lord, a

2

1-6. sign and sac - ra - ment of Christ.

Text and music: Bob Hurd, b. 1950, © 2003, 2009, Bob Hurd. Published by OCP. All rights reserved.

745 · **ONE SPIRIT, ONE CHURCH**

We are a pil-grim peo-ple, we are the Church of God. A fam-'ly of be-liev-ers, dis-ci-ples of the Lord. U-nit-ed in one spir-it, ig-nit-ed by the fire. Still burn-ing through the a-ges, still pres-ent in our lives. lives. A - men! 1. Come, Ho-ly Ghost, Cre-a-tor 2. O Com-fort-er, to thee we

1. blest, and in our hearts take up thy rest; come with thy
2. cry, thou gift of God sent from on high. Thou font of

1. grace and heav'n-ly aid to fill the hearts which thou hast made.
2. life and fire of love, the soul's a-noint-ing from a-bove.

Text: Refrain, Maryanne Quinlivan, OSU, © 1990, Ursuline Academy of Cleveland. Published by OCP. All rights reserved.
Verses fr. *Veni, Creator Spiritus*; attr. to Rabanus Maurus, 776–856; tr. by Edward Caswall, 1814–1878, alt.
Music: Refrain, Kevin Keil (ASCAP), b. 1956; verses based on LAMBILLOTTE, © 1990, Kevin Keil.
Published by OCP. All rights reserved.

746 · **THE CHURCH'S ONE FOUNDATION**

1. The Chur-ch's one foun-da-tion Is Je-sus Christ her Lord;
2. E-lect from ev-'ry na-tion, Yet one o'er all the earth,
3. 'Mid toil and trib-u-la-tion, And tu-mult of her war,
4. Yet she on earth hath un-ion With God, the Three-in-One,

1. She is his new cre-a-tion By wa-ter and the word:
2. Her char-ter of sal-va-tion, "One Lord, one faith, one birth!"
3. She waits the con-sum-ma-tion Of peace for-ev-er-more,
4. And with the saints, com-mu-nion With those whose rest is won.

1. From heav'n he came and sought her To be his ho-ly bride;
2. One ho-ly Name she bless-es, Par-takes one ho-ly food,
3. Till with the vi-sion glo-rious Her long-ing eyes are blest,
4. O hap-py ones and ho-ly! Lord, give us grace that we

1. With his own blood he bought her, And for her life he died.
2. And to one hope she press-es With ev-'ry grace en-dued.
3. And the great Church vic-to-rious Shall be the Church at rest.
4. Like them, the meek and low-ly, On high may dwell with thee.

Text: 76 76 D; Samuel J. Stone, 1839–1900, alt.
Music: AURELIA; Samuel S. Wesley, 1810–1876.

CHRIST IS MADE THE SURE FOUNDATION   747

1. Christ is made the sure foun-da-tion, Christ, the head and
2. To this tem-ple, where we call you, Come, O Lord of
3. Grant, we pray, to all your peo-ple, All the grace they
4. Praise and hon-or to the Fa-ther, Praise and hon-or

1. cor-ner-stone; Cho-sen of the Lord, and pre-cious,
2. hosts, to-day; With your wont-ed lov-ing kind-ness,
3. ask to gain; What they gain from you for ev-er
4. to the Son, Praise and hon-or to the Spir-it,

1. Bind-ing all the Church in one, Ho-ly Si-on's
2. Hear your ser-vants as they pray, And your ful-lest
3. With the bless-ed to re-tain, And here-af-ter
4. Ev-er three and ev-er one, One in might and

1. help for ev-er, And her con-fi-dence a-lone.
2. ben-e-dic-tion, Shed in all its bright-est ray.
3. in your glo-ry, Ev-er-more with you to reign.
4. one in glo-ry, While un-end-ing a-ges run.

Text: 87 87 87; *Angularis fundamentum*, 11th cent.; tr. by John M. Neale, 1818–1866, alt.
Music: WESTMINSTER ABBEY; Henry Purcell, 1659–1695.

748 BY ALL YOUR SAINTS STILL STRIVING

1. By all your saints still striv - ing, For all your saints at rest,
*2. A - pos - tles, proph - ets, mar - tyrs, And all the no - ble throng
3. Then let us praise the Fa - ther And wor - ship God the Son

1. Your ho - ly Name, O Je - sus, For ev - er - more be blessed.
2. Who wear the spot - less rai - ment And raise the cease - less song:
3. And sing to God the Spir - it, E - ter - nal Three in One,

1. You rose, our King vic - to - rious, That they might wear the crown
2. For them and those whose wit - ness Is on - ly known to you
3. Till all the ran - somed num - ber Who stand be - fore the throne,

1. And ev - er shine in splen - dor Re - flect - ed from your throne.
2. By walk - ing in their foot - steps We give you praise a - new.
3. A - scribe all pow'r and glo - ry And praise to God a - lone.

Alternate Verses

4. Conversion of St. Paul (January 25)
Praise for the light from heaven
And for the voice of awe:
Praise for the glorious vision
The persecutor saw.
O Lord, for Paul's conversion,
We bless your Name today.
Come shine within our darkness
And guide us in the Way.

5. Chair of St. Peter (February 22)
We praise you, Lord, for Peter,
So eager and so bold:
Thrice falling, yet repentant,
Thrice charged to feed your fold.
Lord, make your pastors faithful
To guard your flock from harm
And hold them when they waver
With your almighty arm.

**6. St. Joseph, husband of
the Blessed Virgin Mary (March 19)**
All praise, O God, for Joseph,
The guardian of your Son,
Who saved him from King Herod,
When safety there was none.
He taught the trade of builder,
When they to Naz'reth came,
And Joseph's love made "Father"
To be, for Christ, God's name.

7. Annunciation of the Lord (March 25)
We sing with joy of Mary
Whose heart with awe was stirred

When, youthful and unready,
She heard the angel's word;
Yet she her voice upraises
God's glory to proclaim,
As once for our salvation
Your mother she became.

8. St. Mark (April 25)
For Mark, O Lord, we praise you,
The weak by grace made strong:
His witness in his Gospel
Becomes victorious song.
May we, in all our weakness,
Receive your power divine,
And all, as faithful branches,
Grow strong in you, the Vine.

9. Ss. Philip and James (May 3)
We praise you, Lord, for Philip,
Blest guide to Greek and Jew,
And for young James the faithful,
Who heard and followed you,
O grant us grace to know you,
The victor in the strife,
That we with all your servants
May wear the crown of life.

10. St. Matthias (May 13)
For one in place of Judas,
Th'apostles sought God's choice:
The lot fell to Matthias
For whom we now rejoice.
May we like true apostles
Your holy Church defend,

*This verse may be replaced by an appropriate Alternate Verse.

And not betray our calling
But serve you to the end.

11. St. Barnabas (June 11)

For Barnabas we praise you,
Who kept your law of love
And, leaving earthly treasures,
Sought riches from above.
O Christ, our Lord and Savior,
Let gifts of grace descend,
That your true consolation
May through the world extend.

12. Nativity of St. John the Baptist (June 24)

All praise for John the Baptist,
Forerunner of the Word,
Our true Elijah, making
A highway for the Lord.
The last and greatest prophet,
He saw the dawning ray
Of light that grows in splendor
Until the perfect day.

13. Ss. Peter and Paul (June 29)

We praise you for Saint Peter;
We praise you for Saint Paul.
They taught both Jew and Gentile
That Christ is all in all.
To cross and sword they yielded
And saw the kingdom come:
O God, your two apostles
Won life through martyrdom.

14. St. Thomas (July 3)

All praise, O Lord, for Thomas
Whose short-lived doubtings prove
Your perfect twofold nature,
The depth of your true love.
To all who live with questions
A steadfast faith afford;
And grant us grace to know you,
Made flesh, yet God and Lord.

15. St. Mary Magdalene (July 22)

All praise for Mary Magd'lene,
Whose wholeness was restored
By you, her faithful Master,
Her Savior and her Lord.
On Easter morning early,
A word from you sufficed:
Her faith was first to see you,
Her Lord, the risen Christ.

16. St. James (July 25)

O Lord, for James, we praise you,
Who fell to Herod's sword.
He drank the cup of suff'ring
And thus fulfilled your word.
Lord, curb our vain impatience
For glory and for fame,
Equip us for such suff'rings
As glorify your Name.

17. St. Bartholomew (August 24)

Praise for your blest apostle
Surnamed Bartholomew;
We know not his achievements
But know that he was true,
For he at the Ascension
Was an apostle still.
May we discern your presence
And seek, like him, your will.

18. St. Matthew (September 21)

We praise you, Lord, for Matthew,
Whose gospel words declare
That, worldly gain forsaking,
Your path of life we share.
From all unrighteous mammon,
O raise our eyes anew,
That we, whate'er our station
May rise and follow you.

19. St. Luke (October 18)

For Luke, belov'd physician,
All praise; whose Gospel shows
The healer of the nations,
The one who shares our woes.
Your wine and oil, O Savior,
Upon our spirits pour,
And with true balm of Gilead
Anoint us evermore.

20. Ss. Simon and Jude (October 28)

Praise, Lord, for your apostles,
Saint Simon and Saint Jude.
One love, one hope impelled them
To tread the way, renewed.
May we with zeal as earnest
The faith of Christ maintain,
Be bound in love together,
And life eternal gain.

21. St. Andrew (November 30)

All praise, O Lord, for Andrew,
The first to follow you;
He witnessed to his brother,
"This is Messiah true."
You called him from his fishing
Upon Lake Galilee;
He rose to meet your challenge,
"Leave all and follow me."

22. St. Stephen (December 26)

All praise, O Lord, for Stephen
Who, martyred, saw you stand
To help in time of torment,
To plead at God's right hand.
Like you, our suff'ring Savior,
His enemies he blessed,
With "Lord, receive my spirit,"
His faith, in death, confessed.

23. St. John (December 27)

For John, your loved disciple,
Exiled to Patmos' shore,
And for his faithful record,
We praise you evermore;
Praise for the mystic vision
His words to us unfold.
Instill in us his longing,
Your glory to behold.

24. Holy Innocents (December 28)

Praise for your infant martyrs,
Whom your mysterious love
Called early from life's conflicts
To share your peace above.
O Rachel, cease your weeping;
They're free from pain and cares.
Lord, grant us crowns as brilliant
And lives as pure as theirs.

Text: 76 76 D; based on *From All Thy Saints in Warfare* by Horatio Bolton Nelson, 1823–1913;
fr. *The Hymnal 1982*; Jerry D. Godwin, b. 1944, © 1985, The Church Pension Fund. All rights reserved.
Used with permission of Church Publishing, Inc., New York, NY.
Music: ST. THEODULPH; Melchior Teschner, 1584–1635.

749   **BLESSED FEASTS OF BLESSED MARTYRS**

1. Bless-ed feasts of bless-ed mar-tyrs, Ho-ly wom-en,
2. Faith pre-vail-ing, hope un-fail-ing, Lov-ing Christ with
3. There-fore, all that reign in glo-ry, Faith-ful heirs with

1. ho-ly men, With our love and ad-mi-ra-tion, Greet we
2. sin-gle heart, Thus they, glo-rious and vic-to-rious, Brave-ly
3. Christ on high, Join to ours your sup-pli-ca-tion When be-

1. your re-turn a-gain. Wor-thy deeds they wrought, and won-ders,
2. bore the mar-tyr's part, By con-tempt of ev-'ry an-guish,
3. fore Christ we draw nigh, Pray-ing that, this life com-plet-ed,

1. Wor-thy of the name they bore; We, with joy-ful
2. By un-yield-ing bat-tle done; Vic-tors at the
3. All its fleet-ing mo-ments past, By Christ's grace we

1. praise and sing-ing, Hon-or them for ev-er-more.
2. last, they tri-umph, With the host of an-gels one.
3. may be wor-thy Of e-ter-nal bliss at last.

Text: 87 87 D; *O beata beatorum*, 11th cent.; tr. by John M. Neale, 1818–1866, alt.
Music: IN BABILONE; *Oude en Nieuwe Boerenlities en Contradanseu*, ca. 1710.

750   **SING WE NOW THE GLORIOUS MARTYRS**

1. Sing we now the glorious martyrs,
Faithful, fallen, raised on high.
Strong they stood, in ranks of courage,
Loath to live if truth must die.
Grant to us, O God, their wisdom
That could dare to choose the cross,
Christ their one and only treasure,
All else, even life, no loss.

2. Keep alight upon our hilltops
Lamps like these, set high apart,
Flames of faith no night can vanquish,
Beacons for the faint of heart.
Let them burn with such an ardor
That the very dark must quail.
Before love so all-consuming
Death itself cannot prevail.

Music: IN BABILONE; *Oude en Nieuwe Hollanste Boerenlities en Contradanseu*, ca. 1710.

SAINTS OF GOD

Refrain

Saints of God a - bid - ing in the arms of mer - cy, pray for us.

Verses

1. I saw the souls ___ of the saints be - neath the al - tar,
2. I saw a mul - ti - tude from ev - 'ry land and peo - ple
3. Since e - ven now this cloud of wit - ness - es sur-rounds us,

1. slain for bear - ing wit - ness to God's Word,
2. wor - ship - ing be - fore the throne of grace,
3. let us cast a - side the weight of sin,

to Refrain

1. and each one was ___ robed in white.
2. where all tears are ___ washed a - way.
3. so with them we may run the race.

Text: Based on Revelation 6:9–11; 7:9, 17; Hebrews 12:1; Bob Hurd, b. 1950.
Music: Bob Hurd.

752   MINE EYES HAVE SEEN THE GLORY

Verses

1. Mine eyes have seen the glo-ry of the com-ing
2. I have seen him in the watch-fires of a hun-dred
3. He has sound-ed forth the trum-pet that shall nev-er
4. In the beau-ty of the lil-ies Christ was born a-

1. of the Lord; He is tram-pling out the vin-tage where the
2. cir-cling camps; They have build-ed him an al-tar in the
3. call re-treat; He is sift-ing out the hearts of all be-
4. cross the sea, With a glo-ry in his bos-om that trans-

1. grapes of wrath are stored; He hath loosed the fate-ful light-ning
2. eve-ning dews and damps; I can read his righ-teous sen-tence
3. fore his judg-ment seat; O be swift, my soul, to an-swer
4. fig-ures you and me; As he died to make us ho-ly,

1. of his ter-ri-ble swift sword: His truth is march-ing on.
2. by the dim and flar-ing lamps; His day is march-ing on.
3. him; be ju-bi-lant, my feet! Our God is march-ing on.
4. let us die that all be free! While God is march-ing on.

Refrain

Glo-ry! Glo-ry! Hal-le-lu-jah! Glo-ry!

Glo-ry! Hal-le-lu-jah! Glo-ry! Glo-ry! Hal-le-

lu-jah! His truth is march-ing on.

Text: 15 15 15 6 with refrain; Julia W. Howe, 1819–1910, alt.
Music: BATTLE HYMN OF THE REPUBLIC; trad. American Melody; attr. to William Steffe, ca. 1830–1911.

In the Day of the Lord

Refrain

In the day of the Lord, the sun will shine like the dawn of e-ter-nal day. All cre-a-tion will rise to dance and sing the glo-ry of the Lord!

Verses

1. And on that day will jus-tice tri-umph, on that
2. Then shall the na-tions throng to-geth-er to the
3. And they shall beat their swords to plow-shares; there will
4. For Is-ra-el shall be de-liv-ered, and the
5. And on that day of Christ in glo-ry, God will
6. O give us eyes to see your glo-ry, give us

1. day will all be free: free from want, free from
2. moun-tain of the Lord: they shall walk in the
3. be an end to war: one in peace, one in
4. des-ert lands will bloom. Say to all, "Do not
5. wipe a-way our tears, and the dead shall rise
6. hearts to un-der-stand. Let our ears hear your

to Refrain

1. fear, _____ free to live!
2. light _____ of the Lord!
3. love, _____ one in God!
4. fear. Here is your God!"
5. up _____ from their graves!
6. voice _____ 'til you come!

Text: Based on Isaiah 2, 25, 41; M.D. Ridge.
Music: M.D. Ridge.

754   WORTHY IS THE LAMB

Refrain

Wor-thy is the Lamb that was slain to re - ceive

hon - or and glo - ry. Wor - thy are the ones who be - lieve

to re - ceive the good - ness of God.

Verses

1. Wor - thy are you, O Pas - chal Lamb.
2. Wor - thy are you, O Bread of Life. Sal -
3. Wor - thy are you, O Ris - en Christ.

1. Wis - dom and strength be - long now to you. You
2. va - tion and joy be - long now to us. By
3. Won - ders and signs, re - veal - ing your might. Your

1. laid down your life and died up - on the cross: we've be -
2. con - quer - ing death and ris - ing to new life, we've be -
3. pow - er and glo - ry shine up - on our lives: we've be -

2   to Refrain

1. come a peo - ple of hope.
2. come a peo - ple of praise.
3. come your light for the world.

Text: Based on Revelation 5:9–14; Ricky Manalo, CSP, b. 1965.
Music: Ricky Manalo, CSP.
Text and music © 1997, Ricky Manalo, CSP. Published by OCP. All rights reserved.

755   SOON AND VERY SOON

1. Soon and ver - y soon, We are going to see the King;
2. No more cry - ing there, We are going to see the King;
3. No more dy - ing there, We are going to see the King;

1. Soon and ver-y soon, We are going to see the King;
2. No more cry-ing there, We are going to see the King;
3. No more dy-ing there, We are going to see the King;

1. Soon and ver-y soon, We are going to see the King;
2. No more cry-ing there, We are going to see the King; } Hal-le-
3. No more dy-ing there, We are going to see the King;

1-3. lu - jah! Hal-le-lu-jah! We're going to see the King.

Text: 57 57 57 86; Andraé Crouch, b. 1945.
Music: SOON AND VERY SOON; Andraé Crouch; adapt. by William F. Smith, b. 1941.
Text and music © 1976, Bud John Songs, Inc./Crouch Music. All rights reserved. Administered by EMI CMG Publishing.
    Used with permission.

SHALL WE GATHER AT THE RIVER 756

Verses

1. Shall we gath-er at the riv-er, Where bright an-gel feet have
2. On the mar-gin of the riv-er, Wash-ing up its sil-ver
3. Ere we reach the shin-ing riv-er, Lay we ev-'ry bur-den
4. Soon we'll reach the shin-ing riv-er, Soon our pil-grim-age will

1. trod, With its crys-tal tide for-ev - er, Flow-ing
2. spray, We will walk and wor-ship ev - er, All the
3. down; Grace our spir-its will de-liv-er, And pro-
4. cease; Soon our hap-py hearts will quiv-er With the

Refrain

1. by the throne of God? Yes, we'll gath-er at the riv-er, The
2. hap-py gold-en day.
3. vide a robe and crown.
4. mel-o-dy of peace.

beau-ti-ful, the beau-ti-ful riv - er, Gath-er with the

saints at the riv - er That flows by the throne of God.

Text: 87 87 with refrain; Revelation 22:1–5; Robert Lowry, 1826–1899.
Music: HANSON PLACE; Robert Lowry.

757   **STEAL AWAY TO JESUS**

Refrain

Steal a-way, steal a-way, steal a-way to Je-sus!

Steal a-way, steal a-way home, I ain't got long to stay here.

Verses

1. My Lord, he calls me, He calls me by the thun-der; The
2. Green trees are bend-ing, Poor sin-ners stand a-trem-bling; The
3. My Lord, he calls me, He calls me by the light-ning; The

to Refrain

1-3. trum-pet sounds with-in my soul; I ain't got long to stay here.

Text: Traditional.
Music: Spiritual.

758   **JERUSALEM, MY HAPPY HOME**

1. Je - ru - sa - lem, my hap - py home, When shall I
2. O hap - py har - bor of the saints, O sweet and
3. Your gar - dens and your gal - lant walks Con - tin - ual-
4. There trees for - ev - er - more bear fruit And ev - er -
5. Je - ru - sa - lem, Je - ru - sa - lem, God grant that

1. come to thee? When shall my sor - rows
2. pleas - ant soil! In you no sor - row
3. ly are green; There grow such sweet and
4. more do spring; There ev - er - more the
5. I may see Your end - less joy, and

1. have an end? Your joys when shall I see?
2. may be found, No grief, no care, no toil.
3. pleas - ant flow'rs As no - where else are seen.
4. an - gels sit And ev - er - more do sing!
5. of the same Par - tak - er ev - er be!

Text: CM; F. B. P., London, ca. 16th cent., alt.
Music: LAND OF REST; trad. American Melody.

SING WITH ALL THE SAINTS IN GLORY

759

1. Sing with all the saints in glo - ry, Sing the res - ur -
2. Oh, what glo - ry, far ex - ceed - ing All that eye has
3. Life e - ter - nal! heav'n re - joic - es: Je - sus lives who
4. Life e - ter - nal! O what won - ders Crowd on faith; what

1. rec - tion song! Death and sor - row, earth's dark sto - ry,
2. yet per - ceived! Ho - liest hearts for a - ges plead - ing,
3. once was dead; Join with all the heav'n - ly voic - es;
4. joy un - known, When, a - mid earth's clos - ing thun - ders,

1. To the form - er days be - long. All a - round the
2. Nev - er that full joy con - ceived. God has prom - ised,
3. Child of God, lift up your head! Pa - tri - archs from
4. Saints shall stand be - fore the throne! Oh, to en - ter

1. clouds are break-ing, Soon the storms of time shall cease; In God's
2. Christ pre - pares it, There on high our wel-come waits; Ev - 'ry
3. dis - tant a - ges, Saints all long - ing for their heav'n, Proph-ets,
4. that bright por - tal, See that glow - ing fir - ma - ment, Know, with

1. like - ness, peo - ple wak - ing, Know the ev - er - last - ing peace.
2. hum - ble spir - it shares it, Christ has passed th'e - ter - nal gates.
3. psalm-ists, seers, and sa - ges, All a - wait the glo - ry giv'n.
4. you, O God im-mor - tal, Je - sus Christ whom you have sent!

Text: 87 87 D; 1 Corinthians 15:20; William J. Irons, 1812–1893; fr. *Psalms and Hymns*, 1873, alt.
Music: HYMN TO JOY; Ludwig van Beethoven, 1770–1827; adapt. by Edward Hodges, 1796–1867.

760   AS WE GATHER AT YOUR TABLE

1. As we gath-er at your Ta-ble, As we lis-ten to your
2. Turn our wor-ship in-to wit-ness In the sac-ra-ment of
3. Gra-cious Spir-it, help us sum-mon Oth-er guests to share that

1. Word, Help us know, O God, your pres-ence: Let our
2. life; Send us forth to love and serve you, Bring-ing
3. feast Where tri-um-phant Love will wel-come Those who

1. hearts and minds be stirred. Nour-ish us with sa-cred
2. peace where there is strife. Give us, Christ, your great com-
3. had been last and least. There no more will en-vy

1. sto-ry Till we claim it as our own; Teach us
2. pas-sion To for-give as you for-gave; May we
3. blind us Nor will pride our peace de-stroy, As we

1. through this ho-ly ban-quet How to make Love's vic-t'ry known.
2. still be-hold your im-age In the world you died to save.
3. join with saints and an-gels To re-peat the sound-ing joy.

Text: 87 87 D; Carl P. Daw, Jr., b. 1944, © 1989, Hope Publishing Co. All rights reserved. Used with permission.
Music: NETTLETON; J. Wyeth's *Repository of Sacred Music, Part II*, 1813.

761   TABLE OF PLENTY

Refrain

Come to the feast of heav-en and earth! Come to the ta-

-ble of plen-ty! God will pro-vide for all that we

need, here at the ta-ble of plen-ty.

Verses

1. O come and sit at my ta - ble where saints and
2. O come and eat with-out mon-ey; come to
3. My bread will ev - er sus-tain you through days of
4. Your fields will flow - er in full-ness; your homes will

1. sin - ners are friends. I wait to wel-come the lost and
2. drink with - out price. My feast of glad-ness will feed your
3. sor - row and woe. My wine will flow like a sea of
4. flour - ish in peace. For I, the giv - er of home and

to Refrain

1. lone - ly to share the cup of my love.
2. spir - it with faith and full - ness of life.
3. glad-ness to flood the depths of your soul.
4. har - vest, will send my rain on the soil.

Text and music: Dan Schutte, b. 1947, © 1992, OCP. All rights reserved.

WE GATHER TOGETHER   762

1. We gath - er to - geth - er to ask the Lord's bless - ing; He
2. Be - side us to guide us, our God with us join - ing, Whose
3. We all do ex - tol you, our lead - er tri - um-phant, And

1. chas - tens and has - tens his will to make known; The
2. king - dom calls all to the love which en - dures. So
3. pray that you still our de - fend - er will be. Let

1. wick - ed op - press-ing now cease from dis - tress-ing: Sing
2. from the be - gin - ning the fight we were win - ning: You,
3. your con - gre - ga - tion es - cape trib - u - la - tion: Your

1. prais - es to his name; he for - gets not his own.
2. Lord, were at our side; all ___ glo - ry be yours!
3. name be ev - er praised! O ___ Lord, make us free!

Text: 12 11 12 11; *Wilt heden nu treden*; tr. by Theodore Baker, 1851–1934, alt.
Music: KREMSER; Valerius' *Nederlandtsche Gedenckclanck*, Haarlem, 1626.

763   VEN AL BANQUETE/COME TO THE FEAST

Refrain/Estribillo

(Bilingual) Ven, ven al ban-que-te.   Ven a la fies-ta de Dios.
(Español) Ven, ven al ban-que-te.   Ven a la fies-ta de Dios.
(English) Come, come to the ban - quet.   Come,___ come to the feast.

Here the hun-gry find plen - ty,   here the thirst-y shall drink. ___
Los que tie - nen ham - bre   y   sed se-rán __ sa - cia - dos.
Here the hun-gry find plen - ty,   here the thirst-y shall drink, ___

Ven a la ce - na de Cris - to,   come ___ to _ the feast.
Ven a la ce - na de Cris - to,   ven a la fies-ta de Dios.
here at the sup - per of Je - sus,   come ___ to _ the feast.

Verses/Estrofas

1. Like the child whose fish - es and loaves   fed the mul - ti -
__ ¿Quién le pue - de dar de co - mer   a la mul - ti -
2. 'Til the seed is giv - en to earth,   it is just one
__ Hay que dar - se a ___ mo - rir   pa - ra co - se -
3. In the strang - er by ___ our side,   in the least and
__ Los de - sam - pa - ra-dos ven-drán   a par - tir el

1. tude,   in the Lord the lit - tle we have,
__ tud?   Con Je - sús, al com - par - tir lo
2. grain;   but once sown its death brings new birth, the
__ char,   las se - mi - llas de li - ber - tad y
3. last,   in the thirst for jus - tice we share,
__ pan   y ve - rán su dig - ni - dad de

to Refrain/al Estribillo

1. bro - ken and shared, be-comes a - bun-dant food.
__ po - co que hay, re - ci - bi - mos ple - ni - tud.
2. har - vest is rich; what's lost is raised a - gain.
__ re - su - rrec - ción, la pro - me - sa de vi - vir.
3. Christ ___ is here in the break-ing of the bread.
__ nue - vo en Je - sús, Sal - va - dor y Buen Pas - tor.

*Last time, repeat final phrase
Se repite la última vez

Text: Bob Hurd, b. 1950, Pia Moriarty, b. 1948, and Jaime Cortez, b. 1963.
Music: Bob Hurd.

GOD IS HERE! AS WE HIS PEOPLE

764

1. God is here! As we his peo - ple Meet to of - fer
2. Here are sym - bols to re - mind us Of our life - long
3. Here our chil - dren find a wel - come In the Shep - herd's
4. Lord of all, of church and king - dom, In an age of

1. praise and prayer, May we find in full - er mea - sure
2. need of grace; Here are ta - ble, font and pul - pit,
3. flock and fold; Here, as bread and wine are tak - en,
4. change and doubt, Keep us faith - ful to the gos - pel,

1. What it is in Christ we share: Here, as in the world a -
2. Here the cross has cen - tral place: Here in hon - es - ty of
3. Christ sus - tains us as of old: Here the ser - vants of the
4. Help us work your pur - pose out: Here, in this day's ded - i -

1. round us, All our var - ied skills and arts Wait the com - ing
2. preach - ing, Here in si - lence as in speech, Here in new - ness
3. Ser - vant Seek in wor - ship to ex - plore What it means in
4. ca - tion, All we have to give, re - ceive; We who can - not

1. of his Spir - it In - to o - pen minds and hearts.
2. and re - new - al God the Spir - it comes to each.
3. dai - ly liv - ing To be - lieve and to a - dore.
4. live with - out you, We a - dore you! We be - lieve!

Text: 87 87 D; Fred Pratt Green, 1903–2000, © 1979, Hope Publishing Co. All rights reserved. Used with permission.
Music: ABBOT'S LEIGH; Cyril Vincent Taylor, 1907–1991, © 1942, renewed 1970, Hope Publishing Co.
All rights reserved. Used with permission.

765   GATHER US TOGETHER

Refrain

Lord, Je-sus Christ, gath-er us to-geth-er. Make us one bread, one body in your love.

Verses

1. Gath-er your peo - ple, who long
2. We do pro - claim you the Sav-
3. For-give our fail - ings, cre - ate
4. In - to your hands, Lord, we place
5. With-in your tem - ple your prais-

to Refrain

1. to be one, one with you, O Lord, in truth and love.
2. ior of all, Lord of all the earth and sea and sky.
3. us a - new. Speak your words of peace in - to our hearts.
4. all our cares, trust - ing in your love which nev - er fails.
5. es we sing. Glo - rious is your name o'er all the earth.

766   GATHER THE PEOPLE

Refrain

Gath-er the peo-ple! En - ter the feast! All are in - vi - ted, the great-est and least. The ban-quet is read - y, now to be shared. Join in the heav-en - ly

(Fine)   5   to Verses

feast that God has pre - pared.

Verses

1. A - round this ta - ble we dine as kin, be -
2. A - round this ta - ble we tell great tales, the
3. A - round this ta - ble God's boun - ty falls on
4. A - round this ta - ble God's mer - cy flows to
5. A - round this ta - ble new hope is born, the
6. A - round this ta - ble God's heal - ing flows to
7. A - round this ta - ble God's peace will reign in
8. A - round this ta - ble our hearts re - joice in
9. A - round this ta - ble God's jus - tice reigns in
10. A - round this ta - ble God's low - ly ones are

1. lov - ed fam - 'ly of God. We
2. won - drous sto - ries of grace. We
3. all who hun - ger and thirst. We
4. hearts im - pris - oned by shame. We
5. flame of faith in our hearts. We
6. all the wound - ed and worn. We
7. hearts im - pris - oned by fear. We
8. love that's strong - er than death. We'll
9. hearts that la - bor for peace. We
10. clothed in splen - dor and grace. We

1. share the Bod - y of Christ, the Lord. Here we be -
2. hold the mem - 'ry of Christ, the Lord. So we be -
3. drink the full - ness of Christ, the Lord. So we be -
4. know com - pas - sion in Christ, the Lord. Let us be -
5. find our cour - age in Christ, the Lord, till we be -
6. join the suf - f'rings of Christ, the Lord, as we be -
7. live in free - dom through Christ, the Lord, as we be -
8. rise in glo - ry with Christ, the Lord. Then we be -
9. breathe the spir - it of Christ, the Lord, till we be -
10. share the ban - quet of Christ, the Lord. Here we be -

2   to Refrain

1-10. come what we eat.

767   LET US GO TO THE ALTAR

Refrain

Let us go to the al-tar of God, the God of our glad-ness and joy! Let us en-ter the courts of the house of the Lord and sing to the glo-ry of God.

Verses

1. Give praise with blast ___ of trum - pet,
2. Give praise with lyre ___ and tim - brel,
3. Give praise with pipe ___ and or - gan,
4. Give praise, all crea-tures of heav - en,

1. with no - ble sound of the horn. With the clash of the
2. with lute and sound of the harp. With the dance of the
3. with rous - ing beat of the drum. With the call of the
4. and all that dwell on the earth. Come to wor - ship the

to Refrain

1. clang - ing cym - bal, give glo - ry to the Lord!
2. flute and o - boe, give glo - ry to the Lord!
3. bell and bag - pipe, give glo - ry to the Lord!
4. God who made us, and dance be - fore the Lord!

Text: Based on Psalms 42 and 150; Dan Schutte, b. 1947.
Music: Dan Schutte.

768   GATHER YOUR PEOPLE

Refrain

Gath - er your peo - ple, O Lord. Gath - er your peo - ple, O Lord. One bread, one bod - y, one spir - it of love. Gath-er your peo - ple, O Lord.

Verses

1. Draw us forth to the ta - ble of life:
2. We are parts of the bod - y of Christ,
3. No more harm on the moun - tain of God;
4. Wash us, Lord, in the wa - ters of life;

1. broth - ers and sis - ters, each of us called to
2. need - ing each oth - er, each of the gifts the
3. swords in - to plow - shares. Free us, O Lord, from
4. wa - ters of mer - cy, wa - ters of hope that

2   to Refrain

1. walk in your light.
2. Spir - it pro - vides.
3. hard - ness of heart.
4. flow from your side.

Text: Based on 1 Corinthians 12; Isaiah 2:3–4; 11:9; Bob Hurd, b. 1950.
Music: Bob Hurd.
Text and music © 1991, Bob Hurd. Published by OCP. All rights reserved.

WHAT IS THIS PLACE   769

1. What is this place, where we are meet-ing? On - ly a house, the
2. Words from a - far, stars that are fall - ing. Sparks that are sown in
3. And we ac - cept bread at his ta - ble, Bro - ken and shared, a

1. earth its floor. Walls and a roof, shel - ter - ing peo - ple, Win - dows for
2. us like seed: Names for our God, dreams, signs and won - ders Sent from the
3. liv - ing sign. Here in this world, dy - ing and liv - ing, We are each

1. light, an o - pen door. Yet it be - comes a bod - y that lives When
2. past are all we need. We in this place re - mem - ber and speak A-
3. oth - er's bread and wine. This is the place where we can re - ceive What

1. we are gath - ered here, And know our God is near.
2. gain what we have heard: God's free re - deem - ing word.
3. we need to in - crease: Our jus - tice and God's peace.

Text: 98 98 9 66; Huub Oosterhuis, b. 1933; tr. by David Smith, b. 1933.
Music: KOMT NU MET ZANG; trad. Dutch Hymn; Valerius' *Nederlandtsche Gedenckclank*, Haarlem, 1626.
Text and music © 1967, Gooi en Sticht, bv., Baarn, The Netherlands. All rights reserved.
    Exclusive agent for English-language countries: OCP.

770

IN THIS PLACE

Verses

1. We are all hun-gry peo-ple, we need shel-ter and
2. All our lives are a Mys-t'ry; we see not where they
3. Though the world may __ tell us to __ look at our-
4. In the bread that is bro-ken is the Christ that re-

1. strength. We are one in our hurt-ing, we are
2. lead. We are asked now to trust you and we
3. selves, we reach out to an-oth-er where __
4. stores. As we take, now re-ceive him, we find

1. one __ in our pain. In our suf-f'ring and sad-ness,
2. know we must be-lieve. As our feet be-come Christ's feet,
3. suf-fer-ing dwells. As our hands be-come Christ's hands,
4. love __ ev-er-more. As the bread be-comes Bod-y,

1. we are saved by the grace
2. we go forth with the grace   of the pow-er and the
3. we are healed by the grace
4. we are filled with the grace

Refrain

1-4. Spir-it that is here in this place.   We are

gath-ered at ta-ble as __ one in the Lord.   We are
    (*to-geth-er)
gath-ered as peo-ple who are liv-ing the Word.   Our __

hearts and our spir-its are nur-tured by grace.   It is

Je-sus who fills us.   He is here in this place.

*Alternate text.

Text: Victoria Thomson, b. 1969, © 1996, Victoria Thomson. Published by spiritandsong.com®, a division of OCP.
All rights reserved.
Music: Trevor Thomson, b. 1971, © 1996, Trevor Thomson. Published by spiritandsong.com®, a division of OCP.
All rights reserved.

Our God Is Here

Verses

1. Here in this time, here in this place,
2. Here in the Word, God is re-vealed,

1. here we are stand-ing face to face. Here in our hearts,
2. here where the wound-ed can be healed. Here in our hearts,

1. here in our lives, our God is here. Here for the bro-
2. here in our lives, our God is here. Here we be-come

1. - ken, here for the strong, here in this tem-ple we be-long.
2. _____ what we re-ceive, here in this Eu-cha-ris-tic feast.

1. Here in our hearts, _____ here in our lives, our God is here.
2. We are his bod-y, liv-ing as one; our God is here.

Refrain

And we cry: "Ho-ly! Ho-ly! Ho-ly are you!"

We cry: "Ho-ly! Ho-ly! Ho-ly and true!"

A-men, we do be-lieve our God is here.

(Repeat last time)

Our God is here.

Text and music: Chris Muglia, b. 1971, © 2001, Chris Muglia. Published by spiritandsong.com®, a division of OCP.
All rights reserved.

772   WE GATHER HERE TO WORSHIP

1. We gath - er here to wor - ship you, O God.
2. We gath - er here to feed up - on your Word.
3. We gath - er here to pray for those in need.
4. We gath - er here to cel - e - brate your feast.
5. We gath - er here to wor - ship you, O God.

1. We gath - er here to give you thanks and praise. You
2. We gath - er here to learn your way of life. With
3. We gath - er here to place them in your care: The
4. We gath - er at the ta - ble you have spread. As
5. We gath - er here to wor - ship and a - dore The

1. call us from our scat-tered lives To u - ni - fy what we di - vide.
2. bless - ed wis-dom from a - bove You fill our fra - gile hearts with love.
3. hun - gry seek-ing to be fed, The lone - ly, long-ing, dy - ing, dead,
4. once he did in his - to - ry, So now in ho - ly mys - ter - y,
5. Source of all in time and space, The Son who joins the hu - man race,

1. You crown with grace, you crown with grace our hum - ble deeds and
2. You guide our path, you guide our path through strug-gle and through
3. Your wound-ed peo - ple, wound-ed peo - ple here and ev - 'ry -
4. Christ gives him - self, Christ gives him - self in sac - red wine and
5. The Spir - it with them both for - ev - er - more, for - ev - er -

1. days. We gath - er here to wor - ship you, O God.
2. strife. We gath - er here to feed up - on your Word.
3. where. We gath - er here to pray for those in need.
4. bread. We gath - er here to cel - e - brate your feast.
5. more. We gath - er here to wor - ship you, O God.

Text: 10 10 8 8 14 10; Vicki Klima and Michael Joncas, b. 1951, © 2007, Vicki Klima. Published by OCP. All rights reserved.
Music: IRONWOOD; Michael Joncas, © 2007, Jan Michael Joncas Trust. Published by OCP. All rights reserved.

THE GOD OF ALL GRACE

Refrain: 1st time: Cantor, All repeat; thereafter: All

The God of all grace has blessed us this day, all of cre-a-tion joins us in praise; lift-ing our voic-es, lift-ing our hearts to the glo-ry of God for-ev - er!

Verses

1. God of pow-er and might, come in-to our pres-ence this
2. God of mer-cy and truth, who brings us from night in-to
3. God of won-drous love, com-pas-sion and glo-ry are
4a. All the gifts of the Lord shall flow from the glo-ry of
*4b. God of wa-ter and birth, re-new-ing the face of the

1. day. Strength-en us now with a spir-it of
2. day, nour-ish our lives with a spir-it of
3. yours. Come fill our hearts with a spir-it of
4a. God. Let us pro-claim all the won-ders we've
4b. earth; heal-ing us now with the Spir-it of

to Refrain

1. faith; we gath-er in your name.
2. hope and shield us from all fear.
3. love: the joy we find in you.
4a. seen: give thanks, re-joice and sing!
4b. Christ, you cleanse us from our sins.

*Alternate text for use during the Sprinkling Rite.

774 THE SUPPER OF THE LORD

Refrain

Pre-cious bod-y, pre-cious blood, here in bread and wine;

here the Lord pre - pares the feast di - vine.

Bread of love is bro-ken now, cup of life is poured:

come, share the sup-per of the Lord.

Verses

1. This is the bread of God com-ing down from heav'n,
2. "I am the liv-ing spring of e - ter - nal life;
3. "I am the bread of heav'n giv-ing life to you;
4. "All those who feed on me have their life in me,
5. All praise to you, O Christ, pres-ent in this feast,

to Refrain

1. giv-ing life to us, ___ to all the world.
2. you that drink from me shall not thirst a - gain."
3. you that eat this bread ___ shall nev - er die."
4. as I have my life in the liv - ing God."
5. in this bread we share in one life, one Lord.

Text: Verses 1–4 based on John 4, 6; Laurence Rosania, b. 1957.
Music: Laurence Rosania.
Text and music © 1994, Laurence Rosania. Published by OCP. All rights reserved.

775 LOOK BEYOND

Refrain

Look be-yond the bread you eat; see your Sav-ior and your Lord.

Look be-yond the cup you drink; see his love poured out as blood.

1. Give us a sign_____ that we might____ be-lieve in you.
2. I am the bread_____ which from ____ the heav-ens came;
3. The bread I give you_____ will be ____ my ver - y flesh;
4. This man speaks harsh-ly; __ who can lis - ten to his word?
5. You, my dis - ci - ples,_____ will you_____ al - so leave?

to Refrain

1. Mo - ses brought us man - na from the sky.
2. those who eat this bread will nev - er die.
3. my blood_____ will tru - ly be your drink.
4. We ____ shall no long - er fol - low him.
5. Lord,_____ to whom__ can we go?

Text and music: Darryl Ducote, b. 1945, © 1969, 1979, Damean Music. All rights reserved. Used with permission.

UBI CARITAS

776

*U - bi ca - ri - tas est ve - ra, est ve - ra: De - us i - bi

est, De - us i - bi est.

1. The love of Christ joins us to -
2. In true com - mu - nion let us
3. May we who gath - er at this
4. For those in need make us your
5. May we one day be - hold your

1. geth - er. Let us re - joice in him, and in our love and
2. gath - er. May all di - vi - sions cease and in their place be
3. ta - ble to share the bread of life be - come a sac - ra -
4. mer - cy, for those op - pressed, your might. Make us, your Church, a
5. glo - ry and see you face to face, re - joic - ing with the

to Refrain

1. care for all now love God in re - turn.
2. Christ the Lord, our ris - en Prince of Peace.
3. ment of love, your heal - ing touch, O Christ.
4. ho - ly sign of jus - tice and new life.
5. saints of God to sing e - ter - nal praise.

*Where there is true charity, God is present.

Text: Refrain and verses 1, 2 and 5 based on *Ubi Caritas*, 9th cent.; verses 3 and 4, Bob Hurd, b. 1950.
Music: Bob Hurd.
Text and music © 1996, Bob Hurd. Published by OCP. All rights reserved.

777   HERE AT THIS TABLE

Refrain

Come and be filled here at this ta-ble.

Food for all who hun-ger and drink for all who thirst.

Drink of his love, wine of sal - va - tion.

*Final time: repeat from here

You shall live for - ev-er in Je - sus Christ the Lord.

Verses 1, 2, 4

1. You who la - bor for jus-tice,   you who la - bor for
2. You with lives full of pain,   you who sor-row and
4. You, the a - ged a - mong us,   ho - ly, faith-ful and

1. peace,   you who stead - y the plow   in the
2. weep,   you,   be - lov - ed of Christ,   come to
4. wise,   may   the wis-dom you share   form our

to Refrain

1. field   of the Lord,
2. him,   come to him!
4. lives   and our world!

Verses 3, 5

3. Chil - dren of ev - 'ry col - or ___ in ev - 'ry land,
5. Let each wom - an and man ___ learn from the strang-er;

3. you are his own,   he gath - ers you gent - ly.
5. we're not so dif - f'rent   and so much u - nites us.

3. Don't you grow wea-ry, _____ for when you
5. For we are one, _____ blest with the

to Refrain

3. run, ⸕ you run with the Lord!
5. Spir - it and the pow - er of love!

OUR BLESSING CUP 778

Refrain

Our bless-ing cup is a com-mun-ion with the blood of Christ;

and the bread we break, it is a shar - ing in the bod - y of the

Repeat first time only
(or ostinato as desired) Verses
Fine

Lord.
1. How can we make a re - turn
2. Pre-cious in - deed in your sight,
3. Gra-cious and mer - ci-ful God,
4. For you have heard my __ voice,

1. for all the good-ness God has shown? We will take the
2. the life and death of those you love. We__ are your
3. we give you thanks and bless your name: with__ all your
4. for you have heard my plead - ing. Though_ death sur-

to Refrain (or Verse
if ostinato is sung)

1. cup of life, and ___ call up - on God's name.
2. ser - vants, for ___ you have set us free.
3. peo - ple, praise and glo - ry to your name.
4. round-ed me, you ___ heard and an-swered me.

779

IN THE BREAKING OF THE BREAD/
CUANDO PARTIMOS EL PAN DEL SEÑOR

Refrain   In ___ the break - ing ___ of ___ the

Verses   1. Bread for the jour - ney, ___ ♪ strength for our
         2. Bread of the prom - ise, ___ ♪ peo - ple of

Estribillo   Cuan-do par - ti - mos ___ el pan del Se -
Estrofas   1. Pan pa - ra el via - je, ___ pan de la
           2. Pan de pro - me - sa, ___ pan de es - pe -

bread ___ we ___ have known him;
1. years, ___ man - na of ag - es, of
2. hope, ___ wine of com - pas - sion, ___

ñor, ___ lo co - no - ce - mos, nos
1. vi - da, pan de los si - glos de
2. ran - za, vi - no de vi - da, de

we have been fed. ___ Je - sus the ___
1. strug-gle and tears. ___ Cup of sal -
2. life for the world. ___ Gath-ered at ___

da de co - mer. ___ ♪ Je - sús des - co - no -
1. lu - cha y do - lor, ___ y es - te ___
2. su com - pa - sión. ___ En es - ta ___

strang - er, ___ Je - sus the Lord, ___
1. va - tion, ___ fruit of the land, ___
2. ta - ble, ___ joined as his bod - y, ___

ci - do, ___ ♪ Je - sús ___ Se - ñor, ___
1. vi - no, ___ ♪ fru - to de la tie - rra, ___
2. me - sa, ___ un so - lo cuer - po, ___

be our com - pan - ion; ___
1. ___ bless and re - ceive ___ now, ___
2. ___ sealed in the ___ Spir - it, ___

___ nues - tro com-pa - ñe - ro ___
1. ___ ♪ ben - dí - ce - lo ___ Pa - dre, ___
2. ___ en un es - pí - ri - tu, ___

be ___ our hope. (to Verses)
1. ___ 𝄾 the work of our hands. (to Refrain)
2. ___ 𝄾 sent by the Word. (to Refrain)
___ 𝄾 y fuen - te de fe. (a las Estrofas)
1. ___ 𝄾 es tu - yo mi Dios. (al Estribillo)
2. ___ 𝄾 con u - na mi - sión. (al Estribillo)

BREAD FOR THE WORLD 780

Refrain: All

Bread for the world: a world of hun - ger. Wine for all
peo - ples: peo - ple who thirst. May we who eat
be bread for oth - ers. May we who drink pour out our love.

Verses: Cantor

1. Lord Je - sus Christ, you are the bread of life, bro - ken to
2. Lord Je - sus Christ, you are the wine of peace, poured in - to
3. Lord Je - sus Christ, you call us to your feast, at which the

1. reach and heal the wounds of hu - man pain. Where we di -
2. hearts once bro - ken and where dry - ness sleeps. Where we are
3. rich and pow'r - ful have be - come the least. Where we sur -

1. vide your peo - ple you are wait - ing there
2. tired and wea - ry, you are wait - ing there
3. vive on oth - ers in our hu - man greed,

to Refrain

1. on bend - ed knee to wash our feet with end - less care.
2. to be the way which beck - ons us be - yond de - spair.
3. you walk a - mong us beg - ging for your ev - 'ry need.

781   SEED, SCATTERED AND SOWN

Refrain

Seed, scat-tered and sown, wheat, gath-ered and grown,

bread, bro-ken and shared as one, the liv-ing bread of God.

Vine, fruit of the land, wine, work of our hands, one cup that is

shared by all; the liv-ing cup, the liv-ing bread of God.

Verses

1. Is not the bread we break a shar-ing in our Lord?
2. The seed which falls on rock will with-er and will die.
3. As wheat up-on the hills was gath-ered and was grown,

to Refrain

1. Is not the cup we bless the blood of Christ out-poured?
2. The seed with-in good ground will flow-er and have life.
3. so may the church of God be gath-ered in-to one.

Text: 66 66 with refrain; based on Didache 9; 1 Corinthians 10:16–17; Mark 4:3–6; Dan Feiten.
Music: SEED, SCATTERED AND SOWN; Dan Feiten.
Text and music © 1987, International Liturgy Publications, PO Box 50476, Nashville, TN 37205, www.ilpmusic.org
  888-898-SONG. All rights reserved. Used with permission.

782   TASTE AND SEE

Taste and see the good-ness of the Lord, the

good-ness of the Lord. Taste and see the good-

-ness of the Lord, the good-ness of the Lord.

Verses

1. I will bless the Lord at all times.
   Praise will be on my lips.
   My soul will glory in the Lord.
   The poor will hear and be glad.

2. I sought the Lord who answered me,
   delivered me from my fear.
   Look to God that you might shine
   with the radiance of God's joy.

3. The Lord has eyes for justice,
   ears to hear your cry.
   God knows your broken heart.
   The Lord redeems a loyal servant.
   Take refuge in your God.

AMÉN. EL CUERPO DE CRISTO

783

Note: Translation of Spanish refrain: Amen. The Body of Christ. Amen. The Blood of Christ.

784

PAN DE VIDA

Refrain/Estribillo

(Bilingual) *Pan de Vi - da, cuer-po del Se - ñor,
(Spanish) Pan de Vi - da, cuer-po del Se - ñor,

cup of bless - ing, blood of Christ the Lord.
san-ta co - pa, Cris - to Re - den-tor.

At this ta - ble the last shall be first.
Su jus - ti - cia nos con-ver-ti - rá.

**Po - der es ser - vir, por-que Dios es a - mor.
Po - der es ser - vir, por-que Dios es a - mor.

| 1-3 to Verses/a las Estrofas | 4 | Final | Verses/Estrofas |

Po -
Po -

1. We are the
2. You call me
3. There is no
1. So-mos el
2. Us - te - des me
3. No hay es -

1. dwell-ing of God, _____ fra-gile and wound-ed and weak. __
2. Teach-er and Lord; _____ I, who have washed __ your feet. __
3. Jew __ or Greek; _____ there is no slave ___ or free; __
1. tem-plo de Dios, _____ frá - gi - les se - res hu - ma -
2. lla - man "Se - ñor". _____ Me in-cli-no a la - var - les los pies. __
3. cla - vos ni li - bres, no hay mu - je - res ni hom -

1. _____ We are the bod - y of Christ, called to
2. _____ So you must do as I do, so the
3. _____ there is no wom-an or man; on - ly
1. nos. So-mos el cuer-po de Cris - to, lla-
2. _____ Ha-gan lo mis-mo, hu - mil - des, sir-
3. bres, só - lo a - que-llos que he - re - dan el

1. be _____ the com - pas - sion of God. _____
2. great - est must be - come __ the least. _____
3. heirs _____ of the prom - ise of God. _____

1. *ma* - *dos* *a* *ser com - pa - si* - *vos.*
2. *vién* - *do - se* *u - nos* *a* *o* - *tros.*
3. *rei* - *no que Dios pro - me - tió.* _____

*Bread of life, body of the Lord,
**Power is for service, because God is love.

Text: Based on John 13:1–15; Galatians 3:28–29; Bob Hurd, b. 1950, and Pia Moriarty, b. 1948;
  Spanish adapt. by Jaime Cortez, b. 1963, Magali Jerez, Elena García and Gustavo Castillo.
Music: Bob Hurd.
Text and music © 1988, 1995, 1999, Bob Hurd and Pia Moriarty. Published by OCP. All rights reserved.

BEHOLD THE LAMB 785

Verses

1. Those who were in the dark are thank - ful for the
2. Peace - ful now, those whose hearts are blessed with un - der -
3. Gen - tle one, Child of God, join with us at this
4. Lord of all, give us light. De - liv - er us from

1. sun - light; we who live, we who die are grate - ful for his
2. stand - ing of the wheat, of the wine u - nit - ed with his
3. ta - ble. Bless our lives; nour - ish all who hun - ger for this
4. e - vil. Make us one; be our shield. Make still the winds that

Refrain

1. gift, thank - ful for his love. Be - hold, be - hold the Lamb of
2. word and the love we share.
3. feast; shel - ter them with peace.
4. blow; cra - dle us with love.

God. All who eat, all who drink shall live; and all,

all who dwell in God shall come to know his glo - ry.

Text: Refrain based on John 1:29; Martin Willett, b. 1960.
Music: Martin Willett.
Text and music © 1984, OCP. All rights reserved.

786   I Received the Living God

Refrain

I re-ceived the liv-ing God, and my heart is full of joy. I re-ceived the liv-ing God, and my heart is full of joy.

Verses

1. Je-sus said: "I am the Bread Knead-ed long to give you life;
2. Je-sus said: "I am the Way, And my Fa-ther longs for you;
3. Je-sus said: "I am the Truth; If you fol-low close to me,
4. Je-sus said: "I am the Life Far from whom no thing can grow,

to Refrain

1. You who will par-take of me Need not ev-er fear to die."
2. So I come to bring you home To be one with him a-new."
3. You will know me in your heart, And my word shall make you free."
4. But re-ceive this liv-ing bread, And my Spir-it you shall know."

Text: 77 77 with refrain; anon.
Music: LIVING GOD; anon.

787   To Be Your Bread

Refrain

To be your bread now, be your wine now, Lord, come and change us to be a sign of your love. Blest and bro-ken, poured and flow-ing, gift that you gave us, to be your bod-y once a-gain.

Verses

1. We come to your ta-ble with our lives as they are.
2. ˠ Lord, __ we stum-ble through the dark-ness of night.
3. ˠ Give us the bread and wine that bring us to life.

1. Heal us, Lord, __ for we are bro-ken; make us one a-gain.
2. Lead us, now, __ O Lord, we fol-low; bring us home to you.
3. Feed us, ___ and we'll nev-er hun-ger, nev-er thirst a-gain.

BREAD OF LIFE 788

Refrain

Bread of life, hope of the world, Je-sus Christ, our broth-er:

feed us now, give us life, lead us to one an-oth-er.

Verses

1. As we pro-claim your death, as we re-call your life, we re-
2. The bread we break and share was scat-tered once as grain: just as
3. We eat this liv-ing bread, we drink this sav-ing cup: sign of
4. Hold us in u-ni-ty, in love for all to see; that the
5. You are the bread of peace, you are the wine of joy, bro-ken

to Refrain

1. mem-ber your prom - ise to re-turn a - gain.
2. now it is gath - ered, make your peo - ple one.
3. hope in our bro-ken world, source of last - ing love.
4. world may be - lieve in you, God of all who live.
5. now for your peo - ple, poured in end - less love.

Alternate Verses: for Advent/Christmas

Adv. 1. Be with your peo-ple, Lord, send us your sav-ing Word: Je - sus
Adv. 2. Bring to our world of fear the truth we long to hear: Je - sus
Chr. 1. A child is born for us, a son is giv'n to us, In our
Chr. 2. With our own eyes we see, with our own ears we hear The sal-
Chr. 3. You are the hope of all, our prom-ise and our call, Ra-diant

to Refrain

1. Christ, light of glad - ness, come a-mong us now.
2. Christ, hope of a - ges, come to save us now.
1. midst, Christ, our Lord and God comes as one who serves.
2. va - tion of all the world, God's in - car - nate Word.
3. light in our dark - ness, truth to set us free.

789   **LAMB OF GOD/TASTE AND SEE**

Lamb of God, you take a-way the sins of the world, have mer - cy, have

mer - cy on us.   world, grant us, grant us peace.

Refrain

Taste and see the good-ness of the Lord.   Oh,

taste and see the good-ness of the Lord.

Verse 1

1. I will bless the LORD at all times; his praise ev - er in my

1. mouth, let my soul glo - ry in the LORD.

Verse 2

2. Let the low-ly hear and be glad, let us glo - ri - fy his

2. name. To - geth - er let us praise God's name.

Verse 3

3. Glo - ri - fy the LORD with me, to - geth - er let us praise his

3. name; from my fears God set me free.

Verse 4

4. Look to the LORD and shine in the light, let your fac - es not be a - shamed.

to Refrain
7

4. The LORD hears the cry of the poor. Bless-ed be the LORD.

HOLY GIFTS   790

Refrain

Ho-ly gifts for ho-ly peo-ple; come, you hun-gry, and be-lieve;

come and take Christ's bod-y of-fered, come and be what you re-ceive.

Verses

1. This is what we have been told: that on the
2. This is what we un - der - stand: that when we
3. This is how we are to live: that be - ing
4. Christ, our way, our truth and life: we are not

1. night be - fore he died,___ af - ter thanks - giv - ing___
2. eat and drink this feast,___ in this bread which we are
3. joined by Christ's___ gifts,___ we should be Christ to___
4. wor - thy to draw near: but take our praise and thanks -

1. spo - ken, bread blest and___ bro - ken, Christ sealed his
2. break - ing, Christ we are par - tak - ing, Christ's death pro -
3. oth - ers, sis - ters and___ broth - ers, hold - ing them
4. giv - ing, trans - form our___ liv - ing, give us that

to Refrain

1. love with his bod - y and blood.
2. claim - ing un - til his re - turn.
3. pre - cious, as saved by his love.
4. food which is heal - ing and strength.

791   GIFT OF FINEST WHEAT

You sat-is-fy the hun-gry heart With gift of fin-est wheat, Come

give to us, O sav-ing Lord, The bread of life to eat.

Verses

1. As when the
2. With joy - ful
3. Is not the
4. The mys - t'ry
5. You give your-

1. shep - herd calls his sheep, They know and heed his voice; So
2. lips we sing to you Our praise and grat - i - tude, That
3. cup we bless and share The blood of Christ out-poured? Do
4. of your pres - ence, Lord, No mor - tal tongue can tell: Whom
5. self to us, O Lord; Then self - less let us be, To

to Refrain

1. when you call your fam-'ly, Lord, We fol - low and re - joice.
2. you should count us wor-thy, Lord, To share this heav'n-ly food.
3. not one cup, one loaf, de - clare Our one-ness in the Lord?
4. all the world can - not con - tain Comes in our hearts to dwell.
5. serve each oth - er in your name In truth and char - i - ty.

Text: CM with refrain; Omer Westendorf, 1916–1997.
Music: BICENTENNIAL; Robert E. Kreutz, 1922–1996.
Text and music © 1977, Archdiocese of Philadelphia. Published by International Liturgy Publications, PO Box 50476, Nashville, TN 37205. www.ilpmusic.org 888-898-SONG. All rights reserved. Used with permission.

792   GOD'S HOLY GIFTS

God's ho - ly gifts for God's ho - ly peo - ple; come now to share the

ban-quet of Christ. Feed on his love with faith and thanks-giv - ing.

Know in your heart that he died for you.

1. May the Bod - y of Christ be food for our souls
2. May the Blood of the Lord pro - tect us from harm
3. As the grain of this bread was gath - ered as one,
4. As the cup that we share is emp - tied for all,
5. When we eat of this bread and drink of this cup,

1. and bring us to ev - er - last - ing life.
2. and mark us as God's be - lov - ed ones.
3. may we who be - lieve be bound by love.
4. may we of - fer up our lives in love.
5. we hold in our mem - 'ry Christ the Lord.

Text and music: Dan Schutte, b. 1947, © 2006, Daniel L. Schutte. Published by OCP. All rights reserved.

ONE BREAD, ONE BODY 793

One bread, one bod-y, one Lord of all,

one cup of bless-ing which we bless. And we, though

man-y, through-out the earth, we are one bod-y in this

one Lord.

Verses

1. Gen - tile or Jew, ser - vant or
2. Man - y the gifts, man - y the
3. Grain for the fields, scat-tered and

to Refrain

1. free, wom - an or man, no more.
2. works, one in the Lord of all.
3. grown, gath-ered to one, for all.

Text: Based on 1 Corinthians 10:16–17; 12:4, 12–13, 20; Galatians 3:28; Ephesians 4:4–6; The Didache 9;
John Foley, S.J., b. 1939.
Music: John Foley, S.J.
Text and music © 1978, John B. Foley, S.J., and OCP. All rights reserved.

794   I AM THE LIVING BREAD

Refrain

See this bread; take and eat and live in me. See this cup;
take and drink, re-mem-ber me.

Verses

1. I am the liv - ing bread come down from heav - en. _____ All who eat my flesh and drink my blood will __ live, will __ live for-ev-er.
2. I am the liv - ing bread; you shall not hun - ger. _____ If you be - lieve in me you shall not thirst, but __ live, but __ live for-ev-er.
3. I am the liv - ing bread ris - en a - mong you. _____ If you be - lieve in me, __ though you die, you will live; you will live for-ev-er.
4. You are the liv - ing bread; life for the world. _____ O __ Lord, to whom __ shall we go? Your __ words, they __ live for-ev-er.

to Refrain

Text: Based on John 6; David Haas, b. 1957.
Music: David Haas.

795   COME TO THE LORD

Verses

1. Do not let your hearts be trou - bled. Chil-dren, do not fear. I suf - fered, I am al - ways near.
2. I will nev - er leave you or - phans; you are not a - lone. in heav - en, in my fa - ther's home.
3. Eat this bread and nev - er hun - ger; I will give you life. Drink the cup I place be - fore you; you will nev - er die.

Though you suf - fer as I have made your place

Come to the Lord; come to the ta-ble of last-ing life. Bring your bur-dens; there's no price, just come to the Lord.

TASTE AND SEE 796

Refrain

Taste and see, O taste and see, taste and see the good-ness of God.

Verses 1, 2

1. Glo-ry, glo-ry to God most high,
2. Who has fash-ioned the earth and sky,

1. glo-ry, bless-ing and praise. With one voice, O peo-ple, re-
2. who cre-a-ted the deep, who ex-alts the low-ly and

1. joice in our God, who hears _ the cry of all __ in need. O
2. sets cap-tives free, who o-pens the door to all those who seek. O

Verse 3

3. Oh, the love of God! Be-come flesh of our flesh,

3. so that we might live in glo-ry. O

797

COME TO ME AND DRINK

Refrain

Come to me and drink, come to me and drink. Oh, let
all who are thirst-ing come to me and drink.

Verses

1. I will put my spir-it with-in you _____ ʸ and
2. I will pour my spir-it on all flesh; _____ ʸ your
3. ʸ Riv-ers of liv-ing wa-ter ʸ will flow _____
4. ʸ In-to our hearts the love of God _____ has been

to Refrain

1. you shall live and know that I am the LORD.
2. sons _____ and your daugh-ters shall proph-e-sy.
3. from with-in the one who be-lieves in me.
4. poured _____ through the Spir-it that dwells with-in.

Verses (Psalm 42/43)

5. As the deer _____ longs for run-ning streams, _____ ʸ
6. ʸ My soul is thirst-ing for God; _____ ʸ when
7. ʸ Tears are my food by day and night, _____ ʸ and
8. ʸ O God, _____ deep calls un-to deep _____ ʸ
9. ₹ Hope in God, _____ O my soul, _____ ʸ a-
10. ʸ Send forth your light _____ and your truth, _____ ʸ and

to Refrain

5. so my soul is long-ing for you, O God.
6. can I go to see the _____ face of God?
7. all the while they say: "Where _____ is your God?"
8. as your might-y wa-ters sweep o-ver me.
9. gain _____ I shall praise my _____ sav-ing God.
10. they shall lead me to your _____ dwell-ing place.

Text: Refrain based on John 7:37; verses based on Ezekiel 37:14; Joel 3:1; John 7:38; Romans 5:5, 8:11; Psalm 42:2–3; Psalm 43:3; Bob Hurd, b. 1950.
Music: Bob Hurd.

SPIRIT AND GRACE

1. Spir - it and grace, here in this meal;
2. Spir - it and grace, here in this meal;
3. Spir - it and grace, here in this place;
4. Spir - it of God, send - ing us forth;

1. you are the wind that breathes through the field.
2. you are the life that flows through the vine.
3. you are the light that shines in this space.
4. we spread your wis-dom through-out all the earth.

1. Gath - er the wheat___ and form us in Christ.
2. Gath - er this drink___ and form us in Christ.
3. Gath - er your peo - ple and form us in Christ.
4. Gath - er the na - tions and form us in Christ.

1. Come, be our source and breath of life.
2. Come, be our source and blood of life.
3. Come, be the heart - beat of our lives.
4. Come, be the pres - ence in our lives.

Refrain

In the bread, blessed, bro-ken and shared, Christ is our

life, whose pres-ence we bear. Come, O Spir - it, make your

grace re - vealed in this ho - ly meal.

799   BREAD OF LIFE

Refrain

I my-self am the bread of life. You and I are the bread of life, tak-en and blessed, bro-ken and shared by Christ that the world might live. live.

1-3   *to Verses*   *Final*

That the world might live. That the world might live.

Verses

1. This bread is spir - it, gift of the Mak - er's
2. Here is God's king - dom giv - en to us as
3. Lives bro - ken o - pen, sto - ries ___ shared a -

1. love, and we who share it ___ know that we can be
2. food. This is our bod - y, ___ this ___ is our
3. loud, be-come a ban -quet, a shel - ter ___ for the

to Refrain

1. one: ⎫
2. blood: ⎬ a liv-ing sign of God in Christ.
3. world: ⎭

800   LET US BREAK BREAD TOGETHER

Verses

1. Let us break bread to-geth-er on our knees; Let us break
2. Let us drink wine to-geth-er on our knees; Let us drink
3. Let us praise God to-geth-er on our knees; Let us praise

1. bread to-geth-er on our knees;
2. wine to-geth-er on our knees;
3. God to-geth-er on our knees;

When I fall on my knees,

With my face to the ris-ing sun, O Lord, have mer-cy on me.

Text: 10 10 with refrain; Spiritual.
Music: LET US BREAK BREAD; Spiritual.

UNLESS A GRAIN OF WHEAT 801

Un-less a grain of wheat fall to the ground and die, it remains a sin-gle grain. But if it die
it will yield a rich har-vest.

1. In his own bod-
2. Do not draw back

1. y, by his own wounds, he brought your
2. now, do not be shy. Turn not a-

1. sins to the cross, and suf-fer'd for you;
2. way _ from him who paid the price.

1. pour'd out his life - blood up-on the tree,
2. Come to his ta - ble, sit by his side.

to Refrain

1. pour'd out his life - blood for you and for me.
2. There he a-waits you: the Lord __ of Life.

Text: Based on John 12:24 and George Herbert's *Love Bade Me Welcome*; adapt. by Bob Hurd, b. 1950.
Music: Bob Hurd.
Text and music © 1984, Bob Hurd. Published by OCP. All rights reserved.

802   ONE LOVE RELEASED

Refrain

One bread, one bod - y,   one cup, one call,

one faith, one Spir - it   pres-ent in us all.

One prayer, one bless - ing,   one hope, one peace,

one church, one peo - ple,   one love re-leased.

Verses

1. Is not this bread we share, the bod - y of our Lord?
2. I am the bread of life, eat and you shall live.
3. I am the liv - ing bread, as man - na from the sky.
4. No one will come to me, un - less our God has led.

to Refrain

1. Is not this wine we drink, the blood of Christ out-poured?
2. To those who share this meal, my strength I'll al - ways give.
3. This bread I give to you, that you may nev - er die.
4. And I shall raise them up, ___ raise them from the dead!

Text: Bob Frenzel, b. 1953, and Kevin Keil, ASCAP, b. 1956.
Music: Based on O WALY WALY; Bob Frenzel and Kevin Keil, ASCAP.
Text and music © 1999, 2000, Robert H. Frenzel and Kevin Keil. Published by OCP. All rights reserved.

803   SACRAMENTUM CARITATIS

*****Refrain**

Sa - cra - mén - tum ca - ri - tá - tis: pa - nis vi - vus et vi - tá - lis.

Ca - lix no - vi tes - ta - mén - ti: do - num Chri - sti Dó - mi - ni.

*Verses available in accompaniment books. Translation of Refrain:
    The sacrament of love: living and life-giving bread.
    Chalice of the new covenant: gift of Christ the Lord.

Text and music: Michael Joncas, b. 1951, © 2007, Jan Michael Joncas Trust. Published by OCP. All rights reserved.

LORD, WHO AT THY FIRST EUCHARIST

804

1. Lord, who at thy first Eu - cha - rist did pray That
*1. *At that first Eu - cha - rist be - fore you died, O*
2. For all thy Church, O Lord, we in - ter - cede; Make
3. We pray thee, too, for wan - d'rers from thy fold; O
4. So, Lord, at length when sac - ra - ments shall cease, May

1. all thy Church might be for - ev - er one, Grant us at
1. *Lord, you prayed that all be one in you; At this our*
2. thou our sad di - vi - sions soon to cease; Draw us the
3. bring them back, Good Shep-herd of the sheep, Back to the
4. we be one with all thy Church a - bove, One with thy

1. ev - 'ry Eu - cha - rist to say With long - ing heart and
1. *Eu - cha - rist a - gain pre - side, And in our hearts your*
2. near - er each, to each we plead, By draw-ing all to
3. faith which saints be - lieved of old, Back to the Church which
4. saints in one un - bro - ken peace, One with thy saints in

1. soul, "Thy will be done." O may we all one bread, one
1. *law of love re - new. O may we all one bread, one*
2. thee, O Prince of Peace; Thus may we all one bread, one
3. still that faith doth keep; Soon may we all one bread, one
4. one un - bound - ed love; More bless - ed still in peace and

1. bod - y be, Through this blest Sac - ra - ment of U - ni - ty.
1. *bod - y be, Through this blest Sac - ra - ment of U - ni - ty.*
2. bod - y be, Through this blest Sac - ra - ment of U - ni - ty.
3. bod - y be, Through this blest Sac - ra - ment of U - ni - ty.
4. love to be One with the Trin - i - ty in U - ni - ty.

*Alternate version of verse 1.

Text: 10 10 10 10 10 10; William H. Turton, 1859–1938.
Music: UNDE ET MEMORES; William H. Monk, 1823–1889, alt.

805
BREAD OF LIFE

1. Bread of life and cup of hope, we come as gift to
2. Lov-ing Lord, Cre-a-tor God, o-pen our eyes to
3. Liv-ing Word, O Son of God, your love shows us the

1. you. Change our hearts; fill us with peace. Trans-form our
2. see the good that lives in each of us, that called the
3. way that we may live in har-mo-ny, and from you

1. lives a-new. O-pen our eyes so that we might see
2. world to be. And when we fail to __ see the good,
3. nev-er stray. Wipe all op-pres-sion __ from our midst;

1. your pres-ence in one an-oth-er. Your life, poured out in
2. when friend-ships fal-ter and crum-ble, give us the cour-age
3. give us a love for all peo-ple. Your song of jus-tice

(Fine) 4

1. love to-day, u-nites us all in you.
2. to for-give that we may live in peace.
3. sing in us, to live for peace to-day.

Text and music: Bobby Fisher, b. 1952, © 1994, Bobby Fisher. Published by OCP. All rights reserved.

806
AVE VERUM CORPUS/HAIL, TRUE BODY

A - ve ve-rum Cor-pus na-tum de Ma-rí-a
Ve - re pas-sum, im-mo-lá-tum in cru-ce pro

Hail, *true Bod-y!* *Ho-ly Bod-y!* *Of the Vir-gin*
Bod - y bro-ken! *Glo-rious Bod-y!* *By your Cross are*

Vír - gi-ne: Cu-ius la-tus per-fo-rá - tum
hó - mi-ne. Es-to no-bis prae-gu-stá - tum

Ma - ry born. *From your Bod-y flows a riv - er*
we re-born. *Wide your mer-cy! Wide the riv - er!*

flu - xit   a - qua   et   sán - gui - ne:
mor - tis   in   e - xá - mi - ne.
Of wa - ter   and   pre - cious blood.
As wide   as   your   end - less love.

O   Je-su dul - cis!
O   Je-su pi - e!   O   Je - su fi - li Ma-rí - ae.
O   Je-su dul - cis!
O   Je-su pi - e!   *O   Je - sus, O Son of Ma - ry!*

Text: Irregular; ascr. to Innocent VI, d. 1362; Latin, fr. *Liber Cantualis*, 1983;
   tr. by Harry Hagan, OSB, © 2004, St. Meinrad Archabbey. Published by OCP. All rights reserved.
Music: AVE VERUM CORPUS; Chant, Mode VI; fr. *Liber Cantualis*, 1983.

SEE US, LORD, ABOUT YOUR ALTAR   807

1. See us, Lord, a - bout your al - tar,
2. Hear our prayers, O lov - ing Fa - ther,
3. Once were seen the blood and wa - ter:
4. Wheat and grape con - tain the mean - ing:
5. Hear us yet: so much is need - ful
6. Mem - bers of his Mys - tic Bod - y,

1. Tho' so man - y we are one; Man - y souls by
2. Hear in them your Son, our Lord; Hear him speak our
3. Now is seen but bread and wine; Once in hu - man
4. Food and drink he is to all; One in him we
5. In our frail, dis - or - dered life; Stay with us and
6. Now we know our prayer is heard, Heard by you be -

1. love u - ni - ted In the heart of Christ, your Son.
2. love and wor - ship As we sing with one ac - cord.
3. form he suf - fered, Now his form is but a sign.
4. kneel a - dor - ing, Gath-ered by his lov - ing call.
5. tend our weak-ness Till that day of no more strife.
6. cause your chil - dren Have re - ceived th'e - ter - nal Word.

Text: 87 87; John Greally, b. 1934, alt.
Music: DRAKES BROUGHTON; Edward Elgar, 1857–1934.

808

SHEPHERD OF SOULS

1. Shep-herd of souls, re-fresh and bless Your cho-sen pil-grim flock
2. We would not live by bread a-lone, But by your word of grace,
3. Be known to us in break-ing bread, But do not then de-part;
4. Lord, sup with us in love di-vine; Your bod-y and your blood,

1. With man-na in the wil-der-ness, With wa-ter from the rock.
2. In strength of which we trav-el on To our a-bid-ing place.
3. Sav-ior, a-bide with us, and spread Your ta-ble in our heart.
4. That liv-ing bread, that heav'n-ly wine, Be our im-mor-tal food.

Text: CM; verses 1, 2, James Montgomery, 1771–1854; verses 3, 4, anon.
Music: ST. AGNES; John B. Dykes, 1823–1876.

809

AN OLD IRISH BLESSING

May the road rise up to meet you. May the wind be

ev-er at your back. May the sun shine warm up-

on your face and the rains fall soft up-on your fields.

And un-til we meet a-gain, and un-til we meet a-gain,

may you be held in the hol-low of God's hand.

Text: Traditional Irish.
Music: Kevin Keil (ASCAP), b. 1956, © 1998, Kevin Keil. Published by OCP. All rights reserved.

MAY YOU WALK WITH CHRIST

810

Refrain

May you walk with Christ be-side you, saints and an-gels share your way. May the Ho-ly Spir-it guide you to the dawn of end-less day.

Verses

1. Peace in hearth and home, peace sur-round you; peace of
2. Light to bless your eyes, light to lead you, light of
3. Christ to hold and heal, Christ to wel-come: Christ to
4. Three to guard and shield, Three un-sleep-ing, Fa-ther,

to Refrain

1. Christ our God in hearts of those a-round you.
2. Christ to shine and on your jour-ney speed you.
3. bring the wan-d'rer home to fold and shel-ter.
4. Son and Spir-it rest you in their keep-ing.

MAY GOD BLESS AND KEEP YOU

811

1st time: Cantor; thereafter: All

May God bless and keep you. May God's face shine on you.

May God be kind to you and give you peace.

812   TAKE THE WORD OF GOD WITH YOU

Verses

1. Take the word of God with you as you go.
2. Take the peace of God with you as you go.
3. Take the joy of God with you as you go.
4. Take the *love of God with you as you go.

1. Take the seeds of God's word and make them grow.
2. Take the seeds of God's peace and make them grow.
3. Take the seeds of God's joy and make them grow.
4. Take the seeds of God's love and make them grow.

Refrain

Go in peace to serve the world, in peace to serve the world.

Take the love of God, the love of God with you as you go.

*Add other words if needed, such as "faith," "hope," etc.

Text: James Harrison, b. 1979, © 1991, James Harrison. Published by OCP. All rights reserved.
Music: Christopher Walker, b. 1947, © 1991, Christopher Walker. Published by OCP. All rights reserved.

813   CITY OF GOD

Verses 1, 2

1. A-wake from your slum-ber! A - rise from your
2. We are sons of the morn-ing; we are daugh-ters of

1. sleep! A new day is dawn-ing for all those who weep.
2. day. The one who has loved us has bright-ened our way.

1. The peo-ple in dark-ness have seen a great light. The
2. The Lord of all kind-ness has called us to be a

to Refrain

1. Lord of our long-ing has con-quered the night.
2. light for his peo-ple to set their hearts free.

Refrain

Let us build the cit-y of God. May our tears be turned in-to danc - ing! For the Lord, our light and our love, has turned the night in-to day!

Verse 3

3. God is light; in him there is no dark-ness.

3. Let us walk in his light, his chil - dren,

3. one and all. O com-fort my

3. peo-ple; make gen-tle your words. Pro-claim to my

to Refrain

3. cit-y the day of her birth.

Verse 4

4. O cit-y of glad-ness, now lift up your voice!

to Refrain

4. Pro-claim the good tid-ings that all may re - joice!

Text: Based on Isaiah 9; 40:1–9; 1 John 1; Dan Schutte, b. 1947.
Music: Dan Schutte.

814

WITH ONE VOICE

Verses

1. Take the Word and go out to ev - 'ry land:
2. Take the Word to our neigh - bor - hoods and streets:
3. Take the Word to the peo - ple in de - spair:
4. Take the Word to the na - tions ev - 'ry - where:

1-4. shine the light of Christ for all to see!

1. May the lives of those we touch sing
2. May we all set out to live in
3. May our ac - tions and our deeds bring
4. May the wit - ness of our lives trans -

1. praise to God a - bove. Let us sing, we'll sing:
2. peace and har - mo - ny. They will see and sing:
3. com - fort to their needs. And they'll know and sing:
4. form the world a - new. And we'll shine, we'll shine:

Refrain

With one voice we'll pass the Word a - long; with one

voice, bring jus - tice to the world. And with all the an -

- gels we'll spread the good - ness of God. With all

pow - er and glo - ry the Word of God shall reign.

GOD HAS CHOSEN ME

Verses

1. God has cho-sen me, God has cho-sen me to bring good news
2. God has cho-sen me, God has cho-sen me to set a-light
3. God is call-ing me, God is call-ing me in all whose cry

1. to the poor. God has cho-sen me, God has cho-sen me to
2. a new fire. God has cho-sen me, God has cho-sen me to
3. is un-heard. God is call-ing me, God is call-ing me to

1. bring __ new sight to those search-ing for light: God has
2. bring __ to birth a new king-dom on earth: God has
3. raise up the voice with no pow-er or choice: God is

Refrain

1. cho - sen me, cho - sen me: And to tell the world
2. cho - sen me, cho - sen me:
3. call - ing me, call - ing me:

that God's king-dom is near, to re-move op-pres - sion and

break down fear, yes, God's time is near, God's time is near,

God's time is near, God's time is near.

816   THE SERVANT SONG

1, 6. Will you let me be your ser-vant, Let me be as
2. We are pil-grims on a jour-ney, We are trav-'lers
3. I will hold the Christ-light for you In the night-time
4. I will weep when you are weep-ing; When you laugh I'll
5. When we sing to God in heav-en We shall find such

1, 6. Christ to you; Pray that I may have the grace to
2. on the road; We are here to help each oth-er
3. of your fear; I will hold my hand out to you,
4. laugh with you. I will share your joy and sor-row
5. har-mo-ny, Born of all we've known to-geth-er

1, 6. Let you be my ser - vant, too.
2. Walk the mile and bear the load.
3. Speak the peace you long to hear.
4. 'Til we've seen this jour - ney through.
5. Of Christ's love and ag - o - ny.

Text: 87 87; Richard Gillard, b. 1953.
Music: SERVANT SONG; Richard Gillard.
Text and music © 1977, Universal Music Group–Brentwood-Benson Music Publishing (ASCAP). All rights reserved.
   Administrated by Music Services, Inc. Used with permission.

817   THE SPIRIT SENDS US FORTH

1. The Spir-it sends us forth to serve; We go in Je-sus' name
2. We go to com-fort those who mourn And set the bur-dened free;
3. We go to be the hands of Christ, To scat-ter joy like seed
4. Then let us go to serve in peace, The gos-pel to pro-claim.

1. To bring glad ti-dings to the poor, God's fa-vor to pro-claim.
2. Where hope is dim, to share a dream And help the blind to see.
3. And, all our days, to cher-ish life, To do the lov-ing deed.
4. God's Spir-it has em-pow-er'd us; We go in Je-sus' name.

Text: CM; Delores Dufner, OSB, b. 1939, © 1993, The Sisters of St. Benedict, St. Joseph, MN.
   Published by OCP. All rights reserved.
Music: AZMON; Carl Gotthilf Gläser, 1784–1829.

HERE I AM, LORD

818

Verses

1. I, the Lord of sea and sky,   I have heard my peo-ple cry.
2. I, the Lord of snow and rain,   I have borne my peo-ple's pain.
3. I, the Lord of wind and flame,   I will tend the poor and lame.

1. All who dwell in dark and sin   My hand will save.   I, who
2. I have wept for love of them.   They turn a - way.   I will
3. I will set a feast for them.   My hand will save.   Fin-est

1. made the stars of night,   I will make their dark-ness bright.
2. break their hearts of stone,   Give them hearts for love a - lone.
3. bread I will pro - vide   Till their hearts be sat - is - fied.

1. Who will bear my light to them?   Whom shall I send?
2. I will speak my word to them.   Whom shall I send?
3. I will give my life to them.   Whom shall I send?

Refrain

Here I am, Lord.   Is it I, Lord?   I have heard you
call-ing in the night.   I will go, Lord,   if you lead me.
I will hold your peo-ple in my heart.

Text: Based on Isaiah 6; Dan Schutte, b. 1947.
Music: Dan Schutte.

819   WE ARE SENT INTO THE WORLD

Refrain: 1st time: Cantor, All repeat; thereafter: All

We are sent in-to the world to pro-claim the reign of God.

We give glo-ry to the ris-en Christ a-mong us.

Though our eyes have not seen his face, we be-

lieve and we spread the sto-ry of our faith.

Verses

1. Sent out to the world as the fol-low-ers of Christ, we are
2. Sent out to the world as dis-ci-ples of the Word, let us
3. Sent out to the world as am-bas-sa-dors of Christ, we are
4. Sent out to the world as the cho-sen of the Lord, may the

1. called to pro-claim good news. For Christ con-quered death
2. preach to the ends of the earth. For Christ con-quered death
3. sent to all na-tions great and small. For Christ con-quered death
4. Spir-it in-still our hearts a-flame. For Christ con-quered death

to Refrain

1. in his ris-ing to new life: Re-joice in the pow-er of the truth!
2. in his ris-ing to new life: Re-joice in the prom-ise of new birth!
3. in his ris-ing to new life: Re-joice in the splen-dor of our call!
4. in his ris-ing to new life: Re-joice to the glo-ry of his name!

Servant Song

821   CELTIC ALLELUIA: SENDING FORTH

Refrain

Al - le - lu - ia, al - le - lu - ia.

Al - le - lu - ia, al - le - lu - ia.

Verses

1. Now with the strength of your Word,   send us to
2. Fed with the Bread of new life,   filled with the
3. Now make us stead-fast in faith,   joy - ful in
*1. Now he is liv - ing, the Christ.   Out of the
2. Christ is the first-fruits from death,   fill - ing the

1. be your dis - ci - ples,   to bring all the world
2. wine of com - pas - sion,   send us out to serve
3. hope of Christ's com - ing,   and by u - ni - ty
1. tomb he is ris - en;   he has con - quered death,
2. church with his glo - ry!   Dark - ness van - ish - es

to Refrain

1. to the joy ____ of your king - dom. ____
2. all the world ____ in your name. ____
3. let your love ____ fill our lives. ____
1. o - pened heav - en to all be - liev - ers. ____
2. in the light ____ of his pow - er. ____

*Verses for the Easter Season.

Text and music: *Celtic Mass;* Fintan O'Carroll, d. 1977, and Christopher Walker, b. 1947,

822   WE SHALL OVERCOME

1. We shall o - ver - come,   we shall o - ver - come,
2. We'll walk hand in hand,   we'll walk hand in hand,
3. We shall all be free,   we shall all be free,
4. We are not a - fraid,   we are not a - fraid,
5. We shall live in peace,   we shall live in peace,

1. we shall o - ver-come some-day; Oh, deep in my heart
2. we'll walk hand in hand some-day; Oh, deep in my heart
3. we shall all be free some-day; Oh, deep in my heart
4. we are not a - fraid to - day; Oh, deep in my heart
5. we shall live in peace some-day; Oh, deep in my heart

1. I do be - lieve, we shall o - ver-come some - day.
2. I do be - lieve, we'll walk hand in hand some - day.
3. I do be - lieve, we shall all be free some - day.
4. I do be - lieve, we are not a - fraid to - day.
5. I do be - lieve, we shall live in peace some - day.

Text and music: Traditional.

THE CHURCH OF CHRIST IN EVERY AGE   823

1. The Church of Christ in ev - 'ry age Be - set by
2. A - cross the world, a - cross the street, The vic - tims
3. Then let the ser - vant Church a - rise, A car - ing
4. For he a - lone, whose blood was shed, Can cure the
5. We have no mis - sion but to serve In full o -

1. change but Spir - it led, Must claim and test its her - i -
2. of in - jus - tice cry For shel - ter and for bread to
3. Church that longs to be A part - ner in Christ's sac - ri -
4. fe - ver in our blood, And teach us how to share our
5. be - dience to our Lord: To care for all, with - out re -

1. tage And keep on ris - ing from the dead.
2. eat, And nev - er live un - til they die.
3. fice, And clothed in Christ's hu - man - i - ty.
4. bread And feed the starv - ing mul - ti - tude.
5. serve, And spread his lib - er - at - ing Word.

824

CHRIST, BE OUR LIGHT

Verses

1. Long-ing for light, __ we wait in dark-ness. Long-ing for
2. Long-ing for peace, __ our world is trou-bled. Long-ing for
3. Long-ing for food, __ man-y are hun-gry. Long-ing for
4. Long-ing for shel-ter, man-y are home-less. Long-ing for
5. Man-y the gifts, __ man-y the peo-ple, man-y the

1. truth, ____ we turn to you. Make us your own, ____
2. hope, ____ man-y de-spair. Your word a-lone ____
3. wa-ter, man-y still thirst. Make us your bread, ____
4. warmth, __ man-y are cold. Make us your build-ing,
5. hearts that yearn to be-long. Let us be ser-vants

1. your ho-ly peo-ple, light for the world to see.
2. has pow'r to save us. Make us your liv-ing voice.
3. bro-ken for oth-ers, shared un-til all are fed.
4. shel-ter-ing oth-ers, walls made of liv-ing stone.
5. to one an-oth-er, mak-ing your king-dom come.

Refrain

Christ, be our light! Shine in our hearts. Shine through the dark-ness.

Christ, be our light! Shine in your church gath-ered to-day.

Easter Vigil Verses

1. This is the night of new beginnings.
This is the night when heaven meets earth.
This is the night filled with God's glory,
promise of our new birth!

2. This is the night Christ our redeemer
rose from the grave triumphant and free,
leaving the tomb of evil and darkness,
empty for all to see.

3. Now will the fire kindled in darkness
burn to dispel the shadows of night.
Star of the morning, Jesus our Savior,
you are the world's true light!

4. Sing of the hope deeper than dying.
Sing of the pow'r stronger than death.
Sing of the love endless as heaven,
dawning throughout the earth.

5. Into this world morning is breaking.
All of God's people, lift up your voice.
Cry out with joy, tell out the story,
all of the earth rejoice.

LORD, WHOSE LOVE IN HUMBLE SERVICE

1. Lord, whose love in hum-ble ser - vice Bore the
2. Still your chil - dren wan-der home - less; Still the
3. As we wor - ship, grant us vi - sion, Till your
4. Called from wor - ship in - to ser - vice Forth in

1. weight of hu - man need, Who up - on the cross, for-
2. hun - gry cry for bread; Still the cap - tives long for
3. love's re - veal-ing light, Till the height and depth and
4. your great name we go, To the child, the youth, the

1. sak - en, Of - fered mer - cy's per - fect deed; We, your
2. free - dom; Still in grief we mourn our dead. As, O
3. great - ness Dawns up - on our hu - man sight: Mak - ing
4. a - ged, Love in liv - ing deeds to show; Hope and

1. ser - vants, bring the wor - ship Not of voice a -
2. Lord, your deep com - pas - sion Healed the sick and
3. known the needs and bur - dens Your com - pas - sion
4. health, good - will and com - fort, Coun - sel, aid, and

1. lone, but heart: Con - se - crat - ing to your
2. freed the soul, Use the love your Spir - it
3. bids us bear, Stir - ring us to tire - less
4. peace we give, That your chil - dren, Lord, in

1. pur - pose Ev - 'ry gift which you im - part.
2. kin - dles Still to save and make us whole.
3. striv - ing, Your a - bun - dant life to share.
4. free - dom, May your mer - cy know, and live.

Text: 87 87 D; 'Lord, whose love in humble service', by Albert F. Bayly, 1901–1984, alt., © 1988, Oxford University Press.
All rights reserved. Reproduced by permission.
Music: BEACH SPRING; *The Sacred Harp*, 1844.

826 SOMOS EL CUERPO DE CRISTO/ WE ARE THE BODY OF CHRIST

Refrain: All

So-mos el cuer-po de Cris-to.
So-mos el cuer-po de Cris-to.
We are the bod-y of
We are the bod-y of

Christ.
Christ.
He-mos o - í - do el lla - ma-do;
Tra - e - mos su san-to men - sa - je.
we've an-swered
We come to

"Yes," to the call of the Lord.
bring the good news to the
world.
3. Que world.

1 2 to Verses Final
Cantor

Verses
Cantor — All

1. Dios vie-ne al mun-do a tra - vés de no-so-tros.
__ mun-do a cum-plir la mi-sión de la I-gle-sia,
2. Ca - da per - so - na es par-te del rei-no;
__ To - das las ra - zas que ha-bi-tan la tie-rra,
3. nues-tras ac - cio-nes re - fle-jen jus-ti - cia;
Va - mos al mun-do a cui - dar su re - ba - ño.

So-mos el cuer-po de

Cantor

1-3. Cris-to.

1. God is re-vealed when we love one an - oth - er.
__ Bring-ing the light of God's mer-cy to oth - ers,
2. Put - ting a stop to all dis-crim - i - na-tion,
__ All are in - vit - ed to feast in the ban-quet.
3. Stop-ping a - buse and re - liev-ing the hun-gry,
Serv - ing each oth - er we build up the king-dom;

All

1-3. We are the bod-y of Christ.

1 Cantor 2
to Refrain

1. Al
2. ₹   Christ.
3. ₹

Text: Jaime Cortez, b. 1963, and Bob Hurd, b. 1950.
Music: Jaime Cortez.

Alleluia! Raise the Gospel

Refrain

Al - le - lu - ia! Al - le - lu - ia! Raise the Gos - pel o - ver the earth! Al - le - lu - ia! Al - le - lu - ia! Peace and jus - tice bring-ing to birth!

*Verses

1. Bless - ed those whose hearts are gen - tle. Bless - ed
2. Bless - ed those who work for jus - tice. Bless - ed
3. Trem - ble, you who build up rich - es. Trem - ble,
4. Trem - ble, you who thirst for pow - er. Trem - ble
5. Glo - ry like the stars of heav - en— Glo - ry
6. Glo - ry to the Word of Jus - tice. Glo - ry

1. those whose spir - its are strong. Bless - ed those who
2. those who an - swer the call. Bless - ed those who
3. you with op - u - lent lives. Trem - ble, when you
4. you who live for ac - claim. Trem - ble, when you
5. like the sun in the sky— Glo - ry shines up -
6. to the Spir - it of Peace. Glo - ry to the

to Refrain

1. choose to bring forth right where there is wrong.
2. dare to dream of last - ing peace for all.
3. meet the poor and see Christ in their eyes.
4. find no com - fort in your wealth and fame.
5. on all peo - ple, e - qual in God's eyes.
6. God of Love whose bless - ings nev - er cease.

*Alternate verses available in the accompaniment books.

Text: Owen Alstott, b. 1947, © 2002, Owen Alstott. Published by OCP. All rights reserved.
Music: Bernadette Farrell, b. 1957, © 2001, 2002, Bernadette Farrell. Published by OCP. All rights reserved.

828 WHATSOEVER YOU DO

Refrain

What-so-ev-er you do to the least of my peo-ple, that you do un-to me.

Verses

1. When I was hun-gry, you gave me to
2. When I was home-less, you o-pened your
3. When I was wea-ry, you helped me find
4. When in a pris-on, you came to my
5. When I was laughed at, you stood by my

1. eat; When I was thirst-y, you gave me to drink.
2. door; When I was na-ked, you gave me your coat.
3. rest; When I was anx-ious, you calmed all my fears.
4. cell; When on a sick-bed, you cared for my needs.
5. side; When I was hap-py, you shared in my joy.

to Refrain

1-5. Now en-ter in-to the home of my Fa - ther.

829 THE CRY OF THE POOR

Refrain

The Lord hears the cry of the poor. Bless-ed be the Lord.

Verses: Slightly faster

1. I will bless the Lord at all times, with praise
2. Let the low-ly hear and be glad: the Lord
3. Ev-'ry spir-it crushed, God will save; will be
4. We pro-claim your great-ness, O God, your praise

1. ev-er in my mouth. Let my soul glo-ry in the
2. lis-tens to their pleas; and to hearts bro-ken, God is
3. ran-som for their lives; will be safe shel-ter for their
4. ev-er in our mouth; ev-'ry face bright-ened in your

1. Lord, who will hear the cry of the poor.
2. near, who will hear the cry of the poor.
3. fears, and will hear the cry of the poor.
4. light, for you hear the cry of the poor.

Text: Based on Psalm 34:2–3, 18–19a, 19b–20, 4; John Foley, S.J., b. 1939.
Music: John Foley, S.J.

SING A NEW CHURCH 830

Verses

1. Sum-moned by the God who made us Rich in
2. Ra - diant ris - en from the wa - ter, Robed in
3. Trust the good - ness of cre - a - tion; Trust the
4. Bring the hopes of ev - 'ry na - tion; Bring the
5. Draw to - geth - er at one ta - ble All the

1. our di - ver - si - ty, Gath-ered in the name of
2. ho - li - ness and light, Male and fe - male in God's
3. Spir - it strong with - in. Dare to dream the vi - sion
4. art of ev - 'ry race. Weave a song of peace and
5. hu - man fam - i - ly; Shape a cir - cle ev - er

1. Je - sus, Rich - er still in u - ni - ty:
2. im - age, Male and fe - male, God's de - light:
3. prom - ised, Sprung from seed of what has been.
4. jus - tice; Let it sound through time and space.
5. wid - er And a peo - ple ev - er free.

Refrain

Let us bring the gifts that dif - fer And, in

splen - did, var - ied ways, Sing a new church in - to

be - ing, One in faith and love and praise.

Music: NETTLETON; J. Wyeth's *Repository of Sacred Music, Pt. II*, 1813.

831   IN CHRIST THERE IS NO EAST OR WEST

1. In Christ there is no east or west, In
2. In him shall true hearts ev - 'ry - where Their
3. Join hands, dis - ci - ples in the faith, What -
4. In Christ now meet both east and west, In

1. him no south or north; But one great fam - 'ly
2. high com - mu - nion find; His ser - vice is the
3. e'er your race may be! Who serve each oth - er
4. him meet south and north; All Christ - ly souls are

1. bound by love Through - out the whole wide earth.
2. gold - en cord Close - bind - ing hu - man - kind.
3. in Christ's love Are sure - ly kin to me.
4. one in him, Through - out the whole wide earth.

Text: CM; Galatians 3:28; John Oxenham, 1852–1941, alt.
Music: McKEE; Spiritual; adapt. by Harry T. Burleigh, 1866–1949.

832   THEY'LL KNOW WE ARE CHRISTIANS

Verses

1. We are one in the Spir - it, we are one in the Lord,
2. We will walk with each oth - er, we will walk hand in hand,
3. We will work with each oth - er, we will work side by side,
4. All __ praise to the Fa - ther, from __ whom all things come,

1. We are one in the Spir - it, we are one in the Lord,
2. We will walk with each oth - er, we will walk hand in hand,
3. We will work with each oth - er, we will work side by side,
4. And all praise to Christ Je - sus, his __ on - ly __ Son,

1. And we pray that all u - ni - ty may one day be re - stored.
2. And to - geth - er we'll spread the news that God is in our land.
3. And we'll guard each one's dig - ni - ty and save __ each one's pride.
4. And all praise to the Spir - it, who __ makes __ us __ one.

Refrain

And they'll know we are Chris-tians by our love, by our love, Yes they'll know we are Chris-tians by our love.

Text: 13 13 14 with refrain; Peter Scholtes, 1938–2009.
Music: ST. BRENDAN'S; Peter Scholtes.

CHRIST IS THE KING 833

1. Christ is the King! O friends, re - joice:
2. O mag - ni - fy the Lord, and raise
3. They with a faith for ev - er new
4. O Chris - tian wom - en, Chris - tian men,
5. Christ through all a - ges is the same:
6. Let love's all rec - on - cil - ing might
7. So shall God's will on earth be done,

1. Broth - ers and sis - ters, with one voice
2. An - thems of joy and ho - ly praise
3. Fol - lowed the King, and round him drew
4. All the world o - ver, seek a - gain
5. Place the same hope in his great name,
6. Your scat - tered com - pa - nies u - nite
7. New lamps be lit, new tasks be - gun,

1. Let the world know he is your choice.
2. For Christ's brave saints of an - cient days.
3. Thou - sands of men and wom - en true.
4. The Way dis - ci - ples fol - lowed then.
5. With the same faith his word pro - claim.
6. In ser - vice to the Lord of light.
7. And the whole Church at last be one.

1-7. Al - le - lu - ia, al - le - lu - ia, al - le - lu - ia.

Text: 888 with alleluias; 'Christ is the King!' by G K A Bell, 1883–1958, alt.
Music: GELOBT SEI GOTT; Melchior Vulpius, ca. 1560–1616.

834   MANY AND GREAT

Verses

1. Man-y and great are bear-ers of the Word: the Christ
2. Man-y and great are seeds up-on the field: the hand
3. Man-y and great are voic-es of de-spair: the rain
4. Man-y and great are peb-bles in the sand: the sun

1. speaks; the heart seeks. Gath-ered as one, we
2. sows; the seeds grow. Take now and eat the
3. falls; the voice calls. Take now and drink the
4. glows; the wind blows. Take now and spread the

1. lis-ten to the Word and share the meal of new birth.
2. cov-e-nant ful-filled, the bread of prom-ise and life.
3. wine of hope and care; our cup of bless-ing we share.
4. Word to ev-'ry land, the Word of good-ness and hope.

Refrain

The wheat grows from spring-time to fall; the wine flows; in

Christ we re-call the shar-ing of our lives with one and all.

835   COMPANIONS ON THE JOURNEY

Refrain

We are com-pan-ions on the jour - ney, break-ing bread and

shar-ing life; and in the love we bear is the hope we share for we be-

lieve in the love of our God, we be-lieve in the love of our God.

Verse 1

1. No long-er strang-ers to each oth - er; no long-er

1. strang-ers in God's house; we are fed and we are nour-ished by the

to Refrain

1. strength of those who care, by the strength of those who care.

Verse 2

2. We have been gift-ed with each oth - er, and we are called by the

2. Word of the Lord: to act with jus-tice, to love ten-der - ly, and to walk

to Refrain

2. hum-bly with our God, to walk hum-bly with our God.

Verse 3

3. We will seek and we shall find; we will knock and the door will be

3. o-pened; we will ask and it shall be giv-en, for we be-lieve in the

to Refrain

3. love of our God, we be-lieve in the love of our God.

Verse 4

4. We are made for the glo-ry of our God, for ser-vice in the name of

4. Je-sus; to walk side by side with hope in our hearts, for we be-

to Refrain

4. lieve in the love of our God, we be-lieve in the love of our God.

Text: Based on Micah 6:8; Matthew 7:7; Carey Landry, b. 1944.
Music: Carey Landry.

836   Panis Angelicus/Holy and Living Bread

1. Pa - nis an - gé - li - cus, fit_____ pa - nis hó - mi - num,
2. Te, tri - na Dé - i - tas ú - na - que, pó - sci - mus,
1. Ho - ly and liv - ing bread, won - drous food from heav - en sent,
2. God, ho - ly Three - In - One, through this off - 'ring of your Son

1. Dat pa - nis cáe - li - cus fi - gú - ris tér - mi - num.
2. Sic nos tu ví - si - ta, sic - ut te có - li - mus;
1. God's sac - ri - fice fore - told— now in our hands we hold.
2. All now on earth can see what we are called to be:

1. O res mi - rá - bi - lis man - dú - cat Dó - mi - num,
2. Per tu - as sé - mi - tas duc nos quo tén - di - mus,
1. Sign and re - al - i - ty, chal - lenge for us to be
2. Hope for a world in need, signs that love can suc - ceed

1. Pau - per, ser - vus, et hú - mi - lis.
2. Ad lu - cem quam in - há - bi - tas.
1. Hum - ble ser - vants to all the poor.
2. Where true jus - tice and peace en - dure.

Text: 12 12 12 8; Latin; St. Thomas Aquinas, 1227–1274; English, Owen Alstott, b. 1947, © 2001, OCP. All rights reserved.
Music: SACRIS SOLEMNIIS; Louis Lambillotte, SJ, 1796–1855.

837   O Lord, I Am Not Worthy

1. O Lord, I am not wor - thy That thou should'st come to me;
2. And hum - bly I'll re - ceive thee, The Bride - groom of my soul,
3. E - ter - nal Ho - ly Spir - it, Un - wor - thy though I be,
4. In - crease my faith, dear Je - sus, In thy real pres - ence here,

1. But speak the word of com - fort, My spir - it healed shall be.
2. No more by sin to grieve thee Or fly thy sweet con - trol.
3. Pre - pare me to re - ceive him And trust the Word to me.
4. And make me feel most deep - ly That thou to me art near.

Text: 76 76; based on Matthew 8:8; O Herr, ich bin nicht würdig; Landshuter Gesangbuch, 1777; tr. anon.
Music: NON DIGNUS; anon.; Catholic Youth Hymnal, 1871.

O Sacrament Most Holy 838

Verses

1. O Je-sus, we a-dore you, Who, in your love di - vine,
2. O Je-sus, we a-dore you, Our vic-tim and our priest,
3. O Je-sus, we a-dore you, Our Sav-ior and our King,
4. O Je-sus, we a-dore you; Come, live in us we pray,
5. O come, all you who la - bor In sor-row and in pain;

1. Con-ceal your might - y God-head In forms of bread and wine.
2. Whose pre-cious blood and bod - y Be-come our sa - cred feast.
3. And with the saints and an - gels Our hum - ble hom-age bring.
4. That all our thoughts and ac - tions Be yours a - lone to - day.
5. Come, eat this bread from heav - en; Your peace and strength re - gain.

Refrain

O sac - ra - ment most ho - ly, O sac - ra-ment di - vine,

All praise and all thanks-giv - ing Be ev - 'ry mo-ment thine!

Text: 76 76 with refrain; refrain fr. the *Raccolta*, Rome, 19th cent.; tr. unknown; verses by Irvin Udulutsch, OFM, Cap., 1920–2010, © 1958, The Basilian Fathers c/o The Willis Music Company. All rights reserved. Used with permission.
Music: FULDA; *Gebet- und Gesangbuch*, Fulda, 1891.

Soul of My Savior 839

1. Soul of my Sav - ior, sanc - ti - fy my breast; Bod - y of
2. Strength and pro - tec - tion may thy Pas-sion be; O Bless-ed
3. Hear me, Lord Je - sus, lis - ten as I pray; "Lead me from

1. Christ, be thou my sav-ing guest; Blood of my Sav - ior, bathe me
2. Je - sus, hear and an-swer me; Deep in thy wounds, Lord, hide and
3. night to nev - er end-ing day. Fill all the world with love and

1. in thy tide; Wash me with wa - ter flow-ing from his side.
2. shel-ter me; So shall I nev - er, nev - er part from thee.
3. grace di - vine, And glo - ry, laud, and praise be ev - er thine."

Text: 10 10 10 10; verses 1–2 attr. to Pope John XXII, 1249–1334; tr. by Edward Caswall, 1814–1878, alt.;
verse 3, composite, based on *God of Our Fathers*; Daniel C. Roberts, 1841–1907.
Music: ANIMA CHRISTI; William J. Maher, SJ, 1823–1877, alt.

840 ADORO TE DEVOTE/GODHEAD HERE IN HIDING

Verses 1-7: Latin

1. A - dó - ro te de - vó - te, la - tens Dé - i - tas,
2. Vi - sus, ta - ctus, gu - stus in te fál - li - tur,
3. In cru - ce la - té - bat so - la Dé - i - tas,
4. Pla - gas, si - cut Tho - mas, non in - tú - e - or:
5. O me - mo - ri - á - le mor - tis Dó - mi - ni,
6. Pi - e pel - li - cá - ne, Je - su Dó - mi - ne,
7. Je - su, quem ve - lá - tum nunc a - spí - ci - o,

1. Quae sub his fi - gú - ris ve - re lá - ti - tas:
2. Sed au - dí - tu so - lo tu - to cré - di - tur:
3. At hic la - tet si - mul et hu - má - ni - tas:
4. De - um ta - men me - um te con - fí - te - or:
5. Pa - nis vi - vus vi - tam prae - stans hó - mi - ni,
6. Me im - mún - dum mun - da tu - o sán - gui - ne,
7. O - ro fi - at il - lud quod tam sí - ti - o:

1. Ti - bi se cor me - um to - tum súb - ji - cit,
2. Cre - do quid - quid di - xit De - i Fí - li - us:
3. Am - bo ta - men cre - dens at - que cón - fi - tens,
4. Fac me ti - bi sem - per ma - gis cré - de - re,
5. Prae - sta me - ae men - ti de te ví - ve - re,
6. Cu - jus u - na stil - la sal - vum fá - ce - re
7. Ut te re - ve - lá - ta cer - nens fá - ci - e,

(Fine)

1. Qui - a te con - tém - plans to - tum dé - fi - cit.
2. Nil hoc ver - bo ve - ri - tá - tis vé - ri - us.
3. Pe - to quod pe - tí - vit la - tro paé - ni - tens.
4. In te spem ha - bé - re, te di - lí - ge - re.
5. Et te il - li sem - per dul - ce sá - pe - re.
6. To - tum mun - dum quit ab o - mni scé - le - re.
7. Vi - su sim be - á - tus tu - ae gló - ri - ae.

Verses 1-7: English

1. God - head here in hid - ing whom I do a - dore
2. See - ing, touch - ing, tast - ing are in thee de - ceived;
3. On the cross thy god - head made no sign to men;
4. I am not like Thom - as, wounds I can - not see,
5. O thou, our re - mind - er of the Cru - ci - fied,
6. Like what ten - der tales tell of the Pel - i - can,
7. Je - sus whom I look at shroud - ed here be - low,

1. Masked by these bare shad - ows, shape and noth - ing more,
2. How says trust - y hear - ing? that shall be be - lieved;
3. Here thy ver - y man - hood steals from hu - man ken:
4. But I plain - ly call thee Lord and God as he:
5. Liv - ing Bread, the life of us for whom he died,
6. Bathe me, Je - sus Lord, in what thy bos - om ran—
7. I be - seech thee, send me what I thirst for so,

1. See, Lord, at thy ser - vice low lies here a heart
2. What God's Son has told me, take for truth I do;
3. Both are my con - fes - sion, both are my be - lief,
4. This faith each day deep - er be my hold - ing of,
5. Lend this life to me, then; feed and feast my mind,
6. Blood that but one drop of has the pow'r to win
7. Some day to gaze on thee face to face in light

1. Lost, all lost in won - der at the God thou art.
2. Truth him - self speaks tru - ly or there's noth - ing true.
3. And I pray the prayer made by the dy - ing thief.
4. Dai - ly make me hard - er hope and dear - er love.
5. There be thou the sweet - ness man was meant to find.
6. All the world for - give - ness of its world of sin.
7. And be blest for - ev - er with thy glo - ry's sight.

Text: 11 11 11 11; St. Thomas Aquinas, ca. 1224–1274, alt.; tr. by Gerard Manley Hopkins, SJ, 1844–1899, alt.
Music: ADORO TE DEVOTE; Chant, Mode V; *Paris Processionale*, 1697.

841 BEAUTIFUL SAVIOR

1. Beau - ti - ful Sav - ior, King of Cre - a - tion, Son of
2. Fair are the mead - ows, Fair are the wood - lands, Robed in
3. Fair is the sun - shine, Fair is the moon - light, Bright the
4. Beau - ti - ful Sav - ior, Lord of the na - tions, Son of

1. God and Son of Man! Tru - ly I'd love thee, Tru -
2. flow'rs of bloom-ing spring; Je - sus is fair - er, Je -
3. spar-kling stars on high; Je - sus shines bright - er, Je -
4. God and Son of Man! Glo - ry and hon - or, Praise,

1. ly I'd serve thee, Light of my soul, my joy, my crown.
2. sus is pur - er; He makes our sor - r'wing spir - it sing.
3. sus shines pur - er Than all the an - gels in the sky.
4. ad - o - ra - tion, Now and for - ev - er - more be thine!

Text: 55 7 55 8; Psalm 45:3; *Schönster Herr Jesu*, in *Münster Gesangbuch*, 1677; tr. by Joseph A. Seiss, 1823–1904.
Music: ST. ELIZABETH; trad. Silesian Melody; Hoffman and Richter's *Schlesische Volkslieder*, Leipzig, 1842.

842 O GOD OF LOVE, O KING OF PEACE

1. O God of love, O King of peace, Make
2. Re - mem - ber, Lord, your works of old, The
3. Whom shall we trust but you, O Lord? Where
4. Where saints and an - gels dwell a - bove, All

1. wars through-out the world to cease; Our vio - lent ways help
2. won - ders that our fa - thers told; Re - mem - ber not our
3. rest but on your faith - ful word? None ev - er called on
4. hearts are joined in ho - ly love; O bind us in that

1. us con - tain;
2. sin's dark stain,
3. you in vain;
4. heav'n - ly chain; Give peace, O God, give peace a - gain!

*May be sung as a two- or four-voice canon.

Text: LM; Henry W. Baker, 1821–1877.
Music: TALLIS' CANON; Thomas Tallis, ca. 1505–1585.

AMERICA 843

1. My coun-try, 'tis of thee, Sweet land of lib - er - ty,
2. My na - tive coun - try, thee, Land of the no - ble free,
3. Let mu - sic swell the breeze, And ring from all the trees
4. Our fa - thers' God, to thee, Au - thor of lib - er - ty,

1. Of thee I sing; Land where my fa - thers died,
2. Thy name I love; I love thy rocks and rills,
3. Sweet free-dom's song; Let mor - tal tongues a - wake;
4. To thee we sing; Long may our land be bright

1. Land of the pil - grims' pride, From ev - 'ry
2. Thy woods and tem - pled hills; My heart with
3. Let all that breathe par - take; Let rocks their
4. With free - dom's ho - ly light; Pro - tect us

1. moun - tain-side Let free - dom ring!
2. rap - ture thrills, Like that a - bove.
3. si - lence break, The sound pro - long.
4. by thy might, Great God, our King.

Text: 66 4 666 4; Samuel F. Smith, 1808–1895.
Music: AMERICA; *Thesaurus Musicus*, 1744.

FOR THE HEALING OF THE NATIONS 844

1. For the heal-ing of the na-tions, Lord, we pray with one ac-cord;
2. Lead us now, Lord, in - to free-dom, From de-spair your world re-lease;
3. You, cre - a - tor God, have writ-ten Your great name on hu - man-kind;

1. For a just and e - qual shar-ing Of the things that earth af-fords.
2. That re-deemed from war and ha-tred, All may come and go in peace.
3. For our grow - ing in your like-ness Bring the life of Christ to mind:

1. To a life of love and ac - tion Help us rise and pledge our word.
2. Show us how through care and good-ness Fear will die and hope in-crease.
3. That by our re - sponse and ser - vice Earth its des - ti - ny may find.

Text: 87 87 87; based on Revelation 21:1–27; 22:1–5; Fred Kaan, © 1968, Hope Publishing Co.
   All rights reserved. Used with permission.
Music: ST. THOMAS (TANTUM ERGO); John F. Wade, 1711–1786.

845 ### AMERICA THE BEAUTIFUL

1. O beau - ti - ful for spa - cious skies, For am - ber waves of grain,
2. O beau - ti - ful for pil - grim feet, Whose stern, im - pas - sioned stress
3. O beau - ti - ful for he - roes proved In lib - er - at - ing strife,
4. O beau - ti - ful for pa - triot dream That sees be - yond the years

1. For pur - ple moun - tain maj - es - ties A - bove the fruit - ed plain!
2. A thor - ough - fare for free - dom beat A - cross the wil - der - ness!
3. Who more than self their coun - try loved, And mer - cy more than life!
4. Thine al - a - bas - ter cit - ies gleam, Un - dimmed by hu - man tears!

1. A - mer - i - ca! A - mer - i - ca! God shed his grace on thee,
2. A - mer - i - ca! A - mer - i - ca! God mend thine ev - 'ry flaw,
3. A - mer - i - ca! A - mer - i - ca! May God thy gold re - fine,
4. A - mer - i - ca! A - mer - i - ca! God shed his grace on thee,

1. And crown thy good with broth - er - hood From sea to shin - ing sea.
2. Con - firm thy soul in self - con - trol, Thy lib - er - ty in law.
3. Till all suc - cess be no - ble - ness, And ev - 'ry gain di - vine.
4. And crown thy good with broth - er - hood From sea to shin - ing sea.

Text: CMD; Katherine L. Bates, 1859–1929.
Music: MATERNA; Samuel A. Ward, 1848–1903.

846 ### THIS IS MY SONG

1. This is my song, O God of all the na - tions,
2. My coun - try's skies are blu - er than the o - cean,
3. This is my prayer, O Lord of all earth's king - doms:

1. A song of peace for lands a - far and mine.
2. And sun - light beams on clo - ver - leaf and pine;
3. Thy king - dom come; on earth thy will be done.

1. This is my home, the coun - try where my heart is;
2. But oth - er lands have sun - light too, and clo - ver,
3. Let Christ be lift - ed up till all shall serve him,

1. Here are my hopes, my dreams, my ho - ly shrine;
2. And skies are ev - 'ry - where as blue as mine.
3. And hearts u - nit - ed learn to live as one.

1. But oth - er hearts in oth - er lands are beat-ing
2. O hear my song, thou God of all the na - tions,
3. O hear my prayer, thou God of all the na - tions;

1. With hopes and dreams as true and high as mine.
2. A song of peace for their land and for mine.
3. My - self I give thee; let thy will be done.

Text: 11 10 11 10 11 10; verses 1, 2, Lloyd Stone; verse 3, Georgia Harkness, © 1964, Lorenz Corporation.
   All rights reserved. Used with permission.
Music: FINLANDIA; Jean Sibelius, 1865–1957.

GOD OF OUR FATHERS 847

1. God of our fa - thers, whose al - might - y hand
2. Thy love di - vine hath led us in the past,
3. From war's a - larms, from dead - ly pes - ti - lence,
4. Re - fresh thy peo - ple on their toil - some way,

1. Leads forth in beau - ty all the star - ry band
2. In this free land by thee our lot is cast;
3. Be thy strong arm our ev - er sure de - fense;
4. Lead us from night to nev - er - end - ing day;

1. Of shin - ing worlds in splen - dor through the skies,
2. Be thou our rul - er, guard - ian, guide, and stay,
3. Thy true re - li - gion in our hearts in - crease,
4. Fill all our lives with love and grace di - vine,

1. Our grate - ful songs be - fore thy throne a - rise.
2. Thy word our law, thy paths our cho - sen way.
3. Thy boun-teous good - ness nour-ish us in peace.
4. And glo - ry, laud, and praise be ev - er thine.

Text: 10 10 10 10; Daniel Crane Roberts, 1841–1907.
Music: NATIONAL HYMN; George William Warren, 1828–1902.

848 ETERNAL FATHER, STRONG TO SAVE

1. E - ter - nal Fa - ther, strong to save, Whose arm has bound the
2. O Christ, the Lord of hill and plain O'er which our traf - fic
3. O Spir - it, whom the Fa - ther sent To spread a - broad the
4. O Trin - i - ty of love and pow'r, Your chil - dren shield in

1. rest - less wave, Who bids the might - y o - cean deep Its
2. runs a - main By moun - tain pass or val - ley low; Where -
3. fir - ma - ment; O Wind of heav - en, by your might Save
4. dan - ger's hour; From rock and tem - pest, fire and foe, Pro -

1. own ap - point - ed lim - its keep: O hear us when we
2. ev - er, Lord, your loved ones go, Pro - tect them by your
3. all who dare the ea - gle's flight, And keep them by your
4. tect them where - so - e'er they go; And then shall rise with

1. raise our plea For those in per - il on the sea.
2. guard - ing hand From ev - 'ry per - il on the land.
3. watch - ful care From ev - 'ry per - il in the air.
4. voic - es free Glad praise from air and land and sea.

Text: 88 88 88; verses 1, 4, William Whiting, 1825–1878, alt.; verses 2, 3, Robert N. Spencer, 1877–1961, alt.
Music: MELITA; John B. Dykes, 1823–1876.

849 LORD, AS THE DAY BEGINS

1. Lord, as the day be - gins Lift up our hearts in
2. Christ be in work and skill, Serv - ing each oth - er's
3. Grant us the Spir - it's strength, Teach us to walk his
4. Now as the day be - gins Make it the best of

1. praise; Take from us all our sins, Guard us in
2. need; Christ be in thought and will, Christ be in
3. way; So bring us all at length Safe to the
4. days; Take from us all our sins, Guard us in

1. all our ways. Our ev - 'ry step di - rect and
2. word and deed. Our minds be set on things a -
3. close of day. From hour to hour sus - tain and
4. all our ways. Our ev - 'ry step di - rect and

1. guide That Christ in all be glo - ri - fied.
2. bove In joy and peace, in faith and love.
3. bless, And let our song be thank - ful - ness.
4. guide That Christ in all be glo - ri - fied.

THIS DAY GOD GIVES ME   850

1. This day God gives me Strength of high heav - en, Sun and moon
2. This day God sends me Strength as my guard - ian, Might to up -
3. God's way is my way, God's shield is 'round me, God's host de -
4. Ris - ing I thank you, Might - y and Strong One, King of cre -

1. shin - ing, Flame in my hearth, Flash-ing of light - ning, Wind in its
2. hold me, Wis - dom as guide. Your eyes are watch - ful, Your ears are
3. fends me, Sav - ing from ill. An - gels of heav - en, Drive from me
4. a - tion, Giv - er of rest, Firm - ly con - fess - ing Three-ness of

1. swift - ness, Deeps of the o - cean, Firm-ness of earth.
2. lis - t'ning, Your lips are speak - ing, Friend at my side.
3. al - ways All that would harm me, Stand by me still.
4. Per - sons, One-ness of God - head, Trin - i - ty blest.

851   MORNING HAS BROKEN

1. Morn-ing has bro-ken Like the first morn-ing, Black-bird has
2. Sweet the rain's new fall, Sun-lit from heav-en, Like the first
3. Mine is the sun-light! Mine is the morn-ing Born of the

1. spo-ken Like the first bird. Praise for the sing-ing! Praise for the
2. dew-fall On the first grass. Praise for the sweet-ness Of the wet
3. one light E-den saw play! Praise with e-la-tion, Praise ev-'ry

1. morn-ing! Praise for them, spring-ing Fresh from the Word!
2. gar-den, Sprung in com-plete-ness Where his feet pass.
3. morn-ing, God's re-cre-a-tion Of the new day!

Text: 55 54 D; Eleanor Farjeon, 1881–1965, © 1957, Eleanor Farjeon. All rights reserved.
  Reprinted by permission of Harold Ober Assoc., Inc.
Music: BUNESSAN; trad. Gaelic Melody.

852   GOD OF MYSTERY, GOD OF MERCY

1. God of mys-t'ry, God of mer-cy, God of glo-ry,
2. Part the clouds that keep us from you; Rend the heav-ens
3. God of day-light and of dark-ness, God of heav-en,
4. Hold us in the hands that made us; Cra-dle all our

1. hid in light: Let your face shine on your peo-ple
2. and come down; Show your love at work a-mong us;
3. God of earth: You are Lord of all our liv-ing,
4. hopes and fears; Let us praise and give you glo-ry

1. Where we dwell in dark of night.
2. Let us sing your great re-nown.
3. Yours our tears and yours our mirth.
4. With the sum of all our years.

Text: 87 87; Genevieve Glen, OSB, b. 1945, © 2002, The Benedictine Nuns of the Abbey of St. Walburga.
  Published by OCP. All rights reserved.
Music: MOUNT ST. MARY'S; Christopher Walker, b. 1947, © 2005, Christopher Walker.
  Published by OCP. All rights reserved.

DAY IS DONE

1. Day is done, but Love un-fail-ing Dwells ev - er here;
2. Dark de-scends, but Light un-end-ing Shines through our night;
3. Eyes will close, but you un-sleep-ing Watch by our side;

1. Shad-ows fall, but hope, pre-vail-ing, Calms ev - 'ry fear.
2. You are with us, ev - er lend-ing New strength to sight.
3. Death may come, in Love's safe-keep-ing Still we a - bide.

1. God, our Mak - er, none for-sak-ing, Take our hearts, of Love's own
2. One in love, your truth con-fess-ing, One in hope of heav - en's
3. God of love, all e - vil quell-ing, Sin for-giv-ing, fear dis-

1. mak-ing; Watch our sleep-ing, guard our wak-ing, Be al-ways near.
2. bless-ing, May we see, in love's pos-sess-ing, Love's end-less light!
3. pel-ling: Stay with us, our hearts in-dwell-ing, This e - ven-tide.

Text: 84 84 88 84; James D. Quinn, SJ, b. 1919, © 1969, James D. Quinn, SJ. All rights reserved.
Used with permission of Selah Publishing Co., Inc., North American agent.
Music: AR HYD Y NOS; trad. Welsh Melody.

RADIANT LIGHT DIVINE

*Ostinato Refrain

English Ra - diant Light Di - vine, shine through-out this night. Je - sus,
Spanish En la os-cu - ri - dad, bri - lla - rá tu luz. Je - su -
Vietnamese Ôi Nguồn Sáng Linh Thiêng chiếu soi suốt đêm trường. Đoàn con

Ho - ly One, praise to you our Light. As the day-light fades, and come
cris - to, te a-la - ba - mos. Al a - no - che - cer, ya se a-
chúc tụng Ngài là Ánh Sáng chúng con. Khi màu nắng phai tàn, khi hoàng

e - ven-tide, dwell a - mong us, Ho - ly_____ Fire.
ba - jó el sol, Fue - go San - to, da - nos_____ luz.
hôn buông màn, xin ở cùng đoàn con ôi Lửa Thiêng.

*Verses available in accompaniment books.

Text: Based on *Phos Hilaron*, Greek ca. 200; Rufino Zaragoza, OFM, b. 1957; Spanish, Mary Frances Reza;
Vietnamese refrain, Xuân Thảo.
Text and music © 1990, 1999, 2002, 2006, Rufino Zaragoza, OFM. Published by OCP. All rights reserved.

855   THE DAY YOU GAVE US, LORD, IS ENDED

1. The day you gave us, Lord, is end-ed, The
2. We thank you that your Church, un-sleep-ing While
3. A-cross each con - ti - nent and is-land As
4. The sun that bids us rest is wak-ing Your
5. So be it, Lord; your realm shall nev-er, Like

1. dark - ness falls at your be - hest; To
2. earth rolls on - ward in - to light, Through
3. dawn leads on an - oth - er day, The
4. chil - dren un - der west - ern skies And
5. earth's proud em - pires, pass a - way: Your

1. you our morn - ing hymns as - cend-ed, Your
2. all the world its watch is keep-ing, And
3. voice of prayer is nev - er si - lent, Nor
4. hour by hour as day is break-ing, Fresh
5. king - dom stands, and grows for - ev - er, Till

1. praise shall sanc - ti - fy our rest.
2. nev - er rests by day or night.
3. do the prais - es die a - way.
4. hymns of thank - ful praise a - rise.
5. all your crea - tures own your sway.

Text: 98 98; John Ellerton, 1826–1893, alt.
Music: ST. CLEMENT; Clement C. Scholefield, 1839–1904.

856   ABIDE WITH ME

1. A - bide with me! fast falls the e - ven - tide;
2. I need your pres - ence ev - 'ry pass-ing hour:
3. I fear no foe with you at hand to bless;
4. Hold then your cross be - fore my clos-ing eyes;

1. The dark - ness deep - ens; Lord, with me a - bide;
2. What but your grace can foil the tempt-er's pow'r?
3. Ills have no weight, and tears no bit - ter - ness.
4. Shine through the gloom and point me to the skies!

1. When oth-er help-ers fail and com-forts flee,
2. Who like your-self my guide and strength can be?
3. Where is death's sting? Where, grave, your vic-to-ry?
4. Heav'n's morn-ing breaks and earth's vain shad-ows flee;

1. Help of the help-less, O a-bide with me!
2. Through cloud and sun-shine, Lord, a-bide with me!
3. I tri-umph still, if you a-bide with me!
4. In life, in death, O Lord, a-bide with me!

Text: 10 10 10 10; Henry F. Lyte, 1793–1847, alt.; *Remains*, 1850, alt.
Music: EVENTIDE; William Henry Monk, 1823–1889; *Hymns Ancient and Modern*, 1861.

LORD, BID YOUR SERVANT GO IN PEACE   857

1. Lord, bid your ser-vant go in peace, Your
2. This is the Sav-ior of the world, The
3. This child shall see the rise, the fall, Of
4. His moth-er's soul a sword shall pierce, Of
5. Blest be the Fa-ther, who has giv'n His

1. word is now ful-filled. These eyes have seen sal-
2. gen-tiles' prom-ised light, God's glo-ry dwell-ing
3. those in Is-ra-el, God's sign raised high for
4. sor-row keen and deep; And se-cret thoughts of
5. Son to be our Lord, Blest too that Son, and

1. va-tion's dawn, This child so long fore-told.
2. in our midst, The joy of Is-ra-el.
3. all to see, Whom some shall yet de-ny.
4. man-y hearts Through him shall be re-vealed.
5. with them both The Spir-it of their love.

Text: CM; based on Luke 2:29–32, 34–35; *Nunc dimittis*;
    James D. Quinn, SJ, b. 1919, alt., © 1969, 1989, James D. Quinn, SJ. All rights reserved.
    Used with permission of Selah Publishing Co., Inc., North American agent.
Music: MORNING SONG; *Sixteen Tune Settings*, Philadelphia, 1812; *Kentucky Harmony*, 1816.

LECTIONARY READINGS

The word of God proclaimed in worship makes Christ present through the power of the Holy Spirit. In the liturgy of the Church the Sacred Scriptures find their true home, for here both creation and redemption are crowned in mystery. God's word and the liturgy quench the thirst of all who seek the way, the truth and the life. We pray that the word of God be etched indelibly in our heart and on our lips that we may faithfully conform to it and boldly proclaim its love to all. (Additional music for the Responsorial Psalm may be found in #15–125; music for the Gospel Acclamation is also found in #177, 178, 187, 188, 197, 198, 207, 208, 217, 218, 235, 245, 246, 259–266.)

SEASON OF ADVENT

858   FIRST SUNDAY OF ADVENT — A

FIRST READING   *Isaiah 2:1–5*

This is what Isaiah, son of Amoz, saw concerning Judah and Jerusalem.
In days to come,
the mountain of the LORD's house
shall be established as the
highest mountain
and raised above the hills.
All nations shall stream toward it;
many peoples shall come
and say:
"Come, let us climb the
LORD's mountain,
to the house of the God of Jacob,
that he may instruct us in his ways,
and we may walk in his paths."
For from Zion shall go
forth instruction,
and the word of the LORD
from Jerusalem.
He shall judge between
the nations,
and impose terms on
many peoples.
They shall beat their swords
into plowshares
and their spears into
pruning hooks;
one nation shall not raise the
sword against another,
nor shall they train for war again.
O house of Jacob, come,
let us walk in the light of
the LORD!

RESPONSORIAL PSALM   *Psalm 122: 1–2, 3–4, 4–5, 6–7, 8–9*

℟. Let us go re - joic - ing to the house of the Lord.

▶ I rejoiced because they said to me,
  "We will go up to the house of
  the LORD."
And now we have set foot
  within your gates, O Jerusalem. ℟.

▶ Jerusalem, built as a city
  with compact unity.
To it the tribes go up,
  the tribes of the LORD. ℟.

▶ According to the decree for Israel,
  to give thanks to the name of
  the LORD.

In it are set up judgment seats,
  seats for the house of David. ℟.

▶ Pray for the peace of Jerusalem!
  May those who love you prosper!
May peace be within your walls,
  prosperity in your buildings. ℟.

▶ Because of my brothers and friends
  I will say, "Peace be within you!"
Because of the house of the LORD,
  our God,
  I will pray for your good. ℟.

SECOND READING

Romans 13:11–14

Brothers and sisters: You know the time; it is the hour now for you to awake from sleep. For our salvation is nearer now than when we first believed; the night is advanced, the day is at hand. Let us then throw off the works of darkness and put on the armor of light; let us conduct ourselves properly as in the day, not in orgies and drunkenness, not in promiscuity and lust, not in rivalry and jealousy. But put on the Lord Jesus Christ, and make no provision for the desires of the flesh.

GOSPEL ACCLAMATION

cf. Psalm 85:8

℟. Al - le - lu - ia, al - le - lu - ia, al - le - lu - ia.

Music: Owen Alstott, b. 1947, © 1977, 1990, OCP. All rights reserved.   *(Omit if not sung)*

▶ Show us, Lord, your love;
  and grant us your salvation. ℟.

GOSPEL

Matthew 24:37–44

Jesus said to his disciples: "As it was in the days of Noah, so it will be at the coming of the Son of Man. In those days before the flood, they were eating and drinking, marrying and giving in marriage, up to the day that Noah entered the ark. They did not know until the flood came and carried them all away. So will it be also at the coming of the Son of Man. Two men will be out in the field; one will be taken, and one will be left. Two women will be grinding at the mill; one will be taken, and one will be left. Therefore, stay awake! For you do not know on which day your Lord will come. Be sure of this: if the master of the house had known the hour of night when the thief was coming, he would have stayed awake and not let his house be broken into. So too, you also must be prepared, for at an hour you do not expect, the Son of Man will come."

859   FIRST SUNDAY OF ADVENT — B

FIRST READING   *Isaiah 63:16b–17, 19b; 64:2–7*

You, LORD, are our father,
  our redeemer you are
    named forever.
Why do you let us wander, O LORD,
  from your ways,
  and harden our hearts so that we
    fear you not?
Return for the sake of your servants,
  the tribes of your heritage.
Oh, that you would rend the heavens
  and come down,
  with the mountains quaking
    before you,
while you wrought awesome deeds
  we could not hope for,
  such as they had not heard of from
    of old.
No ear has ever heard, no eye ever
  seen, any God but you
  doing such deeds for those who
    wait for him.
Would that you might meet us
  doing right,

that we were mindful of you in
  our ways!
Behold, you are angry, and we
  are sinful;
  all of us have become like
    unclean people,
  all our good deeds are like
    polluted rags;
we have all withered like leaves,
  and our guilt carries us away like
    the wind.
There is none who calls upon
  your name,
  who rouses himself to cling to you;
for you have hidden your face
  from us
  and have delivered us up to
    our guilt.
Yet, O LORD, you are our father;
  we are the clay and you the potter:
  we are all the work of your hands.

RESPONSORIAL PSALM   *Psalm 80:2–3, 15–16, 18–19*

℟. **Lord, make us turn to you;   let us see your face and we shall be saved.**

Music: Owen Alstott, b. 1947, © 1977, 1990, OCP. All rights reserved.

▶ O shepherd of Israel, hearken,
  from your throne upon the
    cherubim, shine forth.
Rouse your power,
  and come to save us. ℟.

▶ Once again, O LORD of hosts,
  look down from heaven, and see;
take care of this vine,
  and protect what your right hand
    has planted,

the son of man whom you yourself
  made strong. ℟.

▶ May your help be with the man of
  your right hand,
  with the son of man whom you
    yourself made strong.
Then we will no more withdraw
  from you;
  give us new life, and we will call
    upon your name. ℟.

SECOND READING   *1 Corinthians 1:3–9*

Brothers and sisters: Grace to you
and peace from God our Father
and the Lord Jesus Christ.

I give thanks to my God always on
your account for the grace of God
bestowed on you in Christ Jesus,
that in him you were enriched in

every way, with all discourse and all knowledge, as the testimony to Christ was confirmed among you, so that you are not lacking in any spiritual gift as you wait for the revelation of our Lord Jesus Christ.

He will keep you firm to the end, irreproachable on the day of our Lord Jesus Christ. God is faithful, and by him you were called to fellowship with his Son, Jesus Christ our Lord.

GOSPEL ACCLAMATION

Psalm 85:8

℟. Al - le - lu - ia, al - le - lu - ia, al - le - lu - ia.

(Omit if not sung)

▶ Show us, Lord, your love;
and grant us your salvation. ℟.

GOSPEL

Mark 13:33–37

Jesus said to his disciples: "Be watchful! Be alert! You do not know when the time will come. It is like a man traveling abroad. He leaves home and places his servants in charge, each with his own work, and orders the gatekeeper to be on the

watch. Watch, therefore; you do not know when the lord of the house is coming, whether in the evening, or at midnight, or at cockcrow, or in the morning. May he not come suddenly and find you sleeping. What I say to you, I say to all: 'Watch!'"

FIRST SUNDAY OF ADVENT — C **860**

FIRST READING

Jeremiah 33:14–16

The days are coming, says the LORD, when I will fulfill the promise I made to the house of Israel and Judah. In those days, in that time, I will raise up for David a just shoot; he shall do what

is right and just in the land. In those days Judah shall be safe and Jerusalem shall dwell secure; this is what they shall call her: "The LORD our justice."

RESPONSORIAL PSALM

Psalm 25:4–5, 8–9, 10, 14

℟. To you, O Lord, I lift my soul.

▶ Your ways, O LORD, make known to me;
   teach me your paths,
 guide me in your truth and teach me,
   for you are God my savior,
   and for you I wait all the day. ℟.

▶ Good and upright is the LORD;
   thus he shows sinners the way.
 He guides the humble to justice,
   and teaches the humble his way. ℟.

▶ All the paths of the LORD are kindness
   and constancy
 toward those who keep his
   covenant and his decrees.
 The friendship of the LORD is with
   those who fear him,
 and his covenant, for their
   instruction. ℟.

SECOND READING

1 Thessalonians 3:12—4:2

Brothers and sisters: May the Lord make you increase and abound in love for one another and for all, just as we have for you, so as to strengthen your hearts, to be blameless in holiness before our God and Father at the coming of our Lord Jesus with all his holy ones. Amen.

Finally, brothers and sisters, we earnestly ask and exhort you in the Lord Jesus that, as you received from us how you should conduct yourselves to please God—and as you are conducting yourselves— you do so even more. For you know what instructions we gave you through the Lord Jesus.

GOSPEL ACCLAMATION

Psalm 85:8

℟. Al - le - lu - ia, al - le - lu - ia, al - le - lu - ia.

Music: Owen Alstott, b. 1947, © 1977, 1990, OCP. All rights reserved.   *(Omit if not sung)*

▶ Show us, Lord, your love;
  and grant us your salvation. ℟.

GOSPEL

Luke 21:25–28, 34–36

Jesus said to his disciples: "There will be signs in the sun, the moon, and the stars, and on earth nations will be in dismay, perplexed by the roaring of the sea and the waves. People will die of fright in anticipation of what is coming upon the world, for the powers of the heavens will be shaken. And then they will see the Son of Man coming in a cloud with power and great glory. But when these signs begin to happen,

stand erect and raise your heads because your redemption is at hand.

"Beware that your hearts do not become drowsy from carousing and drunkenness and the anxieties of daily life, and that day catch you by surprise like a trap. For that day will assault everyone who lives on the face of the earth. Be vigilant at all times and pray that you have the strength to escape the tribulations that are imminent and to stand before the Son of Man."

---

861   SECOND SUNDAY OF ADVENT — A

FIRST READING

Isaiah 11:1–10

On that day, a shoot shall sprout
    from the stump of Jesse,
  and from his roots a bud
    shall blossom.
The spirit of the LORD shall rest
    upon him:
  a spirit of wisdom and
    of understanding,
  a spirit of counsel and of strength,
    a spirit of knowledge and of fear of
      the LORD,

and his delight shall be the fear of
    the LORD.
Not by appearance shall he judge,
    nor by hearsay shall he decide,
  but he shall judge the poor
    with justice,
  and decide aright for the
    land's afflicted.
He shall strike the ruthless with the
    rod of his mouth,
  and with the breath of his lips he
    shall slay the wicked.

Justice shall be the band around
his waist,
and faithfulness a belt upon
his hips.
Then the wolf shall be a guest of
the lamb,
and the leopard shall lie down with
the kid;
the calf and the young lion shall
browse together,
with a little child to guide them.
The cow and the bear shall
be neighbors,
together their young shall rest;

the lion shall eat hay like the ox.
The baby shall play by the
cobra's den,
and the child lay his hand on the
adder's lair.
There shall be no harm or ruin on all
my holy mountain;
for the earth shall be filled with
knowledge of the LORD,
as water covers the sea.
On that day, the root of Jesse,
set up as a signal for the nations,
the Gentiles shall seek out,
for his dwelling shall be glorious.

RESPONSORIAL PSALM

Psalm 72:1–2, 7–8, 12–13, 17

℟. Jus-tice shall flour-ish in his time, and full-ness of peace for ev-er.

Music: Owen Alstott, b. 1947, © 1977, 1990, OCP. All rights reserved.

▶ O God, with your judgment endow
the king,
and with your justice,
the king's son;
he shall govern your people
with justice
and your afflicted ones
with judgment. ℟.

▶ Justice shall flower in his days,
and profound peace, till the moon
be no more.
May he rule from sea to sea,
and from the River to the ends of
the earth. ℟.

▶ For he shall rescue the poor when he
cries out,
and the afflicted when he has no
one to help him.
He shall have pity for the lowly and
the poor;
the lives of the poor he
shall save. ℟.

▶ May his name be blessed forever;
as long as the sun his name
shall remain.
In him shall all the tribes of the earth
be blessed;
all the nations shall proclaim
his happiness. ℟.

SECOND READING

Romans 15:4–9

Brothers and sisters: Whatever was written previously was written for our instruction, that by endurance and by the encouragement of the Scriptures we might have hope. May the God of endurance and encouragement grant you to think in harmony with one another, in keeping with Christ Jesus, that with one accord you may with one voice glorify the God and Father of our Lord Jesus Christ.

Welcome one another, then, as Christ welcomed you, for the glory of God. For I say that Christ became a minister of the circumcised to show God's truthfulness, to confirm the promises to the patriarchs, but so that the Gentiles might glorify God for his mercy. As it is written:
*Therefore, I will praise you among
the Gentiles
and sing praises to your name.*

GOSPEL ACCLAMATION

Luke 3:4, 6

℟. Al - le - lu - ia, al - le - lu - ia, al - le - lu - ia.

(Omit if not sung)

▶ Prepare the way of the Lord, make straight his paths:
all flesh shall see the salvation of God. ℟.

GOSPEL

Matthew 3:1–12

John the Baptist appeared, preaching in the desert of Judea and saying, "Repent, for the kingdom of heaven is at hand!" It was of him that the prophet Isaiah had spoken when he said:

*A voice of one crying out in
the desert,
Prepare the way of the Lord,
make straight his paths.*

John wore clothing made of camel's hair and had a leather belt around his waist. His food was locusts and wild honey. At that time Jerusalem, all Judea, and the whole region around the Jordan were going out to him and were being baptized by him in the Jordan River as they acknowledged their sins.

When he saw many of the Pharisees and Sadducees coming to his baptism, he said to them, "You brood of vipers! Who warned you to flee from the coming wrath? Produce good fruit as evidence of your repentance. And do not presume to say to yourselves, 'We have Abraham as our father.' For I tell you, God can raise up children to Abraham from these stones. Even now the ax lies at the root of the trees. Therefore every tree that does not bear good fruit will be cut down and thrown into the fire. I am baptizing you with water, for repentance, but the one who is coming after me is mightier than I. I am not worthy to carry his sandals. He will baptize you with the Holy Spirit and fire. His winnowing fan is in his hand. He will clear his threshing floor and gather his wheat into his barn, but the chaff he will burn with unquenchable fire."

---

862   SECOND SUNDAY OF ADVENT — B

FIRST READING

Isaiah 40:1–5, 9–11

Comfort, give comfort to my people,
  says your God.
Speak tenderly to Jerusalem, and
    proclaim to her
  that her service is at an end,
  her guilt is expiated;
indeed, she has received from the
    hand of the LORD
  double for all her sins.

    A voice cries out:
In the desert prepare the way
  of the LORD!

Make straight in the wasteland a
    highway for our God!
Every valley shall be filled in,
  every mountain and hill shall be
    made low;
the rugged land shall be made a plain,
  the rough country, a broad valley.
Then the glory of the LORD shall
  be revealed,
  and all people shall see it together;
for the mouth of the LORD
    has spoken.

Go up onto a high mountain,
   Zion, herald of glad tidings;
cry out at the top of your voice,
   Jerusalem, herald of good news!
Fear not to cry out
   and say to the cities of Judah:
   Here is your God!
Here comes with power

the Lord GOD,
   who rules by his strong arm;
here is his reward with him,
   his recompense before him.
Like a shepherd he feeds his flock;
   in his arms he gathers the lambs,
carrying them in his bosom,
   and leading the ewes with care.

RESPONSORIAL PSALM
Psalm 85:9–10, 11–12, 13–14

℞. Lord, let us see your kind - ness, and grant us your sal - va - tion.

Music: Owen Alstott, b. 1947, © 1977, 1990, OCP. All rights reserved.

▸ I will hear what God proclaims;
   the LORD—for he proclaims peace
     to his people.
Near indeed is his salvation to those
   who fear him,
   glory dwelling in our land. ℞.

▸ Kindness and truth shall meet;
   justice and peace shall kiss.

Truth shall spring out of the earth,
   and justice shall look down
     from heaven. ℞.

▸ The LORD himself will give
   his benefits;
   our land shall yield its increase.
Justice shall walk before him,
   and prepare the way of his steps. ℞.

SECOND READING
2 Peter 3:8–14

Do not ignore this one fact, beloved, that with the Lord one day is like a thousand years and a thousand years like one day. The Lord does not delay his promise, as some regard "delay," but he is patient with you, not wishing that any should perish but that all should come to repentance. But the day of the Lord will come like a thief, and then the heavens will pass away with a mighty roar and the elements will be dissolved by fire, and the earth and everything done on it will be found out.

Since everything is to be dissolved in this way, what sort of persons ought you to be, conducting yourselves in holiness and devotion, waiting for and hastening the coming of the day of God, because of which the heavens will be dissolved in flames and the elements melted by fire. But according to his promise we await new heavens and a new earth in which righteousness dwells. Therefore, beloved, since you await these things, be eager to be found without spot or blemish before him, at peace.

GOSPEL ACCLAMATION
Luke 3:4, 6

℞. Al - le - lu - ia, al - le - lu - ia, al - le - lu - ia.

Music: Owen Alstott, b. 1947, © 1977, 1990, OCP. All rights reserved. *(Omit if not sung)*

▸ Prepare the way of the Lord, make straight his paths:
   all flesh shall see the salvation of God. ℞.

GOSPEL *Mark 1:1–8*

The beginning of the gospel of Jesus Christ the Son of God.

As it is written in Isaiah the prophet:

Behold, I am sending my messenger ahead of you;
he will prepare your way.
A voice of one crying out in the desert:
"Prepare the way of the Lord, make straight his paths."

John the Baptist appeared in the desert proclaiming a baptism of repentance for the forgiveness of sins. People of the whole Judean countryside and all the inhabitants of Jerusalem were going out to him and were being baptized by him in the Jordan River as they acknowledged their sins. John was clothed in camel's hair, with a leather belt around his waist. He fed on locusts and wild honey. And this is what he proclaimed: "One mightier than I is coming after me. I am not worthy to stoop and loosen the thongs of his sandals. I have baptized you with water; he will baptize you with the Holy Spirit."

---

863   SECOND SUNDAY OF ADVENT — C

FIRST READING *Baruch 5:1–9*

Jerusalem, take off your robe of mourning and misery;
put on the splendor of glory from God forever:
wrapped in the cloak of justice from God,
bear on your head the mitre that displays the glory of the eternal name.
For God will show all the earth your splendor:
you will be named by God forever the peace of justice, the glory of God's worship.

Up, Jerusalem! stand upon the heights;
look to the east and see your children
gathered from the east and the west at the word of the Holy One,
rejoicing that they are remembered by God.

Led away on foot by their enemies they left you:
but God will bring them back to you
borne aloft in glory as on royal thrones.
For God has commanded that every lofty mountain be made low,
and that the age-old depths and gorges be filled to level ground,
that Israel may advance secure in the glory of God.
The forests and every fragrant kind of tree
have overshadowed Israel at God's command;
for God is leading Israel in joy by the light of his glory,
with his mercy and justice for company.

RESPONSORIAL PSALM *Psalm 126:1–2, 2–3, 4–5, 6*

℟. The Lord has done great things for us; we are filled with joy.

▶ When the Lord brought back the
     captives of Zion,
  we were like men dreaming.
  Then our mouth was filled
     with laughter,
     and our tongue with rejoicing. ℟.

▶ Then they said among the nations,
  "The Lord has done great things
     for them."
  The Lord has done great things
     for us;
     we are glad indeed. ℟.

▶ Restore our fortunes, O Lord,
  like the torrents in the
     southern desert.
  Those who sow in tears
     shall reap rejoicing. ℟.

▶ Although they go forth weeping,
  carrying the seed to be sown,
  they shall come back rejoicing,
  carrying their sheaves. ℟.

SECOND READING   Philippians 1:4–6, 8–11

Brothers and sisters: I pray always
with joy in my every prayer for all of
you, because of your partnership for
the gospel from the first day until now.
I am confident of this, that the one
who began a good work in you will
continue to complete it until the day of
Christ Jesus. God is my witness, how
I long for all of you with the affection
of Christ Jesus. And this is my prayer:
that your love may increase ever more
and more in knowledge and every
kind of perception, to discern what
is of value, so that you may be pure
and blameless for the day of Christ,
filled with the fruit of righteousness
that comes through Jesus Christ
for the glory and praise of God.

GOSPEL ACCLAMATION   Luke 3:4, 6

℟. Al - le - lu - ia,   al - le - lu - ia,   al - le - lu - ia.

(Omit if not sung)

▶ Prepare the way of the Lord, make straight his paths:
  all flesh shall see the salvation of God. ℟.

GOSPEL   Luke 3:1–6

In the fifteenth year of the reign of
Tiberius Caesar, when Pontius Pilate
was governor of Judea, and Herod was
tetrarch of Galilee, and his brother
Philip tetrarch of the region of Ituraea
and Trachonitis, and Lysanias was
tetrarch of Abilene, during the high
priesthood of Annas and Caiaphas,
the word of God came to John the
son of Zechariah in the desert. John
went throughout the whole region
of the Jordan, proclaiming a baptism
of repentance for the forgiveness of
sins, as it is written in the book of
the words of the prophet Isaiah:
  *A voice of one crying out in
     the desert:*
  *"Prepare the way of the Lord,
     make straight his paths.*
  *Every valley shall be filled
     and every mountain and hill shall
     be made low.*
  *The winding roads shall be
     made straight,*
     and the rough ways made smooth,
  *and all flesh shall see the salvation
     of God."*

864 THIRD SUNDAY OF ADVENT — A

FIRST READING *Isaiah 35:1–6a, 10*

The desert and the parched land
     will exult;
  the steppe will rejoice and bloom.
They will bloom with
     abundant flowers,
  and rejoice with joyful song.
The glory of Lebanon will be given
     to them,
  the splendor of Carmel
  and Sharon;
they will see the glory of the LORD,
  the splendor of our God.
Strengthen the hands that are feeble,
  make firm the knees that are weak,
say to those whose hearts
  are frightened:
  Be strong, fear not!

Here is your God,
  he comes with vindication;
with divine recompense
  he comes to save you.
Then will the eyes of the blind
     be opened,
  the ears of the deaf be cleared;
then will the lame leap like a stag,
  then the tongue of the mute
     will sing.

Those whom the LORD has ransomed
  will return
  and enter Zion singing,
  crowned with everlasting joy;
they will meet with joy and gladness,
  sorrow and mourning will flee.

RESPONSORIAL PSALM *Psalm 146:6–7, 8–9, 9–10*

℟. Lord, come and save us.

Music: Owen Alstott, b. 1947, © 1977, 1990, OCP. All rights reserved.

Or ℟. **Alleluia.**

▶ The LORD God keeps faith forever,
  secures justice for the oppressed,
  gives food to the hungry.
  The LORD sets captives free. ℟.

▶ The LORD gives sight to the blind;
  the LORD raises up those who were
     bowed down.
  The LORD loves the just;
  the LORD protects strangers. ℟.

▶ The fatherless and the widow
  he sustains,
  but the way of the wicked
  he thwarts.
  The LORD shall reign forever;
  your God, O Zion, through all
     generations. ℟.

SECOND READING *James 5:7–10*

Be patient, brothers and sisters, until
the coming of the Lord. See how
the farmer waits for the precious
fruit of the earth, being patient with
it until it receives the early and the
late rains. You too must be patient.
Make your hearts firm, because the
coming of the Lord is at hand. Do

not complain, brothers and sisters,
about one another, that you may
not be judged. Behold, the Judge is
standing before the gates. Take as an
example of hardship and patience,
brothers and sisters, the prophets
who spoke in the name of the Lord.

GOSPEL ACCLAMATION

Isaiah 61:1 (cited in Luke 4:18)

℟. Al - le - lu - ia, al - le - lu - ia, al - le - lu - ia.

(Omit if not sung)

▶ The Spirit of the LORD is upon me,
   because he has anointed me
   to bring glad tidings to the poor. ℟.

GOSPEL

Matthew 11:2–11

When John the Baptist heard in prison of the works of the Christ, he sent his disciples to Jesus with this question, "Are you the one who is to come, or should we look for another?" Jesus said to them in reply, "Go and tell John what you hear and see: the blind regain their sight, the lame walk, lepers are cleansed, the deaf hear, the dead are raised, and the poor have the good news proclaimed to them. And blessed is the one who takes no offense at me."

As they were going off, Jesus began to speak to the crowds about John, "What did you go out to the desert to see? A reed swayed by the wind? Then what did you go out to see? Someone dressed in fine clothing? Those who wear fine clothing are in royal palaces. Then why did you go out? To see a prophet? Yes, I tell you, and more than a prophet. This is the one about whom it is written:

*Behold, I am sending my messenger
   ahead of you;
he will prepare your way
   before you.*

Amen, I say to you, among those born of women there has been none greater than John the Baptist; yet the least in the kingdom of heaven is greater than he."

THIRD SUNDAY OF ADVENT — B   865

FIRST READING

Isaiah 61:1–2a, 10–11

The spirit of the Lord GOD is
   upon me,
   because the LORD has anointed me;
he has sent me to bring glad tidings
   to the poor,
   to heal the brokenhearted,
to proclaim liberty to the captives
   and release to the prisoners,
to announce a year of favor from
   the LORD
   and a day of vindication by
   our God.

I rejoice heartily in the LORD,
   in my God is the joy of my soul;
for he has clothed me with a robe
   of salvation
   and wrapped me in a mantle
   of justice,
like a bridegroom adorned with
   a diadem,
   like a bride bedecked with
   her jewels.
As the earth brings forth its plants,
   and a garden makes its growth
   spring up,
so will the Lord GOD make justice
   and praise
   spring up before all the nations.

RESPONSORIAL PSALM

Luke 1:46–48, 49–50, 53–54

℞. My soul re - joic - es in my God.

▶ My soul proclaims the greatness of
   the Lord;
   my spirit rejoices in God my Savior,
for he has looked upon his
   lowly servant.
   From this day all generations will
   call me blessed: ℞.

▶ The Almighty has done great things
   for me,
   and holy is his Name.

He has mercy on those who fear him
   in every generation. ℞.

▶ He has filled the hungry with
   good things,
   and the rich he has sent away
   empty.
He has come to the help of his
   servant Israel
   for he has remembered his promise
   of mercy. ℞.

SECOND READING

1 Thessalonians 5:16–24

Brothers and sisters: Rejoice
always. Pray without ceasing. In all
circumstances give thanks, for this
is the will of God for you in Christ
Jesus. Do not quench the Spirit. Do
not despise prophetic utterances.
Test everything; retain what is good.

Refrain from every kind of evil.
   May the God of peace make you
perfectly holy and may you entirely,
spirit, soul, and body, be preserved
blameless for the coming of our Lord
Jesus Christ. The one who calls you is
faithful, and he will also accomplish it.

GOSPEL ACCLAMATION

Isaiah 61:1 (cited in Luke 4:18)

℞. Al - le - lu - ia, al - le - lu - ia, al - le - lu - ia.

(Omit if not sung)

▶ The Spirit of the Lord is upon me,
   because he has anointed me
   to bring glad tidings to the poor. ℞.

GOSPEL

John 1:6–8, 19–28

A man named John was sent from
God. He came for testimony, to
testify to the light, so that all might
believe through him. He was not the
light, but came to testify to the light.
   And this is the testimony of John.
When the Jews from Jerusalem
sent priests and Levites to him
to ask him, "Who are you?" he
admitted and did not deny it, but
admitted, "I am not the Christ."

So they asked him, "What are you
then? Are you Elijah?" And he said,
"I am not." "Are you the Prophet?"
He answered, "No." So they said to
him, "Who are you, so we can give an
answer to those who sent us? What do
you have to say for yourself?" He said:
   "I am *the voice of one crying out in
   the desert,*
   make straight the way of the Lord,
as Isaiah the prophet said." Some
Pharisees were also sent. They asked

him, "Why then do you baptize if you are not the Christ or Elijah or the Prophet?" John answered them, "I baptize with water; but there is one among you whom you do not recognize, the one who is coming after me, whose sandal strap I am not worthy to untie." This happened in Bethany across the Jordan, where John was baptizing.

THIRD SUNDAY OF ADVENT — C   866

FIRST READING   *Zephaniah 3:14–18a*

Shout for joy, O daughter Zion!
   Sing joyfully, O Israel!
Be glad and exult with all your heart,
   O daughter Jerusalem!
The LORD has removed the judgment
      against you,
   he has turned away your enemies;
the King of Israel, the LORD, is in
      your midst,
   you have no further misfortune
      to fear.

On that day, it shall be said
   to Jerusalem:
Fear not, O Zion, be not
   discouraged!
The LORD, your God, is in your midst,
   a mighty savior;
he will rejoice over you with gladness,
   and renew you in his love,
he will sing joyfully because of you,
   as one sings at festivals.

RESPONSORIAL PSALM   *Isaiah 12:2–3, 4, 5–6*

℟. Cry out with joy and glad-ness: for a-mong you is the great and Ho-ly One of Is - ra - el.

Music: Owen Alstott, b. 1947, © 1977, 1990, OCP. All rights reserved.

▸ God indeed is my savior;
   I am confident and unafraid.
My strength and my courage is
      the LORD,
   and he has been my savior.
With joy you will draw water
   at the fountain of salvation. ℟.

▸ Give thanks to the LORD, acclaim
      his name;
   among the nations make known
      his deeds,

proclaim how exalted is his
   name. ℟.

▸ Sing praise to the LORD for his
      glorious achievement;
   let this be known throughout all
      the earth.
Shout with exultation, O city of Zion,
   for great in your midst
      is the Holy One of Israel! ℟.

SECOND READING   *Philippians 4:4–7*

Brothers and sisters: Rejoice in the Lord always. I shall say it again: rejoice! Your kindness should be known to all. The Lord is near. Have no anxiety at all, but in everything, by prayer and petition, with thanksgiving, make your requests known to God. Then the peace of God that surpasses all understanding will guard your hearts and minds in Christ Jesus.

GOSPEL ACCLAMATION

Isaiah 61:1 (cited in Luke 4:18)

R. Al - le - lu - ia, al - le - lu - ia, al - le - lu - ia.

(Omit if not sung)

▶ The Spirit of the Lord is upon me,
because he has anointed me
to bring glad tidings to the poor. R.

GOSPEL

Luke 3:10–18

The crowds asked John the Baptist, "What should we do?" He said to them in reply, "Whoever has two cloaks should share with the person who has none. And whoever has food should do likewise." Even tax collectors came to be baptized and they said to him, "Teacher, what should we do?" He answered them, "Stop collecting more than what is prescribed." Soldiers also asked him, "And what is it that we should do?" He told them, "Do not practice extortion, do not falsely accuse anyone, and be satisfied with your wages."

Now the people were filled with expectation, and all were asking in their hearts whether John might be the Christ. John answered them all, saying, "I am baptizing you with water, but one mightier than I is coming. I am not worthy to loosen the thongs of his sandals. He will baptize you with the Holy Spirit and fire. His winnowing fan is in his hand to clear his threshing floor and to gather the wheat into his barn, but the chaff he will burn with unquenchable fire." Exhorting them in many other ways, he preached good news to the people.

---

867   FOURTH SUNDAY OF ADVENT — A

FIRST READING

Isaiah 7:10–14

The LORD spoke to Ahaz, saying: Ask for a sign from the LORD, your God; let it be deep as the netherworld, or high as the sky! But Ahaz answered, "I will not ask! I will not tempt the LORD!" Then Isaiah said: Listen, O house of David! Is it not enough for you to weary people, must you also weary my God? Therefore the Lord himself will give you this sign: the virgin shall conceive, and bear a son, and shall name him Emmanuel.

RESPONSORIAL PSALM

Psalm 24:1–2, 3–4, 5–6

R. Let the Lord en - ter; he is king of glo - ry.

▶ The LORD's are the earth and
its fullness;
the world and those who dwell in it.

For he founded it upon the seas
and established it upon
the rivers. R.

▶ Who can ascend the mountain of
the LORD?
or who may stand in his holy place?
One whose hands are sinless, whose
heart is clean,
who desires not what is vain. ℞.

▶ He shall receive a blessing from
the LORD,
a reward from God his savior.
Such is the race that seeks for him,
that seeks the face of the God
of Jacob. ℞.

SECOND READING

Romans 1:1–7

Paul, a slave of Christ Jesus, called to
be an apostle and set apart for the
gospel of God, which he promised
previously through his prophets in
the holy Scriptures, the gospel about
his Son, descended from David
according to the flesh, but established
as Son of God in power according
to the Spirit of holiness through
resurrection from the dead, Jesus
Christ our Lord. Through him we have
received the grace of apostleship, to
bring about the obedience of faith,
for the sake of his name, among
all the Gentiles, among whom are
you also, who are called to belong
to Jesus Christ; to all the beloved
of God in Rome, called to be holy.
Grace to you and peace from God
our Father and the Lord Jesus Christ.

GOSPEL ACCLAMATION

Matthew 1:23

℞. Al - le - lu - ia, al - le - lu - ia, al - le - lu - ia.

Music: Owen Alstott, b. 1947, © 1977, 1990, OCP. All rights reserved.

(Omit if not sung)

▶ The virgin shall conceive, and bear a son,
and they shall name him Emmanuel. ℞.

GOSPEL

Matthew 1:18–24

This is how the birth of Jesus Christ
came about. When his mother Mary
was betrothed to Joseph, but before
they lived together, she was found
with child through the Holy Spirit.
Joseph her husband, since he was a
righteous man, yet unwilling to expose
her to shame, decided to divorce
her quietly. Such was his intention
when, behold, the angel of the Lord
appeared to him in a dream and
said, "Joseph, son of David, do not be
afraid to take Mary your wife into your
home. For it is through the Holy Spirit
that this child has been conceived
in her. She will bear a son and you
are to name him Jesus, because he
will save his people from their sins."
All this took place to fulfill what the
Lord had said through the prophet:
Behold, the virgin shall conceive and
bear a son,
and they shall name him Emmanuel,
which means "God is with us." When
Joseph awoke, he did as the angel
of the Lord had commanded him
and took his wife into his home.

FOURTH SUNDAY OF ADVENT — B   868

FIRST READING

2 Samuel 7:1–5, 8b–12, 14a, 16

When King David was settled in his
palace, and the LORD had given him
rest from his enemies on every side,
he said to Nathan the prophet, "Here I

am living in a house of cedar, while the ark of God dwells in a tent!" Nathan answered the king, "Go, do whatever you have in mind, for the LORD is with you." But that night the LORD spoke to Nathan and said: "Go, tell my servant David, 'Thus says the LORD: Should you build me a house to dwell in?

"'It was I who took you from the pasture and from the care of the flock to be commander of my people Israel. I have been with you wherever you went, and I have destroyed all your enemies before you. And I will make you famous like the great ones of the earth. I will fix a place for my people Israel; I will plant them so that they may dwell in their place without further disturbance. Neither shall the wicked continue to afflict them as they did of old, since the time I first appointed judges over my people Israel. I will give you rest from all your enemies. The LORD also reveals to you that he will establish a house for you. And when your time comes and you rest with your ancestors, I will raise up your heir after you, sprung from your loins, and I will make his kingdom firm. I will be a father to him, and he shall be a son to me. Your house and your kingdom shall endure forever before me; your throne shall stand firm forever.'"

RESPONSIVE PSALM

RESPONSORIAL PSALM *Psalm 89:2–3, 4–5, 27, 29*

℟. For - ev - er I will sing the good - ness of the Lord.

▶ The promises of the LORD I will
   sing forever;
     through all generations my mouth
       shall proclaim your faithfulness.
   For you have said, "My kindness is
     established forever";
     in heaven you have confirmed
       your faithfulness. ℟.

▶ "I have made a covenant with my
     chosen one,
   I have sworn to David my servant:

forever will I confirm your posterity
   and establish your throne for
     all generations." ℟.

▶ "He shall say of me, 'You are
     my father,
   my God, the Rock, my savior.'
   Forever I will maintain my kindness
     toward him,
   and my covenant with him
     stands firm." ℟.

SECOND READING

Romans 16:25–27

Brothers and sisters: To him who can strengthen you, according to my gospel and the proclamation of Jesus Christ, according to the revelation of the mystery kept secret for long ages but now manifested through the prophetic writings and, according to the command of the eternal God, made known to all nations to bring about the obedience of faith, to the only wise God, through Jesus Christ be glory forever and ever. Amen.

GOSPEL ACCLAMATION

Luke 1:38

℟. Al - le - lu - ia, al - le - lu - ia, al - le - lu - ia.

Music: Owen Alstott, b. 1947, © 1977, 1990, OCP. All rights reserved.

(Omit if not sung)

▸ Behold, I am the handmaid of the Lord.
May it be done to me according to your word. ℟.

GOSPEL

Luke 1:26–38

The angel Gabriel was sent from God to a town of Galilee called Nazareth, to a virgin betrothed to a man named Joseph, of the house of David, and the virgin's name was Mary. And coming to her, he said, "Hail, full of grace! The Lord is with you." But she was greatly troubled at what was said and pondered what sort of greeting this might be. Then the angel said to her, "Do not be afraid, Mary, for you have found favor with God.

"Behold, you will conceive in your womb and bear a son, and you shall name him Jesus. He will be great and will be called Son of the Most High, and the Lord God will give him the throne of David his father, and he will rule over the house of Jacob forever, and of his kingdom there will be no end." But Mary said to the angel, "How can this be, since I have no relations with a man?" And the angel said to her in reply, "The Holy Spirit will come upon you, and the power of the Most High will overshadow you. Therefore the child to be born will be called holy, the Son of God. And behold, Elizabeth, your relative, has also conceived a son in her old age, and this is the sixth month for her who was called barren; for nothing will be impossible for God." Mary said, "Behold, I am the handmaid of the Lord. May it be done to me according to your word." Then the angel departed from her.

FOURTH SUNDAY OF ADVENT — C   869

FIRST READING

Micah 5:1–4a

Thus says the LORD:
 You, Bethlehem-Ephrathah,
  too small to be among the clans
   of Judah,
 from you shall come forth for me
  one who is to be ruler in Israel;
 whose origin is from of old,
  from ancient times.
 Therefore the Lord will give them up,
  until the time
   when she who is to give birth
    has borne,
and the rest of his kindred
  shall return
 to the children of Israel.
He shall stand firm and shepherd
  his flock
 by the strength of the LORD,
 in the majestic name of the LORD,
  his God;
and they shall remain, for now
  his greatness
 shall reach to the ends of the earth;
 he shall be peace.

RESPONSORIAL PSALM

Psalm 80:2–3, 15–16, 18–19

℟. Lord, make us turn to you; let us see your face and we shall be saved.

▶ O shepherd of Israel, hearken,
from your throne upon the
cherubim, shine forth.
Rouse your power,
and come to save us. ℟.

▶ Once again, O LORD of hosts,
look down from heaven, and see;
take care of this vine,
and protect what your right hand
has planted,

the son of man whom you yourself
made strong. ℟.

▶ May your help be with the man of
your right hand,
with the son of man whom you
yourself made strong.
Then we will no more withdraw
from you;
give us new life, and we will call
upon your name. ℟.

SECOND READING

Hebrews 10:5–10

Brothers and sisters: When Christ
came into the world, he said:
"Sacrifice and offering you did
not desire,
but a body you prepared for me;
in holocausts and sin offerings you
took no delight.
Then I said, 'As is written of me in
the scroll,
behold, I come to do your will,
O God.'"

First he says, "Sacrifices and
offerings, holocausts and sin
offerings, you neither desired nor
delighted in." These are offered
according to the law. Then he says,
"Behold, I come to do your will." He
takes away the first to establish the
second. By this "will," we have been
consecrated through the offering of
the body of Jesus Christ once for all.

GOSPEL ACCLAMATION

Luke 1:38

℟. Al - le - lu - ia, al - le - lu - ia, al - le - lu - ia.

(Omit if not sung)

▶ Behold, I am the handmaid of the Lord.
May it be done to me according to your word. ℟.

GOSPEL

Luke 1:39–45

Mary set out and traveled to the
hill country in haste to a town of
Judah, where she entered the house
of Zechariah and greeted Elizabeth.
When Elizabeth heard Mary's greeting,
the infant leaped in her womb, and
Elizabeth, filled with the Holy Spirit,
cried out in a loud voice and said,
"Blessed are you among women, and

blessed is the fruit of your womb.
And how does this happen to me,
that the mother of my Lord should
come to me? For at the moment
the sound of your greeting reached
my ears, the infant in my womb
leaped for joy. Blessed are you who
believed that what was spoken to
you by the Lord would be fulfilled."

SEASON OF CHRISTMAS

THE NATIVITY OF THE LORD (CHRISTMAS):   870
AT THE VIGIL MASS — ABC

These readings are used at Mass celebrated on the evening of December 24, either before or after Evening Prayer I of the Nativity.

The texts that follow may also be used for Masses on Christmas Day, with the option of choosing from one or another of the three sets of readings according to the pastoral needs of each assembly.

FIRST READING
Isaiah 62:1–5

For Zion's sake I will not be silent,
  for Jerusalem's sake I will not
    be quiet,
until her vindication shines forth like
  the dawn
  and her victory like a
    burning torch.

Nations shall behold
  your vindication,
  and all the kings your glory;
you shall be called by a new name
  pronounced by the mouth
    of the LORD.
You shall be a glorious crown in the
hand of the LORD,
  a royal diadem held by your God.
No more shall people call
  you "Forsaken,"
  or your land "Desolate,"
but you shall be called "My Delight,"
  and your land "Espoused."
For the LORD delights in you
  and makes your land his spouse.
As a young man marries a virgin,
  your Builder shall marry you;
and as a bridegroom rejoices in
  his bride
so shall your God rejoice in you.

RESPONSORIAL PSALM
Psalm 89:4–5, 16–17, 27, 29

℞. For - ev - er I will sing the good - ness of the Lord.

▶ I have made a covenant with my
  chosen one,
  I have sworn to David my servant:
forever will I confirm your posterity
  and establish your throne for
  all generations. ℞.

▶ Blessed the people who know the
  joyful shout;
  in the light of your countenance,
  O LORD, they walk.

At your name they rejoice all the day,
  and through your justice they
  are exalted. ℞.

▶ He shall say of me, "You are
  my father,
  my God, the Rock, my savior."
Forever I will maintain my kindness
  toward him,
  and my covenant with him
  stands firm. ℞.

SECOND READING
Acts of the Apostles 13:16–17, 22–25

When Paul reached Antioch in Pisidia
and entered the synagogue, he stood
up, motioned with his hand, and said,

"Fellow Israelites and you others who
are God-fearing, listen. The God of
this people Israel chose our ancestors

and exalted the people during their sojourn in the land of Egypt. With uplifted arm he led them out of it. Then he removed Saul and raised up David as king; of him he testified, 'I have found David, son of Jesse, a man after my own heart; he will carry out my every wish.' From this man's descendants God, according to his promise, has brought to Israel a savior, Jesus. John heralded his coming by proclaiming a baptism of repentance to all the people of Israel; and as John was completing his course, he would say, 'What do you suppose that I am? I am not he. Behold, one is coming after me; I am not worthy to unfasten the sandals of his feet.'"

GOSPEL ACCLAMATION

℟. Al - le - lu - ia, al - le - lu - ia, al - le - lu - ia.

(Omit if not sung)

▶ Tomorrow the wickedness of the earth will be destroyed: the Savior of the world will reign over us. ℟.

GOSPEL
Matthew 1:1–25 or 1:18–25

(Include bracketed text for Long Form)

[The book of the genealogy of Jesus Christ, the son of David, the son of Abraham.

Abraham became the father of Isaac, Isaac the father of Jacob, Jacob the father of Judah and his brothers. Judah became the father of Perez and Zerah, whose mother was Tamar. Perez became the father of Hezron, Hezron the father of Ram, Ram the father of Amminadab. Amminadab became the father of Nahshon, Nahshon the father of Salmon, Salmon the father of Boaz, whose mother was Rahab. Boaz became the father of Obed, whose mother was Ruth. Obed became the father of Jesse, Jesse the father of David the king.

David became the father of Solomon, whose mother had been the wife of Uriah. Solomon became the father of Rehoboam, Rehoboam the father of Abijah, Abijah the father of Asaph. Asaph became the father of Jehoshaphat, Jehoshaphat the father of Joram, Joram the father of Uzziah. Uzziah became the father of Jotham, Jotham the father of Ahaz, Ahaz the father of Hezekiah. Hezekiah became the father of Manasseh, Manasseh the father of Amos, Amos the father of Josiah. Josiah became the father of Jechoniah and his brothers at the time of the Babylonian exile.

After the Babylonian exile, Jechoniah became the father of Shealtiel, Shealtiel the father of Zerubbabel, Zerubbabel the father of Abiud. Abiud became the father of Eliakim, Eliakim the father of Azor, Azor the father of Zadok. Zadok became the father of Achim, Achim the father of Eliud, Eliud the father of Eleazar. Eleazar became the father of Matthan, Matthan the father of Jacob, Jacob the father of Joseph, the husband of Mary. Of her was born Jesus who is called the Christ.

Thus the total number of generations from Abraham to David is fourteen generations; from David to the Babylonian exile, fourteen generations; from the Babylonian exile to the Christ, fourteen generations.

Now] this is how the birth of Jesus Christ came about. When his mother Mary was betrothed to Joseph, but before they lived together, she was found with child through the Holy

Spirit. Joseph her husband, since he was a righteous man, yet unwilling to expose her to shame, decided to divorce her quietly. Such was his intention when, behold, the angel of the Lord appeared to him in a dream and said, "Joseph, son of David, do not be afraid to take Mary your wife into your home. For it is through the Holy Spirit that this child has been conceived in her. She will bear a son and you are to name him Jesus, because he will save his people from their sins." All this took place to fulfill what the Lord had said through the prophet:
Behold, the virgin shall conceive and
bear a son,
and they shall name him
Emmanuel,
which means "God is with us." When Joseph awoke, he did as the angel of the Lord had commanded him and took his wife into his home. He had no relations with her until she bore a son, and he named him Jesus.

THE NATIVITY OF THE LORD (CHRISTMAS): 871 AT THE MASS DURING THE NIGHT — ABC

The chant for The Nativity of Our Lord Jesus Christ, found in Appendix I of The Roman Missal *may be sung or proclaimed before the beginning of Mass.*

FIRST READING

Isaiah 9:1–6

The people who walked in darkness
  have seen a great light;
upon those who dwelt in the land
  of gloom
  a light has shone.
You have brought them abundant joy
  and great rejoicing,
as they rejoice before you as at
  the harvest,
  as people make merry when
  dividing spoils.
For the yoke that burdened them,
  the pole on their shoulder,
and the rod of their taskmaster
  you have smashed, as on the day
  of Midian.
For every boot that tramped in battle,

every cloak rolled in blood,
  will be burned as fuel for flames.
For a child is born to us, a son is
  given us;
  upon his shoulder dominion rests.
They name him Wonder-Counselor,
  God-Hero,
  Father-Forever, Prince of Peace.
His dominion is vast
  and forever peaceful,
from David's throne, and over
  his kingdom,
  which he confirms and sustains
by judgment and justice,
  both now and forever.
The zeal of the LORD of hosts will
  do this!

RESPONSORIAL PSALM

Psalm 96: 1–2, 2–3, 11–12, 13

℟. To - day is born our Sav - ior, Christ the Lord.

Music: Owen Alstott, b. 1947, © 1977, 1990, OCP. All rights reserved.

▸ Sing to the LORD a new song;
  sing to the LORD, all you lands.
  Sing to the LORD; bless his name. ℟.

▸ Announce his salvation, day after day.
  Tell his glory among the nations;
  among all peoples, his wondrous
  deeds. ℟.

℟. Today is born our Savior, Christ the Lord.

▶ Let the heavens be glad and the
earth rejoice;
let the sea and what fills it resound;
let the plains be joyful and all that
is in them!
Then shall all the trees of the
forest exult. ℟.

▶ They shall exult before the LORD, for
he comes;
for he comes to rule the earth.
He shall rule the world with justice
and the peoples with
his constancy. ℟.

SECOND READING

Titus 2:11–14

Beloved: The grace of God has
appeared, saving all and training us
to reject godless ways and worldly
desires and to live temperately, justly,
and devoutly in this age, as we await
the blessed hope, the appearance of
the glory of our great God and savior
Jesus Christ, who gave himself for us
to deliver us from all lawlessness and
to cleanse for himself a people as
his own, eager to do what is good.

GOSPEL ACCLAMATION

Luke 2:10–11

℟. Al - le - lu - ia, al - le - lu - ia, al - le - lu - ia.

Music: Owen Alstott, b. 1947, © 1977, 1990, OCP. All rights reserved.

(Omit if not sung)

▶ I proclaim to you good news of great joy:
today a Savior is born for us,
Christ the Lord. ℟.

GOSPEL

Luke 2:1–14

In those days a decree went out from
Caesar Augustus that the whole world
should be enrolled. This was the
first enrollment, when Quirinius was
governor of Syria. So all went to be
enrolled, each to his own town. And
Joseph too went up from Galilee from
the town of Nazareth to Judea, to the
city of David that is called Bethlehem,
because he was of the house and
family of David, to be enrolled with
Mary, his betrothed, who was with
child. While they were there, the time
came for her to have her child, and she
gave birth to her firstborn son. She
wrapped him in swaddling clothes and
laid him in a manger, because there
was no room for them in the inn.

Now there were shepherds in that
region living in the fields and keeping
the night watch over their flock. The
angel of the Lord appeared to them
and the glory of the Lord shone
around them, and they were struck
with great fear. The angel said to
them, "Do not be afraid; for behold, I
proclaim to you good news of great
joy that will be for all the people. For
today in the city of David a savior
has been born for you who is Christ
and Lord. And this will be a sign for
you: you will find an infant wrapped
in swaddling clothes and lying in a
manger." And suddenly there was a
multitude of the heavenly host with
the angel, praising God and saying:
"Glory to God in the highest
and on earth peace to those on
whom his favor rests."

THE NATIVITY OF THE LORD (CHRISTMAS): 872
AT THE MASS AT DAWN — ABC

FIRST READING
Isaiah 62:11–12

See, the LORD proclaims
  to the ends of the earth:
say to daughter Zion,
  your savior comes!
Here is his reward with him,

his recompense before him.
They shall be called the holy people,
  the redeemed of the LORD,
and you shall be called "Frequented,"
  a city that is not forsaken.

RESPONSORIAL PSALM
Psalm 97:1, 6, 11–12

℟. A light will shine on us this day: the Lord is born for us.

▶ The LORD is king; let the earth rejoice;
  let the many isles be glad.
The heavens proclaim his justice,
  and all peoples see his glory. ℟.

▶ Light dawns for the just;
  and gladness, for the upright
  of heart.
Be glad in the LORD, you just,
  and give thanks to his holy name. ℟.

SECOND READING
Titus 3:4–7

Beloved:
  When the kindness and
    generous love
  of God our savior appeared,
  not because of any righteous deeds
    we had done
  but because of his mercy,
he saved us through the bath
  of rebirth

and renewal by the Holy Spirit,
whom he richly poured out on us
  through Jesus Christ our savior,
so that we might be justified
  by his grace
and become heirs in hope
  of eternal life.

GOSPEL ACCLAMATION
Luke 2:14

℟. Al - le - lu - ia, al - le - lu - ia, al - le - lu - ia.

(Omit if not sung)

▶ Glory to God in the highest,
  and on earth peace to those
  on whom his favor rests. ℟.

GOSPEL
Luke 2:15–20

When the angels went away from them
to heaven, the shepherds said to one
another, "Let us go, then, to Bethlehem
to see this thing that has taken place,

which the Lord has made known to
us." So they went in haste and found
Mary and Joseph, and the infant lying
in the manger. When they saw this,

they made known the message that had been told them about this child. All who heard it were amazed by what had been told them by the shepherds. And Mary kept all these things, reflecting on them in her heart. Then the shepherds returned, glorifying and praising God for all they had heard and seen, just as it had been told to them.

873   THE NATIVITY OF THE LORD (CHRISTMAS): AT THE MASS DURING THE DAY — ABC

FIRST READING   *Isaiah 52:7–10*

How beautiful upon the mountains
   are the feet of him who brings
      glad tidings,
announcing peace, bearing
   good news,
announcing salvation, and saying
   to Zion,
"Your God is King!"

Hark! Your sentinels raise a cry,
   together they shout for joy,

for they see directly,
   before their eyes,
      the LORD restoring Zion.
Break out together in song,
   O ruins of Jerusalem!
For the LORD comforts his people,
   he redeems Jerusalem.
The LORD has bared his holy arm
   in the sight of all the nations;
all the ends of the earth will behold
   the salvation of our God.

RESPONSORIAL PSALM   *Psalm 98:1, 2–3, 3–4, 5–6*

℟. All the ends of the earth have seen the sav-ing pow-er of God.

▸ Sing to the LORD a new song,
   for he has done wondrous deeds;
his right hand has won victory
   for him,
his holy arm. ℟.

▸ The LORD has made his
   salvation known:
in the sight of the nations he has
   revealed his justice.
He has remembered his kindness and
   his faithfulness
toward the house of Israel. ℟.

▸ All the ends of the earth have seen
   the salvation by our God.
Sing joyfully to the LORD,
   all you lands;
break into song; sing praise. ℟.

▸ Sing praise to the LORD with the harp,
   with the harp and melodious song.
With trumpets and the sound of
   the horn
sing joyfully before the King,
   the LORD. ℟.

SECOND READING   *Hebrews 1:1–6*

Brothers and sisters: In times past, God spoke in partial and various ways to our ancestors through the prophets; in these last days, he has spoken to us through the Son, whom he made heir of all things and through whom he created the universe, who is the refulgence of his glory, the very imprint of his being, and who sustains all things by his mighty word.

When he had accomplished
purification from sins,
he took his seat at the right hand of
the Majesty on high,
as far superior to the angels
as the name he has inherited is more
excellent than theirs.
For to which of the angels did God
ever say:

*You are my son; this day I have
begotten you?*
Or again:
*I will be a father to him, and he shall
be a son to me?*
And again, when he leads the
firstborn into the world, he says:
*Let all the angels of God
worship him.*

GOSPEL ACCLAMATION

℟. Al - le - lu - ia, al - le - lu - ia, al - le - lu - ia.

Music: Owen Alstott, b. 1947, © 1977, 1990, OCP. All rights reserved.   *(Omit if not sung)*

▶ A holy day has dawned upon us.
Come, you nations, and adore the Lord.
For today a great light has come upon the earth. ℟.

GOSPEL   *John 1:1–18 or 1:1–5, 9–14*

(Include bracketed text for Long Form)

In the beginning was the Word,
and the Word was with God,
and the Word was God.
He was in the beginning with God.
All things came to be through him,
and without him nothing came
to be.
What came to be through him
was life,
and this life was the light of the
human race;
the light shines in the darkness,
and the darkness has not
overcome it.
[A man named John was sent from
God. He came for testimony, to
testify to the light, so that all might
believe through him. He was not
the light, but came to testify to the
light.] The true light, which enlightens
everyone, was coming into the world.
He was in the world,
and the world came to be
through him,
but the world did not know him.

He came to what was his own,
but his own people did not
accept him.

But to those who did accept him
he gave power to become children
of God, to those who believe in his
name, who were born not by natural
generation nor by human choice nor
by a man's decision but of God.
And the Word became flesh
and made his dwelling among us,
and we saw his glory,
the glory as of the Father's
only Son,
full of grace and truth.
[John testified to him and cried
out, saying, "This was he of whom
I said, 'The one who is coming after
me ranks ahead of me because he
existed before me.'" From his fullness
we have all received, grace in place of
grace, because while the law was given
through Moses, grace and truth came
through Jesus Christ. No one has ever
seen God. The only Son, God, who is
at the Father's side, has revealed him.]

874 THE HOLY FAMILY OF JESUS, MARY AND JOSEPH — ABC

FIRST READING *Sirach 3:2–6, 12–14*

God sets a father in honor over
  his children;
  a mother's authority he confirms
  over her sons.
Whoever honors his father atones
  for sins,
  and preserves himself from them.
When he prays, he is heard;
  he stores up riches who reveres
  his mother.
Whoever honors his father is
  gladdened by children,
  and, when he prays, is heard.
Whoever reveres his father will live
  a long life;

he who obeys his father brings
  comfort to his mother.

My son, take care of your father
  when he is old;
  grieve him not as long as he lives.
Even if his mind fail, be considerate
  of him;
  revile him not all the days of
  his life;
kindness to a father will not
  be forgotten,
  firmly planted against the debt
  of your sins
—a house raised in justice to you.

RESPONSORIAL PSALM *Psalm 128:1–2, 3, 4–5*

℟. **Bless-ed are those who fear the Lord and walk in his ways.**

Music: Owen Alstott, b. 1947, © 1977, 1990, OCP. All rights reserved.

▸ Blessed is everyone who fears
  the LORD,
  who walks in his ways!
For you shall eat the fruit
  of your handiwork;
  blessed shall you be,
  and favored. ℟.

▸ Your wife shall be like a fruitful vine
  in the recesses of your home;

your children like olive plants
  around your table. ℟.

▸ Behold, thus is the man blessed
  who fears the LORD.
The LORD bless you from Zion:
  may you see the prosperity
  of Jerusalem
  all the days of your life. ℟.

SECOND READING *Colossians 3:12–21 or 3:12–17*

(Include bracketed text for Long Form)

Brothers and sisters: Put on, as God's
chosen ones, holy and beloved,
heartfelt compassion, kindness,
humility, gentleness, and patience,
bearing with one another and forgiving
one another, if one has a grievance
against another; as the Lord has
forgiven you, so must you also do. And
over all these put on love, that is, the
bond of perfection. And let the peace
of Christ control your hearts, the

peace into which you were also called
in one body. And be thankful. Let the
word of Christ dwell in you richly, as
in all wisdom you teach and admonish
one another, singing psalms, hymns,
and spiritual songs with gratitude in
your hearts to God. And whatever you
do, in word or in deed, do everything
in the name of the Lord Jesus, giving
thanks to God the Father through him.

[Wives, be subordinate to your husbands, as is proper in the Lord. Husbands, love your wives, and avoid any bitterness toward them. Children, obey your parents in everything, for this is pleasing to the Lord. Fathers, do not provoke your children, so they may not become discouraged.]

GOSPEL ACCLAMATION

Colossians 3:15a, 16a

℟. Al - le - lu - ia, al - le - lu - ia, al - le - lu - ia.

Music: Owen Alstott, b. 1947, © 1977, 1990, OCP. All rights reserved.

(Omit if not sung)

▶ Let the peace of Christ control your hearts;
   let the word of Christ dwell in you richly. ℟.

GOSPEL — A

Matthew 2:13–15, 19–23

When the magi had departed, behold, the angel of the Lord appeared to Joseph in a dream and said, "Rise, take the child and his mother, flee to Egypt, and stay there until I tell you. Herod is going to search for the child to destroy him." Joseph rose and took the child and his mother by night and departed for Egypt. He stayed there until the death of Herod, that what the Lord had said through the prophet might be fulfilled, *Out of Egypt I called my son.*

When Herod had died, behold, the angel of the Lord appeared in a dream to Joseph in Egypt and said, "Rise, take the child and his mother and go to the land of Israel, for those who sought the child's life are dead." He rose, took the child and his mother, and went to the land of Israel. But when he heard that Archelaus was ruling over Judea in place of his father Herod, he was afraid to go back there. And because he had been warned in a dream, he departed for the region of Galilee. He went and dwelt in a town called Nazareth, so that what had been spoken through the prophets might be fulfilled, *He shall be called a Nazorean.*

GOSPEL — B

Luke 2:22–40 or 2:22, 39–40

(Include bracketed text for Long Form)

When the days were completed for their purification according to the law of Moses, they took him up to Jerusalem to present him to the Lord, [just as it is written in the law of the Lord, *Every male that opens the womb shall be consecrated to the Lord,* and to offer the sacrifice of *a pair of turtledoves or two young pigeons,* in accordance with the dictate in the law of the Lord.

Now there was a man in Jerusalem whose name was Simeon. This man was righteous and devout, awaiting the consolation of Israel, and the Holy Spirit was upon him. It had been revealed to him by the Holy Spirit that he should not see death before he had seen the Christ of the Lord. He came in the Spirit into the temple; and when the parents brought in the child Jesus to perform the custom of the law in regard to him, he took him into his arms and blessed God, saying:
   "Now, Master, you may let your
      servant go
   in peace, according to your word,
   for my eyes have seen your salvation,
      which you prepared in sight of all
      the peoples,
   a light for revelation to the Gentiles,
      and glory for your people Israel."

The child's father and mother were amazed at what was said about him; and Simeon blessed them and said to Mary his mother, "Behold, this child is destined for the fall and rise of many in Israel, and to be a sign that will be contradicted—and you yourself a sword will pierce—so that the thoughts of many hearts may be revealed." There was also a prophetess, Anna, the daughter of Phanuel, of the tribe of Asher. She was advanced in years, having lived seven years with her husband after her marriage, and then as a widow until she was eighty-four. She never left the temple, but worshiped night and day with fasting and prayer. And coming forward at that very time, she gave thanks to God and spoke about the child to all who were awaiting the redemption of Jerusalem.]

When they had fulfilled all the prescriptions of the law of the Lord, they returned to Galilee, to their own town of Nazareth. The child grew and became strong, filled with wisdom; and the favor of God was upon him.

GOSPEL — C

Luke 2:41–52

Each year Jesus' parents went to Jerusalem for the feast of Passover, and when he was twelve years old, they went up according to festival custom. After they had completed its days, as they were returning, the boy Jesus remained behind in Jerusalem, but his parents did not know it. Thinking that he was in the caravan, they journeyed for a day and looked for him among their relatives and acquaintances, but not finding him, they returned to Jerusalem to look for him. After three days they found him in the temple, sitting in the midst of the teachers, listening to them and asking them questions, and all who heard him were astounded at his understanding and his answers. When his parents saw him, they were astonished, and his mother said to him, "Son, why have you done this to us? Your father and I have been looking for you with great anxiety." And he said to them, "Why were you looking for me? Did you not know that I must be in my Father's house?" But they did not understand what he said to them. He went down with them and came to Nazareth, and was obedient to them; and his mother kept all these things in her heart. And Jesus advanced in wisdom and age and favor before God and man.

---

875   THE HOLY FAMILY OF JESUS, MARY AND JOSEPH
OPTIONAL READINGS — B

FIRST READING

Genesis 15:1–6; 21:1–3

The word of the LORD came to Abram in a vision, saying:
   "Fear not, Abram!
    I am your shield;
    I will make your reward very great."
But Abram said, "O Lord GOD, what good will your gifts be, if I keep on being childless and have as my heir the steward of my house, Eliezer?" Abram continued, "See, you have given me no offspring, and so one of my servants will be my heir." Then the word of the LORD came to him: "No, that one shall not be your heir; your own issue shall be your heir." The Lord took Abram outside and said, "Look up at the sky and count the stars, if you can. Just so," he added, "shall your descendants be." Abram put his faith in the LORD, who credited it to him as an act of righteousness.

The LORD took note of Sarah as he had said he would; he did for her as he had promised. Sarah became pregnant and bore Abraham a son in his old age, at the set time that God had stated. Abraham gave the name Isaac to this son of his whom Sarah bore him.

RESPONSORIAL PSALM

Psalm 105:1–2, 3–4, 5–6, 8–9

℟. The Lord re - mem - bers his cov - e - nant for - ev - er.

▶ Give thanks to the LORD, invoke
  his name;
    make known among the nations
    his deeds.
  Sing to him, sing his praise,
    proclaim all his wondrous deeds. ℟.

▶ Glory in his holy name;
    rejoice, O hearts that seek
    the LORD!
  Look to the LORD in his strength;
    constantly seek his face. ℟.

▶ You descendants of Abraham,
    his servants,
    sons of Jacob, his chosen ones!
  He, the LORD, is our God;
    throughout the earth his judgments
    prevail. ℟.

▶ He remembers forever his covenant
    which he made binding for a
    thousand generations
  which he entered into with Abraham
    and by his oath to Isaac. ℟.

SECOND READING

Hebrews 11:8, 11–12, 17–19

Brothers and sisters: By faith Abraham obeyed when he was called to go out to a place that he was to receive as an inheritance; he went out, not knowing where he was to go. By faith he received power to generate, even though he was past the normal age —and Sarah herself was sterile—for he thought that the one who had made the promise was trustworthy. So it was that there came forth from one man, himself as good as dead, descendants as numerous as the stars in the sky and as countless as the sands on the seashore.

By faith Abraham, when put to the test, offered up Isaac, and he who had received the promises was ready to offer his only son, of whom it was said, "Through Isaac descendants shall bear your name." He reasoned that God was able to raise even from the dead, and he received Isaac back as a symbol.

GOSPEL ACCLAMATION

Hebrews 1:1-2

℟. Al - le - lu - ia, al - le - lu - ia, al - le - lu - ia.

(Omit if not sung)

▶ In the past God spoke to our ancestors through the prophets;
  in these last days, he has spoken to us through the Son. ℟.

Use Gospel Reading for Year B, #874.

876 THE HOLY FAMILY OF JESUS, MARY AND JOSEPH
OPTIONAL READINGS — C

FIRST READING

1 Samuel 1:20–22, 24–28

In those days Hannah conceived, and at the end of her term bore a son whom she called Samuel, since she had asked the LORD for him. The next time her husband Elkanah was going up with the rest of his household to offer the customary sacrifice to the LORD and to fulfill his vows, Hannah did not go, explaining to her husband, "Once the child is weaned, I will take him to appear before the LORD and to remain there forever; I will offer him as a perpetual nazirite."

Once Samuel was weaned, Hannah brought him up with her, along with a three-year-old bull, an ephah of flour, and a skin of wine, and presented him at the temple of the LORD in Shiloh. After the boy's father had sacrificed the young bull, Hannah, his mother, approached Eli and said: "Pardon, my lord! As you live, my lord, I am the woman who stood near you here, praying to the LORD. I prayed for this child, and the LORD granted my request. Now I, in turn, give him to the LORD; as long as he lives, he shall be dedicated to the LORD." Hannah left Samuel there.

RESPONSORIAL PSALM

Psalm 84:2–3, 5–6, 9–10

℟. [Bless - ed are they,] bless-ed are they who dwell in your house, O Lord.

▸ How lovely is your dwelling place,
    O LORD of hosts!
  My soul yearns and pines for the
    courts of the LORD.
  My heart and my flesh cry out for the
    living God. ℟.

▸ Happy they who dwell in your house!
  Continually they praise you.

Happy the men whose strength
    you are!
  Their hearts are set upon the
    pilgrimage. ℟.

▸ O LORD of hosts, hear our prayer;
    hearken, O God of Jacob!
  O God, behold our shield,
    and look upon the face of
      your anointed. ℟.

SECOND READING

1 John 3:1–2, 21–24

Beloved: See what love the Father has bestowed on us that we may be called the children of God. And so we are. The reason the world does not know us is that it did not know him. Beloved, we are God's children now; what we shall be has not yet been revealed. We do know that when it is revealed we shall be like him, for we shall see him as he is.

Beloved, if our hearts do not condemn us, we have confidence in God and receive from him whatever we ask, because we keep his commandments and do what pleases him. And his commandment is this: we should believe in the name of his Son, Jesus Christ, and love one another just as he commanded us. Those who keep his commandments remain in him, and he in them, and the way we know that he remains in us is from the Spirit he gave us.

GOSPEL ACCLAMATION

cf. Acts of the Apostles 16:14b

℟. Al - le - lu - ia,   al - le - lu - ia,   al - le - lu - ia.

(Omit if not sung)

▶ Open our hearts, O Lord,
   to listen to the words of your Son. ℟.

Use Gospel Reading for Year C, #874.

SOLEMNITY OF MARY, THE HOLY MOTHER OF GOD — ABC

877

FIRST READING

Numbers 6:22–27

The LORD said to Moses: "Speak to Aaron and his sons and tell them: This is how you shall bless the Israelites. Say to them:
   The LORD bless you and keep you!
The LORD let his face shine upon you, and be gracious to you!
The LORD look upon you kindly and give you peace!
So shall they invoke my name upon the Israelites, and I will bless them."

RESPONSORIAL PSALM

Psalm 67:2–3, 5, 6, 8

℟. May God bless us in his mer - cy.

▶ May God have pity on us and bless us;
   may he let his face shine upon us.
So may your way be known upon earth;
   among all nations, your salvation. ℟.

▶ May the nations be glad and exult
   because you rule the peoples
   in equity;
the nations on the earth
   you guide. ℟.

▶ May the peoples praise you, O God;
   may all the peoples praise you!
May God bless us,
   and may all the ends of the earth
   fear him! ℟.

SECOND READING

Galatians 4:4–7

Brothers and sisters: When the fullness of time had come, God sent his Son, born of a woman, born under the law, to ransom those under the law, so that we might receive adoption as sons. As proof that you are sons, God sent the Spirit of his Son into our hearts, crying out, "Abba, Father!" So you are no longer a slave but a son, and if a son then also an heir, through God.

GOSPEL ACCLAMATION

Hebrews 1:1–2

℟. Al - le - lu - ia,   al - le - lu - ia,   al - le - lu - ia.

(Omit if not sung)

℟. **Alleluia, alleluia, alleluia.**

▶ In the past God spoke to our ancestors through the prophets;
in these last days, he has spoken to us through the Son. ℟.

GOSPEL
Luke 2:16–21

The shepherds went in haste to Bethlehem and found Mary and Joseph, and the infant lying in the manger. When they saw this, they made known the message that had been told them about this child. All who heard it were amazed by what had been told them by the shepherds. And Mary kept all these things, reflecting on them in her heart. Then the shepherds returned, glorifying and praising God for all they had heard and seen, just as it had been told to them.

When eight days were completed for his circumcision, he was named Jesus, the name given him by the angel before he was conceived in the womb.

---

878   THE EPIPHANY OF THE LORD — ABC

FIRST READING
Isaiah 60:1–6

Rise up in splendor, Jerusalem!
 Your light has come,
  the glory of the Lord shines
   upon you.
See, darkness covers the earth,
  and thick clouds cover the peoples;
but upon you the LORD shines,
  and over you appears his glory.
Nations shall walk by your light,
  and kings by your shining radiance.
Raise your eyes and look about;
  they all gather and come to you:
your sons come from afar,
  and your daughters in the arms
   of their nurses.

Then you shall be radiant at what
  you see,
 your heart shall throb and overflow,
for the riches of the sea shall be
  emptied out before you,
 the wealth of nations shall be
  brought to you.
Caravans of camels shall fill you,
  dromedaries from Midian
   and Ephah;
all from Sheba shall come
  bearing gold and frankincense,
  and proclaiming the praises of
   the LORD.

RESPONSORIAL PSALM
Psalm 72:1–2, 7–8, 10–11, 12–13

℟. Lord, ev-'ry na-tion on earth will a-dore you.

Music: Owen Alstott, b. 1947, © 1977, 1990, OCP. All rights reserved.

▶ O God, with your judgment endow
   the king,
 and with your justice,
   the king's son;
he shall govern your people
   with justice
 and your afflicted ones
   with judgment. ℟.

▶ Justice shall flower in his days,
   and profound peace, till the moon
   be no more.
May he rule from sea to sea,
   and from the River to the ends of
   the earth. ℟.

▶ The kings of Tarshish and the Isles
   shall offer gifts;

the kings of Arabia and Seba shall
  bring tribute.
All kings shall pay him homage,
  all nations shall serve him. ℟.

▸ For he shall rescue the poor when he
  cries out,

and the afflicted when he has no
  one to help him.
He shall have pity for the lowly and
  the poor;
  the lives of the poor he shall save. ℟.

SECOND READING

Ephesians 3:2–3a, 5–6

Brothers and sisters: You have
heard of the stewardship of God's
grace that was given to me for
your benefit, namely, that the
mystery was made known to me by
revelation. It was not made known
to people in other generations as

it has now been revealed to his
holy apostles and prophets by
the Spirit: that the Gentiles are
coheirs, members of the same body,
and copartners in the promise in
Christ Jesus through the gospel.

GOSPEL ACCLAMATION

Matthew 2:2

℟. Al - le - lu - ia, al - le - lu - ia, al - le - lu - ia.

Music: Owen Alstott, b. 1947, © 1977, 1990, OCP. All rights reserved. *(Omit if not sung)*

▸ We saw his star at its rising
  and have come to do him homage. ℟.

GOSPEL

Matthew 2:1–12

When Jesus was born in Bethlehem
of Judea, in the days of King Herod,
behold, magi from the east arrived
in Jerusalem, saying, "Where is the
newborn king of the Jews? We saw his
star at its rising and have come to do
him homage." When King Herod heard
this, he was greatly troubled, and all
Jerusalem with him. Assembling all
the chief priests and the scribes of the
people, he inquired of them where
the Christ was to be born. They said to
him, "In Bethlehem of Judea, for thus it
has been written through the prophet:
  And you, Bethlehem, land of Judah,
    are by no means least among the
      rulers of Judah;
  since from you shall come a ruler,
    who is to shepherd my
      people Israel."
Then Herod called the magi secretly
and ascertained from them the time

of the star's appearance. He sent
them to Bethlehem and said, "Go and
search diligently for the child. When
you have found him, bring me word,
that I too may go and do him homage."
After their audience with the king
they set out. And behold, the star that
they had seen at its rising preceded
them, until it came and stopped over
the place where the child was. They
were overjoyed at seeing the star,
and on entering the house they saw
the child with Mary his mother. They
prostrated themselves and did him
homage. Then they opened their
treasures and offered him gifts of
gold, frankincense, and myrrh. And
having been warned in a dream not
to return to Herod, they departed
for their country by another way.

*The chant for The Announcement of Easter and the Moveable Feats, found in Appendix I
of The Roman Missal, may be sung or proclaimed after the Gospel.*

879   THE BAPTISM OF THE LORD — ABC

FIRST READING

Isaiah 42:1–4, 6–7

Thus says the LORD:
  Here is my servant whom I uphold,
    my chosen one with whom I
      am pleased,
  upon whom I have put my spirit;
    he shall bring forth justice to
      the nations,
  not crying out, not shouting,
    not making his voice heard in
      the street.
  A bruised reed he shall not break,
    and a smoldering wick he shall
      not quench,

until he establishes justice
  on the earth;
  the coastlands will wait for
    his teaching.

I, the LORD, have called you for the
    victory of justice,
  I have grasped you by the hand;
I formed you, and set you
  as a covenant of the people,
  a light for the nations,
to open the eyes of the blind,
  to bring out prisoners from
    confinement,
  and from the dungeon, those who
    live in darkness.

RESPONSORIAL PSALM

Psalm 29:1–2, 3–4, 3, 9–10

℟. The Lord will bless his peo - ple with peace.

▶ Give to the LORD, you sons of God,
  give to the LORD glory and praise,
give to the LORD the glory due
  his name;
  adore the LORD in holy attire. ℟.

▶ The voice of the LORD is over
  the waters,
  the LORD, over vast waters.

The voice of the LORD is mighty;
  the voice of the LORD is majestic. ℟.

▶ The God of glory thunders,
  and in his temple all say, "Glory!"
The LORD is enthroned above
  the flood;
  the LORD is enthroned as
    king forever. ℟.

SECOND READING

Acts of the Apostles 10:34–38

Peter proceeded to speak to those gathered in the house of Cornelius, saying: "In truth, I see that God shows no partiality. Rather, in every nation whoever fears him and acts uprightly is acceptable to him. You know the word that he sent to the Israelites as he proclaimed peace through Jesus Christ, who is Lord of all, what has happened all over Judea, beginning in Galilee after the baptism that John preached, how God anointed Jesus of Nazareth with the Holy Spirit and power. He went about doing good and healing all those oppressed by the devil, for God was with him."

GOSPEL ACCLAMATION

cf. Mark 9:7

℟. Al - le - lu - ia, al - le - lu - ia, al - le - lu - ia.

    (Omit if not sung)

▶ The heavens were opened and the voice of the Father thundered:
This is my beloved Son, listen to him. ℟.

GOSPEL — A

Matthew 3:13–17

Jesus came from Galilee to John at the Jordan to be baptized by him. John tried to prevent him, saying, "I need to be baptized by you, and yet you are coming to me?" Jesus said to him in reply, "Allow it now, for thus it is fitting for us to fulfill all righteousness." Then he allowed him. After Jesus was baptized, he came up from the water and behold, the heavens were opened for him, and he saw the Spirit of God descending like a dove and coming upon him. And a voice came from the heavens, saying, "This is my beloved Son, with whom I am well pleased."

GOSPEL — B

Mark 1:7–11

This is what John the Baptist proclaimed: "One mightier than I is coming after me. I am not worthy to stoop and loosen the thongs of his sandals. I have baptized you with water; he will baptize you with the Holy Spirit."

It happened in those days that Jesus came from Nazareth of Galilee and was baptized in the Jordan by John. On coming up out of the water he saw the heavens being torn open and the Spirit, like a dove, descending upon him. And a voice came from the heavens, "You are my beloved Son; with you I am well pleased."

GOSPEL — C

Luke 3:15–16, 21–22

The people were filled with expectation, and all were asking in their hearts whether John might be the Christ. John answered them all, saying, "I am baptizing you with water, but one mightier than I is coming. I am not worthy to loosen the thongs of his sandals. He will baptize you with the Holy Spirit and fire."

After all the people had been baptized and Jesus also had been baptized and was praying, heaven was opened and the Holy Spirit descended upon him in bodily form like a dove. And a voice came from heaven, "You are my beloved Son; with you I am well pleased."

THE BAPTISM OF THE LORD   880
OPTIONAL READINGS — B

FIRST READING

Isaiah 55:1–11

Thus says the LORD:
　All you who are thirsty,
　　come to the water!
　You who have no money,
　　come, receive grain and eat;
　come, without paying and
　　　without cost,
　　drink wine and milk!

Why spend your money for what is
　　not bread,
　your wages for what fails to satisfy?
Heed me, and you shall eat well,
　you shall delight in rich fare.
Come to me heedfully,
　listen, that you may have life.

I will renew with you the
everlasting covenant,
the benefits assured to David.
As I made him a witness to
the peoples,
a leader and commander
of nations,
so shall you summon a nation you
knew not,
and nations that knew you not shall
run to you,
because of the LORD, your God,
the Holy One of Israel, who has
glorified you.

Seek the LORD while he may
be found,
call him while he is near.
Let the scoundrel forsake his way,
and the wicked man his thoughts;
let him turn to the LORD for mercy;
to our God, who is generous
in forgiving.

For my thoughts are not your thoughts,
nor are your ways my ways, says
the LORD.
As high as the heavens are above
the earth
so high are my ways above
your ways
and my thoughts above
your thoughts.

For just as from the heavens
the rain and snow come down
and do not return there
till they have watered the earth,
making it fertile and fruitful,
giving seed to the one who sows
and bread to the one who eats,
so shall my word be
that goes forth from my mouth;
my word shall not return to me void,
but shall do my will,
achieving the end for which I sent it.

RESPONSORIAL PSALM

Isaiah 12:2–3, 4bcd, 5–6

℟. You will draw wa - ter joy - ful - ly

from the springs of sal - va - tion.

▶ God indeed is my savior;
I am confident and unafraid.
My strength and my courage is
the LORD,
and he has been my savior.
With joy you will draw water
at the fountain of salvation. ℟.

▶ Give thanks to the LORD, acclaim
his name;
among the nations make known
his deeds,

proclaim how exalted is
his name. ℟.

▶ Sing praise to the LORD for his
glorious achievement;
let this be known throughout all
the earth.
Shout with exultation, O city of Zion,
for great in your midst
is the Holy One of Israel! ℟.

SECOND READING

1 John 5:1–9

Beloved: Everyone who believes that
Jesus is the Christ is begotten by God,
and everyone who loves the Father

loves also the one begotten by him.
In this way we know that we love
the children of God when we love

God and obey his commandments.
For the love of God is this, that we
keep his commandments. And his
commandments are not burdensome,
for whoever is begotten by God
conquers the world. And the victory
that conquers the world is our faith.
Who indeed is the victor over the
world but the one who believes
that Jesus is the Son of God?

This is the one who came through
water and blood, Jesus Christ, not by
water alone, but by water and blood.
The Spirit is the one who testifies, and
the Spirit is truth. So there are three
that testify, the Spirit, the water, and
the blood, and the three are of one
accord. If we accept human testimony,
the testimony of God is surely greater.
Now the testimony of God is this, that
he has testified on behalf of his Son.

GOSPEL ACCLAMATION

cf. John 1:29

℟. Al - le - lu - ia, al - le - lu - ia, al - le - lu - ia.

Music: Owen Alstott, b. 1947, © 1977, 1990, OCP. All rights reserved.   *(Omit if not sung)*

▶ John saw Jesus approaching him, and said:
Behold the Lamb of God who takes away the sin of the world. ℟.

Use Gospel Reading for Year B, #879.

THE BAPTISM OF THE LORD   881
OPTIONAL READINGS — C

FIRST READING

Isaiah 40:1–5, 9–11

Comfort, give comfort to my people,
  says your God.
Speak tenderly to Jerusalem, and
      proclaim to her
  that her service is at an end,
  her guilt is expiated;
indeed, she has received from the
    hand of the LORD
  double for all her sins.

  A voice cries out:
In the desert prepare the way
  of the LORD!
  Make straight in the wasteland a
    highway for our God!
Every valley shall be filled in,
  every mountain and hill shall be
    made low;
  the rugged land shall be made a plain,
    the rough country, a broad valley.
Then the glory of the LORD shall
  be revealed,

and all people shall see it together;
  for the mouth of the LORD
    has spoken.

Go up onto a high mountain,
  Zion, herald of glad tidings;
cry out at the top of your voice,
  Jerusalem, herald of good news!
Fear not to cry out
  and say to the cities of Judah:
  Here is your God!
Here comes with power
  the Lord GOD,
  who rules by a strong arm;
here is his reward with him,
  his recompense before him.
Like a shepherd he feeds his flock;
  in his arms he gathers the lambs,
carrying them in his bosom,
  and leading the ewes with care.

RESPONSORIAL PSALM

Psalm 104:1b–2, 3–4, 24–25, 27–28, 29–30

℟. O bless the Lord, my soul.

▶ O LORD, my God, you are
    great indeed!
  you are clothed with majesty
    and glory,
  robed in light as with a cloak.
    You have spread out the heavens
      like a tent-cloth. ℟.

▶ You have constructed your palace
    upon the waters.
  You make the clouds your chariot;
  you travel on the wings of the wind.
    You make the winds
      your messengers,
  and flaming fire your ministers. ℟.

▶ How manifold are your works,
    O LORD!
  In wisdom you have wrought
    them all—

the earth is full of your creatures;
  the sea also, great and wide,
in which are schools without number
  of living things both small
    and great. ℟.

▶ They look to you to give them food
    in due time.
  When you give it to them, they
    gather it;
when you open your hand, they are
  filled with good things. ℟.

▶ If you take away their breath, they
    perish and return to the dust.
  When you send forth your spirit,
    they are created,
and you renew the face of
  the earth. ℟.

SECOND READING

Titus 2:11–14; 3:4–7

Beloved: The grace of God has
appeared, saving all and training us
to reject godless ways and worldly
desires and to live temperately, justly,
and devoutly in this age, as we await
the blessed hope, the appearance of
the glory of our great God and savior
Jesus Christ, who gave himself for us
to deliver us from all lawlessness and
to cleanse for himself a people as
his own, eager to do what is good.
  When the kindness and
    generous love

of God our savior appeared,
not because of any righteous deeds
  we had done
  but because of his mercy,
he saved us through the bath
  of rebirth
  and renewal by the Holy Spirit,
whom he richly poured out on us
  through Jesus Christ our savior,
so that we might be justified by
  his grace
  and become heirs in hope of
    eternal life.

GOSPEL ACCLAMATION

cf. Luke 3:16

℟. Al - le - lu - ia, al - le - lu - ia, al - le - lu - ia.

(Omit if not sung)

▶ John said: One mightier than I is coming;
  he will baptize you with the Holy Spirit and with fire. ℟.

Use Gospel Reading for Year C, #879.

SEASON OF LENT

FIRST READING   *Joel 2:12–18*

Even now, says the LORD,
    return to me with your whole heart,
    with fasting, and weeping,
        and mourning;
Rend your hearts, not your garments,
    and return to the LORD, your God.
For gracious and merciful is he,
    slow to anger, rich in kindness,
    and relenting in punishment.
Perhaps he will again relent
    and leave behind him a blessing,
Offerings and libations
    for the LORD, your God.

Blow the trumpet in Zion!
    proclaim a fast,
    call an assembly;
Gather the people,
    notify the congregation;

Assemble the elders,
    gather the children
    and the infants at the breast;
Let the bridegroom quit his room
    and the bride her chamber.
Between the porch and the altar
    let the priests, the ministers of the
        LORD, weep,
And say, "Spare, O LORD, your people,
    and make not your heritage
    a reproach,
    with the nations ruling over them!
Why should they say among
    the peoples,
    'Where is their God?'"
Then the LORD was stirred
to concern for his land and
took pity on his people.

RESPONSORIAL PSALM   *Psalm 51:3–4, 5–6ab, 12–13, 14 & 17*

℟. Be mer - ci - ful, O Lord, for we have sinned.

▸ Have mercy on me, O God, in
    your goodness;
    in the greatness of your
        compassion wipe out my offense.
Thoroughly wash me from my guilt
and of my sin cleanse me. ℟.

▸ For I acknowledge my offense,
    and my sin is before me always:
"Against you only have I sinned,
    and done what is evil in
        your sight." ℟.

▸ A clean heart create for me, O God,
    and a steadfast spirit renew
    within me.
Cast me not out from your presence,
    and your Holy Spirit take not
    from me. ℟.

▸ Give me back the joy of
    your salvation,
    and a willing spirit sustain in me.
O Lord, open my lips,
    and my mouth shall proclaim
    your praise. ℟.

SECOND READING   *2 Corinthians 5:20—6:2*

Brothers and sisters: We are
ambassadors for Christ, as if God
were appealing through us. We
implore you on behalf of Christ, be

reconciled to God. For our sake he
made him to be sin who did not
know sin, so that we might become
the righteousness of God in him.

Working together, then, we appeal to you not to receive the grace of God in vain. For he says:

In an acceptable time I heard you,
and on the day of salvation
I helped you.
Behold, now is a very acceptable time; behold, now is the day of salvation.

GOSPEL ACCLAMATION

See Psalm 95:8

℟. **Praise to you, Lord Je - sus Christ, King of end - less glo - ry!**

Music: Owen Alstott, b. 1947, © 1977, 1990, OCP. All rights reserved.   *(Omit if not sung)*

▶ If today you hear his voice,
harden not your hearts. ℟.

GOSPEL

Matthew 6:1–6, 16–18

Jesus said to his disciples: "Take care not to perform righteous deeds in order that people may see them; otherwise, you will have no recompense from your heavenly Father. When you give alms, do not blow a trumpet before you, as the hypocrites do in the synagogues and in the streets to win the praise of others. Amen, I say to you, they have received their reward. But when you give alms, do not let your left hand know what your right is doing, so that your almsgiving may be secret. And your Father who sees in secret will repay you.

"When you pray, do not be like the hypocrites, who love to stand and pray in the synagogues and on street corners so that others may see them. Amen, I say to you, they have received their reward. But when you pray, go to your inner room, close the door, and pray to your Father in secret. And your Father who sees in secret will repay you.

"When you fast, do not look gloomy like the hypocrites. They neglect their appearance, so that they may appear to others to be fasting. Amen, I say to you, they have received their reward. But when you fast, anoint your head and wash your face, so that you may not appear to be fasting, except to your Father who is hidden. And your Father who sees what is hidden will repay you."

BLESSING AND DISTRIBUTION OF ASHES

After the homily, the Priest blesses ashes from the branches blessed the preceding year for Palm Sunday of the Passion of the Lord.

After sprinkling the ashes with holy water, the Priest then places the ashes on those who come forward, saying to each, "Repent, and believe in the Gospel," or "Remember that you are dust, and to dust you shall return."

Meanwhile an appropriate chant may be sung (for music see #339–342).

After the distribution of ashes the Priest washes his hands; the rite concludes with the Prayer of the Faithful. The Creed is not said.

FIRST SUNDAY OF LENT — A   883

FIRST READING   *Genesis 2:7–9; 3:1–7*

The LORD God formed man out of the clay of the ground and blew into his nostrils the breath of life, and so man became a living being.

Then the LORD God planted a garden in Eden, in the east, and placed there the man whom he had formed. Out of the ground the LORD God made various trees grow that were delightful to look at and good for food, with the tree of life in the middle of the garden and the tree of the knowledge of good and evil.

Now the serpent was the most cunning of all the animals that the LORD God had made. The serpent asked the woman, "Did God really tell you not to eat from any of the trees in the garden?" The woman answered the serpent: "We may eat of the fruit of the trees in the garden; it is only about the fruit of the tree in the middle of the garden that God said, 'You shall not eat it or even touch it, lest you die.'" But the serpent said to the woman: "You certainly will not die! No, God knows well that the moment you eat of it your eyes will be opened and you will be like gods who know what is good and what is evil." The woman saw that the tree was good for food, pleasing to the eyes, and desirable for gaining wisdom. So she took some of its fruit and ate it; and she also gave some to her husband, who was with her, and he ate it. Then the eyes of both of them were opened, and they realized that they were naked; so they sewed fig leaves together and made loincloths for themselves.

RESPONSORIAL PSALM   *Psalm 51:3–4, 5–6, 12–13, 17*

℟. Be merciful, O Lord, for we have sinned.

Music: Owen Alstott, b. 1947, © 1977, 1990, OCP. All rights reserved.

▶ Have mercy on me, O God, in
    your goodness;
  in the greatness of your
    compassion wipe out
    my offense.
  Thoroughly wash me from my guilt
    and of my sin cleanse me. ℟.

▶ For I acknowledge my offense,
    and my sin is before me always:
  "Against you only have I sinned,
    and done what is evil in
    your sight." ℟.

▶ A clean heart create for me, O God,
    and a steadfast spirit renew
    within me.
  Cast me not out from your presence,
    and your Holy Spirit take not
    from me. ℟.

▶ Give me back the joy of your
    salvation,
    and a willing spirit sustain in me.
  O Lord, open my lips,
    and my mouth shall proclaim
    your praise. ℟.

SECOND READING   *Romans 5:12–19 or 5:12, 17–19*

(Include bracketed text for Long Form)

Brothers and sisters: Through one man sin entered the world, and through sin, death, and thus death came to all men, inasmuch as all sinned—[for up to the time of the law, sin was in the world, though sin is not accounted when there is no law. But death reigned from Adam to Moses, even over those who did not sin after the pattern of the trespass of Adam, who is the type of the one who was to come.

But the gift is not like the transgression. For if by the transgression of the one, the many died, how much more did the grace of God and the gracious gift of the one man Jesus Christ overflow for the many. And the gift is not like the result of the one who sinned. For after one sin there was the judgment that brought condemnation; but the gift, after many transgressions, brought acquittal.] For if, by the transgression of the one, death came to reign through that one, how much more will those who receive the abundance of grace and of the gift of justification come to reign in life through the one Jesus Christ. In conclusion, just as through one transgression condemnation came upon all, so, through one righteous act, acquittal and life came to all. For just as through the disobedience of the one man the many were made sinners, so, through the obedience of the one, the many will be made righteous.

GOSPEL ACCLAMATION
Matthew 4:4b

℟. Praise to you, Lord Je-sus Christ, King of end-less glo-ry!

Music: Owen Alstott, b. 1947, © 1977, 1990, OCP. All rights reserved.   *(Omit if not sung)*

▸ One does not live on bread alone,
  but on every word that comes forth from the mouth of God. ℟.

GOSPEL
Matthew 4:1–11

At that time Jesus was led by the Spirit into the desert to be tempted by the devil. He fasted for forty days and forty nights, and afterwards he was hungry. The tempter approached and said to him, "If you are the Son of God, command that these stones become loaves of bread." He said in reply, "It is written:
One does not live on bread alone,
but on every word that comes
forth from the mouth of God."
Then the devil took him to the holy city, and made him stand on the parapet of the temple, and said to him, "If you are the Son of God, throw yourself down. For it is written:
He will command his angels
concerning you
and with their hands they will
support you,
lest you dash your foot against
a stone."
Jesus answered him, "Again it is written, *You shall not put the Lord, your God, to the test."* Then the devil took him up to a very high mountain, and showed him all the kingdoms of the world in their magnificence, and he said to him, "All these I shall give to you, if you will prostrate yourself and worship me." At this, Jesus said to him, "Get away, Satan! It is written:
The Lord, your God,
shall you worship
and him alone shall you serve."
Then the devil left him and, behold, angels came and ministered to him.

SENDING TO RITE OF ELECTION OR ENROLLMENT OF NAMES

At the beginning of Lent each faith community sends catechumens to the Bishop, who declares in the presence of the community the Church's approval of these candidates.

After the godparents testify to their state of formation, the catechumens are called out by God to prepare for the Easter sacraments of initiation. These elect receive the affirmation of the whole community; all the faithful encircle them with prayer and lead them to meet Christ.

FIRST SUNDAY OF LENT — B 884

FIRST READING

Genesis 9:8–15

God said to Noah and to his sons with him: "See, I am now establishing my covenant with you and your descendants after you and with every living creature that was with you: all the birds, and the various tame and wild animals that were with you and came out of the ark. I will establish my covenant with you, that never again shall all bodily creatures be destroyed by the waters of a flood; there shall not be another flood to devastate the earth." God added: "This is the sign that I am giving for all ages to come, of the covenant between me and you and every living creature with you: I set my bow in the clouds to serve as a sign of the covenant between me and the earth. When I bring clouds over the earth, and the bow appears in the clouds, I will recall the covenant I have made between me and you and all living beings, so that the waters shall never again become a flood to destroy all mortal beings."

RESPONSORIAL PSALM

Psalm 25:4–5, 6–7, 8–9

℟. Your ways, O Lord, are love and truth to those who keep your cov - e - nant.

Music: Owen Alstott, b. 1947, © 1977, 1990, OCP. All rights reserved.

▶ Your ways, O LORD, make known
   to me;
   teach me your paths.
Guide me in your truth and teach me,
   for you are God my savior. ℟.

▶ Remember that your compassion,
   O LORD,
   and your love are from of old.

In your kindness remember me,
   because of your goodness,
   O LORD. ℟.

▶ Good and upright is the LORD,
   thus he shows sinners the way.
He guides the humble to justice,
   and he teaches the humble
   his way. ℟.

SECOND READING

1 Peter 3:18–22

Beloved: Christ suffered for sins once, the righteous for the sake of the unrighteous, that he might lead you to God. Put to death in the flesh, he was brought to life in the Spirit. In it he also went to preach to the spirits in prison, who had once been disobedient while God patiently waited in the days of Noah during the building of the ark, in which a few persons, eight in all, were saved through water. This prefigured baptism, which saves you now. It is not a removal of dirt from the body but an appeal to God for a clear conscience, through the resurrection of Jesus Christ, who has gone into heaven and is at the right hand of God, with angels, authorities, and powers subject to him.

GOSPEL ACCLAMATION

Matthew 4:4b

R. Praise to you, Lord Je-sus Christ, King of end-less glo-ry!

(Omit if not sung)

▶ One does not live on bread alone,
  but on every word that comes forth from the mouth of God. R.

GOSPEL

Mark 1:12–15

The Spirit drove Jesus out into the desert, and he remained in the desert for forty days, tempted by Satan. He was among wild beasts, and the angels ministered to him.

After John had been arrested, Jesus came to Galilee proclaiming the gospel of God: "This is the time of fulfillment. The kingdom of God is at hand. Repent, and believe in the gospel."

SENDING TO RITE OF ELECTION OR ENROLLMENT OF NAMES

See #883.

---

885 FIRST SUNDAY OF LENT — C

FIRST READING

Deuteronomy 26:4–10

Moses spoke to the people, saying: "The priest shall receive the basket from you and shall set it in front of the altar of the LORD, your God. Then you shall declare before the LORD, your God, 'My father was a wandering Aramean who went down to Egypt with a small household and lived there as an alien. But there he became a nation great, strong, and numerous. When the Egyptians maltreated and oppressed us, imposing hard labor upon us, we cried to the LORD, the God of our fathers, and he heard our cry and saw our affliction, our toil, and our oppression. He brought us out of Egypt with his strong hand and outstretched arm, with terrifying power, with signs and wonders; and bringing us into this country, he gave us this land flowing with milk and honey. Therefore, I have now brought you the firstfruits of the products of the soil which you, O LORD, have given me.' And having set them before the Lord, your God, you shall bow down in his presence."

RESPONSORIAL PSALM

Psalm 91:1–2, 10–11, 12–13, 14–15

R. Be with me, Lord, when I am in trou-ble.

▶ You who dwell in the shelter of the
    Most High,
  who abide in the shadow of
    the Almighty,
  say to the LORD, "My refuge
    and fortress,
    my God in whom I trust." ℟.

▶ No evil shall befall you,
  nor shall affliction come near
    your tent,
  for to his angels he has given
    command about you,
  that they guard you in all
    your ways. ℟.

▶ Upon their hands they shall bear
    you up,
  lest you dash your foot against
    a stone.
You shall tread upon the asp and
    the viper;
  you shall trample down the lion
    and the dragon. ℟.

▶ Because he clings to me, I will
    deliver him;
  I will set him on high because he
    acknowledges my name.
He shall call upon me, and I will
    answer him;
  I will be with him in distress;
  I will deliver him and glorify him. ℟.

SECOND READING

Romans 10:8–13

Brothers and sisters: What does Scripture say? *The word is near you, in your mouth and in your heart*—that is, the word of faith that we preach—, for, if you confess with your mouth that Jesus is Lord and believe in your heart that God raised him from the dead, you will be saved. For one believes with the heart and so is justified, and one confesses with the mouth and so is saved. For the Scripture says, *No one who believes in him will be put to shame.* For there is no distinction between Jew and Greek; the same Lord is Lord of all, enriching all who call upon him. For "everyone who calls on the name of the Lord will be saved."

GOSPEL ACCLAMATION

Matthew 4:4b

℟. Praise to you, Lord Je-sus Christ, King of end-less glo-ry!

(Omit if not sung)

▶ One does not live on bread alone,
  but on every word that comes forth from the mouth of God. ℟.

GOSPEL

Luke 4:1–13

Filled with the Holy Spirit, Jesus returned from the Jordan and was led by the Spirit into the desert for forty days, to be tempted by the devil. He ate nothing during those days, and when they were over he was hungry. The devil said to him, "If you are the Son of God, command this stone to become bread." Jesus answered him, "It is written, *One does not live on bread alone.*" Then he took him up and showed him all the kingdoms of the world in a single instant. The devil said to him, "I shall give to you all this power and glory; for it has been handed over to me, and I may give it to whomever I wish. All this will be yours, if you worship me." Jesus said to him in reply, "It is written: *You shall worship the Lord, your God, and him alone shall you serve.*"

Then he led him to Jerusalem, made him stand on the parapet of the temple, and said to him, "If you are the Son of God, throw yourself down from here, for it is written:
He will command his angels
concerning you, to guard you,
and:
With their hands they will support
you,
lest you dash your foot against
a stone."
Jesus said to him in reply, "It also says, *You shall not put the Lord, your God, to the test."* When the devil had finished every temptation, he departed from him for a time.

SENDING TO RITE OF ELECTION OR ENROLLMENT OF NAMES

See #883.

---

886   SECOND SUNDAY OF LENT — A

FIRST READING

Genesis 12:1–4a

The LORD said to Abram: "Go forth from the land of your kinsfolk and from your father's house to a land that I will show you.
  "I will make of you a great nation, and I will bless you;
I will make your name great,
so that you will be a blessing.
I will bless those who bless you and curse those who curse you.
All the communities of the earth shall find blessing in you."
Abram went as the LORD directed him.

RESPONSORIAL PSALM

Psalm 33:4–5, 18–19, 20, 22

℟. Lord, let your mer - cy be on us, as we place our trust in you.

▶ Upright is the word of the LORD,
  and all his works are trustworthy.
He loves justice and right;
  of the kindness of the LORD the
    earth is full. ℟.

▶ See, the eyes of the LORD are upon
  those who fear him,
upon those who hope for
  his kindness,
to deliver them from death
  and preserve them in spite of
    famine. ℟.

▶ Our soul waits for the LORD,
  who is our help and our shield.
May your kindness, O LORD, be
  upon us
who have put our hope in you. ℟.

SECOND READING

2 Timothy 1:8b–10

Beloved: Bear your share of hardship for the gospel with the strength that comes from God.
  He saved us and called us to a holy life, not according to our works but according to his own design and the
grace bestowed on us in Christ Jesus before time began, but now made manifest through the appearance of our savior Christ Jesus, who destroyed death and brought life and immortality to light through the gospel.

GOSPEL ACCLAMATION

cf. Matthew 17:5

℞. Praise to you, Lord Je-sus Christ, King of end-less glo-ry!

(Omit if not sung)

▶ From the shining cloud the Father's voice is heard:
This is my beloved Son, hear him. ℞.

GOSPEL

Matthew 17:1–9

Jesus took Peter, James, and John his brother, and led them up a high mountain by themselves. And he was transfigured before them; his face shone like the sun and his clothes became white as light. And behold, Moses and Elijah appeared to them, conversing with him. Then Peter said to Jesus in reply, "Lord, it is good that we are here. If you wish, I will make three tents here, one for you, one for Moses, and one for Elijah." While he was still speaking, behold, a bright cloud cast a shadow over them, then from the cloud came a voice that said, "This is my beloved Son, with whom I am well pleased; listen to him." When the disciples heard this, they fell prostrate and were very much afraid. But Jesus came and touched them, saying, "Rise, and do not be afraid." And when the disciples raised their eyes, they saw no one else but Jesus alone.

As they were coming down from the mountain, Jesus charged them, "Do not tell the vision to anyone until the Son of Man has been raised from the dead."

SECOND SUNDAY OF LENT — B   887

FIRST READING

Genesis 22:1–2, 9a, 10–13, 15–18

God put Abraham to the test. He called to him, "Abraham!" "Here I am!" he replied. Then God said: "Take your son Isaac, your only one, whom you love, and go to the land of Moriah. There you shall offer him up as a holocaust on a height that I will point out to you."

When they came to the place of which God had told him, Abraham built an altar there and arranged the wood on it. Then he reached out and took the knife to slaughter his son. But the LORD's messenger called to him from heaven, "Abraham, Abraham!" "Here I am!" he answered. "Do not lay your hand on the boy," said the messenger. "Do not do the least thing to him. I know now how devoted you are to God, since you did not withhold from me your own beloved son." As Abraham looked about, he spied a ram caught by its horns in the thicket. So he went and took the ram and offered it up as a holocaust in place of his son.

Again the LORD's messenger called to Abraham from heaven and said: "I swear by myself, declares the LORD, that because you acted as you did in not withholding from me your beloved son, I will bless you abundantly and make your descendants as countless as the stars of the sky and the sands of the seashore; your descendants shall take possession of the gates of their enemies, and in your descendants all the nations of the earth shall find blessing—all this because you obeyed my command."

RESPONSORIAL PSALM

Psalm 116:10, 15, 16–17, 18–19

℞. I will walk be-fore the Lord, in the land of the liv-ing.

▶ I believed, even when I said,
"I am greatly afflicted."
Precious in the eyes of the LORD
is the death of his faithful ones. ℞.

▶ O LORD, I am your servant;
I am your servant, the son of
your handmaid;
you have loosed my bonds.

To you will I offer sacrifice of
thanksgiving,
and I will call upon the name of
the LORD. ℞.

▶ My vows to the LORD I will pay
in the presence of all his people,
in the courts of the house of
the LORD,
in your midst, O Jerusalem. ℞.

SECOND READING

Romans 8:31b–34

Brothers and sisters: If God is for us, who can be against us? He who did not spare his own Son but handed him over for us all, how will he not also give us everything else along with him? Who will bring a charge against God's chosen ones? It is God who acquits us. Who will condemn? Christ Jesus it is who died—or, rather, was raised—who also is at the right hand of God, who indeed intercedes for us.

GOSPEL ACCLAMATION

cf. Matthew 17:5

℞. Praise to you, Lord Je-sus Christ, King of end-less glo-ry!

(Omit if not sung)

▶ From the shining cloud the Father's voice is heard:
This is my beloved Son, listen to him. ℞.

GOSPEL

Mark 9:2–10

Jesus took Peter, James, and John and led them up a high mountain apart by themselves. And he was transfigured before them, and his clothes became dazzling white, such as no fuller on earth could bleach them. Then Elijah appeared to them along with Moses, and they were conversing with Jesus. Then Peter said to Jesus in reply, "Rabbi, it is good that we are here! Let us make three tents: one for you, one for Moses, and one for Elijah." He hardly knew what to say, they were so terrified. Then a cloud came, casting a shadow over them; from the cloud came a voice, "This is my beloved Son. Listen to him." Suddenly, looking around, they no longer saw anyone but Jesus alone with them.

As they were coming down from the mountain, he charged them not to relate what they had seen to anyone, except when the Son of Man had risen from the dead. So they kept the matter to themselves, questioning what rising from the dead meant.

SECOND SUNDAY OF LENT — C 888

FIRST READING *Genesis 15:5–12, 17–18*

The Lord God took Abram outside and said, "Look up at the sky and count the stars, if you can. Just so," he added, "shall your descendants be." Abram put his faith in the LORD, who credited it to him as an act of righteousness.

He then said to him, "I am the LORD who brought you from Ur of the Chaldeans to give you this land as a possession." "O Lord GOD," he asked, "how am I to know that I shall possess it?" He answered him, "Bring me a three-year-old heifer, a three-year-old she-goat, a three-year-old ram, a turtledove, and a young pigeon." Abram brought him all these, split them in two, and placed each half opposite the other; but the birds he did not cut up. Birds of prey swooped down on the carcasses, but Abram stayed with them. As the sun was about to set, a trance fell upon Abram, and a deep, terrifying darkness enveloped him.

When the sun had set and it was dark, there appeared a smoking fire pot and a flaming torch, which passed between those pieces. It was on that occasion that the LORD made a covenant with Abram, saying: "To your descendants I give this land, from the Wadi of Egypt to the Great River, the Euphrates."

RESPONSORIAL PSALM *Psalm 27:1, 7–8, 8–9, 13–14*

℟. The Lord is my light and my sal - va - tion.

Music: Owen Alstott, b. 1947, © 1977, 1990, OCP. All rights reserved.

▸ The LORD is my light and my salvation;
   whom should I fear?
 The LORD is my life's refuge;
   of whom should I be afraid? ℟.

▸ Hear, O LORD, the sound of my call;
   have pity on me, and answer me.
 Of you my heart speaks; you my
   glance seeks. ℟.

▸ Your presence, O LORD, I seek.
   Hide not your face from me;

do not in anger repel your servant.
   You are my helper: cast me
   not off. ℟.

▸ I believe that I shall see the bounty of
   the LORD
 in the land of the living.
 Wait for the LORD with courage;
   be stouthearted, and wait for
   the LORD. ℟.

SECOND READING *Philippians 3:17—4:1 or 3:20—4:1*

(Include bracketed text for Long Form and text in parentheses for Short Form)

[Join with others in being imitators of me,] brothers and sisters, [and observe those who thus conduct themselves according to the model you have in us. For many, as I have often told you and now tell you even in tears, conduct themselves as enemies of the cross of Christ. Their end is destruction. Their God is their stomach; their glory is in their "shame." Their minds are occupied with earthly things. But] our citizenship is in heaven, and from it we also await a savior, the Lord Jesus Christ. He will change our lowly body to conform with his glorified body by the power that enables him also to bring all things into subjection to himself.

Therefore, my brothers and sisters, whom I love and long for, my joy and crown, in this way stand firm in the Lord, (beloved).

GOSPEL ACCLAMATION

cf. Matthew 17:5

℟. Praise to you, Lord Je-sus Christ, King of end-less glo - ry!

(Omit if not sung)

▶ From the shining cloud the Father's voice is heard:
This is my beloved Son, hear him. ℟.

GOSPEL

Luke 9:28b–36

Jesus took Peter, John, and James and went up the mountain to pray. While he was praying his face changed in appearance and his clothing became dazzling white. And behold, two men were conversing with him, Moses and Elijah, who appeared in glory and spoke of his exodus that he was going to accomplish in Jerusalem. Peter and his companions had been overcome by sleep, but becoming fully awake, they saw his glory and the two men standing with him. As they were about to part from him, Peter said to Jesus, "Master, it is good that we are here; let us make three tents, one for you, one for Moses, and one for Elijah." But he did not know what he was saying. While he was still speaking, a cloud came and cast a shadow over them, and they became frightened when they entered the cloud. Then from the cloud came a voice that said, "This is my chosen Son; listen to him." After the voice had spoken, Jesus was found alone. They fell silent and did not at that time tell anyone what they had seen.

---

889   THIRD SUNDAY OF LENT — A

FIRST READING

Exodus 17:3–7

In those days, in their thirst for water, the people grumbled against Moses, saying, "Why did you ever make us leave Egypt? Was it just to have us die here of thirst with our children and our livestock?" So Moses cried out to the LORD, "What shall I do with this people? A little more and they will stone me!" The LORD answered Moses, "Go over there in front of the people, along with some of the elders of Israel, holding in your hand, as you go, the staff with which you struck the river. I will be standing there in front of you on the rock in Horeb. Strike the rock, and the water will flow from it for the people to drink." This Moses did, in the presence of the elders of Israel. The place was called Massah and Meribah, because the Israelites quarreled there and tested the LORD, saying, "Is the LORD in our midst or not?"

RESPONSORIAL PSALM

Psalm 95:1–2, 6–7, 8–9

℟. If to - day you hear his voice, hard - en not your hearts.

▸ Come, let us sing joyfully to the LORD;
  let us acclaim the Rock of
    our salvation.
Let us come into his presence
    with thanksgiving;
  let us joyfully sing psalms to him. ℟.

▸ Come, let us bow down in worship;
  let us kneel before the LORD who
    made us.
For he is our God,
  and we are the people he
shepherds, the flock he
  guides. ℟.

▸ Oh, that today you would hear
    his voice:
  "Harden not your hearts as
    at Meribah,
  as in the day of Massah in
    the desert,
where your fathers tempted me;
  they tested me though they had
    seen my works." ℟.

SECOND READING

Romans 5:1–2, 5–8

Brothers and sisters: Since we have been justified by faith, we have peace with God through our Lord Jesus Christ, through whom we have gained access by faith to this grace in which we stand, and we boast in hope of the glory of God.

And hope does not disappoint, because the love of God has been poured out into our hearts through the Holy Spirit who has been given to us. For Christ, while we were still helpless, died at the appointed time for the ungodly. Indeed, only with difficulty does one die for a just person, though perhaps for a good person one might even find courage to die. But God proves his love for us in that while we were still sinners Christ died for us.

GOSPEL ACCLAMATION

cf. John 4:42, 15

℟. Praise to you, Lord Je - sus Christ, King of end - less glo - ry!

(Omit if not sung)

▸ Lord, you are truly the Savior of the world;
  give me living water, that I may never thirst again. ℟.

GOSPEL

John 4:5–42 or 4:5–15, 19b–26, 39a, 40–42

(Include bracketed text for Long Form and text in parentheses for Short Form)

Jesus came to a town of Samaria called Sychar, near the plot of land that Jacob had given to his son Joseph. Jacob's well was there. Jesus, tired from his journey, sat down there at the well. It was about noon.

A woman of Samaria came to draw water. Jesus said to her, "Give me a drink." His disciples had gone into the town to buy food. The Samaritan woman said to him, "How can you, a Jew, ask me, a Samaritan woman, for a drink?"—For Jews use nothing in common with Samaritans.—Jesus answered and said to her, "If you knew the gift of God and who is saying to you, 'Give me a drink,' you would have asked him and he would have given you living water." The woman said to him, "Sir, you do not even have a bucket and the cistern is deep; where then can you get this living water? Are you greater than our father Jacob, who gave us this cistern and drank from it himself with his children and his flocks?" Jesus answered and said to her, "Everyone who drinks this water will be thirsty again; but whoever drinks the water I shall give will never thirst; the water I shall give will become in him a spring of water welling up to eternal life." The woman said to him, "Sir, give me this water, so that I may not be thirsty or have to keep coming here to draw water."

[Jesus said to her, "Go call your husband and come back." The woman answered and said to him, "I do not have a husband." Jesus answered her, "You are right in saying, 'I do not have a husband.' For you have had five husbands, and the one you have now is not your husband. What you have said is true." The woman said to him, "Sir,] I can see that you are a prophet. Our ancestors worshiped on this mountain; but you people say that the place to worship is in Jerusalem." Jesus said to her, "Believe me, woman, the hour is coming when you will worship the Father neither on this mountain nor in Jerusalem. You people worship what you do not understand; we worship what we understand, because salvation is from the Jews. But the hour is coming, and is now here, when true worshipers will worship the Father in Spirit and truth; and indeed the Father seeks such people to worship him. God is Spirit, and those who worship him must worship in Spirit and truth." The woman said to him, "I know that the Messiah is coming, the one called the Christ; when he comes, he will tell us everything." Jesus said to her, "I am he, the one (who is) speaking with you."

[At that moment his disciples returned, and were amazed that he was talking with a woman, but still no one said, "What are you looking for?" or "Why are you talking with her?" The woman left her water jar and went into the town and said to the people, "Come see a man who told me everything I have done. Could he possibly be the Christ?" They went out of the town and came to him. Meanwhile, the disciples urged him, "Rabbi, eat." But he said to them, "I have food to eat of which you do not know." So the disciples said to one another, "Could someone have brought him something to eat?" Jesus said to them, "My food is to do the will of the one who sent me and to finish his work. Do you not say, 'In four months the harvest will be here'? I tell you, look up and see the fields ripe for the harvest. The reaper is already receiving payment and gathering crops for eternal life, so that the sower and reaper can rejoice together. For here the saying is verified that 'One sows and another reaps.' I sent you to reap what you have not worked for; others have done the work, and you are sharing the fruits of their work."]

Many of the Samaritans of that town began to believe in him [because of the word of the woman who testified, "He told me everything I have done."] When the Samaritans came to him, they invited him to stay with them; and he stayed there two days. Many more began to believe in him because of his word, and they said to the woman, "We no longer believe because of your word; for we have heard for ourselves, and we know that this is truly the savior of the world."

First Scrutiny

After the homily the elect come before the community for exorcisms and prayers. Like the woman at the well, they seek Christ's merciful wisdom and long to worship the Father in spirit and in truth. For music, see #128.

Third Sunday of Lent — B 890

When celebrating the Scrutinies, the readings given for Year A, #889, may be used in place of these.

FIRST READING
Exodus 20:1–17 or 20:1–3, 7–8, 12–17

(Include bracketed text for Long Form)

In those days, God delivered all these commandments:

"I, the LORD, am your God, who brought you out of the land of Egypt, that place of slavery. You shall not have other gods besides me. [You shall not carve idols for yourselves in the shape of anything in the sky above or on the earth below or in the waters beneath the earth; you shall not bow down before them or worship them. For I, the LORD, your God, am a jealous God, inflicting punishment for their fathers' wickedness on the children of those who hate me, down to the third and fourth generation; but bestowing mercy down to the thousandth generation on the children of those who love me and keep my commandments.]

"You shall not take the name of the LORD, your God, in vain. For the LORD will not leave unpunished the one who takes his name in vain.

"Remember to keep holy the sabbath day. [Six days you may labor and do all your work, but the seventh day is the sabbath of the LORD, your God. No work may be done then either by you, or your son or daughter, or your male or female slave, or your beast, or by the alien who lives with you. In six days the LORD made the heavens and the earth, the sea and all that is in them; but on the seventh day he rested. That is why the LORD has blessed the sabbath day and made it holy.]

"Honor your father and your mother, that you may have a long life in the land which the LORD, your God, is giving you.
You shall not kill.
You shall not commit adultery.
You shall not steal.
You shall not bear false witness against your neighbor.
You shall not covet your neighbor's house.
You shall not covet your neighbor's wife, nor his male or female slave, nor his ox or ass, nor anything else that belongs to him."

RESPONSORIAL PSALM
Psalm 19:8, 9, 10, 11

℟. Lord, you have the words of ev-er-last-ing life.

Music: Owen Alstott, b. 1947, © 1977, 1990, OCP. All rights reserved.

▶ The law of the LORD is perfect, refreshing the soul;
the decree of the LORD is trustworthy, giving wisdom to the simple. ℟.

▶ The precepts of the LORD are right, rejoicing the heart;
the command of the LORD is clear, enlightening the eye. ℟.

▶ The fear of the LORD is pure, enduring forever;
the ordinances of the LORD are true, all of them just. ℟.

▶ They are more precious than gold, than a heap of purest gold;
sweeter also than syrup or honey from the comb. ℟.

SECOND READING
1 Corinthians 1:22–25

Brothers and sisters: Jews demand signs and Greeks look for wisdom, but we proclaim Christ crucified, a stumbling block to Jews and foolishness to Gentiles, but to those who are called, Jews and Greeks alike, Christ the power of God and the wisdom of God. For the foolishness of God is wiser than human wisdom, and the weakness of God is stronger than human strength.

GOSPEL ACCLAMATION
John 3:16

℟. Praise to you, Lord Je‑sus Christ, King of end‑less glo‑ry!

(Omit if not sung)

▸ God so loved the world that he gave his only Son,
so that everyone who believes in him might have eternal life. ℟.

GOSPEL
John 2:13–25

Since the Passover of the Jews was near, Jesus went up to Jerusalem. He found in the temple area those who sold oxen, sheep, and doves, as well as the money changers seated there. He made a whip out of cords and drove them all out of the temple area, with the sheep and oxen, and spilled the coins of the money changers and overturned their tables, and to those who sold doves he said, "Take these out of here, and stop making my Father's house a marketplace." His disciples recalled the words of Scripture, *Zeal for your house will consume me.* At this the Jews answered and said to him, "What sign can you show us for doing this?" Jesus answered and said to them, "Destroy this temple and in three days I will raise it up." The Jews said, "This temple has been under construction for forty-six years, and you will raise it up in three days?" But he was speaking about the temple of his body. Therefore, when he was raised from the dead, his disciples remembered that he had said this, and they came to believe the Scripture and the word Jesus had spoken.

While he was in Jerusalem for the feast of Passover, many began to believe in his name when they saw the signs he was doing. But Jesus would not trust himself to them because he knew them all, and did not need anyone to testify about human nature. He himself understood it well.

---

891   THIRD SUNDAY OF LENT — C

When celebrating the Scrutinies, the readings given for Year A, #889, may be used in place of these.

FIRST READING
Exodus 3:1–8a, 13–15

Moses was tending the flock of his father-in-law Jethro, the priest of Midian. Leading the flock across the desert, he came to Horeb, the mountain of God. There an angel of the LORD appeared to Moses in fire flaming out of a bush. As he looked on, he was surprised to see that the bush, though on fire, was not consumed. So Moses decided, "I must go over to look at this remarkable sight, and see why the bush is not burned."

When the LORD saw him coming over to look at it more closely, God called out to him from the bush, "Moses! Moses!" He answered, "Here I am." God said, "Come no nearer! Remove the sandals from your feet, for the place where you stand is holy ground. I am the God of your fathers," he continued, "the God of Abraham, the God of Isaac, the God of Jacob." Moses hid his face, for he was afraid to look at God. But the LORD said, "I have witnessed the affliction of my people in Egypt and have heard their cry of complaint against their slave drivers, so I know well what they are suffering. Therefore I have come down to rescue them from the hands of the Egyptians and lead them out of that land into a good and spacious land, a land flowing with milk and honey."

Moses said to God, "But when I go to the Israelites and say to them, 'The God of your fathers has sent me to you,' if they ask me, 'What is his name?' what am I to tell them?" God replied, "I am who am." Then he added, "This is what you shall tell the Israelites: I AM sent me to you."

God spoke further to Moses, "Thus shall you say to the Israelites: The LORD, the God of your fathers, the God of Abraham, the God of Isaac, the God of Jacob, has sent me to you.

"This is my name forever;
thus am I to be remembered
through all generations."

RESPONSORIAL PSALM

Psalm 103: 1–2, 3–4, 6–7, 8, 11

℟. The Lord is kind and mer - ci - ful.

Music: Owen Alstott, b. 1947, © 1977, 1990, OCP. All rights reserved.

▶ Bless the LORD, O my soul;
and all my being, bless his
holy name.
Bless the LORD, O my soul,
and forget not all his benefits. ℟.

▶ He pardons all your iniquities,
he heals all your ills.
He redeems your life
from destruction,
he crowns you with kindness
and compassion. ℟.

▶ The LORD secures justice
and the rights of all the oppressed.
He has made known his ways
to Moses,
and his deeds to the children
of Israel. ℟.

▶ Merciful and gracious is the LORD,
slow to anger and abounding
in kindness.
For as the heavens are high above
the earth,
so surpassing is his kindness
toward those who fear him. ℟.

SECOND READING

1 Corinthians 10:1–6, 10–12

I do not want you to be unaware, brothers and sisters, that our ancestors were all under the cloud and all passed through the sea, and all of them were baptized into Moses in the cloud and in the sea. All ate the same spiritual food, and all drank the same spiritual drink, for they drank from a spiritual rock that followed them, and the rock was the Christ. Yet God was not pleased with most of them, for they were struck down in the desert.

These things happened as examples for us, so that we might not desire evil things, as they did. Do not grumble as some of them did, and suffered death by the destroyer. These things happened to them as an example, and they have been written down as a warning to us, upon whom the end of the ages has come. Therefore, whoever thinks he is standing secure should take care not to fall.

GOSPEL ACCLAMATION

Matthew 4:17

℟. Praise to you, Lord Jesus Christ, King of endless glory!

Music: Owen Alstott, b. 1947, © 1977, 1990, OCP. All rights reserved.

(Omit if not sung)

▶ Repent, says the Lord;
the kingdom of heaven is at hand. ℟.

GOSPEL

Luke 13:1–9

Some people told Jesus about the Galileans whose blood Pilate had mingled with the blood of their sacrifices. Jesus said to them in reply, "Do you think that because these Galileans suffered in this way they were greater sinners than all other Galileans? By no means! But I tell you, if you do not repent, you will all perish as they did! Or those eighteen people who were killed when the tower at Siloam fell on them—do you think they were more guilty than everyone else who lived in Jerusalem? By no means! But I tell you, if you do not repent, you will all perish as they did!"

And he told them this parable: "There once was a person who had a fig tree planted in his orchard, and when he came in search of fruit on it but found none, he said to the gardener, 'For three years now I have come in search of fruit on this fig tree but have found none. So cut it down. Why should it exhaust the soil?' He said to him in reply, 'Sir, leave it for this year also, and I shall cultivate the ground around it and fertilize it; it may bear fruit in the future. If not you can cut it down.'"

892 FOURTH SUNDAY OF LENT — A

FIRST READING

1 Samuel 16:1b, 6–7, 10–13a

The LORD said to Samuel: "Fill your horn with oil, and be on your way. I am sending you to Jesse of Bethlehem, for I have chosen my king from among his sons."

As Jesse and his sons came to the sacrifice, Samuel looked at Eliab and thought, "Surely the LORD's anointed is here before him." But the LORD said to Samuel: "Do not judge from his appearance or from his lofty stature, because I have rejected him. Not as man sees does God see, because man sees the appearance but the LORD looks into the heart." In the same way Jesse presented seven sons before Samuel, but Samuel said to Jesse, "The LORD has not chosen any one of these." Then Samuel asked Jesse, "Are these all the sons you have?" Jesse replied, "There is still the youngest, who is tending the sheep." Samuel said to Jesse, "Send for him; we will not begin the sacrificial banquet until he arrives here." Jesse sent and had the young man brought to them. He was ruddy, a youth handsome to behold and making a splendid appearance. The LORD said, "There— anoint him, for this is the one!" Then Samuel, with the horn of oil in hand, anointed David in the presence of his brothers; and from that day on, the spirit of the LORD rushed upon David.

RESPONSORIAL PSALM
Psalm 23: 1–3a, 3b–4, 5, 6

℟. The Lord is my shep-herd; there is noth-ing I shall want.

▶ The LORD is my shepherd; I shall
    not want.
  In verdant pastures he gives
    me repose;
beside restful waters he leads me;
  he refreshes my soul. ℟.

▶ He guides me in right paths
  for his name's sake.
Even though I walk in the dark valley
  I fear no evil; for you are at my side
with your rod and your staff
  that give me courage. ℟.

▶ You spread the table before me
  in the sight of my foes;
you anoint my head with oil;
  my cup overflows. ℟.

▶ Only goodness and kindness
  follow me
all the days of my life;
and I shall dwell in the house of
  the LORD
  for years to come. ℟.

SECOND READING
Ephesians 5:8–14

Brothers and sisters: You were once darkness, but now you are light in the Lord. Live as children of light, for light produces every kind of goodness and righteousness and truth. Try to learn what is pleasing to the Lord. Take no part in the fruitless works of darkness; rather expose them, for it is shameful even to mention the things done by them in secret; but everything exposed by the light becomes visible, for everything that becomes visible is light. Therefore, it says:
  "Awake, O sleeper,
  and arise from the dead,
  and Christ will give you light."

GOSPEL ACCLAMATION
John 8:12

℟. Praise to you, Lord Je-sus Christ, King of end-less glo-ry!

(Omit if not sung)

▶ I am the light of the world, says the Lord;
  whoever follows me will have the light of life. ℟.

GOSPEL
John 9:1–41 or 9:1, 6–9, 13–17, 34–38

(Include bracketed text for Long Form)

As Jesus passed by he saw a man blind from birth. [His disciples asked him, "Rabbi, who sinned, this man or his parents, that he was born blind?" Jesus answered, "Neither he nor his parents sinned; it is so that the works of God might be made visible through him. We have to do the works of the one who sent me while it is day. Night is coming when no one can work.

While I am in the world, I am the light of the world." When he had said this,] he spat on the ground and made clay with the saliva, and smeared the clay on his eyes, and said to him, "Go wash in the Pool of Siloam"—which means Sent—. So he went and washed, and came back able to see.

His neighbors and those who had seen him earlier as a beggar said, "Isn't this the one who used to sit and beg?" Some said, "It is," but others said, "No, he just looks like him." He said, "I am." [So they said to him, "How were your eyes opened?" He replied, "The man called Jesus made clay and anointed my eyes and told me, 'Go to Siloam and wash.' So I went there and washed and was able to see." And they said to him, "Where is he?" He said, "I don't know."]

They brought the one who was once blind to the Pharisees. Now Jesus had made clay and opened his eyes on a sabbath. So then the Pharisees also asked him how he was able to see. He said to them, "He put clay on my eyes, and I washed, and now I can see." So some of the Pharisees said, "This man is not from God, because he does not keep the sabbath." But others said, "How can a sinful man do such signs?" And there was a division among them. So they said to the blind man again, "What do you have to say about him, since he opened your eyes?" He said, "He is a prophet."

[Now the Jews did not believe that he had been blind and gained his sight until they summoned the parents of the one who had gained his sight. They asked them, "Is this your son, who you say was born blind? How does he now see?" His parents answered and said, "We know that this is our son and that he was born blind. We do not know how he sees now, nor do we know who opened his eyes. Ask him, he is of age; he can speak for himself." His parents said this

because they were afraid of the Jews, for the Jews had already agreed that if anyone acknowledged him as the Christ, he would be expelled from the synagogue. For this reason his parents said, "He is of age; question him."

So a second time they called the man who had been blind and said to him, "Give God the praise! We know that this man is a sinner." He replied, "If he is a sinner, I do not know. One thing I do know is that I was blind and now I see." So they said to him, "What did he do to you? How did he open your eyes?" He answered them, "I told you already and you did not listen. Why do you want to hear it again? Do you want to become his disciples, too?" They ridiculed him and said, "You are that man's disciple; we are disciples of Moses! We know that God spoke to Moses, but we do not know where this one is from." The man answered and said to them, "This is what is so amazing, that you do not know where he is from, yet he opened my eyes. We know that God does not listen to sinners, but if one is devout and does his will, he listens to him. It is unheard of that anyone ever opened the eyes of a person born blind. If this man were not from God, he would not be able to do anything."] They answered and said to him, "You were born totally in sin, and are you trying to teach us?" Then they threw him out.

When Jesus heard that they had thrown him out, he found him and said, "Do you believe in the Son of Man?" He answered and said, "Who is he, sir, that I may believe in him?" Jesus said to him, "You have seen him, and the one speaking with you is he." He said, "I do believe, Lord," and he worshiped him. [Then Jesus said, "I came into this world for judgment, so that those who do not see might see, and those who do see might become blind."

Some of the Pharisees who were with him heard this and said to him, "Surely we are not also blind, are we?" Jesus said to them, "If you were blind, you would have no sin; but now you are saying, 'We see,' so your sin remains."]

Second Scrutiny

After the readings and the homily, the elect come forward with their godparents. With the faithful they pray to God, who led the man born blind to the kingdom of light, to be their light in darkness as well. For music, see #128.

Fourth Sunday of Lent — B   893

When celebrating the Scrutinies, the readings given for Year A, #892, may be used in place of these.

First Reading   *2 Chronicles 36:14–16, 19–23*

In those days, all the princes of Judah, the priests, and the people added infidelity to infidelity, practicing all the abominations of the nations and polluting the LORD's temple which he had consecrated in Jerusalem.

Early and often did the LORD, the God of their fathers, send his messengers to them, for he had compassion on his people and his dwelling place. But they mocked the messengers of God, despised his warnings, and scoffed at his prophets, until the anger of the LORD against his people was so inflamed that there was no remedy. Their enemies burnt the house of God, tore down the walls of Jerusalem, set all its palaces afire, and destroyed all its precious objects. Those who escaped the sword were carried captive to Babylon, where they became servants of the king of the Chaldeans and his sons until the kingdom of the Persians came to power. All this was to fulfill the word of the LORD spoken by Jeremiah: "Until the land has retrieved its lost sabbaths, during all the time it lies waste it shall have rest while seventy years are fulfilled."

In the first year of Cyrus, king of Persia, in order to fulfill the word of the LORD spoken by Jeremiah, the LORD inspired King Cyrus of Persia to issue this proclamation throughout his kingdom, both by word of mouth and in writing: "Thus says Cyrus, king of Persia: All the kingdoms of the earth the LORD, the God of heaven, has given to me, and he has also charged me to build him a house in Jerusalem, which is in Judah. Whoever, therefore, among you belongs to any part of his people, let him go up, and may his God be with him!"

Responsorial Psalm   *Psalm 137:1–2, 3, 4–5, 6*

℟. Let my tongue be si-lenced, if I ev - er for - get you!

Music: Owen Alstott, b. 1947, © 1977, 1990, OCP. All rights reserved.

▶ By the streams of Babylon
we sat and wept
when we remembered Zion.

On the aspens of that land
we hung up our harps. ℟.

℟. Let my tongue be silenced, if I ever forget you!

▶ For there our captors asked of us
　　the lyrics of our songs,
　and our despoilers urged us to
　　　be joyous:
　　"Sing for us the songs of Zion!" ℟.

▶ How could we sing a song of the LORD
　　in a foreign land?
　If I forget you, Jerusalem,
　　may my right hand be forgotten! ℟.

▶ May my tongue cleave to my palate
　　if I remember you not,
　if I place not Jerusalem
　　ahead of my joy. ℟.

SECOND READING   *Ephesians 2:4–10*

Brothers and sisters: God, who is rich in mercy, because of the great love he had for us, even when we were dead in our transgressions, brought us to life with Christ—by grace you have been saved—, raised us up with him, and seated us with him in the heavens in Christ Jesus, that in the ages to come he might show the immeasurable riches of his grace in his kindness to us in Christ Jesus. For by grace you have been saved through faith, and this is not from you; it is the gift of God; it is not from works, so no one may boast. For we are his handiwork, created in Christ Jesus for the good works that God has prepared in advance, that we should live in them.

GOSPEL ACCLAMATION   *John 3:16*

℟. Praise to you, Lord   Je-sus Christ,   King of end-less glo - ry!

(Omit if not sung)

▶ God so loved the world that he gave his only Son,
　so everyone who believes in him might have eternal life. ℟.

GOSPEL   *John 3:14–21*

Jesus said to Nicodemus: "Just as Moses lifted up the serpent in the desert, so must the Son of Man be lifted up, so that everyone who believes in him may have eternal life."

For God so loved the world that he gave his only Son, so that everyone who believes in him might not perish but might have eternal life. For God did not send his Son into the world to condemn the world, but that the world might be saved through him. Whoever believes in him will not be condemned, but whoever does not believe has already been condemned, because he has not believed in the name of the only Son of God. And this is the verdict, that the light came into the world, but people preferred darkness to light, because their works were evil. For everyone who does wicked things hates the light and does not come toward the light, so that his works might not be exposed. But whoever lives the truth comes to the light, so that his works may be clearly seen as done in God.

Fourth Sunday of Lent — C

When celebrating the Scrutinies, the readings given for Year A, #892, may be used in place of these.

First Reading

Joshua 5:9a, 10–12

The LORD said to Joshua, "Today I have removed the reproach of Egypt from you."

While the Israelites were encamped at Gilgal on the plains of Jericho, they celebrated the Passover on the evening of the fourteenth of the month. On the day after the Passover, they ate of the produce of the land in the form of unleavened cakes and parched grain. On that same day after the Passover, on which they ate of the produce of the land, the manna ceased. No longer was there manna for the Israelites, who that year ate of the yield of the land of Canaan.

Responsorial Psalm

Psalm 34:2–3, 4–5, 6–7

℟. Taste and see the good-ness of the Lord.

▶ I will bless the LORD at all times;
  his praise shall be ever in
    my mouth.
Let my soul glory in the LORD;
  the lowly will hear me and
    be glad. ℟.

▶ Glorify the LORD with me,
  let us together extol his name.
I sought the LORD, and he
    answered me

and delivered me from all
  my fears. ℟.

▶ Look to him that you may be radiant
    with joy,
and your faces may not blush
    with shame.
When the poor one called out,
  the LORD heard,
and from all his distress he
  saved him. ℟.

Second Reading

2 Corinthians 5:17–21

Brothers and sisters: Whoever is in Christ is a new creation: the old things have passed away; behold, new things have come. And all this is from God, who has reconciled us to himself through Christ and given us the ministry of reconciliation, namely, God was reconciling the world to himself in Christ, not counting their trespasses against them and entrusting to us the message of reconciliation. So we are ambassadors for Christ, as if God were appealing through us. We implore you on behalf of Christ, be reconciled to God. For our sake he made him to be sin who did not know sin, so that we might become the righteousness of God in him.

Gospel Acclamation

Luke 15:18

℟. Praise to you, Lord Je-sus Christ, King of end-less glo-ry!

(Omit if not sung)

℟. **Praise to you, Lord Jesus Christ, King of endless glory!**

▶ I will get up and go to my Father and shall say to him:
Father, I have sinned against heaven and against you. ℟.

GOSPEL   *Luke 15:1–3, 11–32*

Tax collectors and sinners were all drawing near to listen to Jesus, but the Pharisees and scribes began to complain, saying, "This man welcomes sinners and eats with them." So to them Jesus addressed this parable: "A man had two sons, and the younger son said to his father, 'Father, give me the share of your estate that should come to me.' So the father divided the property between them. After a few days, the younger son collected all his belongings and set off to a distant country where he squandered his inheritance on a life of dissipation. When he had freely spent everything, a severe famine struck that country, and he found himself in dire need. So he hired himself out to one of the local citizens who sent him to his farm to tend the swine. And he longed to eat his fill of the pods on which the swine fed, but nobody gave him any. Coming to his senses he thought, 'How many of my father's hired workers have more than enough food to eat, but here am I, dying from hunger. I shall get up and go to my father and I shall say to him, "Father, I have sinned against heaven and against you. I no longer deserve to be called your son; treat me as you would treat one of your hired workers."' So he got up and went back to his father. While he was still a long way off, his father caught sight of him, and was filled with compassion. He ran to his son, embraced him and kissed him. His son said to him, 'Father, I have sinned against heaven and against you; I no longer deserve to be called your son.' But his father ordered his servants, 'Quickly bring the finest robe and put it on him; put a ring on his finger and sandals on his feet. Take the fattened calf and slaughter it. Then let us celebrate with a feast, because this son of mine was dead, and has come to life again; he was lost, and has been found.' Then the celebration began. Now the older son had been out in the field and, on his way back, as he neared the house, he heard the sound of music and dancing. He called one of the servants and asked what this might mean. The servant said to him, 'Your brother has returned and your father has slaughtered the fattened calf because he has him back safe and sound.' He became angry, and when he refused to enter the house, his father came out and pleaded with him. He said to his father in reply, 'Look, all these years I served you and not once did I disobey your orders; yet you never gave me even a young goat to feast on with my friends. But when your son returns who swallowed up your property with prostitutes, for him you slaughter the fattened calf.' He said to him, 'My son, you are here with me always; everything I have is yours. But now we must celebrate and rejoice, because your brother was dead and has come to life again; he was lost and has been found.'"

---

895   FIFTH SUNDAY OF LENT — A

FIRST READING   *Ezekiel 37:12–14*

Thus says the Lord GOD: O my people, I will open your graves and have you rise from them, and bring you back to the land of Israel. Then you shall know

that I am the LORD, when I open your
graves and have you rise from them, O
my people! I will put my spirit in you
that you may live, and I will settle you
upon your land; thus you shall know
that I am the LORD. I have promised,
and I will do it, says the LORD.

RESPONSORIAL PSALM
Psalm 130:1–2, 3–4, 5–6, 7–8

℟. With the Lord there is mer-cy and full-ness of re-demp-tion.

▸ Out of the depths I cry to you,
O LORD;
LORD, hear my voice!
Let your ears be attentive
to my voice in supplication. ℟.

▸ If you, O LORD, mark iniquities,
LORD, who can stand?
But with you is forgiveness,
that you may be revered. ℟.

▸ I trust in the LORD;
my soul trusts in his word.
More than sentinels wait for
the dawn,
let Israel wait for the LORD. ℟.

▸ For with the LORD is kindness
and with him is plenteous
redemption;
and he will redeem Israel
from all their iniquities. ℟.

SECOND READING
Romans 8:8–11

Brothers and sisters: Those who
are in the flesh cannot please God.
But you are not in the flesh; on the
contrary, you are in the spirit, if
only the Spirit of God dwells in you.
Whoever does not have the Spirit of
Christ does not belong to him. But
if Christ is in you, although the body
is dead because of sin, the spirit is
alive because of righteousness. If the
Spirit of the One who raised Jesus
from the dead dwells in you, the One
who raised Christ from the dead will
give life to your mortal bodies also,
through his Spirit dwelling in you.

GOSPEL ACCLAMATION
John 11:25a, 26

℟. Praise to you, Lord Je-sus Christ, King of end-less glo-ry!

(Omit if not sung)

▸ I am the resurrection and the life, says the Lord;
whoever believes in me, even if he dies, will never die. ℟.

GOSPEL
John 11:1–45 or 11:3–7, 17, 20–27, 33b–45

(Include bracketed text for Long Form and text in parentheses for Short Form)

[Now a man was ill, Lazarus from
Bethany, the village of Mary and her
sister Martha. Mary was the one who
had anointed the Lord with perfumed
oil and dried his feet with her hair; it
was her brother Lazarus who was ill.
So] the sisters (of Lazarus) sent word
to Jesus saying, "Master, the one you
love is ill." When Jesus heard this he
said, "This illness is not to end in death,

but is for the glory of God, that the Son of God may be glorified through it." Now Jesus loved Martha and her sister and Lazarus. So when he heard that he was ill, he remained for two days in the place where he was. Then after this he said to his disciples, "Let us go back to Judea." [The disciples said to him, "Rabbi, the Jews were just trying to stone you, and you want to go back there?" Jesus answered, "Are there not twelve hours in a day? If one walks during the day, he does not stumble, because he sees the light of this world. But if one walks at night, he stumbles, because the light is not in him." He said this, and then told them, "Our friend Lazarus is asleep, but I am going to awaken him." So the disciples said to him, "Master, if he is asleep, he will be saved." But Jesus was talking about his death, while they thought that he meant ordinary sleep. So then Jesus said to them clearly, "Lazarus has died. And I am glad for you that I was not there, that you may believe. Let us go to him." So Thomas, called Didymus, said to his fellow disciples, "Let us also go to die with him."]

When Jesus arrived, he found that Lazarus had already been in the tomb for four days. [Now Bethany was near Jerusalem, only about two miles away. And many of the Jews had come to Martha and Mary to comfort them about their brother.] When Martha heard that Jesus was coming, she went to meet him; but Mary sat at home. Martha said to Jesus, "Lord, if you had been here, my brother would not have died. But even now I know that whatever you ask of God, God will give you." Jesus said to her, "Your brother will rise." Martha said to him, "I know he will rise, in the resurrection on the last day." Jesus told her, "I am the resurrection and the life; whoever believes in me, even if he dies, will live, and everyone who lives and believes in me will never die. Do you

believe this?" She said to him, "Yes, Lord. I have come to believe that you are the Christ, the Son of God, the one who is coming into the world."

[When she had said this, she went and called her sister Mary secretly, saying, "The teacher is here and is asking for you." As soon as she heard this, she rose quickly and went to him. For Jesus had not yet come into the village, but was still where Martha had met him. So when the Jews who were with her in the house comforting her saw Mary get up quickly and go out, they followed her, presuming that she was going to the tomb to weep there. When Mary came to where Jesus was and saw him, she fell at his feet and said to him, "Lord, if you had been here, my brother would not have died." When Jesus saw her weeping and the Jews who had come with her weeping,] he became perturbed and deeply troubled, and said, "Where have you laid him?" They said to him, "Sir, come and see." And Jesus wept. So the Jews said, "See how he loved him." But some of them said, "Could not the one who opened the eyes of the blind man have done something so that this man would not have died?"

So Jesus, perturbed again, came to the tomb. It was a cave, and a stone lay across it. Jesus said, "Take away the stone." Martha, the dead man's sister, said to him, "Lord, by now there will be a stench; he has been dead for four days." Jesus said to her, "Did I not tell you that if you believe you will see the glory of God?" So they took away the stone. And Jesus raised his eyes and said, "Father, I thank you for hearing me. I know that you always hear me; but because of the crowd here I have said this, that they may believe that you sent me." And when he had said this, he cried out in a loud voice, "Lazarus, come out!" The dead man came out, tied hand and foot with burial bands, and his face was wrapped in a cloth. So Jesus said to them, "Untie him and let him go."

Now many of the Jews who had come to Mary and seen what he had done began to believe in him.

THIRD SCRUTINY

The community prays for the elect with the Priest who says with hands outstretched, "God of the living, as your Son Jesus raised Lazarus from the dead, save us too on the last day." For music, see #128.

FIFTH SUNDAY OF LENT — B   896

When celebrating the Scrutinies, the readings given for Year A, #895, may be used in place of these.

FIRST READING   *Jeremiah 31:31–34*

The days are coming, says the LORD, when I will make a new covenant with the house of Israel and the house of Judah. It will not be like the covenant I made with their fathers the day I took them by the hand to lead them forth from the land of Egypt; for they broke my covenant, and I had to show myself their master, says the LORD. But this is the covenant that I will make with the house of Israel after those days, says the LORD. I will place my law within them and write it upon their hearts; I will be their God, and they shall be my people. No longer will they have need to teach their friends and relatives how to know the LORD. All, from least to greatest, shall know me, says the LORD, for I will forgive their evildoing and remember their sin no more.

RESPONSORIAL PSALM   *Psalm 51:3–4, 12–13, 14–15*

℟. Cre - ate [a clean heart,] a clean heart in me, O God.

Music: Owen Alstott, b. 1947, © 1977, 1990, OCP. All rights reserved.

▶ Have mercy on me, O God, in
   your goodness;
in the greatness of your
   compassion wipe out
   my offense.
Thoroughly wash me from my guilt
and of my sin cleanse me. ℟.

▶ A clean heart create for me, O God,
   and a steadfast spirit renew
   within me.

Cast me not out from your presence,
   and your Holy Spirit take not
   from me. ℟.

▶ Give me back the joy of
   your salvation,
   and a willing spirit sustain in me.
I will teach transgressors your ways,
   and sinners shall return to you. ℟.

SECOND READING   *Hebrews 5:7–9*

In the days when Christ Jesus was in the flesh, he offered prayers and supplications with loud cries and tears to the one who was able to save him from death, and he was heard because of his reverence. Son though he was, he learned obedience from what he suffered; and when he was made perfect, he became the source of eternal salvation for all who obey him.

GOSPEL ACCLAMATION

John 12:26

℟. Praise to you, Lord Je-sus Christ, King of end-less glo-ry!

Music: Owen Alstott, b. 1947, © 1977, 1990, OCP. All rights reserved.

(Omit if not sung)

▶ Whoever serves me must follow me, says the Lord; and where I am, there also will my servant be. ℟.

GOSPEL

John 12:20–33

Some Greeks who had come to worship at the Passover Feast came to Philip, who was from Bethsaida in Galilee, and asked him, "Sir, we would like to see Jesus." Philip went and told Andrew; then Andrew and Philip went and told Jesus. Jesus answered them, "The hour has come for the Son of Man to be glorified. Amen, amen, I say to you, unless a grain of wheat falls to the ground and dies, it remains just a grain of wheat; but if it dies, it produces much fruit. Whoever loves his life loses it, and whoever hates his life in this world will preserve it for eternal life. Whoever serves me must follow me, and where I am, there also will my servant be. The Father will honor whoever serves me.

"I am troubled now. Yet what should I say? 'Father, save me from this hour'? But it was for this purpose that I came to this hour. Father, glorify your name." Then a voice came from heaven, "I have glorified it and will glorify it again." The crowd there heard it and said it was thunder; but others said, "An angel has spoken to him." Jesus answered and said, "This voice did not come for my sake but for yours. Now is the time of judgment on this world; now the ruler of this world will be driven out. And when I am lifted up from the earth, I will draw everyone to myself." He said this indicating the kind of death he would die.

---

897   FIFTH SUNDAY OF LENT — C

When celebrating the Scrutinies, the readings given for Year A, #895, may be used in place of these.

FIRST READING

Isaiah 43:16–21

Thus says the LORD,
  who opens a way in the sea
  and a path in the mighty waters,
who leads out chariots
    and horsemen,
  a powerful army,
till they lie prostrate together, never
    to rise,
  snuffed out and quenched like
    a wick.

Remember not the events of the past,
  the things of long ago consider not;
see, I am doing something new!
  Now it springs forth, do you not
    perceive it?
In the desert I make a way,
  in the wasteland, rivers.
Wild beasts honor me,
  jackals and ostriches,

for I put water in the desert
  and rivers in the wasteland
  for my chosen people to drink,

the people whom I formed
  for myself,
  that they might announce
  my praise.

RESPONSORIAL PSALM

Psalm 126:1–2, 2–3, 4–5, 6

℟. The Lord has done great things for us; we are filled with joy.

▶ When the LORD brought back the
    captives of Zion,
  we were like men dreaming.
  Then our mouth was filled
    with laughter,
    and our tongue with rejoicing. ℟.

▶ Then they said among the nations,
    "The LORD has done great things
    for them."
  The LORD has done great things for us;
    we are glad indeed. ℟.

▶ Restore our fortunes, O LORD,
    like the torrents in the
    southern desert.
  Those that sow in tears
    shall reap rejoicing. ℟.

▶ Although they go forth weeping,
    carrying the seed to be sown,
  they shall come back rejoicing,
    carrying their sheaves. ℟.

SECOND READING

Philippians 3:8–14

Brothers and sisters: I consider everything as a loss because of the supreme good of knowing Christ Jesus my Lord. For his sake I have accepted the loss of all things and I consider them so much rubbish, that I may gain Christ and be found in him, not having any righteousness of my own based on the law but that which comes through faith in Christ, the righteousness from God, depending on faith to know him and the power of his resurrection and the sharing of his sufferings by being conformed to his death, if somehow I may attain the resurrection from the dead.

It is not that I have already taken hold of it or have already attained perfect maturity, but I continue my pursuit in hope that I may possess it, since I have indeed been taken possession of by Christ Jesus. Brothers and sisters, I for my part do not consider myself to have taken possession. Just one thing: forgetting what lies behind but straining forward to what lies ahead, I continue my pursuit toward the goal, the prize of God's upward calling, in Christ Jesus.

GOSPEL ACCLAMATION

Joel 2:12–13

℟. Praise to you, Lord Jesus Christ, King of endless glory!

(Omit if not sung)

▶ Even now, says the Lord,
  return to me with your whole heart;
  for I am gracious and merciful. ℟.

GOSPEL

John 8:1–11

Jesus went to the Mount of Olives. But early in the morning he arrived again in the temple area, and all the people started coming to him, and he sat down and taught them. Then the scribes and the Pharisees brought a woman who had been caught in adultery and made her stand in the middle. They said to him, "Teacher, this woman was caught in the very act of committing adultery. Now in the law, Moses commanded us to stone such women. So what do you say?" They said this to test him, so that they could have some charge to bring against him. Jesus bent down and began to write on the ground with his finger. But when they continued asking him, he straightened up and said to them, "Let the one among you who is without sin be the first to throw a stone at her." Again he bent down and wrote on the ground. And in response, they went away one by one, beginning with the elders. So he was left alone with the woman before him. Then Jesus straightened up and said to her, "Woman, where are they? Has no one condemned you?" She replied, "No one, sir." Then Jesus said, "Neither do I condemn you. Go, and from now on do not sin any more."

HOLY WEEK

898   PALM SUNDAY OF THE PASSION OF THE LORD — ABC

THE COMMEMORATION OF THE LORD'S ENTRANCE INTO JERUSALEM

On this day, the Church celebrates Christ's entrance into Jerusalem to accomplish the Paschal Mystery of his death and resurrection. The memorial of this event is included in every Mass, with the Procession or the Solemn Entrance before the principal Mass and with the Simple Entrance before the other Masses. The Solemn Entrance, but not the Procession, may be repeated before other Masses.

FIRST FORM: THE PROCESSION

At the scheduled time, the assembly gathers in a suitable place distinct from the church to which the Procession will move. The faithful carry palm or other branches. The Priest and ministers put on red vestments for Mass and go to the place where the people have assembled. Meanwhile, an appropriate chant is sung (for music, see #365, 367).

After greeting the people, the Priest sprinkles the branches with holy water in silence. Then the account of the Lord's entrance is proclaimed from one of the four gospels. This is done by a Deacon or, if there is no Deacon, by the Priest.

GOSPEL — A

Matthew 21:1–11

When Jesus and the disciples drew near Jerusalem and came to Bethphage on the Mount of Olives, Jesus sent two disciples, saying to them, "Go into the village opposite you, and immediately you will find an ass tethered, and a colt with her. Untie them and bring them here to me. And if anyone should say anything to you, reply, 'The master has need of them.' Then he will send them at once." This happened so that what had been spoken through the prophet might be fulfilled:

Say to daughter Zion,
"Behold, your king comes to you,
meek and riding on an ass,
and on a colt, the foal of a beast
of burden."

The disciples went and did as Jesus had ordered them. They brought the ass and the colt and laid their cloaks over them, and he sat upon them. The very large crowd spread their cloaks on the road, while others cut branches from the trees and strewed them on the road. The crowds preceding him and those following kept crying out and saying:

"Hosanna to the Son of David;
blessed is he who comes in the name of the Lord;
hosanna in the highest."

And when he entered Jerusalem the whole city was shaken and asked, "Who is this?" And the crowds replied, "This is Jesus the prophet, from Nazareth in Galilee."

GOSPEL — B

Mark 11:1–10

When Jesus and his disciples drew near to Jerusalem, to Bethphage and Bethany at the Mount of Olives, he sent two of his disciples and said to them, "Go into the village opposite you, and immediately on entering it, you will find a colt tethered on which no one has ever sat. Untie it and bring it here. If anyone should say to you, 'Why are you doing this?' reply, 'The Master has need of it and will send it back here at once.'" So they went off and found a colt tethered at a gate outside on the street, and they untied it. Some of the bystanders said to them, "What are you doing, untying the colt?" They answered them just as Jesus had told them to, and they permitted them to do it. So they brought the colt to Jesus and put their cloaks over it. And he sat on it. Many people spread their cloaks on the road, and others spread leafy branches that they had cut from the fields. Those preceding him as well as those following kept crying out:

"Hosanna!
Blessed is he who comes in the name of the Lord!
Blessed is the kingdom of our father David that is to come!
Hosanna in the highest!"

Or

GOSPEL — B

John 12:12–16

When the great crowd that had come to the feast heard that Jesus was coming to Jerusalem, they took palm branches and went out to meet him, and cried out:

"Hosanna!
Blessed is he who comes in the name of the Lord,
the king of Israel."

Jesus found an ass and sat upon it, as is written:

Fear no more, O daughter Zion;
see, your king comes, seated upon
an ass's colt.

His disciples did not understand this at first, but when Jesus had been glorified they remembered that these things were written about him and that they had done this for him.

GOSPEL — C
Luke 19:28–40

Jesus proceeded on his journey up to Jerusalem. As he drew near to Bethphage and Bethany at the place called the Mount of Olives, he sent two of his disciples. He said, "Go into the village opposite you, and as you enter it you will find a colt tethered on which no one has ever sat. Untie it and bring it here. And if anyone should ask you, 'Why are you untying it?' you will answer, 'The Master has need of it.'" So those who had been sent went off and found everything just as he had told them. And as they were untying the colt, its owners said to them, "Why are you untying this colt?" They answered, "The Master has need of it." So they brought it to Jesus, threw their cloaks over the colt, and helped Jesus to mount. As he rode along, the people were spreading their cloaks on the road; and now as he was approaching the slope of the Mount of Olives, the whole multitude of his disciples began to praise God aloud with joy for all the mighty deeds they had seen. They proclaimed:

"Blessed is the king who comes
in the name of the Lord.
Peace in heaven
and glory in the highest."

Some of the Pharisees in the crowd said to him, "Teacher, rebuke your disciples." He said in reply, "I tell you, if they keep silent, the stones will cry out!"

After the Gospel, a brief homily may be given. The Procession to the church where the Mass will be celebrated then begins. During the Procession, the people sing a hymn to Christ the King or another appropriate hymn or song (for music, see #366).

When the Priest arrives at the altar, he venerates it. Then he goes to his chair and, omitting the other Introductory Rites and, if appropriate, the Kyrie, eleison (Lord, have mercy), continues with the Collect of the Mass, followed by the Liturgy of the Word.

SECOND FORM: THE SOLEMN ENTRANCE

If the Procession cannot be held outside the church, the commemoration of the Lord's entrance may be celebrated before the principal Mass with the Solemn Entrance, which takes place within the church.

The faithful, holding the branches, assemble either in front of the church door or inside the church. The Priest and ministers, with a representative group of the faithful, go to a suitable place in the church outside the sanctuary so that most of the people will be able to see the rite.

While the Priest goes to the appointed place, the rite proceeds according to the First Form. After the Priest goes to his place in the sanctuary following the Procession, he immediately says the Collect of the Mass, omitting the Introductory Rites and, if appropriate, the Kyrie, eleison (Lord, have mercy). Mass then continues in the usual way.

THIRD FORM: THE SIMPLE ENTRANCE

At all other Masses, when the Solemn Entrance is not held, the commemoration of the Lord's entrance takes place by means of a Simple Entrance. While the Priest goes to the altar, the Entrance Antiphon, or a suitable hymn, may be sung (for music, see #366). After the Priest venerates the altar, he goes to his chair and greets the people. At Masses where singing cannot take place, after the Priest greets the people, the Entrance Antiphon may be read. Mass continues in the usual way with the Introductory Rites.

The Liturgy of the Word

First Reading
Isaiah 50:4–7

The Lord GOD has given me
  a well-trained tongue,
that I might know how to speak to
    the weary
  a word that will rouse them.
Morning after morning
  he opens my ear that I may hear;
and I have not rebelled,
  have not turned back.
I gave my back to those who beat me,

my cheeks to those who plucked
  my beard;
my face I did not shield
  from buffets and spitting.

The Lord GOD is my help,
  therefore I am not disgraced;
I have set my face like flint,
  knowing that I shall not be put
    to shame.

Responsorial Psalm
Psalm 22:8–9, 17–18, 19–20, 23–24

℟. My God, my God, why have you a-ban-doned me?

Music: Owen Alstott, b. 1947, © 1977, 1990, OCP. All rights reserved.

▶ All who see me scoff at me;
  they mock me with parted lips,
  they wag their heads:
"He relied on the LORD; let him
  deliver him,
  let him rescue him, if he
  loves him." ℟.

▶ Indeed, many dogs surround me,
  a pack of evildoers closes in
  upon me;
they have pierced my hands and
  my feet;
  I can count all my bones. ℟.

▶ They divide my garments
  among them,
  and for my vesture they cast lots.
But you, O LORD, be not far from me;
  O my help, hasten to aid me. ℟.

▶ I will proclaim your name to
  my brethren;
  in the midst of the assembly I will
  praise you:
"You who fear the LORD, praise him;
  all you descendants of Jacob, give
  glory to him;
  revere him, all you descendants
  of Israel!" ℟.

Second Reading
Philippians 2:6–11

Christ Jesus, though he was in the
  form of God,
  did not regard equality with God
  something to be grasped.
Rather, he emptied himself,
  taking the form of a slave,
  coming in human likeness;
  and found human in appearance,
  he humbled himself,
  becoming obedient to the point
    of death,
  even death on a cross.

Because of this, God greatly
  exalted him
  and bestowed on him the name
  which is above every name,
  that at the name of Jesus
  every knee should bend,
  of those in heaven and on earth
    and under the earth,
  and every tongue confess that
  Jesus Christ is Lord,
  to the glory of God the Father.

GOSPEL ACCLAMATION

Philippians 2:8–9

℟. Praise to you, Lord Je-sus Christ, King of end-less glo-ry!

(Omit if not sung)

▶ Christ became obedient to the point of death,
even death on a cross.
Because of this, God greatly exalted him
and bestowed on him the name which is above every name. ℟.

THE PASSION OF THE LORD — A

Matthew 26:14—27:66 or 27:11–54

The Passion according to St. Matthew is proclaimed by the Deacon, or if there is no Deacon, by the Priest. It may also be read by lay readers, with the part of Christ reserved to the Priest, if possible. Speakers in the Passion Narrative are represented by these abbreviations:

N. – Narrator	V. – Voice
† – Christ	**C. – Crowd**

(Include bracketed text for Long Form and text in parentheses for Short Form)

N. The Passion of our Lord Jesus Christ according to Matthew

[One of the Twelve, who was called Judas Iscariot, went to the chief priests and said,

V. "What are you willing to give me if I hand him over to you?"

N. They paid him thirty pieces of silver, and from that time on he looked for an opportunity to hand him over.

On the first day of the Feast of Unleavened Bread, the disciples approached Jesus and said,

V. "Where do you want us to prepare for you to eat the Passover?"

N. He said,

† "Go into the city to a certain man and tell him, 'The teacher says, "My appointed time draws near; in your house I shall celebrate the Passover with my disciples."'"

N. The disciples then did as Jesus had ordered, and prepared the Passover.

When it was evening, he reclined at table with the Twelve. And while they were eating, he said,

† "Amen, I say to you, one of you will betray me."

N. Deeply distressed at this, they began to say to him one after another,

V. "Surely it is not I, Lord?"

N. He said in reply,

† "He who has dipped his hand into the dish with me is the one who will betray me. The Son of Man indeed goes, as it is written of him, but woe to that man by whom the Son of Man is betrayed. It would be better for that man if he had never been born."

N. Then Judas, his betrayer, said in reply,

V. "Surely it is not I, Rabbi?"

N. He answered,

† "You have said so."

N. While they were eating, Jesus took bread, said the blessing, broke it, and giving it to his disciples said,

† "Take and eat; this is my body."

N. Then he took a cup, gave thanks, and gave it to them, saying,

† "Drink from it, all of you, for this is my blood of the covenant, which will be shed on behalf of many for the forgiveness of sins. I tell you, from now on I shall not drink this fruit of the vine until the day

when I drink it with you new in the kingdom of my Father."

N. Then, after singing a hymn, they went out to the Mount of Olives.

Then Jesus said to them,

† "This night all of you will have your faith in me shaken, for it is written:
*I will strike the shepherd,
   and the sheep of the flock will
      be dispersed;*
but after I have been raised up, I shall go before you to Galilee."

N. Peter said to him in reply,

V. "Though all may have their faith in you shaken, mine will never be."

N. Jesus said to him,

† "Amen, I say to you, this very night before the cock crows, you will deny me three times."

N. Peter said to him,

V. "Even though I should have to die with you, I will not deny you."

N. And all the disciples spoke likewise.

Then Jesus came with them to a place called Gethsemane, and he said to his disciples,

† "Sit here while I go over there and pray."

N. He took along Peter and the two sons of Zebedee, and began to feel sorrow and distress. Then he said to them,

† "My soul is sorrowful even to death. Remain here and keep watch with me."

N. He advanced a little and fell prostrate in prayer, saying,

† "My Father, if it is possible, let this cup pass from me; yet, not as I will, but as you will."

N. When he returned to his disciples he found them asleep. He said to Peter,

† "So you could not keep watch with me for one hour? Watch and pray that you may not undergo the test. The spirit is willing, but the flesh is weak."

N. Withdrawing a second time, he prayed again,

† "My Father, if it is not possible that this cup pass without my drinking it, your will be done!"

N. Then he returned once more and found them asleep, for they could not keep their eyes open. He left them and withdrew again and prayed a third time, saying the same thing again. Then he returned to his disciples and said to them,

† "Are you still sleeping and taking your rest? Behold, the hour is at hand when the Son of Man is to be handed over to sinners. Get up, let us go. Look, my betrayer is at hand."

N. While he was still speaking, Judas, one of the Twelve, arrived, accompanied by a large crowd, with swords and clubs, who had come from the chief priests and the elders of the people. His betrayer had arranged a sign with them, saying,

V. "The man I shall kiss is the one; arrest him."

N. Immediately he went over to Jesus and said,

V. "Hail, Rabbi!"

N. and he kissed him. Jesus answered him,

† "Friend, do what you have come for."

N. Then stepping forward they laid hands on Jesus and arrested him. And behold, one of those who accompanied Jesus put his hand to his sword, drew it, and struck the high priest's servant, cutting off his ear. Then Jesus said to him,

† "Put your sword back into its sheath, for all who take the sword will perish by the sword. Do you think that I cannot call upon my Father and he will not provide me at this moment with more than twelve legions of angels? But then how would the Scriptures be fulfilled which say that it must come to pass in this way?"

N. At that hour Jesus said to the crowds,

† "Have you come out as against a robber, with swords and clubs to seize me? Day after day I sat

teaching in the temple area, yet you did not arrest me. But all this has come to pass that the writings of the prophets may be fulfilled."

N. Then all the disciples left him and fled.

Those who had arrested Jesus led him away to Caiaphas the high priest, where the scribes and the elders were assembled. Peter was following him at a distance as far as the high priest's courtyard, and going inside he sat down with the servants to see the outcome. The chief priests and the entire Sanhedrin kept trying to obtain false testimony against Jesus in order to put him to death, but they found none, though many false witnesses came forward. Finally two came forward who stated,

C. **"This man said, 'I can destroy the temple of God and within three days rebuild it.'"**

N. The high priest rose and addressed him,

V. "Have you no answer? What are these men testifying against you?"

N. But Jesus was silent. Then the high priest said to him,

V. "I order you to tell us under oath before the living God whether you are the Christ, the Son of God."

N. Jesus said to him in reply,

† "You have said so. But I tell you: From now on you will see
'the Son of Man
seated at the right hand of the Power'
and 'coming on the clouds of heaven.'"

N. Then the high priest tore his robes and said,

V. "He has blasphemed! What further need have we of witnesses? You have now heard the blasphemy; what is your opinion?"

N. They said in reply,

C. **"He deserves to die!"**

N. Then they spat in his face and struck him, while some slapped him, saying,

C. **"Prophesy for us, Christ: who is it that struck you?"**

N. Now Peter was sitting outside in the courtyard. One of the maids came over to him and said,

C. **"You too were with Jesus the Galilean."**

N. But he denied it in front of everyone, saying,

V. "I do not know what you are talking about!"

N. As he went out to the gate, another girl saw him and said to those who were there,

C. **"This man was with Jesus the Nazorean."**

N. Again he denied it with an oath,

V. "I do not know the man!"

N. A little later the bystanders came over and said to Peter,

C. **"Surely you too are one of them; even your speech gives you away."**

N. At that he began to curse and to swear,

V. "I do not know the man."

N. And immediately a cock crowed. Then Peter remembered the word that Jesus had spoken: "Before the cock crows you will deny me three times." He went out and began to weep bitterly.

When it was morning, all the chief priests and the elders of the people took counsel against Jesus to put him to death. They bound him, led him away, and handed him over to Pilate, the governor.

Then Judas, his betrayer, seeing that Jesus had been condemned, deeply regretted what he had done. He returned the thirty pieces of silver to the chief priests and elders, saying,

V. "I have sinned in betraying innocent blood."

N. They said,

C. "What is that to us? Look to it yourself."

N. Flinging the money into the temple, he departed and went off and hanged himself. The chief priests gathered up the money, but said,

C. "It is not lawful to deposit this in the temple treasury, for it is the price of blood."

N. After consultation, they used it to buy the potter's field as a burial place for foreigners. That is why that field even today is called the Field of Blood. Then was fulfilled what had been said through Jeremiah the prophet, *And they took the thirty pieces of silver, the value of a man with a price on his head, a price set by some of the Israelites, and they paid it out for the potter's field just as the Lord had commanded me.*

Now] Jesus stood before the governor, (Pontius Pilate,) and he questioned him,

V. "Are you the king of the Jews?"

N. Jesus said,

† "You say so."

N. And when he was accused by the chief priests and elders, he made no answer. Then Pilate said to him,

V. "Do you not hear how many things they are testifying against you?"

N. But he did not answer him one word, so that the governor was greatly amazed.

Now on the occasion of the feast the governor was accustomed to release to the crowd one prisoner whom they wished. And at that time they had a notorious prisoner called Barabbas. So when they had assembled, Pilate said to them,

V. "Which one do you want me to release to you, Barabbas, or Jesus called Christ?"

N. For he knew that it was out of envy that they had handed him over. While he was still seated on the bench, his wife sent him a message, "Have nothing to do with that righteous man. I suffered much in a dream today because of him." The chief priests and the elders persuaded the crowds to ask for Barabbas but to destroy Jesus. The governor said to them in reply,

V. "Which of the two do you want me to release to you?"

N. They answered,

C. "Barabbas!"

N. Pilate said to them,

V. "Then what shall I do with Jesus called Christ?"

N. They all said,

C. "Let him be crucified!"

N. But he said,

V. "Why? What evil has he done?"

N. They only shouted the louder,

C. "Let him be crucified!"

N. When Pilate saw that he was not succeeding at all, but that a riot was breaking out instead, he took water and washed his hands in the sight of the crowd, saying,

V. "I am innocent of this man's blood. Look to it yourselves."

N. And the whole people said in reply,

C. "His blood be upon us and upon our children."

N. Then he released Barabbas to them, but after he had Jesus scourged, he handed him over to be crucified.

Then the soldiers of the governor took Jesus inside the praetorium and gathered the whole cohort around him. They stripped off his clothes and threw a scarlet military cloak about him. Weaving a crown out of thorns, they placed it on his head, and a reed in his right hand. And kneeling before him, they mocked him, saying,

C. "Hail, King of the Jews!"

N. They spat upon him and took the reed and kept striking him on the head. And when they had mocked him, they stripped him of the cloak, dressed him in his own clothes, and led him off to crucify him.

As they were going out, they met a Cyrenian named Simon; this man they pressed into service to carry his cross.

And when they came to a place called Golgotha—which means Place of the Skull—, they gave Jesus wine to drink mixed with gall. But when he had tasted it, he refused to drink. After they had crucified him, they divided his garments by casting lots; then they sat down and kept watch over him there. And they placed over his head the written charge against him: This is Jesus, the King of the Jews. Two revolutionaries were crucified with him, one on his right and the other on his left. Those passing by reviled him, shaking their heads and saying,

C. **"You who would destroy the temple and rebuild it in three days, save yourself, if you are the Son of God, and come down from the cross!"**

N. Likewise the chief priests with the scribes and elders mocked him and said,

C. **"He saved others; he cannot save himself. So he is the king of Israel! Let him come down from the cross now, and we will believe in him. He trusted in God; let him deliver him now if he wants him. For he said, 'I am the Son of God.'"**

N. The revolutionaries who were crucified with him also kept abusing him in the same way.

From noon onward, darkness came over the whole land until three in the afternoon. And about three o'clock Jesus cried out in a loud voice,

✝ *"Eli, Eli, lema sabachthani?"*

N. which means,

✝ *"My God, my God, why have you forsaken me?"*

N. Some of the bystanders who heard it said,

C. **"This one is calling for Elijah."**

N. Immediately one of them ran to get a sponge; he soaked it in wine, and putting it on a reed, gave it to him to drink. But the rest said,

C. **"Wait, let us see if Elijah comes to save him."**

N. But Jesus cried out again in a loud voice, and gave up his spirit.

Here all kneel and pause for a short time.

N. And behold, the veil of the sanctuary was torn in two from top to bottom. The earth quaked, rocks were split, tombs were opened, and the bodies of many saints who had fallen asleep were raised. And coming forth from their tombs after his resurrection, they entered the holy city and appeared to many. The centurion and the men with him who were keeping watch over Jesus feared greatly when they saw the earthquake and all that was happening, and they said,

C. **"Truly, this was the Son of God!"**

N. [There were many women there, looking on from a distance, who had followed Jesus from Galilee, ministering to him. Among them were Mary Magdalene and Mary the mother of James and Joseph, and the mother of the sons of Zebedee.

When it was evening, there came a rich man from Arimathea named Joseph, who was himself a disciple of Jesus. He went to Pilate and asked for the body of Jesus; then Pilate ordered it to be handed over. Taking the body, Joseph wrapped it in clean linen and laid it in his new tomb that he had hewn in the rock. Then he rolled a huge stone across the entrance to the tomb and departed. But Mary Magdalene and the other Mary remained sitting there, facing the tomb.

The next day, the one following the day of preparation, the chief priests and the Pharisees gathered before Pilate and said,

C. "Sir, we remember that this impostor while still alive said, 'After three days I will be raised up.' Give orders, then, that the grave be secured until the third day, lest his disciples come and steal him and say to the people, 'He has been raised from the dead.' This last imposture would be worse than the first."

N. Pilate said to them,

V. "The guard is yours; go, secure it as best you can."

N. So they went and secured the tomb by fixing a seal to the stone and setting the guard.]

THE PASSION OF THE LORD — B

Mark 14:1—15:47 or 15:1–39

The Passion according to St. Mark is proclaimed by the Deacon, or if there is no Deacon, by the Priest. It may also be read by lay readers, with the part of Christ reserved to the Priest, if possible. Speakers in the Passion Narrative are represented by these abbreviations:

N. – Narrator
† – Christ

V. – Voice
C. – Crowd

(Include bracketed text for Long Form)

N. The Passion of our Lord Jesus Christ according to Mark

[The Passover and the Feast of Unleavened Bread were to take place in two days' time. So the chief priests and the scribes were seeking a way to arrest him by treachery and put him to death. They said,

C. "Not during the festival, for fear that there may be a riot among the people."

N. When he was in Bethany reclining at table in the house of Simon the leper, a woman came with an alabaster jar of perfumed oil, costly genuine spikenard. She broke the alabaster jar and poured it on his head. There were some who were indignant.

C. "Why has there been this waste of perfumed oil? It could have been sold for more than three hundred days' wages and the money given to the poor."

N. They were infuriated with her. Jesus said,

† "Let her alone. Why do you make trouble for her? She has done a good thing for me. The poor you will always have with you, and whenever you wish you can do good to them, but you will not always have me. She has done what she could. She has anticipated anointing my body for burial. Amen, I say to you, wherever the gospel is proclaimed to the whole world, what she has done will be told in memory of her."

N. Then Judas Iscariot, one of the Twelve, went off to the chief priests to hand him over to them. When they heard him they were pleased and promised to pay him money. Then he looked for an opportunity to hand him over.

On the first day of the Feast of Unleavened Bread, when they sacrificed the Passover lamb, his disciples said to him,

V. "Where do you want us to go and prepare for you to eat the Passover?"

N. He sent two of his disciples and said to them,

† "Go into the city and a man will meet you, carrying a jar of water. Follow him. Wherever he enters, say to the master of the house, 'The Teacher says, "Where is my guest room where I may eat the Passover with my disciples?"' Then he will show you a large upper room

N. furnished and ready. Make the preparations for us there."

N. The disciples then went off, entered the city, and found it just as he had told them; and they prepared the Passover.

When it was evening, he came with the Twelve. And as they reclined at table and were eating, Jesus said,

† "Amen, I say to you,
one of you will betray me,
one who is eating with me."

N. They began to be distressed and to say to him, one by one,

V. "Surely it is not I?"

N. He said to them,

† "One of the Twelve, the one who dips with me into the dish. For the Son of Man indeed goes, as it is written of him, but woe to that man by whom the Son of Man is betrayed. It would be better for that man if he had never been born."

N. While they were eating, he took bread, said the blessing, broke it, and gave it to them, and said,

† "Take it; this is my body."

N. Then he took a cup, gave thanks, and gave it to them, and they all drank from it. He said to them,

† "This is my blood of the covenant, which will be shed for many. Amen, I say to you, I shall not drink again the fruit of the vine until the day when I drink it new in the kingdom of God."

N. Then, after singing a hymn, they went out to the Mount of Olives.

Then Jesus said to them,

† "All of you will have your faith shaken, for it is written:
'I will strike the shepherd,
and the sheep will
be dispersed.'
But after I have been raised up,
I shall go before you to Galilee."

N. Peter said to him,

V. "Even though all should have their faith shaken, mine will not be."

N. Then Jesus said to him,

† "Amen, I say to you, this very night before the cock crows twice you will deny me three times."

N. But he vehemently replied,

V. "Even though I should have to die with you, I will not deny you."

N. And they all spoke similarly.

Then they came to a place named Gethsemane, and he said to his disciples,

† "Sit here while I pray."

N. He took with him Peter, James, and John, and began to be troubled and distressed. Then he said to them,

† "My soul is sorrowful even to death. Remain here and keep watch."

N. He advanced a little and fell to the ground and prayed that if it were possible the hour might pass by him; he said,

† "Abba, Father, all things are possible to you. Take this cup away from me, but not what I will but what you will."

N. When he returned he found them asleep. He said to Peter,

† "Simon, are you asleep? Could you not keep watch for one hour? Watch and pray that you may not undergo the test. The spirit is willing but the flesh is weak."

N. Withdrawing again, he prayed, saying the same thing. Then he returned once more and found them asleep, for they could not keep their eyes open and did not know what to answer him. He returned a third time and said to them,

† "Are you still sleeping and taking your rest? It is enough. The hour has come. Behold, the Son of Man is to be handed over to sinners. Get up, let us go. See, my betrayer is at hand."

N. Then, while he was still speaking, Judas, one of the Twelve, arrived, accompanied by a crowd with swords and clubs who had come from the chief priests, the scribes, and the elders. His betrayer had arranged a signal with them, saying,

V. "The man I shall kiss is the one; arrest him and lead him away securely."

N. He came and immediately went over to him and said,

V. "Rabbi."

N. And he kissed him. At this they laid hands on him and arrested him. One of the bystanders drew his sword, struck the high priest's servant, and cut off his ear. Jesus said to them in reply,

† "Have you come out as against a robber, with swords and clubs, to seize me? Day after day I was with you teaching in the temple area, yet you did not arrest me; but that the Scriptures may be fulfilled."

N. And they all left him and fled. Now a young man followed him wearing nothing but a linen cloth about his body. They seized him, but he left the cloth behind and ran off naked.

They led Jesus away to the high priest, and all the chief priests and the elders and the scribes came together. Peter followed him at a distance into the high priest's courtyard and was seated with the guards, warming himself at the fire. The chief priests and the entire Sanhedrin kept trying to obtain testimony against Jesus in order to put him to death, but they found none. Many gave false witness against him, but their testimony did not agree. Some took the stand and testified falsely against him, alleging,

C. "We heard him say, 'I will destroy this temple made with hands and within three days I will build another not made with hands.'"

N. Even so their testimony did not agree. The high priest rose before the assembly and questioned Jesus, saying,

V. "Have you no answer? What are these men testifying against you?"

N. But he was silent and answered nothing. Again the high priest asked him and said to him,

V. "Are you the Christ, the son of the Blessed One?"

N. Then Jesus answered,

† "I am;
   and 'you will see the Son of Man
      seated at the right hand
         of the Power
      and coming with the clouds
         of heaven.'"

N. At that the high priest tore his garments and said,

V. "What further need have we of witnesses? You have heard the blasphemy. What do you think?"

N. They all condemned him as deserving to die. Some began to spit on him. They blindfolded him and struck him and said to him,

C. "Prophesy!"

N. And the guards greeted him with blows.

While Peter was below in the courtyard, one of the high priest's maids came along. Seeing Peter warming himself, she looked intently at him and said,

C. "You too were with the Nazarene, Jesus."

N. But he denied it saying,

V. "I neither know nor understand what you are talking about."

N. So he went out into the outer court. Then the cock crowed. The maid saw him and began again to say to the bystanders,

C. "This man is one of them."

N. Once again he denied it. A little later the bystanders said to Peter once more,

C. "Surely you are one of them; for you too are a Galilean."

N. He began to curse and to swear,

V. "I do not know this man about whom you are talking."

N. And immediately a cock crowed a second time. Then Peter remembered the word that Jesus had said to him, "Before the cock crows twice you will deny me three times." He broke down and wept.]

As soon as morning came, the chief priests with the elders and the scribes, that is, the whole Sanhedrin, held a council. They bound Jesus, led him away, and handed him over to Pilate. Pilate questioned him,

V. "Are you the king of the Jews?"

N. He said to him in reply,

† "You say so."

N. The chief priests accused him of many things. Again Pilate questioned him,

V. "Have you no answer? See how many things they accuse you of."

N. Jesus gave him no further answer, so that Pilate was amazed.

Now on the occasion of the feast he used to release to them one prisoner whom they requested. A man called Barabbas was then in prison along with the rebels who had committed murder in a rebellion. The crowd came forward and began to ask him to do for them as he was accustomed. Pilate answered,

V. "Do you want me to release to you the king of the Jews?"

N. For he knew that it was out of envy that the chief priests had handed him over. But the chief priests stirred up the crowd to have him release Barabbas for them instead. Pilate again said to them in reply,

V. "Then what do you want me to do with the man you call the king of the Jews?"

N. They shouted again,

C. **"Crucify him."**

N. Pilate said to them,

V. "Why? What evil has he done?"

N. They only shouted the louder,

C. **"Crucify him."**

N. So Pilate, wishing to satisfy the crowd, released Barabbas to them and, after he had Jesus scourged, handed him over to be crucified.

The soldiers led him away inside the palace, that is, the praetorium, and assembled the whole cohort. They clothed him in purple and, weaving a crown of thorns, placed it on him. They began to salute him with,

C. **"Hail, King of the Jews!"**

N. and kept striking his head with a reed and spitting upon him. They knelt before him in homage. And when they had mocked him, they stripped him of the purple cloak, dressed him in his own clothes, and led him out to crucify him.

They pressed into service a passer-by, Simon, a Cyrenian, who was coming in from the country, the father of Alexander and Rufus, to carry his cross.

They brought him to the place of Golgotha—which is translated Place of the Skull—. They gave him wine drugged with myrrh, but he did not take it. Then they crucified him and divided his garments by casting lots for them to see what each should take. It was nine o'clock in the morning when they crucified him. The inscription of the charge against him read, "The King of the Jews." With him they crucified two revolutionaries, one on his right and one on his left. Those passing by reviled him, shaking their heads and saying,

C. **"Aha! You who would destroy the temple and rebuild it in three days, save yourself by coming down from the cross."**

N. Likewise the chief priests, with the scribes, mocked him among themselves and said,

C. **"He saved others; he cannot save himself. Let the Christ, the King of Israel, come down now from the cross that we may see and believe."**

N. Those who were crucified with him also kept abusing him.

At noon darkness came over the whole land until three in the afternoon. And at three o'clock Jesus cried out in a loud voice,

† *"Eloi, Eloi, lema sabachthani?"*

N. which is translated,

† "My God, my God, why have you forsaken me?"

N. Some of the bystanders who heard it said,

C. **"Look, he is calling Elijah."**

N. One of them ran, soaked a sponge with wine, put it on a reed and gave it to him to drink, saying,

V. "Wait, let us see if Elijah comes to take him down."

N. Jesus gave a loud cry and breathed his last.

Here all kneel and pause for a short time.

N. The veil of the sanctuary was torn in two from top to bottom. When the centurion who stood facing him saw how he breathed his last he said,

V. "Truly this man was the Son of God!"

N. [There were also women looking on from a distance. Among them were Mary Magdalene, Mary the mother of the younger James and of Joses, and Salome. These women had followed him when he was in Galilee and ministered to him. There were also many other women who had come up with him to Jerusalem.

When it was already evening, since it was the day of preparation, the day before the sabbath, Joseph of Arimathea, a distinguished member of the council, who was himself awaiting the kingdom of God, came and courageously went to Pilate and asked for the body of Jesus. Pilate was amazed that he was already dead. He summoned the centurion and asked him if Jesus had already died. And when he learned of it from the centurion, he gave the body to Joseph. Having bought a linen cloth, he took him down, wrapped him in the linen cloth, and laid him in a tomb that had been hewn out of the rock. Then he rolled a stone against the entrance to the tomb. Mary Magdalene and Mary the mother of Joses watched where he was laid.]

THE PASSION OF THE LORD — C

Luke 22:14—23:56 or 23:1-49

The Passion according to St. Luke is proclaimed by the Deacon, or if there is no Deacon, by the Priest. It may also be read by lay readers, with the part of Christ reserved to the Priest, if possible. Speakers in the Passion Narrative are represented by these abbreviations:

N. – Narrator   V. – Voice

† – Christ   **C. – Crowd**

(Include bracketed text for Long Form)

N. The Passion of our Lord Jesus Christ according to Luke

[When the hour came, Jesus took his place at table with the apostles. He said to them,

† "I have eagerly desired to eat this Passover with you before I suffer, for, I tell you, I shall not eat it again until there is fulfillment in the kingdom of God."

N. Then he took a cup, gave thanks, and said,

† "Take this and share it among yourselves; for I tell you that from this time on I shall not drink of the fruit of the vine until the kingdom of God comes."

N. Then he took the bread, said the blessing, broke it, and gave it to them, saying,

† "This is my body, which will be given for you; do this in memory of me."

N. And likewise the cup after they had eaten, saying,

† "This cup is the new covenant in my blood, which will be shed for you.

"And yet behold, the hand of the one who is to betray me is with me on the table; for the Son of Man indeed goes as it has been determined; but woe to that man by whom he is betrayed."

N. And they began to debate among themselves who among them would do such a deed.

Then an argument broke out among them about which of them should be regarded as the greatest. He said to them,

† "The kings of the Gentiles lord it over them and those in authority over them are addressed as 'Benefactors'; but among you it shall not be so. Rather, let the greatest among you be as the youngest, and the leader as the servant. For who is greater: the one seated at table or the one who serves? Is it not the one seated at table? I am among you as the one who serves. It is you who have stood by me in my trials; and I confer a kingdom on you, just as my Father has conferred one on me, that you may eat and drink at my table in my kingdom; and you will sit on thrones judging the twelve tribes of Israel.

"Simon, Simon, behold Satan has demanded to sift all of you like wheat, but I have prayed that your own faith may not fail; and once you have turned back, you must strengthen your brothers."

N. He said to him,

V. "Lord, I am prepared to go to prison and to die with you."

N. But he replied,

† "I tell you, Peter, before the cock crows this day, you will deny three times that you know me."

N. He said to them,

† "When I sent you forth without a money bag or a sack or sandals, were you in need of anything?"

C. "No, nothing,"

N. they replied. He said to them,

† "But now one who has a money bag should take it, and likewise a sack, and one who does not have a sword should sell his cloak and buy one. For I tell you that this Scripture must be fulfilled in me, namely, *He was counted among the wicked*; and indeed what is written about me is coming to fulfillment."

N. Then they said,

C. "Lord, look, there are two swords here."

N. But he replied,

† "It is enough!"

N. Then going out, he went, as was his custom, to the Mount of Olives, and the disciples followed him. When he arrived at the place he said to them,

† "Pray that you may not undergo the test."

N. After withdrawing about a stone's throw from them and kneeling, he prayed, saying,

† "Father, if you are willing, take this cup away from me; still, not my will but yours be done."

N. And to strengthen him an angel from heaven appeared to him. He was in such agony and he prayed so fervently that his sweat became like drops of blood falling on the ground. When he rose from prayer and returned to his disciples, he found them sleeping from grief. He said to them,

† "Why are you sleeping? Get up and pray that you may not undergo the test."

N. While he was still speaking, a crowd approached and in front was one of the Twelve, a man named Judas. He went up to Jesus to kiss him. Jesus said to him,

† "Judas, are you betraying the Son of Man with a kiss?"

N. His disciples realized what was about to happen, and they asked,

C. **"Lord, shall we strike with a sword?"**

N. And one of them struck the high priest's servant and cut off his right ear. But Jesus said in reply,

† "Stop, no more of this!"

N. Then he touched the servant's ear and healed him. And Jesus said to the chief priests and temple guards and elders who had come for him,

† "Have you come out as against a robber, with swords and clubs? Day after day I was with you in the temple area, and you did not seize me; but this is your hour, the time for the power of darkness."

N. After arresting him they led him away and took him into the house of the high priest; Peter was following at a distance. They lit a fire in the middle of the courtyard and sat around it, and Peter sat down with them. When a maid saw him seated in the light, she looked intently at him and said,

C. **"This man too was with him."**

N. But he denied it saying,

V. "Woman, I do not know him."

N. A short while later someone else saw him and said,

C. **"You too are one of them";**

N. but Peter answered,

V. "My friend, I am not."

N. About an hour later, still another insisted,

C. **"Assuredly, this man too was with him, for he also is a Galilean."**

N. But Peter said,

V. "My friend, I do not know what you are talking about."

N. Just as he was saying this, the cock crowed, and the Lord turned and looked at Peter; and Peter remembered the word of the Lord, how he had said to him, "Before the cock crows today, you will deny me three times." He went out and began to weep bitterly. The men who held Jesus in custody were ridiculing and beating him. They blindfolded him and questioned him, saying,

C. **"Prophesy! Who is it that struck you?"**

N. And they reviled him in saying many other things against him.

When day came the council of elders of the people met, both chief priests and scribes, and they brought him before their Sanhedrin. They said,

C. **"If you are the Christ, tell us,"**

N. but he replied to them,

† "If I tell you, you will not believe, and if I question, you will not respond. But from this time on the Son of Man will be seated at the right hand of the power of God."

N. They all asked,

C. **"Are you then the Son of God?"**

N. He replied to them,

† "You say that I am."

N. Then they said,

C. **"What further need have we for testimony? We have heard it from his own mouth."]**

N. *Then the whole assembly of them arose and brought him before Pilate. They brought charges against him, saying,

C. **"We found this man misleading our people; he opposes the payment of taxes to Caesar and maintains that he is the Christ, a king."**

N. Pilate asked him,

V. "Are you the king of the Jews?"

N. He said to him in reply,

† "You say so."

N. Pilate then addressed the chief priests and the crowds,

*The shorter form replaces this sentence with the words: "The elders of the people, chief priests and scribes, arose and brought Jesus before Pilate."

V. "I find this man not guilty."

N. But they were adamant and said,

C. **"He is inciting the people with his teaching throughout all Judea, from Galilee where he began even to here."**

N. On hearing this Pilate asked if the man was a Galilean; and upon learning that he was under Herod's jurisdiction, he sent him to Herod who was in Jerusalem at that time. Herod was very glad to see Jesus; he had been wanting to see him for a long time, for he had heard about him and had been hoping to see him perform some sign. He questioned him at length, but he gave him no answer. The chief priests and scribes, meanwhile, stood by accusing him harshly. Herod and his soldiers treated him contemptuously and mocked him, and after clothing him in resplendent garb, he sent him back to Pilate. Herod and Pilate became friends that very day, even though they had been enemies formerly. Pilate then summoned the chief priests, the rulers, and the people and said to them,

V. "You brought this man to me and accused him of inciting the people to revolt. I have conducted my investigation in your presence and have not found this man guilty of the charges you have brought against him, nor did Herod, for he sent him back to us. So no capital crime has been committed by him. Therefore I shall have him flogged and then release him."

N. But all together they shouted out,

C. **"Away with this man! Release Barabbas to us."**

N. —Now Barabbas had been imprisoned for a rebellion that had taken place in the city and for murder.—Again Pilate addressed them, still wishing to release Jesus, but they continued their shouting,

C. **"Crucify him! Crucify him!"**

N. Pilate addressed them a third time,

V. "What evil has this man done? I found him guilty of no capital crime. Therefore I shall have him flogged and then release him."

N. With loud shouts, however, they persisted in calling for his crucifixion, and their voices prevailed. The verdict of Pilate was that their demand should be granted. So he released the man who had been imprisoned for rebellion and murder, for whom they asked, and he handed Jesus over to them to deal with as they wished.

As they led him away they took hold of a certain Simon, a Cyrenian, who was coming in from the country; and after laying the cross on him, they made him carry it behind Jesus. A large crowd of people followed Jesus, including many women who mourned and lamented him. Jesus turned to them and said,

† "Daughters of Jerusalem, do not weep for me; weep instead for yourselves and for your children, for indeed, the days are coming when people will say, 'Blessed are the barren, the wombs that never bore and the breasts that never nursed.' At that time people will say to the mountains, 'Fall upon us!' and to the hills, 'Cover us!' for if these things are done when the wood is green what will happen when it is dry?"

N. Now two others, both criminals, were led away with him to be executed.

When they came to the place called the Skull, they crucified him and the criminals there, one on his right, the other on his left. Then Jesus said,

† "Father, forgive them, they know not what they do."

N. They divided his garments by casting lots. The people stood by and watched; the rulers, meanwhile, sneered at him and said,

C. **"He saved others, let him save himself if he is the chosen one, the Christ of God."**

N. Even the soldiers jeered at him. As they approached to offer him wine they called out,

C. **"If you are King of the Jews, save yourself."**

N. Above him there was an inscription that read, "This is the King of the Jews."

Now one of the criminals hanging there reviled Jesus, saying,

V. "Are you not the Christ? Save yourself and us."

N. The other, however, rebuking him, said in reply,

V. "Have you no fear of God, for you are subject to the same condemnation? And indeed, we have been condemned justly, for the sentence we received corresponds to our crimes, but this man has done nothing criminal."

N. Then he said,

V. "Jesus, remember me when you come into your kingdom."

N. He replied to him,

† "Amen, I say to you, today you will be with me in Paradise."

N. It was now about noon and darkness came over the whole land until three in the afternoon because of an eclipse of the sun. Then the veil of the temple was torn down the middle. Jesus cried out in a loud voice,

† "Father, into your hands I commend my spirit";

N. and when he had said this he breathed his last.

Here all kneel and pause for a short time.

N. The centurion who witnessed what had happened glorified God and said,

V. "This man was innocent beyond doubt."

N. When all the people who had gathered for this spectacle saw what had happened, they returned home beating their breasts; but all his acquaintances stood at a distance, including the women who had followed him from Galilee and saw these events.

[Now there was a virtuous and righteous man named Joseph who, though he was a member of the council, had not consented to their plan of action. He came from the Jewish town of Arimathea and was awaiting the kingdom of God. He went to Pilate and asked for the body of Jesus. After he had taken the body down, he wrapped it in a linen cloth and laid him in a rock-hewn tomb in which no one had yet been buried. It was the day of preparation, and the sabbath was about to begin. The women who had come from Galilee with him followed behind, and when they had seen the tomb and the way in which his body was laid in it, they returned and prepared spices and perfumed oils. Then they rested on the sabbath according to the commandment.]

THE SACRED PASCHAL TRIDUUM AND SEASON OF EASTER

899 THURSDAY OF THE LORD'S SUPPER (HOLY THURSDAY): AT THE EVENING MASS — ABC

At the Last Supper, on the night when he was betrayed, our Savior instituted the Eucharistic Sacrifice of his body and blood. The tabernacle should be entirely empty; a sufficient amount of bread should be consecrated at this Mass for the Communion of clergy and laity today and tomorrow. The reception of the holy oils blessed at the Chrism Mass may be received by the local community during this liturgy. Mass begins with the Entrance Antiphon or an appropriate song (see #454, 458, 803, 804, 808), followed by the Introductory Rites. During the singing of the "Gloria" the church bells are rung and then remain silent until the Easter Vigil. Likewise, during this same period, the organ and other musical instruments may be used only so as to support the singing.

THE LITURGY OF THE WORD

FIRST READING *Exodus 12:1–8, 11–14*

The LORD said to Moses and Aaron in the land of Egypt, "This month shall stand at the head of your calendar; you shall reckon it the first month of the year. Tell the whole community of Israel: On the tenth of this month every one of your families must procure for itself a lamb, one apiece for each household. If a family is too small for a whole lamb, it shall join the nearest household in procuring one and shall share in the lamb in proportion to the number of persons who partake of it. The lamb must be a year-old male and without blemish. You may take it from either the sheep or the goats. You shall keep it until the fourteenth day of this month, and then, with the whole assembly of Israel present, it shall be slaughtered during the evening twilight. They shall take some of its blood and apply it to the two doorposts and the lintel of every house in which they partake of the lamb. That same night they shall eat its roasted flesh with unleavened bread and bitter herbs.

"This is how you are to eat it: with your loins girt, sandals on your feet and your staff in hand, you shall eat like those who are in flight. It is the Passover of the LORD. For on this same night I will go through Egypt, striking down every firstborn of the land, both man and beast, and executing judgment on all the gods of Egypt— I, the LORD! But the blood will mark the houses where you are. Seeing the blood, I will pass over you; thus, when I strike the land of Egypt, no destructive blow will come upon you.

"This day shall be a memorial feast for you, which all your generations shall celebrate with pilgrimage to the LORD, as a perpetual institution."

RESPONSORIAL PSALM *Psalm 116:12–13, 15–16bc, 17–18*

℟. Our bless-ing-cup is a com-mu - nion with the Blood of Christ.

Music: Owen Alstott, b. 1947, © 1977, 1990, OCP. All rights reserved.

▸ How shall I make a return to the LORD
for all the good he has done
for me?
The cup of salvation I will take up,
and I will call upon the name of
the LORD. ℟.

▸ Precious in the eyes of the LORD
is the death of his faithful ones.

I am your servant, the son of
your handmaid;
you have loosed my bonds. ℟.

▸ To you will I offer sacrifice of
thanksgiving,
and I will call upon the name of
the LORD.
My vows to the LORD I will pay
in the presence of all his people. ℟.

SECOND READING

1 Corinthians 11:23–26

Brothers and sisters: I received from the Lord what I also handed on to you, that the Lord Jesus, on the night he was handed over, took bread, and, after he had given thanks, broke it and said, "This is my body that is for you. Do this in remembrance of me."

In the same way also the cup, after supper, saying, "This cup is the new covenant in my blood. Do this, as often as you drink it, in remembrance of me." For as often as you eat this bread and drink the cup, you proclaim the death of the Lord until he comes.

GOSPEL ACCLAMATION

John 13:34

℟. Praise to you, Lord Je-sus Christ, King of end-less glo-ry!

Music: Owen Alstott, b. 1947, © 1977, 1990, OCP. All rights reserved.　　　*(Omit if not sung)*

▸ I give you a new commandment, says the Lord:
love one another as I have loved you. ℟.

GOSPEL

John 13:1–15

Before the feast of Passover, Jesus knew that his hour had come to pass from this world to the Father. He loved his own in the world and he loved them to the end. The devil had already induced Judas, son of Simon the Iscariot, to hand him over. So, during supper, fully aware that the Father had put everything into his power and that he had come from God and was returning to God, he rose from supper and took off his outer garments. He took a towel and tied it around his waist. Then he poured water into a basin and began to wash the disciples' feet and dry them with the towel around his waist. He came to Simon Peter, who said to him, "Master, are you going to wash my feet?" Jesus answered and said to him, "What I am doing, you do not understand now, but you will understand later." Peter said to him, "You will never wash my

feet." Jesus answered him, "Unless I wash you, you will have no inheritance with me." Simon Peter said to him, "Master, then not only my feet, but my hands and head as well." Jesus said to him, "Whoever has bathed has no need except to have his feet washed, for he is clean all over; so you are clean, but not all." For he knew who would betray him; for this reason, he said, "Not all of you are clean."

So when he had washed their feet and put his garments back on and reclined at table again, he said to them, "Do you realize what I have done for you? You call me 'teacher' and 'master,' and rightly so, for indeed I am. If I, therefore, the master and teacher, have washed your feet, you ought to wash one another's feet. I have given you a model to follow, so that as I have done for you, you should also do."

THE WASHING OF FEET

During the washing of feet an appropriate hymn may be sung (see #371–373).

Mass continues with the Prayer of the Faithful, followed by the Liturgy of the Eucharist.

At the beginning of the Liturgy of the Eucharist, there may be a procession of the faithful in which gifts for the poor may be presented with the bread and wine.

Meanwhile the "Ubi Caritas," or another appropriate chant, is sung. The Creed is not said at this Mass.

THE TRANSFER OF THE MOST BLESSED SACRAMENT

Following the prayer after Communion, all kneel as the Priest incenses the Blessed Sacrament on the altar. The Blessed Sacrament is then carried through the church to the place of reposition. The hosts will be distributed to the people on Good Friday. During the procession, a suitable hymn is sung (see #377, 378).

After the Priest incenses and places the Blessed Sacrament in the tabernacle the people are encouraged to remain for a period of quiet adoration. All depart in silence.

---

900   FRIDAY OF THE PASSION OF THE LORD (GOOD FRIDAY) — ABC

According to the Church's ancient tradition, Mass is not celebrated today. The celebration of the Lord's Passion consists of three parts: Liturgy of the Word, Adoration of the Cross, and Holy Communion.

The Priest and the Deacon go to the altar in silence and, after making a reverence to the altar, prostrate themselves or, if appropriate, kneel and pray in silence, while all others kneel. Then the Priest goes to his chair, faces the people, and begins with a brief prayer.

FIRST PART: THE LITURGY OF THE WORD

FIRST READING   *Isaiah 52:13—53:12*

See, my servant shall prosper,
  he shall be raised high and
    greatly exalted.
Even as many were amazed at him—
  so marred was his look beyond
    human semblance
  and his appearance beyond that of
    the sons of man—
so shall he startle many nations,
  because of him kings shall
    stand speechless;
for those who have not been told
    shall see,
  those who have not heard shall
    ponder it.

Who would believe what we
  have heard?

To whom has the arm of the LORD
  been revealed?
He grew up like a sapling before him,
  like a shoot from the
    parched earth;
there was in him no stately bearing
  to make us look at him,
  nor appearance that would attract
    us to him.
He was spurned and avoided
  by people,
a man of suffering, accustomed
  to infirmity,
one of those from whom people hide
  their faces,
  spurned, and we held him in
    no esteem.

Yet it was our infirmities that he bore,
  our sufferings that he endured,
while we thought of him as stricken,
  as one smitten by God
    and afflicted.
But he was pierced for our offenses,
  crushed for our sins;
upon him was the chastisement that
    makes us whole,
  by his stripes we were healed.
We had all gone astray like sheep,
  each following his own way;
but the LORD laid upon him
  the guilt of us all.

Though he was harshly treated,
    he submitted
  and opened not his mouth;
like a lamb led to the slaughter
  or a sheep before the shearers,
  he was silent and opened not
    his mouth.
Oppressed and condemned, he was
    taken away,
  and who would have thought any
    more of his destiny?
When he was cut off from the land of
    the living,
  and smitten for the sin of
    his people,

a grave was assigned him among
    the wicked
  and a burial place with evildoers,
though he had done no wrong
  nor spoken any falsehood.
But the LORD was pleased
  to crush him in infirmity.

If he gives his life as an offering for sin,
  he shall see his descendants in a
    long life,
  and the will of the LORD shall be
    accomplished through him.

Because of his affliction
  he shall see the light
    in fullness of days;
through his suffering, my servant
    shall justify many,
  and their guilt he shall bear.
Therefore I will give him his portion
    among the great,
  and he shall divide the spoils with
    the mighty,
because he surrendered himself
    to death
  and was counted among
    the wicked;
and he shall take away the sins
    of many,
  and win pardon for their offenses.

RESPONSORIAL PSALM

Psalm 31:2, 6, 12–13, 15–16, 17, 25

℟. Fa - ther, in - to your hands I com - mend my spir - it.

Music: Owen Alstott, b. 1947, © 1977, 1990, OCP. All rights reserved.

▸ In you, O LORD, I take refuge;
    let me never be put to shame.
  In your justice rescue me.
  Into your hands I commend my spirit;
    you will redeem me, O LORD,
      O faithful God. ℟.

▸ For all my foes I am an object
    of reproach,
    a laughingstock to my neighbors,
      and a dread to my friends;
    they who see me abroad flee
      from me.

I am forgotten like the
    unremembered dead;
  I am like a dish that is broken. ℟.

▸ But my trust is in you, O LORD;
  I say, "You are my God.
  In your hands is my destiny; rescue me
    from the clutches of my enemies
      and my persecutors." ℟.

▸ Let your face shine upon your
    servant;
  save me in your kindness.
  Take courage and be stouthearted,
    all you who hope in the LORD. ℟.

SECOND READING
Hebrews 4:14–16; 5:7–9

Brothers and sisters: Since we have a great high priest who has passed through the heavens, Jesus, the Son of God, let us hold fast to our confession. For we do not have a high priest who is unable to sympathize with our weaknesses, but one who has similarly been tested in every way, yet without sin. So let us confidently approach the throne of grace to receive mercy and to find grace for timely help.

In the days when Christ was in the flesh, he offered prayers and supplications with loud cries and tears to the one who was able to save him from death, and he was heard because of his reverence. Son though he was, he learned obedience from what he suffered; and when he was made perfect, he became the source of eternal salvation for all who obey him.

GOSPEL ACCLAMATION
Philippians 2:8–9

℟. Praise to you, Lord Jesus Christ, King of endless glory!

Music: Owen Alstott, b. 1947, © 1977, 1990, OCP. All rights reserved. *(Omit if not sung)*

▶ Christ became obedient to the point of death,
even death on a cross.
Because of this, God greatly exalted him
and bestowed on him the name which is above every other name. ℟.

THE PASSION OF THE LORD*
John 18:1—19:42

The Passion according to St. John is proclaimed by the Deacon, or is there is no Deacon, by the Priest. It may also be read by lay readers, with the part of Christ reserved to the Priest, if possible. Speakers in the Passion Narrative are represented by these abbreviations:

| N. – Narrator | V. – Voice |
| † – Christ | **C. – Crowd** |

N. The Passion of our Lord Jesus Christ according to John

Jesus went out with his disciples across the Kidron valley to where there was a garden, into which he and his disciples entered. Judas his betrayer also knew the place, because Jesus had often met there with his disciples. So Judas got a band of soldiers and guards from the chief priests and the Pharisees and went there with lanterns, torches, and weapons. Jesus, knowing everything that was going to happen to him, went out and said to them,

† "Whom are you looking for?"

N. They answered him,

C. "Jesus the Nazorean."

N. He said to them,

† "I AM."

N. Judas his betrayer was also with them. When he said to them, "I AM," they turned away and fell to the ground. So he again asked them,

† "Whom are you looking for?"

N. They said,

C. "Jesus the Nazorean."

N. Jesus answered,

† "I told you that I AM. So if you are looking for me, let these men go."

N. This was to fulfill what he had said, "I have not lost any of those you gave me." Then Simon Peter, who had a sword, drew it, struck the high priest's slave, and cut off his right ear. The slave's name was Malchus. Jesus said to Peter,

† "Put your sword into its scabbard. Shall I not drink the cup that the Father gave me?"

N. So the band of soldiers, the tribune, and the Jewish guards seized Jesus, bound him, and brought him to Annas first. He was the father-in-law of Caiaphas, who was high priest that year. It was Caiaphas who had counseled the Jews that it was better that one man should die rather than the people.

Simon Peter and another disciple followed Jesus. Now the other disciple was known to the high priest, and he entered the courtyard of the high priest with Jesus. But Peter stood at the gate outside. So the other disciple, the acquaintance of the high priest, went out and spoke to the gatekeeper and brought Peter in. Then the maid who was the gatekeeper said to Peter,

C. **"You are not one of this man's disciples, are you?"**

N. He said,

V. "I am not."

N. Now the slaves and the guards were standing around a charcoal fire that they had made, because it was cold, and were warming themselves. Peter was also standing there keeping warm.

The high priest questioned Jesus about his disciples and about his doctrine. Jesus answered him,

† "I have spoken publicly to the world. I have always taught in a synagogue or in the temple area where all the Jews gather, and in secret I have said nothing. Why ask me? Ask those who heard me what I said to them. They know what I said."

N. When he had said this, one of the temple guards standing there struck Jesus and said,

V. "Is this the way you answer the high priest?"

N. Jesus answered him,

† "If I have spoken wrongly, testify to the wrong; but if I have spoken rightly, why do you strike me?"

N. Then Annas sent him bound to Caiaphas the high priest.

Now Simon Peter was standing there keeping warm. And they said to him,

C. **"You are not one of his disciples, are you?"**

N. He denied it and said,

V. "I am not."

N. One of the slaves of the high priest, a relative of the one whose ear Peter had cut off, said,

C. **"Didn't I see you in the garden with him?"**

N. Again Peter denied it. And immediately the cock crowed.

Then they brought Jesus from Caiaphas to the praetorium. It was morning. And they themselves did not enter the praetorium, in order not to be defiled so that they could eat the Passover. So Pilate came out to them and said,

V. "What charge do you bring against this man?"

N. They answered and said to him,

C. **"If he were not a criminal, we would not have handed him over to you."**

N. At this, Pilate said to them,

V. "Take him yourselves, and judge him according to your law."

N. The Jews answered him,

C. **"We do not have the right to execute anyone,"**

N. in order that the word of Jesus might be fulfilled that he said indicating the kind of death he would die. So Pilate went back into the praetorium and summoned Jesus and said to him,

V. "Are you the King of the Jews?"

N. Jesus answered,

† "Do you say this on your own or have others told you about me?"

N. Pilate answered,

V. "I am not a Jew, am I? Your own nation and the chief priests handed you over to me. What have you done?"

N. Jesus answered,

✝ "My kingdom does not belong to this world. If my kingdom did belong to this world, my attendants would be fighting to keep me from being handed over to the Jews. But as it is, my kingdom is not here."

N. So Pilate said to him,

V. "Then you are a king?"

N. Jesus answered,

✝ "You say I am a king. For this I was born and for this I came into the world, to testify to the truth. Everyone who belongs to the truth listens to my voice."

N. Pilate said to him,

V. "What is truth?"

N. When he had said this, he again went out to the Jews and said to them,

V. "I find no guilt in him. But you have a custom that I release one prisoner to you at Passover. Do you want me to release to you the King of the Jews?"

N. They cried out again,

C. **"Not this one but Barabbas!"**

N. Now Barabbas was a revolutionary.

Then Pilate took Jesus and had him scourged. And the soldiers wove a crown out of thorns and placed it on his head, and clothed him in a purple cloak, and they came to him and said,

C. **"Hail, King of the Jews!"**

N. And they struck him repeatedly. Once more Pilate went out and said to them,

V. "Look, I am bringing him out to you, so that you may know that I find no guilt in him."

N. So Jesus came out, wearing the crown of thorns and the purple cloak. And Pilate said to them,

V. "Behold, the man!"

N. When the chief priests and the guards saw him they cried out,

C. **"Crucify him, crucify him!"**

N. Pilate said to them,

V. "Take him yourselves and crucify him. I find no guilt in him."

N. The Jews answered,

C. **"We have a law, and according to that law he ought to die, because he made himself the Son of God."**

N. Now when Pilate heard this statement, he became even more afraid, and went back into the praetorium and said to Jesus,

V. "Where are you from?"

N. Jesus did not answer him. So Pilate said to him,

V. "Do you not speak to me? Do you not know that I have power to release you and I have power to crucify you?"

N. Jesus answered him,

✝ "You would have no power over me if it had not been given to you from above. For this reason the one who handed me over to you has the greater sin."

N. Consequently, Pilate tried to release him; but the Jews cried out,

C. **"If you release him, you are not a Friend of Caesar. Everyone who makes himself a king opposes Caesar."**

N. When Pilate heard these words he brought Jesus out and seated him on the judge's bench in the place called Stone Pavement, in Hebrew, Gabbatha. It was preparation day for Passover, and it was about noon. And he said to the Jews,

V. "Behold, your king!"

N. They cried out,

C. **"Take him away, take him away! Crucify him!"**

N. Pilate said to them,

V. "Shall I crucify your king?"

N. The chief priests answered,

C. **"We have no king but Caesar."**

N. Then he handed him over to them to be crucified.

So they took Jesus, and, carrying the cross himself, he went out to what is called the Place of the Skull, in Hebrew, Golgotha. There they crucified him, and with him two others, one on either side, with Jesus in the middle. Pilate also had an inscription written and put on the cross. It read, "Jesus the Nazorean, the King of the Jews." Now many of the Jews read this inscription, because the place where Jesus was crucified was near the city; and it was written in Hebrew, Latin, and Greek. So the chief priests of the Jews said to Pilate,

C. **"Do not write 'The King of the Jews,' but that he said, 'I am the King of the Jews.'"**

N. Pilate answered,

V. "What I have written, I have written."

N. When the soldiers had crucified Jesus, they took his clothes and divided them into four shares, a share for each soldier. They also took his tunic, but the tunic was seamless, woven in one piece from the top down. So they said to one another,

C. **"Let's not tear it, but cast lots for it to see whose it will be,"**

N. in order that the passage of Scripture might be fulfilled that says:
> They divided my garments
> among them,
> and for my vesture they cast lots.

This is what the soldiers did. Standing by the cross of Jesus were his mother and his mother's sister, Mary the wife of Clopas, and Mary of Magdala. When Jesus saw his mother and the disciple there whom he loved he said to his mother,

† "Woman, behold, your son."

N. Then he said to the disciple,

† "Behold, your mother."

N. And from that hour the disciple took her into his home.

After this, aware that everything was now finished, in order that the Scripture might be fulfilled, Jesus said,

† "I thirst."

N. There was a vessel filled with common wine. So they put a sponge soaked in wine on a sprig of hyssop and put it up to his mouth. When Jesus had taken the wine, he said,

† "It is finished."

N. And bowing his head, he handed over the spirit.

Here all kneel and pause for a short time.

N. Now since it was preparation day, in order that the bodies might not remain on the cross on the sabbath, for the sabbath day of that week was a solemn one, the Jews asked Pilate that their legs be broken and that they be taken down. So the soldiers came and broke the legs of the first and then of the other one who was crucified with Jesus. But when they came to Jesus and saw that he was already dead, they did not break his legs, but one soldier thrust his lance into his side, and immediately blood and water flowed out. An eyewitness has testified, and his testimony is true; he knows that he is speaking the truth, so that you also may come to believe. For this happened so that the Scripture passage might be fulfilled:
> Not a bone of it will be broken.
And again another passage says:
> They will look upon him whom
> they have pierced.

After this, Joseph of Arimathea, secretly a disciple of Jesus for fear of the Jews, asked Pilate if he could remove the body of Jesus. And Pilate permitted it. So he came and took his body. Nicodemus, the one who had first come to him at night, also came bringing a mixture of myrrh and aloes weighing about one hundred pounds. They took the body of Jesus and bound it with burial cloths along with the spices, according to the Jewish burial custom. Now in the place where he had been crucified there was a garden, and in the garden a new tomb, in which no one had yet been buried. So they laid Jesus there because of the Jewish preparation day; for the tomb was close by.

The message of the liturgy in proclaiming the passion narratives in full is to enable the assembly to see vividly the love of Christ for each person, despite their sins, a love that even death could not vanquish. The crimes during the Passion of Christ cannot be attributed indiscriminately to all Jews of that time, nor to Jews today. The Jewish people should not be referred to as though rejected or cursed, as if this view followed from Scripture. The Church ever keeps in mind that Jesus, his mother Mary, and the Apostles all were Jewish. As the Church has always held, Christ freely suffered his passion and death because of the sins of all, that all might be saved.

— Bishops' Committee on Ecumenical and Interreligious Affairs

---

Note: A chanted musical version of the St. John Passion is available (edition 20042).

THE SOLEMN INTERCESSIONS

The Solemn Intercessions conclude the Liturgy of the Word. The Deacon, standing at the ambo, sings or says the invitation in which each intention is stated. In the absence of a Deacon, a lay minister may do this. All pray silently for a while, and then the Priest, with hands extended, standing either at the chair or at the altar, sings or says the prayer, after which the assembly responds, "Amen." The people may either kneel or stand throughout the entire period of the prayers.

SECOND PART: THE ADORATION OF THE HOLY CROSS

After the Showing of the Holy Cross, the Priest, clergy, and faithful approach to venerate the Cross as if in procession. They make a simple genuflection or perform some other appropriate sign of reverence according to local custom, for example, kissing the Cross. The "Stabat Mater" (song #363), or another appropriate chant in memory of the compassion of the Blessed Virgin Mary, may also be sung (for additional music, see #375, 380–384, 387–389).

When the adoration is concluded, the Cross is carried by the Deacon, or another minister, to its place at the altar.

THIRD PART: HOLY COMMUNION

The Deacon or the Priest brings the ciborium with the Blessed Sacrament from the place of reposition to the altar without any procession while all stand in silence. Two ministers with lighted candles accompany him and place their candles near the altar or on it. After the Lord's Prayer is recited by all, Communion is distributed to the faithful. An appropriate song may be sung during Communion (see #385, 386, 390–393).

A period of silence may be observed after Communion. Following the Prayer after Communion and the Prayer over the People, all depart in silence, after genuflecting toward the Cross. The altar is stripped at a later time.

THE EASTER VIGIL IN THE HOLY NIGHT — ABC 901

The entire celebration of the Easter Vigil must take place at night, so that it begins after nightfall and ends before daybreak on the Sunday. This Vigil is arranged in four parts: after a service of light and the Easter Proclamation (I), the Church meditates on all the wonderful things God has done for his people from the beginning; this is the Liturgy of the Word (II). As the day of resurrection approaches, new members of the Church are reborn in Baptism (III), and the whole Church is called to the table the Lord prepared for his people through his Death and Resurrection; this is the Liturgy of the Eucharist (IV).

FIRST PART:
THE SOLEMN BEGINNING OF THE VIGIL OR LUCERNARIUM

THE BLESSING OF THE FIRE AND PREPARATION OF THE CANDLE

A large fire is prepared in a suitable place. The people and the Priest assemble there with the other ministers (carrying the paschal candle). The Priest then greets the assembly in the usual manner and briefly instructs them about the vigil and blesses the fire. The paschal candle is then prepared and lighted from the new fire.

PROCESSION

One of the ministers takes burning coals from the fire and places them in the thurible; the Priest then places incense into it. The Deacon, or other appropriate minister, accepts the paschal candle from the Priest, and a procession is formed. The Priest and ministers follow the smoking thurible and lit paschal candle, leading the people, who are holding unlit candles, to the door of the church. At the door of the darkened Church, the Deacon then takes the paschal candle, lifts it high, and sings the acclamation "The Light of Christ." All respond, "Thanks be to God."

After this, the Priest lights his candle. When the procession reaches the middle of the church, the Deacon lifts the candle high and sings the acclamation "The Light of Christ" a second time. All respond, "Thanks be to God."

All light their candles from the paschal candle and the procession continues. When the Deacon arrives before the altar, he faces the people and sings a third time, "The Light of Christ," and all respond, "Thanks be to God."

After the paschal candle is placed in a large candle holder, the lights in the church are put on, except for the altar candles.

THE EASTER PROCLAMATION (EXSULTET)

The Easter Proclamation is proclaimed by the Deacon or, in his absence, by the Priest. If necessary, a lay cantor may sing the Proclamation. In this case, the words "Therefore, dearest friends" up to the end of the invitation are omitted, as is the greeting "The Lord be with you." All stand and hold lighted candles.

After the Easter Proclamation, the candles are put aside and all are seated.

SECOND PART: THE LITURGY OF THE WORD

There are seven readings from the Old Testament and two from the New (the Epistle and Gospel), all of which should be read whenever this can be done, so that the character of the Vigil, which demands an extended period of time, may be preserved. Nevertheless, where more serious pastoral circumstances demand it, the number of readings from the Old Testament may be reduced, always bearing in mind that the reading of the Word of God is a fundamental part of this Easter Vigil. At least three readings should be read from the Old Testament, both from the Law and from the Prophets, and their respective Responsorial Psalms should be sung. Never, moreover, should the reading of chapter 14 of Exodus with its canticle be omitted.

Following each reading from the Old Testament the Responsorial Psalm is sung. Then all rise, the Priest says, "Let us pray" and, after all have prayed for a while in silence, he says the prayer corresponding to the reading. In place of the Responsorial Psalm a period of sacred silence may be observed, in which case the pause after "Let us pray" is omitted.

FIRST READING

Genesis 1:1—2:2 or 1:1, 26–31a

(Include bracketed text for Long Form)

In the beginning, when God created the heavens and the earth, [the earth was a formless wasteland, and darkness covered the abyss, while a mighty wind swept over the waters.

Then God said, "Let there be light," and there was light. God saw how good the light was. God then separated the light from the darkness. God called the light "day," and the darkness he called "night." Thus evening came, and morning followed—the first day.

Then God said, "Let there be a dome in the middle of the waters, to separate one body of water from the other." And so it happened: God made the dome, and it separated the water above the dome from the water below it. God called the dome "the sky." Evening came, and morning followed—the second day.

Then God said, "Let the water under the sky be gathered into a single basin, so that the dry land may appear." And so it happened: the water under the sky was gathered into its basin, and the dry land appeared. God called the dry land "the earth," and the basin of the water he called "the sea." God saw how good it was. Then God said, "Let the earth bring forth vegetation:

every kind of plant that bears seed and every kind of fruit tree on earth that bears fruit with its seed in it." And so it happened: the earth brought forth every kind of plant that bears seed and every kind of fruit tree on earth that bears fruit with its seed in it. God saw how good it was. Evening came, and morning followed—the third day.

Then God said: "Let there be lights in the dome of the sky, to separate day from night. Let them mark the fixed times, the days and the years, and serve as luminaries in the dome of the sky, to shed light upon the earth." And so it happened: God made the two great lights, the greater one to govern the day, and the lesser one to govern the night; and he made the stars. God set them in the dome of the sky, to shed light upon the earth, to govern the day and the night, and to separate the light from the darkness. God saw how good it was. Evening came, and morning followed—the fourth day.

Then God said, "Let the water teem with an abundance of living creatures, and on the earth let birds fly beneath the dome of the sky." And so it happened: God created the great sea monsters and all kinds of swimming creatures with which the water teems, and all kinds of winged birds. God saw how good it was, and God blessed them, saying, "Be fertile, multiply, and fill the water of the seas; and let the birds multiply on the earth." Evening came, and morning followed—the fifth day.

Then God said, "Let the earth bring forth all kinds of living creatures: cattle, creeping things, and wild animals of all kinds." And so it happened: God made all kinds of wild animals, all kinds of cattle, and all kinds of creeping things of the earth. God saw how good it was. Then] God said: "Let us make man in our image, after our likeness. Let them have dominion over the fish of the sea, the birds of the air, and the cattle, and over all the wild animals and all the creatures that crawl on the ground."

God created man in his image;
   in the image of God he
     created him;
   male and female he created them.

God blessed them, saying: "Be fertile and multiply; fill the earth and subdue it. Have dominion over the fish of the sea, the birds of the air, and all the living things that move on the earth." God also said: "See, I give you every seed-bearing plant all over the earth and every tree that has seed-bearing fruit on it to be your food; and to all the animals of the land, all the birds of the air, and all the living creatures that crawl on the ground, I give all the green plants for food." And so it happened. God looked at everything he had made, and he found it very good. [Evening came, and morning followed—the sixth day.

Thus the heavens and the earth and all their array were completed. Since on the seventh day God was finished with the work he had been doing, he rested on the seventh day from all the work he had undertaken.]

RESPONSORIAL PSALM

Psalm 104:1–2, 5–6, 10, 12, 13–14, 24, 35

℟. Lord, send out your Spir - it, and re - new the face of the earth.

Music: Owen Alstott, b. 1947, © 1977, 1990, OCP. All rights reserved.

▸ Bless the LORD, O my soul!
  O LORD, my God, you are
    great indeed!
You are clothed with majesty
    and glory,
  robed in light as with a cloak. ℟.

▸ You fixed the earth upon
    its foundation,
  not to be moved forever;
with the ocean, as with a garment,
    you covered it;
  above the mountains the
    waters stood. ℟.

▸ You send forth springs into
    the watercourses
  that wind among the mountains.
Beside them the birds of
    heaven dwell;

from among the branches they
    send forth their song. ℟.

▸ You water the mountains from
    your palace;
  the earth is replete with the fruit of
    your works.
You raise grass for the cattle,
    and vegetation for man's use,
  producing bread from the earth. ℟.

▸ How manifold are your works,
    O LORD!
  In wisdom you have wrought
    them all—
the earth is full of your creatures.
  Bless the LORD, O my soul! ℟.

Or

RESPONSORIAL PSALM

Psalm 33:4–5, 6–7, 12–13, 20 & 22

℟. The earth is full of the good-ness of the Lord.

▸ Upright is the word of the LORD,
  and all his works are trustworthy.
He loves justice and right;
  of the kindness of the LORD the
  earth is full. ℟.

▸ By the word of the LORD the heavens
  were made;
  by the breath of his mouth all
  their host.
He gathers the waters of the sea as in
  a flask;
  in cellars he confines the deep. ℟.

▸ Blessed the nation whose God is
  the LORD,
  the people he has chosen for his
  own inheritance.
From heaven the LORD looks down;
  he sees all mankind. ℟.

▸ Our soul waits for the LORD,
  who is our help and our shield.
May your kindness, O LORD, be
  upon us
  who have put our hope in you. ℟.

SECOND READING

Genesis 22:1–18 or 22:1–2, 9a, 10–13, 15–18

(Include bracketed text for Long Form)

God put Abraham to the test. He called to him, "Abraham!" "Here I am," he replied. Then God said: "Take your son Isaac, your only one, whom you love, and go to the land of Moriah. There you shall offer him up as a holocaust on a height that I will point out to you." [Early the next morning Abraham saddled his donkey, took with him his son Isaac and two of his servants as well, and with the wood that he had cut for the holocaust, set out for the place of which God had told him.

On the third day Abraham got sight of the place from afar. Then he said to his servants: "Both of you stay here with the donkey, while the boy and I go on over yonder. We will worship and then come back to you." Thereupon Abraham took the wood for the holocaust and laid it on his son Isaac's shoulders, while he himself carried the fire and the knife. As the two walked on together, Isaac spoke to his father Abraham: "Father!" Isaac said. "Yes, son," he replied. Isaac continued, "Here are the fire and the wood, but where is the sheep for the holocaust?" "Son," Abraham answered, "God himself will provide the sheep for the holocaust." Then the two continued going forward.]

When they came to the place of which God had told him, Abraham built an altar there and arranged the wood on it. [Next he tied up his son Isaac, and put him on top of the wood on the altar.] Then he reached out and took the knife to slaughter his son. But the LORD's messenger called to him from heaven, "Abraham, Abraham!" "Here I am," he answered. "Do not lay your hand on the boy," said the messenger. "Do not do the least thing to him. I know now how devoted you are to God, since you did not withhold from me your own beloved son." As Abraham looked about, he spied a ram caught by its horns in the thicket. So he went and took the ram and offered it up as a holocaust in place of his son. [Abraham named the site Yahweh-yireh; hence people now say, "On the mountain the LORD will see."]

Again the LORD's messenger called to Abraham from heaven and said: "I swear by myself, declares the LORD, that because you acted as you did in not withholding from me your beloved son, I will bless you abundantly and make your descendants as countless as the stars of the sky and the sands of the seashore; your descendants shall take possession of the gates of their enemies, and in your descendants all the nations of the earth shall find blessing—all this because you obeyed my command."

RESPONSORIAL PSALM

Psalm 16:5, 8, 9–10, 11

℟. You are my in - her - i - tance, O Lord.

▶ O LORD, my allotted portion and my cup,
  you it is who hold fast my lot.
I set the LORD ever before me;
  with him at my right hand I shall not be disturbed. ℟.

▶ Therefore my heart is glad and my soul rejoices,
  my body, too, abides in confidence;
because you will not abandon my soul to the netherworld,
  nor will you suffer your faithful one to undergo corruption. ℟.

▶ You will show me the path to life,
  fullness of joys in your presence,
  the delights at your right hand forever. ℟.

THIRD READING

Exodus 14:15—15:1

The LORD said to Moses, "Why are you crying out to me? Tell the Israelites to go forward. And you, lift up your staff and, with hand outstretched over the sea, split the sea in two, that the Israelites may pass through it on dry land. But I will make the Egyptians so obstinate that they will go in after them. Then I will receive glory through Pharaoh and all his army, his chariots and charioteers. The Egyptians shall know that I am the LORD, when I receive glory through Pharaoh and his chariots and charioteers."

The angel of God, who had been leading Israel's camp, now moved and went around behind them. The column of cloud also, leaving the front, took up its place behind them, so that it came between the camp of the Egyptians and that of Israel. But the cloud now became dark, and thus the night passed without the rival camps coming any closer together all night long. Then Moses stretched out his hand over the sea, and the LORD swept the sea with a strong east wind throughout the night and so turned it into dry land. When the water was thus divided, the Israelites marched into the midst of the sea on dry land, with the water like a wall to their right and to their left.

The Egyptians followed in pursuit; all Pharaoh's horses and chariots and charioteers went after them right into the midst of the sea. In the night watch just before dawn the LORD cast through the column of the fiery cloud upon the Egyptian force a glance that threw it into a panic; and he so clogged their chariot wheels that they could hardly drive. With that the Egyptians sounded the retreat before Israel, because the LORD was fighting for them against the Egyptians.

Then the LORD told Moses, "Stretch out your hand over the sea, that the water may flow back upon the Egyptians, upon their chariots and their charioteers." So Moses stretched out his hand over the sea, and at dawn the sea flowed back to its normal depth. The Egyptians were fleeing head on toward the sea, when the LORD hurled them into its midst. As the water flowed back, it covered the chariots and the charioteers of Pharaoh's whole army which had followed the Israelites into the sea. Not a single one of them escaped. But the Israelites had marched on dry land through the midst of the sea, with the water like a wall to their right and to their left. Thus the LORD saved Israel on that day from the power of the Egyptians. When Israel saw the Egyptians lying dead on the seashore and beheld the great power that the LORD had shown against the Egyptians, they feared the LORD and believed in him and in his servant Moses.

Then Moses and the Israelites sang this song to the LORD:
I will sing to the LORD, for he is
    gloriously triumphant;
horse and chariot he has cast into
    the sea.

RESPONSORIAL PSALM

Exodus 15:1–2, 3–4, 5–6, 17–18

℟. Let us sing to the Lord; he has cov-ered him - self in glo - ry.

▶ I will sing to the LORD, for he is
    gloriously triumphant;
horse and chariot he has cast into
    the sea.
My strength and my courage is
    the LORD,
    and he has been my savior.
He is my God, I praise him;
    the God of my father, I extol him. ℟.

▶ The LORD is a warrior,
    LORD is his name!
Pharaoh's chariots and army he
    hurled into the sea;
    the elite of his officers were
        submerged in the Red Sea. ℟.

▶ The flood waters covered them,
    they sank into the depths like
    a stone.
Your right hand, O LORD, magnificent
    in power,
    your right hand, O LORD, has
        shattered the enemy. ℟.

▶ You brought in the people
    you redeemed
and planted them on the mountain
    of your inheritance—
the place where you made your seat,
    O LORD,
    the sanctuary, LORD, which your
        hands established.
The LORD shall reign forever
    and ever. ℟.

FOURTH READING

Isaiah 54:5–14

The One who has become your
    husband is your Maker;
his name is the LORD of hosts;
your redeemer is the Holy One
    of Israel,
    called God of all the earth.
The LORD calls you back,
    like a wife forsaken and grieved
        in spirit,
a wife married in youth and then
    cast off,
says your God.
For a brief moment I abandoned you,
    but with great tenderness I will
        take you back.
In an outburst of wrath, for a moment
    I hid my face from you;

but with enduring love I take pity
  on you,
  says the LORD, your redeemer.
This is for me like the days of Noah,
  when I swore that the waters
    of Noah
  should never again deluge
    the earth;
so I have sworn not to be angry
    with you,
  or to rebuke you.
Though the mountains leave
    their place
  and the hills be shaken,
my love shall never leave you
  nor my covenant of peace
    be shaken,

says the LORD, who has mercy
  on you.
O afflicted one, storm-battered
    and unconsoled,
  I lay your pavements in carnelians,
  and your foundations in sapphires;
I will make your battlements
    of rubies,
  your gates of carbuncles,
  and all your walls of
    precious stones.
All your children shall be taught by
    the LORD,
  and great shall be the peace of
    your children.
In justice shall you be established,
  far from the fear of oppression,
  where destruction cannot come
    near you.

RESPONSORIAL PSALM

Psalm 30:2, 4, 5–6, 11–12, 13

℟. I will praise you, Lord, for you have res - cued me.

▶ I will extol you, O LORD, for you drew
    me clear
  and did not let my enemies rejoice
    over me.
O LORD, you brought me up from the
    netherworld;
  you preserved me from among
    those going down into the pit. ℟.

▶ Sing praise to the LORD, you his
    faithful ones,
  and give thanks to his holy name.

For his anger lasts but a moment;
  a lifetime, his good will.
At nightfall, weeping enters in,
  but with the dawn, rejoicing. ℟.

▶ Hear, O LORD, and have pity on me;
  O LORD, be my helper.
You changed my mourning
    into dancing;
  O LORD, my God, forever will I give
    you thanks. ℟.

FIFTH READING

Isaiah 55:1–11

Thus says the LORD:
  All you who are thirsty,
    come to the water!
  You who have no money,
    come, receive grain and eat;
  come, without paying and
      without cost,
    drink wine and milk!
  Why spend your money for what is
      not bread,
    your wages for what fails to satisfy?

Heed me, and you shall eat well,
  you shall delight in rich fare.
Come to me heedfully,
  listen, that you may have life.
I will renew with you the everlasting
    covenant,
  the benefits assured to David.
As I made him a witness to
    the peoples,
  a leader and commander of nations,

so shall you summon a nation you
knew not,
and nations that knew you not shall
run to you,
because of the LORD, your God,
the Holy One of Israel, who has
glorified you.

Seek the LORD while he may
be found,
call him while he is near.
Let the scoundrel forsake his way,
and the wicked man his thoughts;
let him turn to the LORD for mercy;
to our God, who is generous
in forgiving.
For my thoughts are not your
thoughts,
nor are your ways my ways, says
the LORD.

As high as the heavens are above
the earth,
so high are my ways above
your ways
and my thoughts above
your thoughts.

For just as from the heavens
the rain and snow come down
and do not return there
till they have watered the earth,
making it fertile and fruitful,
giving seed to the one who sows
and bread to the one who eats,
so shall my word be
that goes forth from my mouth;
my word shall not return to me void,
but shall do my will,
achieving the end for which I
sent it.

RESPONSORIAL PSALM

Isaiah 12:2–3, 4bcd, 5–6

Music: Owen Alstott, b. 1947, © 1977, 1990, OCP. All rights reserved.

▶ God indeed is my savior;
I am confident and unafraid.
My strength and my courage is
the LORD,
and he has been my savior.
With joy you will draw water
at the fountain of salvation. ℟.

▶ Give thanks to the LORD, acclaim
his name;
among the nations make known
his deeds,

proclaim how exalted is
his name. ℟.

▶ Sing praise to the LORD for his
glorious achievement;
let this be known throughout all
the earth.
Shout with exultation, O city of Zion,
for great in your midst
is the Holy One of Israel! ℟.

SIXTH READING

Baruch 3:9–15, 32—4:4

Hear, O Israel, the commandments
of life:
listen, and know prudence!
How is it, Israel,
that you are in the land of
your foes,

grown old in a foreign land,
defiled with the dead,
accounted with those destined for
the netherworld?
You have forsaken the fountain
of wisdom!

Had you walked in the way of God,
you would have dwelt in
enduring peace.
Learn where prudence is,
where strength, where
understanding;
that you may know also
where are length of days, and life,
where light of the eyes, and peace.
Who has found the place of wisdom,
who has entered into
her treasuries?

The One who knows all things
knows her;
he has probed her by his
knowledge—
the One who established the earth
for all time,
and filled it with four-footed beasts;
he who dismisses the light,
and it departs,
calls it, and it obeys him trembling;
before whom the stars at their posts
shine and rejoice;

when he calls them, they answer,
"Here we are!"
shining with joy for their Maker.
Such is our God;
no other is to be compared to him:
he has traced out the whole way
of understanding,
and has given her to Jacob,
his servant,
to Israel, his beloved son.

Since then she has appeared
on earth,
and moved among people.
She is the book of the precepts
of God,
the law that endures forever;
all who cling to her will live,
but those will die who forsake her.
Turn, O Jacob, and receive her:
walk by her light toward splendor.
Give not your glory to another,
your privileges to an alien race.
Blessed are we, O Israel;
for what pleases God is known
to us!

RESPONSORIAL PSALM
Psalm 19:8, 9, 10, 11

℟. Lord, you have the words of ev - er - last - ing life.

Music: Owen Alstott, b. 1947, © 1977, 1990, OCP. All rights reserved.

▸ The law of the LORD is perfect,
refreshing the soul;
the decree of the LORD is trustworthy,
giving wisdom to the simple. ℟.

▸ The precepts of the LORD are right,
rejoicing the heart;
the command of the LORD is clear,
enlightening the eye. ℟.

▸ The fear of the LORD is pure,
enduring forever;
the ordinances of the LORD are true,
all of them just. ℟.

▸ They are more precious than gold,
than a heap of purest gold;
sweeter also than syrup
or honey from the comb. ℟.

SEVENTH READING
Ezekiel 36:16–17a, 18–28

The word of the LORD came to me, saying: Son of man, when the house of Israel lived in their land, they defiled it by their conduct and deeds. Therefore I poured out my fury upon them because of the blood that they poured out on the ground, and because they defiled it with idols. I scattered them among the nations, dispersing them over foreign lands; according to their conduct and deeds I judged them. But when they came among the nations wherever they came, they served to profane my holy name, because it was said of them: "These are the people of the LORD, yet they had to leave their land." So I have relented because of my holy name which the house of Israel profaned among the nations where they came. Therefore say to the house of Israel: Thus says the Lord GOD: Not for your sakes do I act, house of Israel, but for the sake of my holy name, which you profaned among the nations to which you came. I will prove the holiness of my great name, profaned among the nations, in whose midst you have profaned it. Thus the nations shall know that I am the LORD, says the Lord GOD, when in their sight I prove my holiness through you. For I will take you away from among the nations, gather you from all the foreign lands, and bring you back to your own land. I will sprinkle clean water upon you to cleanse you from all your impurities, and from all your idols I will cleanse you. I will give you a new heart and place a new spirit within you, taking from your bodies your stony hearts and giving you natural hearts. I will put my spirit within you and make you live by my statutes, careful to observe my decrees. You shall live in the land I gave your fathers; you shall be my people, and I will be your God.

RESPONSORIAL PSALM

(When baptism is celebrated) Psalms 42:3, 5; 43:3, 4

Music: Owen Alstott, b. 1947, © 1977, 1990, OCP. All rights reserved.

▶ Athirst is my soul for God, the
    living God.
  When shall I go and behold the
    face of God? ℟.

▶ I went with the throng
    and led them in procession to the
      house of God,
  amid loud cries of joy
    and thanksgiving,
  with the multitude keeping
    festival. ℟.

▶ Send forth your light and
    your fidelity;
  they shall lead me on
  and bring me to your holy mountain,
    to your dwelling-place. ℟.

▶ Then will I go in to the altar of God,
    the God of my gladness and joy;
  then will I give you thanks upon
    the harp,
  O God, my God! ℟.

Or

RESPONSORIAL PSALM

(When baptism is not celebrated)   Isaiah 12:2–3, 4bcd, 5–6

℟. You will draw wa - ter joy - ful - ly

from the springs of sal - va - tion.

Music: Owen Alstott, b. 1947, © 1977, 1990, OCP. All rights reserved.

▶ God indeed is my savior;
  I am confident and unafraid.
My strength and my courage is
    the LORD,
  and he has been my savior.
With joy you will draw water
  at the fountain of salvation. ℟.

▶ Give thanks to the LORD, acclaim
    his name;
  among the nations make known
    his deeds,

proclaim how exalted is
  his name. ℟.

▶ Sing praise to the LORD for his
    glorious achievement;
  let this be known throughout all
    the earth.
Shout with exultation, O city of Zion,
  for great in your midst
  is the Holy One of Israel! ℟.

Or

RESPONSORIAL PSALM

(When baptism is not celebrated)   Psalm 51:12–13, 14–15, 18–19

℟. Cre - ate [a clean heart,] a clean heart in me, O God.

Music: Owen Alstott, b. 1947, © 1977, 1990, OCP. All rights reserved.

▶ A clean heart create for me, O God,
  and a steadfast spirit renew
    within me.
Cast me not out from your presence,
  and your Holy Spirit take not
    from me. ℟.

▶ Give me back the joy of your
    salvation,
  and a willing spirit sustain in me.

I will teach transgressors your ways,
  and sinners shall return to you. ℟.

▶ For you are not pleased with
    sacrifices;
  should I offer a holocaust, you
    would not accept it.
My sacrifice, O God, is a contrite
    spirit;
  a heart contrite and humbled,
    O God, you will not spurn. ℟.

*After the last reading from the Old Testament with its Responsorial Psalm and prayer,
the altar candles are lit and the Priest intones the "Gloria," which is taken up by all
present (for music, see #146, 169, 176, 186, 196, 206, 216, 226, 234, 244). The church bells
are rung, according to local custom.*

COLLECT

EPISTLE
Romans 6:3–11

Brothers and sisters: Are you unaware that we who were baptized into Christ Jesus were baptized into his death? We were indeed buried with him through baptism into death, so that, just as Christ was raised from the dead by the glory of the Father, we too might live in newness of life.

For if we have grown into union with him through a death like his, we shall also be united with him in the resurrection. We know that our old self was crucified with him, so that our sinful body might be done away with, that we might no longer be in slavery to sin. For a dead person has been absolved from sin. If, then, we have died with Christ, we believe that we shall also live with him. We know that Christ, raised from the dead, dies no more; death no longer has power over him. As to his death, he died to sin once and for all; as to his life, he lives for God. Consequently, you too must think of yourselves as being dead to sin and living for God in Christ Jesus.

After the Epistle has been read, all rise, then the Priest solemnly intones the Alleluia three times, raising his voice by a step each time, with all repeating it. If necessary, the psalmist intones the Alleluia. Then the psalmist or cantor proclaims Psalm 118 (below) with the people responding "Alleluia."

RESPONSORIAL PSALM
Psalm 118:1–2, 16–17, 22–23

℟. Al - le - lu - ia, al - le - lu - ia, al - le - lu - ia.

Music: Owen Alstott, b. 1947, © 1977, 1990, OCP. All rights reserved.

▶ Give thanks to the LORD, for he
    is good,
  for his mercy endures forever.
Let the house of Israel say,
  "His mercy endures forever." ℟.

▶ "The right hand of the LORD has struck
    with power;
  the right hand of the LORD
    is exalted.

I shall not die, but live,
  and declare the works of
    the LORD." ℟.

▶ The stone which the builders rejected
  has become the cornerstone.
By the LORD has this been done;
  it is wonderful in our eyes. ℟.

GOSPEL — A
Matthew 28:1–10

After the sabbath, as the first day of the week was dawning, Mary Magdalene and the other Mary came to see the tomb. And behold, there was a great earthquake; for an angel of the Lord descended from heaven, approached, rolled back the stone, and sat upon it. His appearance was like lightning and his clothing was white as snow. The guards were shaken with fear of him and became like dead men. Then the angel said to the women in reply, "Do not be afraid! I know that you are seeking Jesus the crucified. He is not here, for he has been raised just as he said. Come and see the place where he lay. Then go quickly and tell his disciples, 'He has been raised from the dead, and he is going before you to Galilee; there you

will see him.' Behold, I have told you."
Then they went away quickly from the
tomb, fearful yet overjoyed, and ran
to announce this to his disciples. And
behold, Jesus met them on their way
and greeted them. They approached,
embraced his feet, and did him
homage. Then Jesus said to them, "Do
not be afraid. Go tell my brothers to go
to Galilee, and there they will see me."

GOSPEL — B

Mark 16:1–7

When the sabbath was over, Mary
Magdalene, Mary, the mother of James,
and Salome bought spices so that
they might go and anoint him. Very
early when the sun had risen, on the
first day of the week, they came to
the tomb. They were saying to one
another, "Who will roll back the stone
for us from the entrance to the tomb?"
When they looked up, they saw that
the stone had been rolled back; it
was very large. On entering the tomb
they saw a young man sitting on the
right side, clothed in a white robe, and
they were utterly amazed. He said to
them, "Do not be amazed! You seek
Jesus of Nazareth, the crucified. He
has been raised; he is not here. Behold
the place where they laid him. But go
and tell his disciples and Peter, 'He
is going before you to Galilee; there
you will see him, as he told you.'"

GOSPEL — C

Luke 24:1–12

At daybreak on the first day of the
week the women who had come from
Galilee with Jesus took the spices they
had prepared and went to the tomb.
They found the stone rolled away from
the tomb; but when they entered, they
did not find the body of the Lord Jesus.
While they were puzzling over this,
behold, two men in dazzling garments
appeared to them. They were terrified
and bowed their faces to the ground.
They said to them, "Why do you seek
the living one among the dead? He
is not here, but he has been raised.
Remember what he said to you while
he was still in Galilee, that the Son of
Man must be handed over to sinners
and be crucified, and rise on the
third day." And they remembered his
words. Then they returned from the
tomb and announced all these things
to the eleven and to all the others. The
women were Mary Magdalene, Joanna,
and Mary the mother of James; the
others who accompanied them also
told this to the apostles, but their story
seemed like nonsense and they did
not believe them. But Peter got up and
ran to the tomb, bent down, and saw
the burial cloths alone; then he went
home amazed at what had happened.

*The homily follows the Gospel. After the homily, the sacraments of Baptism and
Confirmation take place. If there are no candidates for Baptism and Confirmation, the
Renewal of Baptismal Promises occurs instead.*

THIRD PART: BAPTISMAL LITURGY

CELEBRATION OF BAPTISM

*Following the homily, the Deacon or another minister calls the candidates for Baptism,
along with their godparents, forth from the assembly. The invitation to prayer and the
Litany of the Saints follow (for music, see #394, 503). When there are no baptisms and
the font is not to be blessed, the Litany of the Saints is omitted and the Blessing of
Water for all the faithful takes place at once.*

Blessing of Baptismal Water

If there are candidates for Baptism, the Priest then blesses the water which will be used for Baptism. After saying the words "...through water and the Holy Spirit," he may lower the paschal candle into the water once or three times, then hold it there for the remainder of the blessing. After the paschal candle has been lifted out of the water, the people sing a suitable acclamation (see #399). If there are no candidates for Baptism, the Priest blesses the water and continues with the Renewal of Baptismal Promises.

Renunciation of Sin and Profession of Faith

The Priest then asks the candidates to renounce sin. Then the Priest, informed again of each baptismal candidate's name by the godparents, asks each of them (or the group as a whole, if it is large) to profess his or her faith.

Baptism

Immediately after his or her profession of faith, the Priest baptizes each candidate either by a threefold immersion or pouring of water using the words, "N., I baptize you in the name of the Father, and of the Son, and of the Holy Spirit."

After each Baptism, the assembly may sing a suitable acclamation (for music, see #254–256). If there are great numbers to be baptized, the baptisms may be accompanied by singing.

Anointing after Baptism and Clothing with a Baptismal Garment

If the Confirmation of those baptized is separated from their Baptism, the Priest anoints them immediately. The newly baptized are then clothed with baptismal garments (this rite is optional and may be omitted). At the words "Receive this baptismal garment" the godparents place the garment on the newly baptized.

Presentation of a Lighted Candle

A godparent of each of the newly baptized goes to the Priest, lights a candle from the paschal candle, then presents it to the newly baptized.

The Renewal of Baptismal Promises

When the Rite of Baptism (and Confirmation) has been completed or, if this has not taken place, after the blessing of water, all stand, holding lighted candles in their hands, and renew the promise of baptismal faith, unless this has already been done together with those to be baptized.

Following this, the Priest sprinkles the whole assembly with the blessed baptismal water, while all sing a song that is baptismal in character (for music, see #167, 242, 254–256).

If there are no candidates for reception into full communion of the Catholic Church, continue with the Celebration of Confirmation, on next page.

Celebration of Reception

The Priest invites the candidates for reception, along with their sponsors, to come into the sanctuary and before the community to make a profession of faith. Then the candidates with their sponsors go individually to the Priest, to be received into the full communion of the Catholic Church.

CELEBRATION OF CONFIRMATION

The newly baptized with their godparents and, if they have not received the Sacrament of Confirmation, the newly received with their sponsors, now stand before the Priest. After a brief prayer, each candidate, with godparents or sponsors, goes to the Priest (or, if circumstances require, the Priest may go to the candidates). Either or both godparents and sponsors place the right hand on the shoulder of the candidate; a godparent or a sponsor gives the candidate's name to the minister of the sacrament. The minister anoints each candidate using the words, "N., be sealed with the Gift of the Holy Spirit."

During the conferral of the sacrament an appropriate song may be sung (for music, see #432–444). After all have received the sacrament, the newly confirmed as well as the godparents and sponsors return to their places in the assembly.

Since the Creed is not said, the Prayer of the Faithful begins immediately.

FOURTH PART: THE LITURGY OF THE EUCHARIST

The rite continues with the Liturgy of the Eucharist. The Easter Vigil liturgy ends with a Solemn Blessing or the final blessing formula from the Rite of Baptism of Adults or of Children, according to circumstances.

EASTER SUNDAY OF THE RESURRECTION OF THE LORD: 902 AT THE MASS DURING THE DAY — ABC

FIRST READING   *Acts of the Apostles 10:34a, 37–43*

Peter proceeded to speak and said: "You know what has happened all over Judea, beginning in Galilee after the baptism that John preached, how God anointed Jesus of Nazareth with the Holy Spirit and power. He went about doing good and healing all those oppressed by the devil, for God was with him. We are witnesses of all that he did both in the country of the Jews and in Jerusalem. They put him to death by hanging him on a tree. This man God raised on the third day and granted that he be visible, not to all the people, but to us, the witnesses chosen by God in advance, who ate and drank with him after he rose from the dead. He commissioned us to preach to the people and testify that he is the one appointed by God as judge of the living and the dead. To him all the prophets bear witness, that everyone who believes in him will receive forgiveness of sins through his name."

RESPONSORIAL PSALM   *Psalm 118:1–2, 16–17, 22–23*

℟. This is the day the Lord has made; let us re-joice and be glad.

Music: Owen Alstott, b. 1947, © 1977, 1990, OCP. All rights reserved.

Or ℟. **Alleluia.**

℟. **This is the day the Lord has made; let us rejoice and be glad.**
Or ℟. **Alleluia.**

▸ Give thanks to the LORD, for he
  is good,
   for his mercy endures forever.
  Let the house of Israel say,
   "His mercy endures forever." ℟.

▸ "The right hand of the LORD has
   struck with power;
   the right hand of the LORD
   is exalted.

I shall not die, but live,
 and declare the works of
  the LORD." ℟.

▸ The stone which the builders rejected
  has become the cornerstone.
 By the LORD has this been done;
  it is wonderful in our eyes. ℟.

SECOND READING

Colossians 3:1–4

Brothers and sisters: If then you
were raised with Christ, seek what
is above, where Christ is seated at
the right hand of God. Think of what
is above, not of what is on earth.

For you have died, and your life is
hidden with Christ in God. When
Christ your life appears, then you
too will appear with him in glory.

Or

SECOND READING

1 Corinthians 5:6b–8

Brothers and sisters: Do you not know
that a little yeast leavens all the dough?
Clear out the old yeast, so that you
may become a fresh batch of dough,
inasmuch as you are unleavened.
For our paschal lamb, Christ, has

been sacrificed. Therefore, let us
celebrate the feast, not with the
old yeast, the yeast of malice and
wickedness, but with the unleavened
bread of sincerity and truth.

SEQUENCE

Victimae Paschali Laudes

The Sequence, Victimae Paschali Laudes, *is sung before the Gospel Acclamation on
Easter Sunday. (For music, see #396–398.)*

**Christians, to the Paschal Victim
 Offer your thankful praises!
A Lamb the sheep redeems;
 Christ, who only is sinless,
 Reconciles sinners to the Father.
Death and life have contended in that
 combat stupendous:
 The Prince of life, who died,
 reigns immortal.
Speak, Mary, declaring
 What you saw, wayfaring.**

**"The tomb of Christ, who is living,
 The glory of Jesus' resurrection;
Bright angels attesting,
 The shroud and napkin resting.
Yes, Christ my hope is arisen;
 To Galilee he goes before you."
Christ indeed from death is risen,
 our new life obtaining.
Have mercy, victor King,
 ever reigning!
Amen. Alleluia.**

GOSPEL ACCLAMATION

cf. 1 Corinthians 5:7b–8a

℟. Al - le - lu - ia, al - le - lu - ia, al - le - lu - ia.

(Omit if not sung)

▶ Christ, our paschal lamb, has been sacrificed;
let us then feast with joy in the Lord. ℟.

(Options: At an afternoon or evening Mass, another Gospel may be read: Luke 24:13–35 [see Lectionary number 46]. The Gospel from the Easter Vigil [see Lectionary number 41] may also be read in place of the following Gospel at any time of the day.)

GOSPEL
John 20:1–9

On the first day of the week, Mary of Magdala came to the tomb early in the morning, while it was still dark, and saw the stone removed from the tomb. So she ran and went to Simon Peter and to the other disciple whom Jesus loved, and told them, "They have taken the Lord from the tomb, and we don't know where they put him." So Peter and the other disciple went out and came to the tomb. They both ran, but the other disciple ran faster than Peter and arrived at the tomb first; he bent down and saw the burial cloths there, but did not go in. When Simon Peter arrived after him, he went into the tomb and saw the burial cloths there, and the cloth that had covered his head, not with the burial cloths but rolled up in a separate place. Then the other disciple also went in, the one who had arrived at the tomb first, and he saw and believed. For they did not yet understand the Scripture that he had to rise from the dead.

THE RENEWAL OF BAPTISMAL PROMISES
The renewal of baptismal promises takes place at all Masses today. The form followed is the same as at the Easter Vigil. The Creed is omitted. Mass continues with the Prayer of the Faithful.

SECOND SUNDAY OF EASTER
(OR SUNDAY OF DIVINE MERCY) — ABC
903

FIRST READING — A
Acts of the Apostles 2:42–47

They devoted themselves to the teaching of the apostles and to the communal life, to the breaking of bread and to the prayers. Awe came upon everyone, and many wonders and signs were done through the apostles. All who believed were together and had all things in common; they would sell their property and possessions and divide them among all according to each one's need. Every day they devoted themselves to meeting together in the temple area and to breaking bread in their homes. They ate their meals with exultation and sincerity of heart, praising God and enjoying favor with all the people. And every day the Lord added to their number those who were being saved.

FIRST READING — B
Acts of the Apostles 4:32–35

The community of believers was of one heart and mind, and no one claimed that any of his possessions was his own, but they had everything in common. With great power the apostles bore witness to the resurrection of the Lord Jesus, and great favor was accorded them all. There was no needy person among them, for those who owned property or houses would sell them, bring the proceeds of the sale, and put them at the feet of the apostles, and they were distributed to each according to need.

FIRST READING — C

Acts of the Apostles 5:12–16

Many signs and wonders were done among the people at the hands of the apostles. They were all together in Solomon's portico. None of the others dared to join them, but the people esteemed them. Yet more than ever, believers in the Lord, great numbers of men and women, were added to them. Thus they even carried the sick out into the streets and laid them on cots and mats so that when Peter came by, at least his shadow might fall on one or another of them. A large number of people from the towns in the vicinity of Jerusalem also gathered, bringing the sick and those disturbed by unclean spirits, and they were all cured.

RESPONSORIAL PSALM

Psalm 118:2–4, 13–15, 22–24

℞. Give thanks to the Lord for he is good, his love is ev-er-last-ing.

Music: Owen Alstott, b. 1947, © 1977, 1990, OCP. All rights reserved.

Or ℞. *Alleluia.*

▶ Let the house of Israel say,
  "His mercy endures forever."
Let the house of Aaron say,
  "His mercy endures forever."
Let those who fear the LORD say,
  "His mercy endures forever." ℞.

▶ I was hard pressed and was falling,
  but the LORD helped me.
My strength and my courage is
  the LORD,

and he has been my savior.
The joyful shout of victory
  in the tents of the just. ℞.

▶ The stone which the builders rejected
  has become the cornerstone.
By the LORD has this been done;
  it is wonderful in our eyes.
This is the day the LORD has made;
  let us be glad and rejoice in it. ℞.

SECOND READING — A

1 Peter 1:3–9

Blessed be the God and Father of our Lord Jesus Christ, who in his great mercy gave us a new birth to a living hope through the resurrection of Jesus Christ from the dead, to an inheritance that is imperishable, undefiled, and unfading, kept in heaven for you who by the power of God are safeguarded through faith, to a salvation that is ready to be revealed in the final time. In this you rejoice, although now for a little while you may have to suffer through various trials, so that the genuineness of your faith, more precious than gold that is perishable even though tested by fire, may prove to be for praise, glory, and honor at the revelation of Jesus Christ. Although you have not seen him you love him; even though you do not see him now yet believe in him, you rejoice with an indescribable and glorious joy, as you attain the goal of your faith, the salvation of your souls.

SECOND READING — B

1 John 5:1–6

Beloved: Everyone who believes that Jesus is the Christ is begotten by God, and everyone who loves the Father loves also the one begotten by him.

In this way we know that we love the children of God when we love God and obey his commandments. For the love of God is this, that we keep his commandments. And his commandments are not burdensome, for whoever is begotten by God conquers the world. And the victory that conquers the world is our faith.

Who indeed is the victor over the world but the one who believes that Jesus is the Son of God?

This is the one who came through water and blood, Jesus Christ, not by water alone, but by water and blood. The Spirit is the one that testifies, and the Spirit is truth.

SECOND READING — C
Revelation 1:9–11a, 12–13, 17–19

I, John, your brother, who share with you the distress, the kingdom, and the endurance we have in Jesus, found myself on the island called Patmos because I proclaimed God's word and gave testimony to Jesus. I was caught up in spirit on the Lord's day and heard behind me a voice as loud as a trumpet, which said, "Write on a scroll what you see." Then I turned to see whose voice it was that spoke to me, and when I turned, I saw seven gold lampstands and in the midst of the lampstands one like a son of man, wearing an ankle-length robe, with a gold sash around his chest.

When I caught sight of him, I fell down at his feet as though dead. He touched me with his right hand and said, "Do not be afraid. I am the first and the last, the one who lives. Once I was dead, but now I am alive forever and ever. I hold the keys to death and the netherworld. Write down, therefore, what you have seen, and what is happening, and what will happen afterwards."

GOSPEL ACCLAMATION
John 20:29

℟. Al - le - lu - ia, al - le - lu - ia, al - le - lu - ia.

Music: Owen Alstott, b. 1947, © 1977, 1990, OCP. All rights reserved. *(Omit if not sung)*

▸ You believe in me, Thomas, because you have seen me, says the Lord; blessed are they who have not seen me, but still believe! ℟.

GOSPEL
John 20:19–31

On the evening of that first day of the week, when the doors were locked, where the disciples were, for fear of the Jews, Jesus came and stood in their midst and said to them, "Peace be with you." When he had said this, he showed them his hands and his side. The disciples rejoiced when they saw the Lord. Jesus said to them again, "Peace be with you. As the Father has sent me, so I send you." And when he had said this, he breathed on them and said to them, "Receive the Holy Spirit. Whose sins you forgive are forgiven them, and whose sins you retain are retained."

Thomas, called Didymus, one of the Twelve, was not with them when Jesus came. So the other disciples said to him, "We have seen the Lord." But he said to them, "Unless I see the mark of the nails in his hands and put my finger into the nailmarks and put my hand into his side, I will not believe."

Now a week later his disciples were again inside and Thomas was with them. Jesus came, although the doors were locked, and stood in their midst and said, "Peace be with you." Then he said to Thomas, "Put your finger here and see my hands, and bring your hand and put it into my side, and do not be unbelieving, but believe." Thomas answered and said to him, "My Lord and my God!" Jesus said to him, "Have you come to believe because you have seen me? Blessed are those who have not seen and have believed."

Now Jesus did many other signs in the presence of his disciples that are not written in this book. But these are written that you may come to believe that Jesus is the Christ, the Son of God, and that through this belief you may have life in his name.

904   THIRD SUNDAY OF EASTER — A

FIRST READING

Acts of the Apostles 2:14, 22–33

Then Peter stood up with the Eleven, raised his voice, and proclaimed: "You who are Jews, indeed all of you staying in Jerusalem. Let this be known to you, and listen to my words. You who are Israelites, hear these words. Jesus the Nazorean was a man commended to you by God with mighty deeds, wonders, and signs, which God worked through him in your midst, as you yourselves know. This man, delivered up by the set plan and foreknowledge of God, you killed, using lawless men to crucify him. But God raised him up, releasing him from the throes of death, because it was impossible for him to be held by it. For David says of him:
I saw the Lord ever before me,
   with him at my right hand I shall
     not be disturbed.
Therefore my heart has been glad
   and my tongue has exulted;
my flesh, too, will dwell in hope,
because you will not abandon my
   soul to the netherworld,
   nor will you suffer your holy one
     to see corruption.
You have made known to me
   the paths of life;
   you will fill me with joy
     in your presence.

"My brothers, one can confidently say to you about the patriarch David that he died and was buried, and his tomb is in our midst to this day. But since he was a prophet and knew that God had sworn an oath to him that he would set one of his descendants upon his throne, he foresaw and spoke of the resurrection of the Christ, that neither was he abandoned to the netherworld nor did his flesh see corruption. God raised this Jesus; of this we are all witnesses. Exalted at the right hand of God, he received the promise of the Holy Spirit from the Father and poured him forth, as you see and hear."

RESPONSORIAL PSALM

Psalm 16:1–2, 5, 7–8, 9–10, 11

℟. Lord, you will show us the path of life.

Music: Owen Alstott, b. 1947, © 1977, 1990, OCP. All rights reserved.

Or ℟. **Alleluia.**

▶ Keep me, O God, for in you
   I take refuge;
   I say to the LORD, "My Lord
   are you."

O LORD, my allotted portion and
   my cup,
   you it is who hold fast my lot. ℟.

▸ I bless the LORD who counsels me;
    even in the night my heart
      exhorts me.
I set the LORD ever before me;
    with him at my right hand I shall
      not be disturbed. ℟.

▸ Therefore my heart is glad and my
    soul rejoices,
    my body, too, abides in confidence;

because you will not abandon my
    soul to the netherworld,
    nor will you suffer your faithful one
      to undergo corruption. ℟.

▸ You will show me the path to life,
    abounding joy in your presence,
    the delights at your right
      hand forever. ℟.

SECOND READING

1 Peter 1:17–21

Beloved: If you invoke as Father him who judges impartially according to each one's works, conduct yourselves with reverence during the time of your sojourning, realizing that you were ransomed from your futile conduct, handed on by your ancestors, not with perishable things like silver or gold but with the precious blood of Christ as of a spotless unblemished lamb.

He was known before the foundation of the world but revealed in the final time for you, who through him believe in God who raised him from the dead and gave him glory, so that your faith and hope are in God.

GOSPEL ACCLAMATION

cf. Luke 24:32

℟. Al - le - lu - ia,   al - le - lu - ia,   al - le - lu - ia.

     (Omit if not sung)

▸ Lord Jesus, open the Scriptures to us;
  make our hearts burn while you speak to us. ℟.

GOSPEL

Luke 24:13–35

That very day, the first day of the week, two of Jesus' disciples were going to a village seven miles from Jerusalem called Emmaus, and they were conversing about all the things that had occurred. And it happened that while they were conversing and debating, Jesus himself drew near and walked with them, but their eyes were prevented from recognizing him. He asked them, "What are you discussing as you walk along?" They stopped, looking downcast. One of them, named Cleopas, said to him in reply, "Are you the only visitor to Jerusalem who does not know of the things that have taken place there in these days?" And he replied to them, "What sort of things?" They said to him, "The things that happened to Jesus the Nazarene, who was a prophet mighty in deed and word before God and all the people, how our chief priests and rulers both handed him over to a sentence of death and crucified him. But we were hoping that he would be the one to redeem Israel; and besides all this, it is now the third day since this took place. Some women from our group, however, have astounded us: they were at the tomb early in the morning and did not find his body; they came back and reported that they had indeed seen a vision of angels who announced that he was alive. Then some of those with us went to the tomb and found things just as the women had described, but him they did not see." And he said to them, "Oh, how foolish you are! How slow of heart to believe all that the prophets spoke! Was it not necessary that the Christ should suffer these things and enter into his glory?" Then beginning with Moses and all the prophets, he interpreted to them what referred to him in all the Scriptures. As they approached the village to which they were going, he gave the impression that he was going on farther. But they urged him, "Stay with us, for it is nearly evening and the day is almost over." So he went in to stay with them. And it happened that, while he was with them at table, he took bread, said the blessing, broke it, and gave it to them.

With that their eyes were opened and they recognized him, but he vanished from their sight. Then they said to each other, "Were not our hearts burning within us while he spoke to us on the way and opened the Scriptures to us?" So they set out at once and returned to Jerusalem where they found gathered together the eleven and those with them who were saying, "The Lord has truly been raised and has appeared to Simon!" Then the two recounted what had taken place on the way and how he was made known to them in the breaking of bread.

---

905 THIRD SUNDAY OF EASTER — B

FIRST READING
Acts of the Apostles 3:13–15, 17–19

Peter said to the people: "The God of Abraham, the God of Isaac, and the God of Jacob, the God of our fathers, has glorified his servant Jesus, whom you handed over and denied in Pilate's presence when he had decided to release him. You denied the Holy and Righteous One and asked that a murderer be released to you. The author of life you put to

death, but God raised him from the dead; of this we are witnesses. Now I know, brothers, that you acted out of ignorance, just as your leaders did; but God has thus brought to fulfillment what he had announced beforehand through the mouth of all the prophets, that his Christ would suffer. Repent, therefore, and be converted, that your sins may be wiped away."

RESPONSORIAL PSALM
Psalm 4:2, 4, 7–8, 9

℟. Lord, let your face shine on us.

Music: Owen Alstott, b. 1947, © 1977, 1990, OCP. All rights reserved.

Or ℟. **Alleluia.**

▸ When I call, answer me, O my
  just God,
  you who relieve me when I am
  in distress;
  have pity on me, and hear
  my prayer! ℟.

▸ Know that the LORD does wonders for
  his faithful one;
  the LORD will hear me when I call
  upon him. ℟.

▸ O LORD, let the light of your
  countenance shine upon us!
  You put gladness into my heart. ℟.

▸ As soon as I lie down, I fall
  peacefully asleep,
  for you alone, O LORD,
  bring security to my dwelling. ℟.

SECOND READING

1 John 2:1–5a

My children, I am writing this to you so that you may not commit sin. But if anyone does sin, we have an Advocate with the Father, Jesus Christ the righteous one. He is expiation for our sins, and not for our sins only but for those of the whole world. The way we may be sure that we know him is to keep his commandments. Those who say, "I know him," but do not keep his commandments are liars, and the truth is not in them. But whoever keeps his word, the love of God is truly perfected in him.

GOSPEL ACCLAMATION

cf. Luke 24:32

℟. Al - le - lu - ia, al - le - lu - ia, al - le - lu - ia.

(Omit if not sung)

▶ Lord Jesus, open the Scriptures to us;
  make our hearts burn while you speak to us. ℟.

GOSPEL

Luke 24:35–48

The two disciples recounted what had taken place on the way, and how Jesus was made known to them in the breaking of bread.

While they were still speaking about this, he stood in their midst and said to them, "Peace be with you." But they were startled and terrified and thought that they were seeing a ghost. Then he said to them, "Why are you troubled? And why do questions arise in your hearts? Look at my hands and my feet, that it is I myself. Touch me and see, because a ghost does not have flesh and bones as you can see I have." And as he said this, he showed them his hands and his feet. While they were still incredulous for joy and were amazed, he asked them, "Have you anything here to eat?" They gave him a piece of baked fish; he took it and ate it in front of them.

He said to them, "These are my words that I spoke to you while I was still with you, that everything written about me in the law of Moses and in the prophets and psalms must be fulfilled." Then he opened their minds to understand the Scriptures. And he said to them, "Thus it is written that the Christ would suffer and rise from the dead on the third day and that repentance, for the forgiveness of sins, would be preached in his name to all the nations, beginning from Jerusalem. You are witnesses of these things."

THIRD SUNDAY OF EASTER — C   906

FIRST READING

Acts of the Apostles 5:27–32, 40b–41

When the captain and the court officers had brought the apostles in and made them stand before the Sanhedrin, the high priest questioned them, "We gave you strict orders, did we not, to stop teaching in that name? Yet you have filled Jerusalem with your teaching and want to bring this man's blood upon us." But Peter and the apostles said in reply, "We must obey God rather than men. The God of our ancestors raised Jesus, though you had him killed by hanging him on a tree. God exalted him at his right hand as leader and savior to grant Israel repentance and forgiveness of sins. We are witnesses of these things, as is the Holy Spirit whom God has given to those who obey him."

   The Sanhedrin ordered the apostles to stop speaking in the name of Jesus, and dismissed them. So they left the presence of the Sanhedrin, rejoicing that they had been found worthy to suffer dishonor for the sake of the name.

RESPONSORIAL PSALM
Psalm 30:2, 4, 5–6, 11–12, 13

℟. I will praise you, Lord, for you have res-cued me.

Or ℟. **Alleluia.**

▸ I will extol you, O LORD, for you drew me clear
   and did not let my enemies rejoice over me.
O LORD, you brought me up from the netherworld;
   you preserved me from among those going down into the pit. ℟.

▸ Sing praise to the LORD, you his faithful ones,
   and give thanks to his holy name.

For his anger lasts but a moment;
   a lifetime, his good will.
At nightfall, weeping enters in,
   but with the dawn, rejoicing. ℟.

▸ Hear, O LORD, and have pity on me;
   O LORD, be my helper.
You changed my mourning into dancing;
   O LORD, my God, forever will I give you thanks. ℟.

SECOND READING
Revelation 5:11–14

I, John, looked and heard the voices of many angels who surrounded the throne and the living creatures and the elders. They were countless in number, and they cried out in a loud voice:
   "Worthy is the Lamb that was slain
      to receive power and riches,
         wisdom and strength,
      honor and glory and blessing."
Then I heard every creature in heaven and on earth and under the earth and in the sea, everything in the universe, cry out:
   "To the one who sits on the throne
      and to the Lamb
      be blessing and honor, glory
         and might,
      forever and ever."
The four living creatures answered, "Amen," and the elders fell down and worshiped.

GOSPEL ACCLAMATION

℟. Al-le-lu - ia, al - le - lu - ia, al-le-lu - ia.

(Omit if not sung)

▸ Christ is risen, creator of all;
   he has shown pity on all people. ℟.

GOSPEL

John 21:1–19 or 21:1–14

(Include bracketed text for Long Form)

At that time, Jesus revealed himself again to his disciples at the Sea of Tiberias. He revealed himself in this way. Together were Simon Peter, Thomas called Didymus, Nathanael from Cana in Galilee, Zebedee's sons, and two others of his disciples. Simon Peter said to them, "I am going fishing." They said to him, "We also will come with you." So they went out and got into the boat, but that night they caught nothing. When it was already dawn, Jesus was standing on the shore; but the disciples did not realize that it was Jesus. Jesus said to them, "Children, have you caught anything to eat?" They answered him, "No." So he said to them, "Cast the net over the right side of the boat and you will find something." So they cast it, and were not able to pull it in because of the number of fish. So the disciple whom Jesus loved said to Peter, "It is the Lord." When Simon Peter heard that it was the Lord, he tucked in his garment, for he was lightly clad, and jumped into the sea. The other disciples came in the boat, for they were not far from shore, only about a hundred yards, dragging the net with the fish. When they climbed out on shore, they saw a charcoal fire with fish on it and bread. Jesus said to them, "Bring some of the fish you just caught." So Simon Peter went over and dragged the net ashore full of one hundred fifty-three large fish. Even though there were so many, the net was not torn. Jesus said to them, "Come, have breakfast." And none of the disciples dared to ask him, "Who are you?" because they realized it was the Lord. Jesus came over and took the bread and gave it to them, and in like manner the fish. This was now the third time Jesus was revealed to his disciples after being raised from the dead.

[When they had finished breakfast, Jesus said to Simon Peter, "Simon, son of John, do you love me more than these?" Simon Peter answered him, "Yes, Lord, you know that I love you." Jesus said to him, "Feed my lambs." He then said to Simon Peter a second time, "Simon, son of John, do you love me?" Simon Peter answered him, "Yes, Lord, you know that I love you." Jesus said to him, "Tend my sheep." Jesus said to him the third time, "Simon, son of John, do you love me?" Peter was distressed that Jesus had said to him a third time, "Do you love me?" and he said to him, "Lord, you know everything; you know that I love you." Jesus said to him, "Feed my sheep. Amen, amen, I say to you, when you were younger, you used to dress yourself and go where you wanted; but when you grow old, you will stretch out your hands, and someone else will dress you and lead you where you do not want to go." He said this signifying by what kind of death he would glorify God. And when he had said this, he said to him, "Follow me."]

FOURTH SUNDAY OF EASTER — A   907

FIRST READING

Acts of the Apostles 2:14a, 36–41

Then Peter stood up with the Eleven, raised his voice, and proclaimed: "Let the whole house of Israel know for certain that God has made both Lord and Christ, this Jesus whom you crucified."

Now when they heard this, they were cut to the heart, and they asked Peter and the other apostles, "What are we to do, my brothers?" Peter said to them, "Repent and be baptized, every one of you, in the name of Jesus Christ for the forgiveness of your sins; and you will receive the gift of the Holy Spirit. For the promise is made to you and to your children and to all those far off, whomever the Lord our God will call." He testified with many other arguments, and was exhorting them, "Save yourselves from this corrupt generation." Those who accepted his message were baptized, and about three thousand persons were added that day.

RESPONSORIAL PSALM

Psalm 23:1–3a, 3b–4, 5, 6

R. The Lord is my shep-herd; there is noth-ing I shall want.

Or R. **Alleluia.**

▶ The LORD is my shepherd; I shall
  not want.
 In verdant pastures he gives
  me repose;
 beside restful waters he leads me;
  he refreshes my soul. R.

▶ He guides me in right paths
  for his name's sake.
 Even though I walk in the dark valley
  I fear no evil; for you are at my side
 with your rod and your staff
  that give me courage. R.

▶ You spread the table before me
  in the sight of my foes;
 you anoint my head with oil;
  my cup overflows. R.

▶ Only goodness and kindness
  follow me
 all the days of my life;
 and I shall dwell in the house of
  the LORD
  for years to come. R.

SECOND READING

1 Peter 2:20b–25

Beloved: If you are patient when you suffer for doing what is good, this is a grace before God. For to this you have been called, because Christ also suffered for you, leaving you an example that you should follow in his footsteps.
 He committed no sin, and no deceit
  was found in his mouth.
When he was insulted, he returned no insult; when he suffered, he did not threaten; instead, he handed himself over to the one who judges justly. He himself bore our sins in his body upon the cross, so that, free from sin, we might live for righteousness. By his wounds you have been healed. For you had gone astray like sheep, but you have now returned to the shepherd and guardian of your souls.

GOSPEL ACCLAMATION

John 10:14

R. Al - le - lu - ia, al - le - lu - ia, al - le - lu - ia.

(Omit if not sung)

▶ I am the good shepherd, says the Lord;
 I know my sheep, and mine know me. R.

GOSPEL

John 10:1–10

Jesus said: "Amen, amen, I say to you, whoever does not enter a sheepfold through the gate but climbs over elsewhere is a thief and a robber. But whoever enters through the gate is the shepherd of the sheep. The gatekeeper opens it for him, and the sheep hear his voice, as the shepherd calls his own sheep by name and leads them out. When he has driven out all his own, he walks ahead of them, and the sheep follow him, because they recognize his voice. But they will not follow a stranger; they will run away from him, because they do not recognize the voice of strangers." Although Jesus used this figure of speech, the Pharisees did not realize what he was trying to tell them.

So Jesus said again, "Amen, amen, I say to you, I am the gate for the sheep. All who came before me are thieves and robbers, but the sheep did not listen to them. I am the gate. Whoever enters through me will be saved, and will come in and go out and find pasture. A thief comes only to steal and slaughter and destroy; I came so that they might have life and have it more abundantly."

FOURTH SUNDAY OF EASTER — B   908

FIRST READING

Acts of the Apostles 4:8–12

Peter, filled with the Holy Spirit, said: "Leaders of the people and elders: If we are being examined today about a good deed done to a cripple, namely, by what means he was saved, then all of you and all the people of Israel should know that it was in the name of Jesus Christ the Nazorean whom you crucified, whom God raised from the dead; in his name this man stands before you healed. He is *the stone rejected by you, the builders, which has become the cornerstone.* There is no salvation through anyone else, nor is there any other name under heaven given to the human race by which we are to be saved."

RESPONSORIAL PSALM

Psalm 118:1, 8–9, 21–23, 26, 28, 29

℟. The stone re-ject-ed by the build-ers has be-come the cor-ner-stone.

Music: Owen Alstott, b. 1947, © 1977, 1990, OCP. All rights reserved.

Or ℟. Alleluia.

▶ Give thanks to the LORD, for he
  is good,
  for his mercy endures forever.
It is better to take refuge in the LORD
  than to trust in man.
It is better to take refuge in the LORD
  than to trust in princes. ℟.

▶ I will give thanks to you, for you have
  answered me
  and have been my savior.
The stone which the builders rejected
  has become the cornerstone.

By the LORD has this been done;
  it is wonderful in our eyes. ℟.

▶ Blessed is he who comes in the name
  of the LORD;
  we bless you from the house of
  the LORD.
I will give thanks to you, for you have
  answered me
  and have been my savior.
Give thanks to the LORD, for he
  is good;
  for his kindness endures forever. ℟.

SECOND READING

1 John 3:1–2

Beloved: See what love the Father has bestowed on us that we may be called the children of God. Yet so we are. The reason the world does not know us is that it did not know him. Beloved, we are God's children now; what we shall be has not yet been revealed. We do know that when it is revealed we shall be like him, for we shall see him as he is.

GOSPEL ACCLAMATION

John 10:14

℟. Al - le - lu - ia, al - le - lu - ia, al - le - lu - ia.

(Omit if not sung)

▶ I am the good shepherd, says the Lord;
I know my sheep, and mine know me. ℟.

GOSPEL

John 10:11–18

Jesus said: "I am the good shepherd. A good shepherd lays down his life for the sheep. A hired man, who is not a shepherd and whose sheep are not his own, sees a wolf coming and leaves the sheep and runs away, and the wolf catches and scatters them. This is because he works for pay and has no concern for the sheep. I am the good shepherd, and I know mine and mine know me, just as the Father knows me and I know the Father; and I will lay down my life for the sheep. I have other sheep that do not belong to this fold. These also I must lead, and they will hear my voice, and there will be one flock, one shepherd. This is why the Father loves me, because I lay down my life in order to take it up again. No one takes it from me, but I lay it down on my own. I have power to lay it down, and power to take it up again. This command I have received from my Father."

909　FOURTH SUNDAY OF EASTER — C

FIRST READING

Acts of the Apostles 13:14, 43–52

Paul and Barnabas continued on from Perga and reached Antioch in Pisidia. On the sabbath they entered the synagogue and took their seats. Many Jews and worshipers who were converts to Judaism followed Paul and Barnabas, who spoke to them and urged them to remain faithful to the grace of God.

On the following sabbath almost the whole city gathered to hear the word of the Lord. When the Jews saw the crowds, they were filled with jealousy and with violent abuse contradicted what Paul said. Both Paul and Barnabas spoke out boldly and said, "It was necessary that the word of God be spoken to you first, but since you reject it and condemn yourselves as unworthy of eternal life, we now turn to the Gentiles. For so the Lord has commanded us, *I have made you a light to the Gentiles, that you may be an instrument of salvation to the ends of the earth.*"

The Gentiles were delighted when they heard this and glorified the word of the Lord. All who were destined for eternal life came to believe, and the word of the Lord continued to spread through the whole region. The Jews, however, incited the women of prominence who were worshipers and the leading men of the city, stirred up a persecution against Paul and Barnabas, and expelled them from their territory. So they shook the dust from their feet in protest against them, and went to Iconium. The disciples were filled with joy and the Holy Spirit.

RESPONSORIAL PSALM

Psalm 100:1–2, 3, 5

℟. We are his peo - ple, the sheep of his flock.

Or ℟. **Alleluia.**

▸ Sing joyfully to the LORD,
all you lands;
serve the Lord with gladness;
come before him with
joyful song. ℟.

▸ Know that the LORD is God;
he made us, his we are;
his people, the flock he tends. ℟.

▸ The LORD is good:
his kindness endures forever,
and his faithfulness, to all
generations. ℟.

SECOND READING

Revelation 7:9, 14b–17

I, John, had a vision of a great multitude, which no one could count, from every nation, race, people, and tongue. They stood before the throne and before the Lamb, wearing white robes and holding palm branches in their hands.

Then one of the elders said to me, "These are the ones who have survived the time of great distress; they have washed their robes and made them white in the blood of the Lamb.

"For this reason they stand before God's throne

and worship him day and night in
his temple.
The one who sits on the throne will
shelter them.
They will not hunger or thirst
anymore,
nor will the sun or any heat
strike them.
For the Lamb who is in the center of
the throne
will shepherd them
and lead them to springs of life-
giving water,
and God will wipe away every tear
from their eyes."

GOSPEL ACCLAMATION

John 10:14

℟. Al - le - lu - ia, al - le - lu - ia, al - le - lu - ia.

(Omit if not sung)

▸ I am the good shepherd, says the Lord;
I know my sheep, and mine know me. ℟.

GOSPEL *John 10:27–30*

Jesus said: "My sheep hear my voice; I know them, and they follow me. I give them eternal life, and they shall never perish. No one can take them out of my hand. My Father, who has given them to me, is greater than all, and no one can take them out of the Father's hand. The Father and I are one."

---

910 FIFTH SUNDAY OF EASTER — A

FIRST READING *Acts of the Apostles 6:1–7*

As the number of disciples continued to grow, the Hellenists complained against the Hebrews because their widows were being neglected in the daily distribution. So the Twelve called together the community of the disciples and said, "It is not right for us to neglect the word of God to serve at table. Brothers, select from among you seven reputable men, filled with the Spirit and wisdom, whom we shall appoint to this task, whereas we shall devote ourselves to prayer and to the ministry of the word." The proposal was acceptable to the whole community, so they chose Stephen, a man filled with faith and the Holy Spirit, also Philip, Prochorus, Nicanor, Timon, Parmenas, and Nicholas of Antioch, a convert to Judaism. They presented these men to the apostles who prayed and laid hands on them. The word of God continued to spread, and the number of the disciples in Jerusalem increased greatly; even a large group of priests were becoming obedient to the faith.

RESPONSORIAL PSALM *Psalm 33:1–2, 4–5, 18–19*

℟. Lord, let your mer - cy be on us, as we place our trust in you.

Music: Owen Alstott, b. 1947, © 1977, 1990, OCP. All rights reserved.

Or ℟. **Alleluia.**

▸ Exult, you just, in the LORD;
  praise from the upright is fitting.
Give thanks to the LORD on the harp;
  with the ten-stringed lyre chant
    his praises. ℟.

▸ Upright is the word of the LORD,
  and all his works are trustworthy.
He loves justice and right;
  of the kindness of the LORD the

earth is full. ℟.

▸ See, the eyes of the LORD are
    upon those who fear him,
  upon those who hope for
    his kindness,
to deliver them from death
  and preserve them in spite
    of famine. ℟.

SECOND READING *1 Peter 2:4–9*

Beloved: Come to him, a living stone, rejected by human beings but chosen and precious in the sight of God, and, like living stones, let yourselves be built into a spiritual house to be a holy priesthood to offer spiritual sacrifices acceptable to God through Jesus Christ. For it says in Scripture:
Behold, I am laying a stone in Zion,
a cornerstone, chosen and precious,
and whoever believes in it shall not
  be put to shame.
Therefore, its value is for you who have faith, but for those without faith:

The stone that the builders rejected
has become the cornerstone,
and
A stone that will make people
stumble,
and a rock that will make them fall.

They stumble by disobeying
the word, as is their destiny.
You are "a chosen race, a royal
priesthood, a holy nation, a people of
his own, so that you may announce
the praises" of him who called you out
of darkness into his wonderful light.

GOSPEL ACCLAMATION
John 14:6

℟. Al - le - lu - ia, al - le - lu - ia, al - le - lu - ia.

(Omit if not sung)

▶ I am the way, the truth and the life, says the Lord;
no one comes to the Father, except through me. ℟.

GOSPEL
John 14:1–12

Jesus said to his disciples: "Do not let your hearts be troubled. You have faith in God; have faith also in me. In my Father's house there are many dwelling places. If there were not, would I have told you that I am going to prepare a place for you? And if I go and prepare a place for you, I will come back again and take you to myself, so that where I am you also may be. Where I am going you know the way." Thomas said to him, "Master, we do not know where you are going; how can we know the way?" Jesus said to him, "I am the way and the truth and the life. No one comes to the Father except through me. If you know me, then you will also know my Father. From now on you do know him and have seen him." Philip said to him, "Master, show us the Father, and that will be enough for us." Jesus said to him, "Have I been with you for so long a time and you still do not know me, Philip? Whoever has seen me has seen the Father. How can you say, 'Show us the Father'? Do you not believe that I am in the Father and the Father is in me? The words that I speak to you I do not speak on my own. The Father who dwells in me is doing his works. Believe me that I am in the Father and the Father is in me, or else, believe because of the works themselves. Amen, amen, I say to you, whoever believes in me will do the works that I do, and will do greater ones than these, because I am going to the Father."

FIFTH SUNDAY OF EASTER — B 911

FIRST READING
Acts of the Apostles 9:26–31

When Saul arrived in Jerusalem he tried to join the disciples, but they were all afraid of him, not believing that he was a disciple. Then Barnabas took charge of him and brought him to the apostles, and he reported to them how he had seen the Lord, and that he had spoken to him, and how in Damascus he had spoken out boldly in the name of Jesus. He moved about freely with them in Jerusalem, and spoke out boldly in the name of the Lord. He also spoke and debated with the Hellenists, but they tried to kill him. And when the brothers learned of this, they took him down to Caesarea and sent him on his way to Tarsus.

The church throughout all Judea, Galilee, and Samaria was at peace. It was being built up and walked in the fear of the Lord, and with the consolation of the Holy Spirit it grew in numbers.

RESPONSORIAL PSALM
Psalm 22:26–27, 28, 30, 31–32

℞. I will praise you, Lord, in the as-sem-bly of your peo - ple.

Or ℞. **Alleluia.**

▸ I will fulfill my vows before those
who fear the LORD.
The lowly shall eat their fill;
they who seek the LORD shall
praise him:
"May your hearts live forever!" ℞.

▸ All the ends of the earth
shall remember and turn to
the LORD;
all the families of the nations
shall bow down before him. ℞.

▸ To him alone shall bow down
all who sleep in the earth;
before him shall bend
all who go down into the dust. ℞.

▸ And to him my soul shall live;
my descendants shall serve him.
Let the coming generation be told of
the LORD
that they may proclaim to a people
yet to be born
the justice he has shown. ℞.

SECOND READING
1 John 3:18–24

Children, let us love not in word or speech but in deed and truth.
Now this is how we shall know that we belong to the truth and reassure our hearts before him in whatever our hearts condemn, for God is greater than our hearts and knows everything. Beloved, if our hearts do not condemn us, we have confidence in God and receive from him whatever we ask, because we keep his commandments and do what pleases him. And his commandment is this: we should believe in the name of his Son, Jesus Christ, and love one another just as he commanded us. Those who keep his commandments remain in him, and he in them, and the way we know that he remains in us is from the Spirit he gave us.

GOSPEL ACCLAMATION
John 15:4a, 5b

℞. Al - le - lu - ia, al - le - lu - ia, al - le - lu - ia.

(Omit if not sung)

▸ Remain in me as I remain in you, says the Lord.
Whoever remains in me will bear much fruit. ℞.

GOSPEL
John 15:1–8

Jesus said to his disciples: "I am the true vine, and my Father is the vine grower. He takes away every branch in me that does not bear fruit, and every one that does he prunes so that it bears more fruit. You are already pruned because of the word that I spoke to you. Remain in me, as I remain in you. Just as a branch cannot bear fruit on its own unless it remains on the vine, so neither can you unless you remain in me. I am the vine, you are the branches. Whoever remains in me and I in him will bear much fruit, because without me you can do nothing. Anyone who does not remain in me will be thrown out like a branch and wither; people will gather them and throw them into a fire and they will be burned. If you remain in me and my words remain in you, ask for whatever you want and it will be done for you. By this is my Father glorified, that you bear much fruit and become my disciples."

FIFTH SUNDAY OF EASTER — C 912

FIRST READING

Acts of the Apostles 14:21–27

After Paul and Barnabas had proclaimed the good news to that city and made a considerable number of disciples, they returned to Lystra and to Iconium and to Antioch. They strengthened the spirits of the disciples and exhorted them to persevere in the faith, saying, "It is necessary for us to undergo many hardships to enter the kingdom of God." They appointed elders for them in each church and, with prayer and fasting, commended them to the Lord in whom they had put their faith. Then they traveled through Pisidia and reached Pamphylia. After proclaiming the word at Perga they went down to Attalia. From there they sailed to Antioch, where they had been commended to the grace of God for the work they had now accomplished. And when they arrived, they called the church together and reported what God had done with them and how he had opened the door of faith to the Gentiles.

RESPONSORIAL PSALM

Psalm 145:8–9, 10–11, 12–13

℟. I will praise your name for ev - er, my king and my God.

Or ℟. **Alleluia.**

▸ The LORD is gracious and merciful,
  slow to anger and of great kindness.
The LORD is good to all
  and compassionate toward all
    his works. ℟.

▸ Let all your works give you thanks,
  O LORD,
  and let your faithful ones bless you.
Let them discourse of the glory of
  your kingdom
  and speak of your might. ℟.

▸ Let them make known your might to
  the children of Adam,
  and the glorious splendor of
    your kingdom.
Your kingdom is a kingdom for
  all ages,
  and your dominion endures
    through all generations. ℟.

SECOND READING
Revelation 21:1–5a

Then I, John, saw a new heaven and a new earth. The former heaven and the former earth had passed away, and the sea was no more. I also saw the holy city, a new Jerusalem, coming down out of heaven from God, prepared as a bride adorned for her husband. I heard a loud voice from the throne saying, "Behold, God's dwelling is with the human race. He will dwell with them and they will be his people and God himself will always be with them as their God. He will wipe every tear from their eyes, and there shall be no more death or mourning, wailing or pain, for the old order has passed away."

The One who sat on the throne said, "Behold, I make all things new."

GOSPEL ACCLAMATION
John 13:34

℟. Al - le - lu - ia, al - le - lu - ia, al - le - lu - ia.

Music: Owen Alstott, b. 1947, © 1977, 1990, OCP. All rights reserved. *(Omit if not sung)*

▸ I give you a new commandment, says the Lord:
love one another as I have loved you. ℟.

GOSPEL
John 13:31–33a, 34–35

When Judas had left them, Jesus said, "Now is the Son of Man glorified, and God is glorified in him. If God is glorified in him, God will also glorify him in himself, and God will glorify him at once. My children, I will be with you only a little while longer. I give you a new commandment: love one another. As I have loved you, so you also should love one another. This is how all will know that you are my disciples, if you have love for one another."

---

913 SIXTH SUNDAY OF EASTER — A

When the Ascension of the Lord is celebrated the following Sunday, the second reading and Gospel from the Seventh Sunday of Easter (see #917) may be read on the Sixth Sunday of Easter.

FIRST READING
Acts of the Apostles 8:5–8, 14–17

Philip went down to the city of Samaria and proclaimed the Christ to them. With one accord, the crowds paid attention to what was said by Philip when they heard it and saw the signs he was doing. For unclean spirits, crying out in a loud voice, came out of many possessed people, and many paralyzed or crippled people were cured. There was great joy in that city. Now when the apostles in Jerusalem heard that Samaria had accepted the word of God, they sent them Peter and John, who went down and prayed for them, that they might receive the Holy Spirit, for it had not yet fallen upon any of them; they had only been baptized in the name of the Lord Jesus. Then they laid hands on them and they received the Holy Spirit.

RESPONSORIAL PSALM

Psalm 66:1–3, 4–5, 6–7, 16, 20

℟. Let all the earth cry out to God with joy.

Or ℟. **Alleluia.**

▶ Shout joyfully to God, all the earth,
    sing praise to the glory of his name;
    proclaim his glorious praise.
Say to God, "How tremendous are
    your deeds!" ℟.

▶ "Let all on earth worship and sing
    praise to you,
sing praise to your name!"
Come and see the works of God,
    his tremendous deeds among the
    children of Adam. ℟.

▶ He has changed the sea into dry land;
    through the river they passed
    on foot;
    therefore let us rejoice in him.
He rules by his might forever. ℟.

▶ Hear now, all you who fear God,
    while I declare
what he has done for me.
Blessed be God who refused me not
    my prayer or his kindness! ℟.

SECOND READING

1 Peter 3:15–18

Beloved: Sanctify Christ as Lord in your hearts. Always be ready to give an explanation to anyone who asks you for a reason for your hope, but do it with gentleness and reverence, keeping your conscience clear, so that, when you are maligned, those who defame your good conduct in Christ may themselves be put to shame. For it is better to suffer for doing good, if that be the will of God, than for doing evil. For Christ also suffered for sins once, the righteous for the sake of the unrighteous, that he might lead you to God. Put to death in the flesh, he was brought to life in the Spirit.

GOSPEL ACCLAMATION

John 14:23

℟. Al - le - lu - ia, al - le - lu - ia, al - le - lu - ia.

(Omit if not sung)

▶ Whoever loves me will keep my word, says the Lord,
    and my Father will love him and we will come to him. ℟.

GOSPEL

John 14:15–21

Jesus said to his disciples: "If you love me, you will keep my commandments. And I will ask the Father, and he will give you another Advocate to be with you always, the Spirit of truth, whom the world cannot accept, because it neither sees nor knows him. But you know him, because he remains with you, and will be in you. I will not leave you orphans; I will come to you. In a little while the world will no longer see me, but you will see me, because I live and you will live. On that day you will realize that I am in my Father and you are in me and I in you. Whoever has my commandments and observes them is the one who loves me. And whoever loves me will be loved by my Father, and I will love him and reveal myself to him."

914   SIXTH SUNDAY OF EASTER — B

When the Ascension of the Lord is celebrated the following Sunday, the second reading and Gospel from the Seventh Sunday of Easter (see #918) may be read on the Sixth Sunday of Easter.

FIRST READING   *Acts of the Apostles 10:25–26, 34–35, 44–48*

When Peter entered, Cornelius met him and, falling at his feet, paid him homage. Peter, however, raised him up, saying, "Get up. I myself am also a human being."

Then Peter proceeded to speak and said, "In truth, I see that God shows no partiality. Rather, in every nation whoever fears him and acts uprightly is acceptable to him."

While Peter was still speaking these things, the Holy Spirit fell upon all who were listening to the word. The circumcised believers who had accompanied Peter were astounded that the gift of the Holy Spirit should have been poured out on the Gentiles also, for they could hear them speaking in tongues and glorifying God. Then Peter responded, "Can anyone withhold the water for baptizing these people, who have received the Holy Spirit even as we have?" He ordered them to be baptized in the name of Jesus Christ.

RESPONSORIAL PSALM   *Psalm 98:1, 2–3, 3–4*

℟. The Lord has re-vealed to the na-tions his sav-ing pow'r.

Music: Owen Alstott, b. 1947, © 1977, 1990, OCP. All rights reserved.

Or ℟. **Alleluia.**

▸ Sing to the LORD a new song,
    for he has done wondrous deeds;
  his right hand has won victory for him,
    his holy arm. ℟.

▸ The LORD has made his
    salvation known:
  in the sight of the nations he has
    revealed his justice.

He has remembered his kindness and
    his faithfulness
  toward the house of Israel. ℟.

▸ All the ends of the earth have seen
    the salvation by our God.
Sing joyfully to the LORD, all
    you lands;
  break into song; sing praise. ℟.

SECOND READING   *1 John 4:7–10*

Beloved, let us love one another, because love is of God; everyone who loves is begotten by God and knows God. Whoever is without love does not know God, for God is love. In this way the love of God was revealed to us: God sent his only Son into the world so that we might have life through him. In this is love: not that we have loved God, but that he loved us and sent his Son as expiation for our sins.

GOSPEL ACCLAMATION

John 14:23

℟. Al - le - lu - ia, al - le - lu - ia, al - le - lu - ia.

(Omit if not sung)

▶ Whoever loves me will keep my word, says the Lord,
  and my Father will love him and we will come to him. ℟.

GOSPEL

John 15:9–17

Jesus said to his disciples: "As the Father loves me, so I also love you. Remain in my love. If you keep my commandments, you will remain in my love, just as I have kept my Father's commandments and remain in his love.

  "I have told you this so that my joy may be in you and your joy might be complete. This is my commandment: love one another as I love you. No one has greater love than this, to lay down one's life for one's friends. You are my friends if you do what I command you. I no longer call you slaves, because a slave does not know what his master is doing. I have called you friends, because I have told you everything I have heard from my Father. It was not you who chose me, but I who chose you and appointed you to go and bear fruit that will remain, so that whatever you ask the Father in my name he may give you. This I command you: love one another."

SIXTH SUNDAY OF EASTER — C   915

When the Ascension of the Lord is celebrated the following Sunday, the second reading and Gospel from the Seventh Sunday of Easter (see #919) may be read on the Sixth Sunday of Easter.

FIRST READING

Acts of the Apostles 15:1–2, 22–29

Some who had come down from Judea were instructing the brothers, "Unless you are circumcised according to the Mosaic practice, you cannot be saved." Because there arose no little dissension and debate by Paul and Barnabas with them, it was decided that Paul, Barnabas, and some of the others should go up to Jerusalem to the apostles and elders about this question.

  The apostles and elders, in agreement with the whole church, decided to choose representatives and to send them to Antioch with Paul and Barnabas. The ones chosen were Judas, who was called Barsabbas, and Silas, leaders among the brothers. This is the letter delivered by them: "The apostles and the elders, your brothers, to the brothers in Antioch, Syria, and Cilicia of Gentile origin: greetings. Since we have heard that some of our number who went out without any mandate from us have upset you with their teachings and disturbed your peace of mind, we have with one accord decided to choose representatives and to send them to you along with our beloved Barnabas and Paul, who have dedicated their lives to the name of our Lord Jesus Christ. So we are sending Judas and Silas who will also convey this same message by word of mouth: 'It is the decision of the Holy Spirit and of us not to place on you any burden beyond these necessities, namely, to abstain from meat sacrificed to idols, from blood, from meats of strangled animals, and from unlawful marriage.

If you keep free of these, you will be doing what is right. Farewell.'"

RESPONSORIAL PSALM

Psalm 67:2–3, 5, 6, 8

℟. O God, let all the na - tions praise you!

Or ℟. **Alleluia.**

▶ May God have pity on us and
    bless us;
  may he let his face shine upon us.
So may your way be known
    upon earth;
  among all nations, your salvation. ℟.

▶ May the nations be glad and exult
  because you rule the peoples
    in equity;

the nations on the earth
  you guide. ℟.

▶ May the peoples praise you, O God;
  may all the peoples praise you!
May God bless us,
  and may all the ends of the earth
    fear him! ℟.

SECOND READING

Revelation 21:10–14, 22–23

The angel took me in spirit to a great, high mountain and showed me the holy city Jerusalem coming down out of heaven from God. It gleamed with the splendor of God. Its radiance was like that of a precious stone, like jasper, clear as crystal. It had a massive, high wall, with twelve gates where twelve angels were stationed and on which names were inscribed, the names of the twelve tribes of the Israelites. There were three gates facing east, three north, three south, and three west. The wall of the city had twelve courses of stones as its foundation, on which were inscribed the twelve names of the twelve apostles of the Lamb.

I saw no temple in the city for its temple is the Lord God almighty and the Lamb. The city had no need of sun or moon to shine on it, for the glory of God gave it light, and its lamp was the Lamb.

GOSPEL ACCLAMATION

John 14:23

℟. Al - le - lu - ia, al - le - lu - ia, al - le - lu - ia.

(Omit if not sung)

▶ Whoever loves me will keep my word, says the Lord,
  and my Father will love him and we will come to him. ℟.

GOSPEL

John 14:23–29

Jesus said to his disciples: "Whoever loves me will keep my word, and my Father will love him, and we will come to him and make our dwelling with him. Whoever does not love me does not keep my words; yet the word you hear is not mine but that of the Father who sent me.

"I have told you this while I am with you. The Advocate, the Holy Spirit, whom the Father will send in my name, will teach you everything and remind you of all that I told you. Peace I leave with you; my peace I give to you. Not as the world gives do I give it to you. Do not let your hearts be troubled or afraid. You heard me tell you, 'I am going away and I will come back to you.' If you loved me, you would rejoice that I am going to the Father; for the Father is greater than I. And now I have told you this before it happens, so that when it happens you may believe."

THE ASCENSION OF THE LORD — ABC   916

This solemnity is transferred to the following Sunday in many archdioceses and dioceses of the United States. In those churches, Thursday is observed as an Easter Weekday.

FIRST READING

Acts of the Apostles 1:1–11

In the first book, Theophilus, I dealt with all that Jesus did and taught until the day he was taken up, after giving instructions through the Holy Spirit to the apostles whom he had chosen. He presented himself alive to them by many proofs after he had suffered, appearing to them during forty days and speaking about the kingdom of God. While meeting with them, he enjoined them not to depart from Jerusalem, but to wait for "the promise of the Father about which you have heard me speak; for John baptized with water, but in a few days you will be baptized with the Holy Spirit."

When they had gathered together they asked him, "Lord, are you at this time going to restore the kingdom to Israel?" He answered them, "It is not for you to know the times or seasons that the Father has established by his own authority. But you will receive power when the Holy Spirit comes upon you, and you will be my witnesses in Jerusalem, throughout Judea and Samaria, and to the ends of the earth." When he had said this, as they were looking on, he was lifted up, and a cloud took him from their sight. While they were looking intently at the sky as he was going, suddenly two men dressed in white garments stood beside them. They said, "Men of Galilee, why are you standing there looking at the sky? This Jesus who has been taken up from you into heaven will return in the same way as you have seen him going into heaven."

RESPONSORIAL PSALM

Psalm 47:2–3, 6–7, 8–9

℟. God mounts his throne to shouts of joy: a blare of trumpets for the Lord.

Or ℟. **Alleluia.**

℞. **God mounts his throne to shouts of joy: a blare of trumpets for the Lord.**
Or ℞. **Alleluia.**

▸ All you peoples, clap your hands,
    shout to God with cries of gladness.
For the LORD, the Most High,
    the awesome,
    is the great king over all
    the earth. ℞.

▸ God mounts his throne amid shouts
    of joy;

the LORD, amid trumpet blasts.
Sing praise to God, sing praise;
    sing praise to our king,
    sing praise. ℞.

▸ For king of all the earth is God;
    sing hymns of praise.
God reigns over the nations,
    God sits upon his holy throne. ℞.

SECOND READING — ABC

Ephesians 1:17–23

Brothers and sisters: May the God of our Lord Jesus Christ, the Father of glory, give you a Spirit of wisdom and revelation resulting in knowledge of him. May the eyes of your hearts be enlightened, that you may know what is the hope that belongs to his call, what are the riches of glory in his inheritance among the holy ones, and what is the surpassing greatness of his power for us who believe, in accord with the exercise of his great might, which he worked in Christ, raising him from the dead and seating him at his right hand in the heavens, far above every principality, authority, power, and dominion, and every name that is named not only in this age but also in the one to come. And he put all things beneath his feet and gave him as head over all things to the church, which is his body, the fullness of the one who fills all things in every way.

Or

SECOND READING — B

Ephesians 4:1–13 or 4:1–7, 11–13

(Include bracketed text for Long Form)

Brothers and sisters, I, a prisoner for the Lord, urge you to live in a manner worthy of the call you have received, with all humility and gentleness, with patience, bearing with one another through love, striving to preserve the unity of the spirit through the bond of peace: one body and one Spirit, as you were also called to the one hope of your call; one Lord, one faith, one baptism; one God and Father of all, who is over all and through all and in all.

But grace was given to each of us according to the measure of Christ's gift. [Therefore, it says:
*He ascended on high and took
    prisoners captive;
he gave gifts to men.*

What does "he ascended" mean except that he also descended into the lower regions of the earth? The one who descended is also the one who ascended far above all the heavens, that he might fill all things.]

And he gave some as apostles, others as prophets, others as evangelists, others as pastors and teachers, to equip the holy ones for the work of ministry, for building up the body of Christ, until we all attain to the unity of faith and knowledge of the Son of God, to mature manhood, to the extent of the full stature of Christ.

Or

SECOND READING — C

Hebrews 9:24–28; 10:19–23

Christ did not enter into a sanctuary made by hands, a copy of the true one, but heaven itself, that he might now appear before God on our behalf. Not that he might offer himself repeatedly, as the high priest enters each year into the sanctuary with blood that is not his own; if that were so, he would have had to suffer repeatedly from the foundation of the world. But now once for all he has appeared at the end of the ages to take away sin by his sacrifice. Just as it is appointed that men and women die once, and after this the judgment, so also Christ, offered once to take away the sins of many, will appear a second time, not to take away sin but to bring salvation to those who eagerly await him.

Therefore, brothers and sisters, since through the blood of Jesus we have confidence of entrance into the sanctuary by the new and living way he opened for us through the veil, that is, his flesh, and since we have "a great priest over the house of God," let us approach with a sincere heart and in absolute trust, with our hearts sprinkled clean from an evil conscience and our bodies washed in pure water. Let us hold unwaveringly to our confession that gives us hope, for he who made the promise is trustworthy.

GOSPEL ACCLAMATION

Matthew 28:19a, 20b

℟. Al - le - lu - ia, al - le - lu - ia, al - le - lu - ia.

(Omit if not sung)

▶ Go and teach all nations, says the Lord;
 I am with you always, until the end of the world. ℟.

GOSPEL — A

Matthew 28:16–20

The eleven disciples went to Galilee, to the mountain to which Jesus had ordered them. When they saw him, they worshiped, but they doubted. Then Jesus approached and said to them, "All power in heaven and on earth has been given to me. Go, therefore, and make disciples of all nations, baptizing them in the name of the Father, and of the Son, and of the Holy Spirit, teaching them to observe all that I have commanded you. And behold, I am with you always, until the end of the age."

GOSPEL — B

Mark 16:15–20

Jesus said to his disciples: "Go into the whole world and proclaim the gospel to every creature. Whoever believes and is baptized will be saved; whoever does not believe will be condemned. These signs will accompany those who believe: in my name they will drive out demons, they will speak new languages. They will pick up serpents with their hands, and if they drink any deadly thing, it will not harm them. They will lay hands on the sick, and they will recover."

So then the Lord Jesus, after he spoke to them, was taken up into heaven and took his seat at the right hand of God. But they went forth and preached everywhere, while the Lord worked with them and confirmed the word through accompanying signs.

GOSPEL — C

Luke 24:46–53

Jesus said to his disciples: "Thus it is written that the Christ would suffer and rise from the dead on the third day and that repentance, for the forgiveness of sins, would be preached in his name to all the nations, beginning from Jerusalem. You are witnesses of these things. And behold I am sending the promise of my Father upon you; but stay in the city until you are clothed with power from on high."

Then he led them out as far as Bethany, raised his hands, and blessed them. As he blessed them he parted from them and was taken up to heaven. They did him homage and then returned to Jerusalem with great joy, and they were continually in the temple praising God.

---

917   SEVENTH SUNDAY OF EASTER — A

In those places where the observance of the solemnity of the Ascension of the Lord has been transferred to this day, the Mass and readings of the Ascension, #916, are used.

FIRST READING

Acts of the Apostles 1:12–14

After Jesus had been taken up to heaven the apostles returned to Jerusalem from the mount called Olivet, which is near Jerusalem, a sabbath day's journey away.

When they entered the city they went to the upper room where they were staying, Peter and John and

James and Andrew, Philip and Thomas, Bartholomew and Matthew, James son of Alphaeus, Simon the Zealot, and Judas son of James. All these devoted themselves with one accord to prayer, together with some women, and Mary the mother of Jesus, and his brothers.

RESPONSORIAL PSALM

Psalm 27:1, 4, 7–8

℟. I be-lieve that I shall see the good things of the Lord in the land of the liv - ing.

Music: Owen Alstott, b. 1947, © 1977, 1990, OCP. All rights reserved.

Or ℟. **Alleluia.**

▶ The LORD is my light and my salvation;
   whom should I fear?
The LORD is my life's refuge;
   of whom should I be afraid? ℟.

▶ One thing I ask of the LORD;
   this I seek:
to dwell in the house of the LORD
   all the days of my life,

that I may gaze on the loveliness of
   the LORD
   and contemplate his temple. ℟.

▶ Hear, O LORD, the sound of my call;
   have pity on me, and answer me.
Of you my heart speaks; you my
   glance seeks. ℟.

SECOND READING
1 Peter 4:13–16

Beloved: Rejoice to the extent that you share in the sufferings of Christ, so that when his glory is revealed you may also rejoice exultantly. If you are insulted for the name of Christ, blessed are you, for the Spirit of glory and of God rests upon you. But let no one among you be made to suffer as a murderer, a thief, an evildoer, or as an intriguer. But whoever is made to suffer as a Christian should not be ashamed but glorify God because of the name.

GOSPEL ACCLAMATION
cf. John 14:18

℟. Al - le - lu - ia, al - le - lu - ia, al - le - lu - ia.

Music: Owen Alstott, b. 1947, © 1977, 1990, OCP. All rights reserved. *(Omit if not sung)*

▸ I will not leave you orphans, says the Lord.
I will come back to you, and your hearts will rejoice. ℟.

GOSPEL
John 17:1–11a

Jesus raised his eyes to heaven and said, "Father, the hour has come. Give glory to your son, so that your son may glorify you, just as you gave him authority over all people, so that your son may give eternal life to all you gave him. Now this is eternal life, that they should know you, the only true God, and the one whom you sent, Jesus Christ. I glorified you on earth by accomplishing the work that you gave me to do. Now glorify me, Father, with you, with the glory that I had with you before the world began.

"I revealed your name to those whom you gave me out of the world. They belonged to you, and you gave them to me, and they have kept your word. Now they know that everything you gave me is from you, because the words you gave to me I have given to them, and they accepted them and truly understood that I came from you, and they have believed that you sent me. I pray for them. I do not pray for the world but for the ones you have given me, because they are yours, and everything of mine is yours and everything of yours is mine, and I have been glorified in them. And now I will no longer be in the world, but they are in the world, while I am coming to you."

SEVENTH SUNDAY OF EASTER — B   918

In those places where the observance of the solemnity of the Ascension of the Lord has been transferred to this day, the Mass and readings of the Ascension, #916, are used.

FIRST READING
Acts of the Apostles 1:15–17, 20a, 20c–26

Peter stood up in the midst of the brothers—there was a group of about one hundred and twenty persons in the one place—. He said, "My brothers, the Scripture had to be fulfilled which the Holy Spirit spoke beforehand through the mouth of David, concerning Judas, who was the guide for those who arrested Jesus. He was numbered among us and was allotted a share in this ministry.

"For it is written in the Book of Psalms:
May another take his office.

"Therefore, it is necessary that one of the men who accompanied us the whole time the Lord Jesus came and went among us, beginning from the baptism of John until the day on which he was taken up from us, become with us a witness to his resurrection." So they proposed two, Judas called Barsabbas, who was also known as Justus, and Matthias. Then they prayed,

"You, Lord, who know the hearts of all, show which one of these two you have chosen to take the place in this apostolic ministry from which Judas turned away to go to his own place." Then they gave lots to them, and the lot fell upon Matthias, and he was counted with the eleven apostles.

RESPONSORIAL PSALM

Psalm 103:1–2, 11–12, 19–20

℟. The Lord has set his throne in heav - en.

Or ℟. Alleluia.

▶ Bless the LORD, O my soul;
and all my being, bless his
holy name.
Bless the LORD, O my soul,
and forget not all his benefits. ℟.

▶ For as the heavens are high above
the earth,
so surpassing is his kindness
toward those who fear him.

As far as the east is from the west,
so far has he put our transgressions
from us. ℟.

▶ The LORD has established his throne
in heaven,
and his kingdom rules over all.
Bless the LORD, all you his angels,
you mighty in strength, who do
his bidding. ℟.

SECOND READING

1 John 4:11–16

Beloved, if God so loved us, we also must love one another. No one has ever seen God. Yet, if we love one another, God remains in us, and his love is brought to perfection in us.

This is how we know that we remain in him and he in us, that he has given us of his Spirit. Moreover, we have

seen and testify that the Father sent his Son as savior of the world. Whoever acknowledges that Jesus is the Son of God, God remains in him and he in God. We have come to know and to believe in the love God has for us.

God is love, and whoever remains in love remains in God and God in him.

GOSPEL ACCLAMATION

cf. John 14:18

℟. Al - le - lu - ia, al - le - lu - ia, al - le - lu - ia.

(Omit if not sung)

▶ I will not leave you orphans, says the Lord.
I will come back to you, and your hearts will rejoice. ℟.

GOSPEL

John 17:11b–19

Lifting up his eyes to heaven, Jesus prayed, saying: "Holy Father, keep them in your name that you have given me, so that they may be one

just as we are one. When I was with them I protected them in your name that you gave me, and I guarded them, and none of them was lost except the son of destruction, in order that the Scripture might be fulfilled. But now I am coming to you. I speak this in the world so that they may share my joy completely. I gave them your word, and the world hated them, because they do not belong to the world any more than I belong to the world. I do not ask that you take them out of the world but that you keep them from the evil one. They do not belong to the world any more than I belong to the world. Consecrate them in the truth. Your word is truth. As you sent me into the world, so I sent them into the world. And I consecrate myself for them, so that they also may be consecrated in truth."

SEVENTH SUNDAY OF EASTER — C   919

In those places where the observance of the solemnity of the Ascension of the Lord has been transferred to this day, the Mass and readings of the Ascension, #916, are used.

FIRST READING

Acts of the Apostles 7:55–60

Stephen, filled with the Holy Spirit, looked up intently to heaven and saw the glory of God and Jesus standing at the right hand of God, and Stephen said, "Behold, I see the heavens opened and the Son of Man standing at the right hand of God." But they cried out in a loud voice, covered their ears, and rushed upon him together. They threw him out of the city, and began to stone him. The witnesses laid down their cloaks at the feet of a young man named Saul. As they were stoning Stephen, he called out, "Lord Jesus, receive my spirit." Then he fell to his knees and cried out in a loud voice, "Lord, do not hold this sin against them"; and when he said this, he fell asleep.

RESPONSORIAL PSALM

Psalm 97:1–2, 6–7, 9

℟. The Lord is king, the most high over all the earth.

Music: Owen Alstott, b. 1947, © 1977, 1990, OCP. All rights reserved.

Or ℟. **Alleluia.**

▶ The LORD is king; let the earth rejoice;
   let the many islands be glad.
Justice and judgment are the
   foundation of his throne. ℟.

▶ The heavens proclaim his justice,
   and all peoples see his glory.
All gods are prostrate before him. ℟.

▶ You, O LORD, are the Most High over
   all the earth,
   exalted far above all gods. ℟.

SECOND READING

Revelation 22:12–14, 16–17, 20

I, John, heard a voice saying to me: "Behold, I am coming soon. I bring with me the recompense I will give to each according to his deeds. I am the Alpha and the Omega, the first and the last, the beginning and the end."

Blessed are they who wash their robes so as to have the right to the tree of life and enter the city through its gates.

"I, Jesus, sent my angel to give you this testimony for the churches.

I am the root and offspring of David, the bright morning star."

The Spirit and the bride say, "Come." Let the hearer say, "Come." Let the one who thirsts come forward, and the one who wants it receive the gift of life-giving water.

The one who gives this testimony says, "Yes, I am coming soon." Amen! Come, Lord Jesus!

GOSPEL ACCLAMATION

cf. John 14:18

℟. Al - le - lu - ia, al - le - lu - ia, al - le - lu - ia.

Music: Owen Alstott, b. 1947, © 1977, 1990, OCP. All rights reserved.

(Omit if not sung)

▶ I will not leave you orphans, says the Lord.
I will come back to you, and your hearts will rejoice. ℟.

GOSPEL

John 17:20–26

Lifting up his eyes to heaven, Jesus prayed, saying: "Holy Father, I pray not only for them, but also for those who will believe in me through their word, so that they may all be one, as you, Father, are in me and I in you, that they also may be in us, that the world may believe that you sent me. And I have given them the glory you gave me, so that they may be one, as we are one, I in them and you in me, that they may be brought to perfection as one, that the world may know that you sent me, and that you loved them even as you loved me. Father, they are your gift to me. I wish that where I am they also may be with me, that they may see my glory that you gave me, because you loved me before the foundation of the world. Righteous Father, the world also does not know you, but I know you, and they know that you sent me. I made known to them your name and I will make it known, that the love with which you loved me may be in them and I in them."

---

920 PENTECOST SUNDAY: AT THE VIGIL MASS — ABC

These readings are used at Saturday Evening Mass celebrated either before or after Evening Prayer I of Pentecost Sunday. An extended form of this Mass is given in The Roman Missal *which, after omitting the Penitential Act, includes four Old Testament readings with their responsories. Following this, the Gloria is sung; then the reading from the Apostle takes place. Mass then continues in the usual way.*

FIRST READING

Genesis 11:1–9

The whole world spoke the same language, using the same words. While the people were migrating in the east, they came upon a valley in the land of Shinar and settled there. They said to one another, "Come, let us mold bricks and harden them with fire." They used bricks for stone, and bitumen for mortar. Then they said, "Come, let us build ourselves a city and a tower with its top in the sky, and so make a name for ourselves; otherwise we shall be scattered all over the earth."

The LORD came down to see the city and the tower that the people had built. Then the LORD said: "If now, while they are one people, all speaking the same language, they have started to do this, nothing will later stop them from doing whatever they presume to do. Let us then go down there and confuse their language, so that one will not understand what another says." Thus the LORD scattered them from there all over the earth, and they stopped building the city. That is why it was called Babel, because there the LORD confused the speech of all the world. It was from that place that he scattered them all over the earth.

Or

FIRST READING

Exodus 19:3–8a, 16–20b

Moses went up the mountain to God. Then the LORD called to him and said, "Thus shall you say to the house of Jacob; tell the Israelites: You have seen for yourselves how I treated the Egyptians and how I bore you up on eagle wings and brought you here to myself. Therefore, if you hearken to my voice and keep my covenant, you shall be my special possession, dearer to me than all other people, though all the earth is mine. You shall be to me a kingdom of priests, a holy nation. That is what you must tell the Israelites." So Moses went and summoned the elders of the people. When he set before them all that the LORD had ordered him to tell them, the people all answered together, "Everything the LORD has said, we will do."

On the morning of the third day there were peals of thunder and lightning, and a heavy cloud over the mountain, and a very loud trumpet blast, so that all the people in the camp trembled. But Moses led the people out of the camp to meet God, and they stationed themselves at the foot of the mountain. Mount Sinai was all wrapped in smoke, for the LORD came down upon it in fire. The smoke rose from it as though from a furnace, and the whole mountain trembled violently. The trumpet blast grew louder and louder, while Moses was speaking, and God answering him with thunder.

When the LORD came down to the top of Mount Sinai, he summoned Moses to the top of the mountain.

Or

FIRST READING

Ezekiel 37:1–14

The hand of the LORD came upon me, and he led me out in the spirit of the LORD and set me in the center of the plain, which was now filled with bones. He made me walk among the bones in every direction so that I saw how many they were on the surface of the plain. How dry they were! He asked me: Son of man, can these bones come to life? I answered, "Lord GOD, you alone know that." Then he said to me: Prophesy over these bones, and say to them: Dry bones, hear the word of the LORD! Thus says the Lord GOD to these bones: See! I will bring spirit into you, that you may come to life. I will put sinews upon you, make flesh grow over you, cover you with skin, and put spirit in you so that you may come to life and know that I am the LORD. I, Ezekiel, prophesied as I had been told, and even as I was prophesying I heard a noise; it was a rattling as the bones came together, bone joining bone. I saw the sinews and the flesh come upon them, and the skin cover them, but there was no spirit in them. Then the LORD said to me: Prophesy to the spirit, prophesy, son of man, and say to the spirit: Thus says the Lord GOD: From the four winds come, O spirit, and breathe into these slain that they may come to life. I prophesied as he told me, and the spirit came into them; they came alive and stood upright, a vast army. Then he said to me: Son of man, these bones are the whole house of Israel. They have been saying,

"Our bones are dried up, our hope is lost, and we are cut off." Therefore, prophesy and say to them: Thus says the Lord GOD: O my people, I will open your graves and have you rise from them, and bring you back to the land of Israel. Then you shall know that I am the LORD, when I open your graves and have you rise from them, O my people! I will put my spirit in you that you may live, and I will settle you upon your land; thus you shall know that I am the LORD. I have promised, and I will do it, says the LORD.

Or

FIRST READING

Joel 3:1–5

Thus says the LORD:
  I will pour out my spirit upon all flesh.
  Your sons and daughters
      shall prophesy,
  your old men shall dream dreams,
  your young men shall see visions;
  even upon the servants and
      the handmaids,
  in those days, I will pour out
      my spirit.
  And I will work wonders in the
      heavens and on the earth,
  blood, fire, and columns of smoke;
  the sun will be turned to darkness,
      and the moon to blood,
  at the coming of the day of the LORD,
      the great and terrible day.
  Then everyone shall be rescued
      who calls on the name of the LORD;
  for on Mount Zion there shall be
      a remnant,
      as the LORD has said,
  and in Jerusalem survivors
      whom the LORD shall call.

RESPONSORIAL PSALM

Psalm 104:1–2, 24 & 35, 27–28, 29, 30

℟. Lord, send out your Spir - it, and re - new the face of the earth.

Music: Owen Alstott, b. 1947, © 1977, 1990, OCP. All rights reserved.

Or ℟. **Alleluia.**

▸ Bless the LORD, O my soul!
    O LORD, my God, you are
        great indeed!
  You are clothed with majesty
        and glory,
    robed in light as with a cloak. ℟.

▸ How manifold are your works,
        O LORD!
    In wisdom you have wrought
        them all—
  the earth is full of your creatures;
    bless the LORD, O my soul!
        Alleluia. ℟.

▸ Creatures all look to you
    to give them food in due time.
  When you give it to them, they
        gather it;
    when you open your hand, they are
        filled with good things. ℟.

▸ If you take away their breath,
        they perish
    and return to their dust.
  When you send forth your spirit, they
        are created,
    and you renew the face of
        the earth. ℟.

SECOND READING

Romans 8:22–27

Brothers and sisters: We know that all creation is groaning in labor pains even until now; and not only that, but we ourselves, who have the firstfruits of the Spirit, we also groan within ourselves as we wait for adoption, the redemption of our bodies. For in hope we were saved. Now hope that sees is not hope. For who hopes for what one sees? But if we hope for what we do not see, we wait with endurance.

In the same way, the Spirit too comes to the aid of our weakness; for we do not know how to pray as we ought, but the Spirit himself intercedes with inexpressible groanings. And the one who searches hearts knows what is the intention of the Spirit, because he intercedes for the holy ones according to God's will.

GOSPEL ACCLAMATION

℟. Al - le - lu - ia, al - le - lu - ia, al - le - lu - ia.

(Omit if not sung)

▶ Come, Holy Spirit, fill the hearts of the faithful and kindle in them the fire of your love. **℟.**

GOSPEL
John 7:37–39

On the last and greatest day of the feast, Jesus stood up and exclaimed, "Let anyone who thirsts come to me and drink. As Scripture says:
Rivers of living water will flow from within him who believes in me." He said this in reference to the Spirit that those who came to believe in him were to receive. There was, of course, no Spirit yet, because Jesus had not yet been glorified.

PENTECOST SUNDAY: 921
AT THE MASS DURING THE DAY — ABC

If it is customary or obligatory for the faithful to attend Mass on the Monday or even the Tuesday after Pentecost, the readings from the Mass of Pentecost Sunday may be repeated or the readings of the Ritual Mass for Confirmation, Lectionary numbers 764–768, or a Mass of the Holy Spirit may be used in its place.

FIRST READING
Acts of the Apostles 2:1–11

When the time for Pentecost was fulfilled, they were all in one place together. And suddenly there came from the sky a noise like a strong driving wind, and it filled the entire house in which they were. Then there appeared to them tongues as of fire, which parted and came to rest on each one of them. And they were all filled with the Holy Spirit and began to speak in different tongues, as the Spirit enabled them to proclaim.

Now there were devout Jews from every nation under heaven staying in Jerusalem. At this sound, they gathered in a large crowd, but they were confused because each one heard them speaking in his own language. They were astounded, and in amazement they asked, "Are not all these people who are speaking Galileans? Then how does each of us hear them in his native language? We are Parthians, Medes, and Elamites, inhabitants of Mesopotamia, Judea and Cappadocia, Pontus and Asia, Phrygia and Pamphylia, Egypt and the districts of Libya near Cyrene, as well as travelers from Rome, both Jews and converts to Judaism, Cretans and Arabs, yet we hear them speaking in our own tongues of the mighty acts of God."

RESPONSORIAL PSALM

Psalm 104:1, 24, 29–30, 31, 34

℟. Lord, send out your Spir-it, and re-new the face of the earth.

Or ℟. Alleluia.

▶ Bless the LORD, O my soul!
　O LORD, my God, you are
　　great indeed!
　How manifold are your works,
　　O LORD!
　The earth is full of your creatures. ℟.

▶ If you take away their breath,
　　they perish
　and return to their dust.

When you send forth your spirit, they
　　are created,
　and you renew the face of
　　the earth. ℟.

▶ May the glory of the LORD
　　endure forever;
　may the LORD be glad in his works!
　Pleasing to him be my theme;
　I will be glad in the LORD. ℟.

SECOND READING — ABC

1 Corinthians 12:3b–7, 12–13

Brothers and sisters: No one can say, "Jesus is Lord," except by the Holy Spirit.

There are different kinds of spiritual gifts but the same Spirit; there are different forms of service but the same Lord; there are different workings but the same God who produces all of them in everyone. To each individual the manifestation of the Spirit is given for some benefit.

As a body is one though it has many parts, and all the parts of the body, though many, are one body, so also Christ. For in one Spirit we were all baptized into one body, whether Jews or Greeks, slaves or free persons, and we were all given to drink of one Spirit.

Or

SECOND READING — B

Galatians 5:16–25

Brothers and sisters, live by the Spirit and you will certainly not gratify the desire of the flesh. For the flesh has desires against the Spirit, and the Spirit against the flesh; these are opposed to each other, so that you may not do what you want. But if you are guided by the Spirit, you are not under the law. Now the works of the flesh are obvious: immorality, impurity, lust, idolatry, sorcery, hatreds, rivalry, jealousy, outbursts of fury, acts of selfishness, dissensions, factions, occasions of envy, drinking bouts, orgies, and the like. I warn you, as I warned you before, that those who do such things will not inherit the kingdom of God. In contrast, the fruit of the Spirit is love, joy, peace, patience, kindness, generosity, faithfulness, gentleness, self-control. Against such there is no law. Now those who belong to Christ Jesus have crucified their flesh with its passions and desires. If we live in the Spirit, let us also follow the Spirit.

Or

SECOND READING — C

Romans 8:8–17

Brothers and sisters: Those who are in the flesh cannot please God. But you are not in the flesh; on the contrary, you are in the spirit, if only the Spirit of God dwells in you. Whoever does not have the Spirit of

Christ does not belong to him. But if Christ is in you, although the body is dead because of sin, the spirit is alive because of righteousness. If the Spirit of the one who raised Jesus from the dead dwells in you, the one who raised Christ from the dead will give life to your mortal bodies also, through his Spirit that dwells in you. Consequently, brothers and sisters, we are not debtors to the flesh, to live according to the flesh. For if you live according to the flesh, you will die, but if by the Spirit you put to death the deeds of the body, you will live.

For those who are led by the Spirit of God are sons of God. For you did not receive a spirit of slavery to fall back into fear, but you received a Spirit of adoption, through whom we cry, "Abba, Father!" The Spirit himself bears witness with our spirit that we are children of God, and if children, then heirs, heirs of God and joint heirs with Christ, if only we suffer with him so that we may also be glorified with him.

SEQUENCE
Veni, Sancte Spiritus

The Sequence, Veni, Sancte Spiritus, *is sung before the Gospel Acclamation on Pentecost Sunday. (For music, see #432, 434, 435, 437, 439, 441.)*

Come, Holy Spirit, come!
And from your celestial home
  Shed a ray of light divine!

Come, Father of the poor!
Come, source of all our store!
  Come, within our bosoms shine.

You, of comforters the best;
You, the soul's most welcome guest;
  Sweet refreshment here below;

In our labor, rest most sweet;
Grateful coolness in the heat;
  Solace in the midst of woe.

O most blessed Light divine,
Shine within these hearts of yours,
  And our inmost being fill!

Where you are not, we have naught,
Nothing good in deed or thought,
  Nothing free from taint of ill.

Heal our wounds, our strength renew;
On our dryness pour your dew;
  Wash the stains of guilt away:

Bend the stubborn heart and will;
Melt the frozen, warm the chill;
  Guide the steps that go astray.

On the faithful, who adore
And confess you, evermore
  In your sevenfold gift descend;

Give them virtue's sure reward;
Give them your salvation, Lord;
  Give them joys that never end.
    Amen.
    Alleluia.

GOSPEL ACCLAMATION

℟. Al - le - lu - ia, al - le - lu - ia, al - le - lu - ia.

(Omit if not sung)

▶ Come, Holy Spirit, fill the hearts of your faithful and kindle in them the fire of your love. ℟.

GOSPEL — ABC
John 20:19–23

On the evening of that first day of the week, when the doors were locked, where the disciples were, for fear of the Jews, Jesus came and stood in their midst and said to them, "Peace be with you." When he had said this, he showed them his hands and his side. The disciples rejoiced when they saw the Lord. Jesus said to them again, "Peace be with you. As the Father has sent me, so I send you." And when he had said this, he breathed on them and said to them, "Receive the Holy Spirit. Whose sins you forgive are forgiven them, and whose sins you retain are retained."

Or

GOSPEL — B
John 15:26–27; 16:12–15

Jesus said to his disciples: "When the Advocate comes whom I will send you from the Father, the Spirit of truth that proceeds from the Father, he will testify to me. And you also testify, because you have been with me from the beginning.

"I have much more to tell you, but you cannot bear it now. But when he comes, the Spirit of truth, he will guide you to all truth. He will not speak on his own, but he will speak what he hears, and will declare to you the things that are coming. He will glorify me, because he will take from what is mine and declare it to you. Everything that the Father has is mine; for this reason I told you that he will take from what is mine and declare it to you."

Or

GOSPEL — C
John 14:15–16, 23b–26

Jesus said to his disciples: "If you love me, you will keep my commandments. And I will ask the Father, and he will give you another Advocate to be with you always.

"Whoever loves me will keep my word, and my Father will love him, and we will come to him and make our dwelling with him. Those who do not love me do not keep my words; yet the word you hear is not mine but that of the Father who sent me.

"I have told you this while I am with you. The Advocate, the Holy Spirit whom the Father will send in my name, will teach you everything and remind you of all that I told you."

SOLEMNITIES OF THE LORD DURING ORDINARY TIME

922 THE MOST HOLY TRINITY — A

FIRST READING
Exodus 34:4b–6, 8–9

Early in the morning Moses went up Mount Sinai as the LORD had commanded him, taking along the two stone tablets.

Having come down in a cloud, the LORD stood with Moses there and proclaimed his name, "LORD." Thus the LORD passed before him and cried out, "The LORD, the LORD, a merciful and gracious God, slow to anger and rich in kindness and fidelity." Moses at once bowed down to the ground in worship. Then he said, "If I find favor with you, O LORD, do come along in our company. This is indeed a stiff-necked people; yet pardon our wickedness and sins, and receive us as your own."

RESPONSORIAL PSALM

Daniel 3:52, 53, 54, 55

℟. Glo - ry and praise for ev - er!

▸ Blessed are you, O Lord, the God of
   our fathers,
   praiseworthy and exalted above
   all forever;
and blessed is your holy and
   glorious name,
   praiseworthy and exalted above all
   for all ages. ℟.

▸ Blessed are you in the temple of your
   holy glory,
   praiseworthy and glorious above
   all forever. ℟.

▸ Blessed are you on the throne of
   your kingdom,
   praiseworthy and exalted above
   all forever. ℟.

▸ Blessed are you who look into
   the depths
from your throne upon
   the cherubim,
   praiseworthy and exalted above
   all forever. ℟.

SECOND READING

2 Corinthians 13:11–13

Brothers and sisters, rejoice. Mend your ways, encourage one another, agree with one another, live in peace, and the God of love and peace will be with you. Greet one another with a holy kiss. All the holy ones greet you.
   The grace of the Lord Jesus Christ and the love of God and the fellowship of the Holy Spirit be with all of you.

GOSPEL ACCLAMATION

cf. Revelation 1:8

℟. Al - le - lu - ia, al - le - lu - ia, al - le - lu - ia.

(Omit if not sung)

▸ Glory to the Father, the Son, and the Holy Spirit;
   to God who is, who was, and who is to come. ℟.

GOSPEL

John 3:16–18

God so loved the world that he gave his only Son, so that everyone who believes in him might not perish but might have eternal life. For God did not send his Son into the world to condemn the world, but that the world might be saved through him. Whoever believes in him will not be condemned, but whoever does not believe has already been condemned, because he has not believed in the name of the only Son of God.

923 THE MOST HOLY TRINITY — B

FIRST READING

Deuteronomy 4:32–34, 39–40

Moses said to the people: "Ask now of the days of old, before your time, ever since God created man upon the earth; ask from one end of the sky to the other: Did anything so great ever happen before? Was it ever heard of? Did a people ever hear the voice of God speaking from the midst of fire, as you did, and live? Or did any god venture to go and take a nation for himself from the midst of another nation, by testings, by signs and wonders, by war, with strong hand and outstretched arm, and by great terrors, all of which the LORD, your God, did for you in Egypt before your very eyes? This is why you must now know, and fix in your heart, that the LORD is God in the heavens above and on earth below, and that there is no other. You must keep his statutes and commandments that I enjoin on you today, that you and your children after you may prosper, and that you may have long life on the land which the LORD, your God, is giving you forever."

RESPONSORIAL PSALM

Psalm 33:4–5, 6, 9, 18–19, 20, 22

℟. Bless-ed the peo-ple the Lord has [cho-sen,] cho-sen to be his own.

▶ Upright is the word of the LORD,
　and all his works are trustworthy.
He loves justice and right;
　of the kindness of the LORD the
　　earth is full. ℟.

▶ By the word of the LORD the heavens
　　were made;
　by the breath of his mouth all
　　their host.
For he spoke, and it was made;
　he commanded, and it
　　stood forth. ℟.

▶ See, the eyes of the LORD are upon
　　those who fear him,
　upon those who hope for
　　his kindness,
to deliver them from death
　and preserve them in spite
　　of famine. ℟.

▶ Our soul waits for the LORD,
　who is our help and our shield.
May your kindness, O LORD,
　be upon us
who have put our hope in you. ℟.

SECOND READING

Romans 8:14–17

Brothers and sisters: Those who are led by the Spirit of God are sons of God. For you did not receive a spirit of slavery to fall back into fear, but you received a Spirit of adoption, through whom we cry, "Abba, Father!" The Spirit himself bears witness with our spirit that we are children of God, and if children, then heirs, heirs of God and joint heirs with Christ, if only we suffer with him so that we may also be glorified with him.

GOSPEL ACCLAMATION

Revelation 1:8

℟. Al - le - lu - ia, al - le - lu - ia, al - le - lu - ia.

(Omit if not sung)

▸ Glory to the Father, the Son, and the Holy Spirit;
to God who is, who was, and who is to come. ℟.

GOSPEL

Matthew 28:16–20

The eleven disciples went to Galilee, to the mountain to which Jesus had ordered them. When they all saw him, they worshiped, but they doubted. Then Jesus approached and said to them, "All power in heaven and on earth has been given to me. Go, therefore, and make disciples of all nations, baptizing them in the name of the Father, and of the Son, and of the Holy Spirit, teaching them to observe all that I have commanded you. And behold, I am with you always, until the end of the age."

THE MOST HOLY TRINITY — C   924

FIRST READING

Proverbs 8:22–31

Thus says the wisdom of God:
"The LORD possessed me, the
    beginning of his ways,
      the forerunner of his prodigies of
      long ago;
  from of old I was poured forth,
    at the first, before the earth.
When there were no depths I was
    brought forth,
    when there were no fountains or
      springs of water;
before the mountains were settled
    into place,
    before the hills, I was
      brought forth;
while as yet the earth and fields were
    not made,
    nor the first clods of the world.

"When the Lord established the
    heavens I was there,
    when he marked out the vault over
      the face of the deep;
when he made firm the skies above,
    when he fixed fast the foundations
      of the earth;
when he set for the sea its limit,
    so that the waters should not
      transgress his command;
then was I beside him as
    his craftsman,
  and I was his delight day by day,
playing before him all the while,
    playing on the surface of his earth;
and I found delight in the
    human race."

RESPONSORIAL PSALM

Psalm 8:4–5, 6–7, 8–9

℟. O Lord, our God, how won-der-ful your name in all the earth!

▸ When I behold your heavens, the
    work of your fingers,
    the moon and the stars which you
      set in place—
what is man that you should be
    mindful of him,
    or the son of man that you should
    care for him? ℟.

▸ You have made him little less than
    the angels,
    and crowned him with glory
    and honor.
You have given him rule over the
    works of your hands,
    putting all things under his feet. ℟.

℟. O Lord, our God, how wonderful your name in all the earth!

▶ All sheep and oxen,
   yes, and the beasts of the field,
 the birds of the air, the fishes of the sea,

and whatever swims the paths of
  the seas. **℟.**

SECOND READING
Romans 5:1–5

Brothers and sisters: Therefore, since we have been justified by faith, we have peace with God through our Lord Jesus Christ, through whom we have gained access by faith to this grace in which we stand, and we boast in hope of the glory of God. Not only that, but we even boast of our afflictions, knowing that affliction produces endurance, and endurance, proven character, and proven character, hope, and hope does not disappoint, because the love of God has been poured out into our hearts through the Holy Spirit that has been given to us.

GOSPEL ACCLAMATION
cf. Revelation 1:8

℟. Al - le-lu - ia,   **al - le - lu - ia,**   **al - le - lu - ia.**

Music: Owen Alstott, b. 1947, © 1977, 1990, OCP. All rights reserved.   *(Omit if not sung)*

▶ Glory to the Father, the Son, and the Holy Spirit;
 to God who is, who was, and who is to come. **℟.**

GOSPEL
John 16:12–15

Jesus said to his disciples: "I have much more to tell you, but you cannot bear it now. But when he comes, the Spirit of truth, he will guide you to all truth. He will not speak on his own, but he will speak what he hears, and will declare to you the things that are coming. He will glorify me, because he will take from what is mine and declare it to you. Everything that the Father has is mine; for this reason I told you that he will take from what is mine and declare it to you."

---

925   THE MOST HOLY BODY AND BLOOD OF CHRIST (CORPUS CHRISTI) — A

FIRST READING
Deuteronomy 8:2–3, 14b–16a

Moses said to the people: "Remember how for forty years now the LORD, your God, has directed all your journeying in the desert, so as to test you by affliction and find out whether or not it was your intention to keep his commandments. He therefore let you be afflicted with hunger, and then fed you with manna, a food unknown to you and your fathers, in order to show you that not by bread alone does one live, but by every word that comes forth from the mouth of the LORD.

"Do not forget the LORD, your God, who brought you out of the land of Egypt, that place of slavery; who guided you through the vast and terrible desert with its saraph serpents and scorpions, its parched and waterless ground; who brought forth water for you from the flinty rock and fed you in the desert with manna, a food unknown to your fathers."

RESPONSORIAL PSALM   *Psalm 147:12–13, 14–15, 19–20*

℟. Praise the Lord, Je - ru - sa - lem.   [Al - le - lu - ia!]

Or ℟. **Alleluia.**

▸ Glorify the LORD, O Jerusalem;
    praise your God, O Zion.
  For he has strengthened the bars of
      your gates;
    he has blessed your children
      within you. ℟.

▸ He has granted peace in
    your borders;
  with the best of wheat he fills you.

He sends forth his command to
    the earth;
  swiftly runs his word! ℟.

▸ He has proclaimed his word to Jacob,
    his statutes and his ordinances
    to Israel.
  He has not done thus for any
    other nation;
  his ordinances he has not
    made known to them. Alleluia. ℟.

SECOND READING   *1 Corinthians 10:16–17*

Brothers and sisters: The cup of
blessing that we bless, is it not a
participation in the blood of Christ?
The bread that we break, is it not a
participation in the body of Christ?
Because the loaf of bread is one,
we, though many, are one body, for
we all partake of the one loaf.

SEQUENCE (Optional)   *Lauda Sion*

The sequence Laud, O Zion (Lauda Sion), *or the shorter form beginning with the verse*
Lo! the angel's food is given, *may be sung before the Gospel Acclamation. (For music, see #453.)*

Laud, O Zion, your salvation,
Laud with hymns of exultation,
    Christ, your king and shepherd true:

Bring him all the praise you know,
He is more than you bestow.
    Never can you reach his due.

Special theme for glad thanksgiving
Is the quick'ning and the living
    Bread today before you set:

From his hands of old partaken,
As we know, by faith unshaken,
    Where the Twelve at supper met.

Full and clear ring out your chanting,
Joy nor sweetest grace be wanting,
    From your heart let praises burst:

For today the feast is holden,
When the institution olden
    Of that supper was rehearsed.

Here the new law's new oblation,
By the new king's revelation,
    Ends the form of ancient rite:

Now the new the old effaces,
Truth away the shadow chases,
    Light dispels the gloom of night.

What he did at supper seated,
Christ ordained to be repeated,
    His memorial ne'er to cease:

And his rule for guidance taking,
Bread and wine we hallow, making
    Thus our sacrifice of peace.

This the truth each Christian learns,
Bread into his flesh he turns,
    To his precious blood the wine:

Sight has fail'd, nor thought conceives,
But a dauntless faith believes,
    Resting on a pow'r divine.

Here beneath these signs are hidden
Priceless things to sense forbidden;
  Signs, not things are all we see:

Blood is poured and flesh is broken,
Yet in either wondrous token
  Christ entire we know to be.

Whoso of this food partakes,
Does not rend the Lord nor breaks;
  Christ is whole to all that taste:

Thousands are, as one, receivers,
One, as thousands of believers,
  Eats of him who cannot waste.

Bad and good the feast are sharing,
Of what divers dooms preparing,
  Endless death, or endless life.

Life to these, to those damnation,
See how like participation
  Is with unlike issues rife.

When the sacrament is broken,
Doubt not, but believe 'tis spoken,
  That each sever'd outward token
    doth the very whole contain.

Nought the precious gift divides,
Breaking but the sign betides

Jesus still the same abides,
  still unbroken does remain.

*The shorter form of the sequence
begins here.*

Lo! the angel's food is given
To the pilgrim who has striven;
  See the children's bread from heaven,
    which on dogs may not be spent.

Truth the ancient types fulfilling,
Isaac bound, a victim willing,
  Paschal lamb, its lifeblood spilling,
  manna to the fathers sent.

Very bread, good shepherd, tend us,
Jesu, of your love befriend us,
  You refresh us, you defend us,
  Your eternal goodness send us
In the land of life to see.

You who all things can and know,
Who on earth such food bestow,
  Grant us with your saints,
    though lowest,
  Where the heav'nly feast you show,
Fellow heirs and guests to be.
  Amen. Alleluia.

GOSPEL ACCLAMATION

John 6:51

℟. Al - le - lu - ia, al - le - lu - ia, al - le - lu - ia.

(Omit if not sung)

▸ I am the living bread that came down from heaven, says the Lord;
whoever eats this bread will live forever. ℟.

GOSPEL

John 6:51–58

Jesus said to the Jewish crowds: "I am the living bread that came down from heaven; whoever eats this bread will live forever; and the bread that I will give is my flesh for the life of the world."

The Jews quarreled among themselves, saying, "How can this man give us his flesh to eat?" Jesus said to them, "Amen, amen, I say to you, unless you eat the flesh of the Son of Man and drink his blood, you do not have life within you. Whoever eats my flesh and drinks my blood has eternal life, and I will raise him on the last day. For my flesh is true food, and my blood is true drink. Whoever eats my flesh and drinks my blood remains in me and I in him. Just as the living Father sent me and I have life because of the Father, so also the one who feeds on me will have life because of me. This is the bread that came down from heaven. Unlike your ancestors who ate and still died, whoever eats this bread will live forever."

It is desirable that a procession take place after the Mass in which the Host to be carried in the procession is consecrated. This may be done even after a public and lengthy period of adoration following the Mass. If a procession takes place after Mass, when Communion is over, the monstrance in which the consecrated Host has been placed is set on the altar. After the Prayer after Communion is said, the Concluding Rites are omitted and the procession forms.

THE MOST HOLY BODY AND BLOOD OF CHRIST 926
(CORPUS CHRISTI) — B

FIRST READING
Exodus 24:3–8

When Moses came to the people and related all the words and ordinances of the LORD, they all answered with one voice, "We will do everything that the LORD has told us." Moses then wrote down all the words of the LORD and, rising early the next day, he erected at the foot of the mountain an altar and twelve pillars for the twelve tribes of Israel. Then, having sent certain young men of the Israelites to offer holocausts and sacrifice young bulls as peace offerings to the LORD, Moses took half of the blood and put it in large bowls; the other half he splashed on the altar. Taking the book of the covenant, he read it aloud to the people, who answered, "All that the LORD has said, we will heed and do." Then he took the blood and sprinkled it on the people, saying, "This is the blood of the covenant that the LORD has made with you in accordance with all these words of his."

RESPONSORIAL PSALM
Psalm 116:12–13, 15–16, 17–18

℟. I will take the cup of sal-va-tion, and call on the name of the Lord.

Music: Owen Alstott, b. 1947, © 1977, 1990, OCP. All rights reserved.

Or ℟. **Alleluia.**

▶ How shall I make a return to the LORD
for all the good he has done
for me?
The cup of salvation I will take up,
and I will call upon the name of
the LORD. ℟.

▶ Precious in the eyes of the LORD
is the death of his faithful ones.

I am your servant, the son of
your handmaid;
you have loosed my bonds. ℟.

▶ To you will I offer a sacrifice
of thanksgiving,
and I will call upon the name of
the LORD.
My vows to the LORD I will pay
in the presence of all his people. ℟.

SECOND READING
Hebrews 9:11–15

Brothers and sisters: When Christ came as high priest of the good things that have come to be, passing through the greater and more perfect tabernacle not made by hands, that is, not belonging to this creation, he entered once for all into the sanctuary, not with the blood of goats and calves but with his own blood, thus obtaining eternal redemption. For if the blood of goats and bulls and the sprinkling of a heifer's ashes

can sanctify those who are defiled
so that their flesh is cleansed, how
much more will the blood of Christ,
who through the eternal Spirit
offered himself unblemished to God,
cleanse our consciences from dead
works to worship the living God.

For this reason he is mediator of
a new covenant: since a death has
taken place for deliverance from
transgressions under the first covenant,
those who are called may receive
the promised eternal inheritance.

SEQUENCE (Optional)   *Lauda Sion*

The sequence Laud, O Zion (Lauda Sion), *or the shorter form beginning with the verse* Lo! the angel's food is given, *may be sung before the Gospel Acclamation. (For music, see #453.)*

Laud, O Zion, your salvation,
Laud with hymns of exultation,
    Christ, your king and shepherd true:

Bring him all the praise you know,
He is more than you bestow.
    Never can you reach his due.

Special theme for glad thanksgiving
Is the quick'ning and the living
    Bread today before you set:

From his hands of old partaken,
As we know, by faith unshaken,
    Where the Twelve at supper met.

Full and clear ring out your chanting,
Joy nor sweetest grace be wanting,
    From your heart let praises burst:

For today the feast is holden,
When the institution olden
    Of that supper was rehearsed.

Here the new law's new oblation,
By the new king's revelation,
    Ends the form of ancient rite:

Now the new the old effaces,
Truth away the shadow chases,
    Light dispels the gloom of night.

What he did at supper seated,
Christ ordained to be repeated,
    His memorial ne'er to cease:

And his rule for guidance taking,
Bread and wine we hallow, making
    Thus our sacrifice of peace.

This the truth each Christian learns,
Bread into his flesh he turns,
    To his precious blood the wine:

Sight has fail'd, nor thought conceives,
But a dauntless faith believes,
    Resting on a pow'r divine.

Here beneath these signs are hidden
Priceless things to sense forbidden;
    Signs, not things are all we see:

Blood is poured and flesh is broken,
Yet in either wondrous token
    Christ entire we know to be.

Whoso of this food partakes,
Does not rend the Lord nor breaks;
    Christ is whole to all that taste:

Thousands are, as one, receivers,
One, as thousands of believers,
    Eats of him who cannot waste.

Bad and good the feast are sharing,
Of what divers dooms preparing,
    Endless death, or endless life.

Life to these, to those damnation,
See how like participation
    Is with unlike issues rife.

When the sacrament is broken,
Doubt not, but believe 'tis spoken,
    That each sever'd outward token
    doth the very whole contain.

Nought the precious gift divides,
Breaking but the sign betides
    Jesus still the same abides,
    still unbroken does remain.

*The shorter form of the sequence
begins here.*

Lo! the angel's food is given
To the pilgrim who has striven;
  See the children's bread from heaven,
    which on dogs may not be spent.

Truth the ancient types fulfilling,
Isaac bound, a victim willing,
  Paschal lamb, its lifeblood spilling,
  manna to the fathers sent.

Very bread, good shepherd, tend us,
Jesu, of your love befriend us,
  You refresh us, you defend us,
  Your eternal goodness send us
In the land of life to see.

You who all things can and know,
Who on earth such food bestow,
  Grant us with your saints,
    though lowest,
  Where the heav'nly feast you show,
Fellow heirs and guests to be.
  Amen. Alleluia.

GOSPEL ACCLAMATION

John 6:51

R. Al - le - lu - ia, al - le - lu - ia, al - le - lu - ia.

(Omit if not sung)

▶ I am the living bread that came down from heaven, says the Lord;
  whoever eats this bread will live forever. R.

GOSPEL

Mark 14:12–16, 22–26

On the first day of the Feast of Unleavened Bread, when they sacrificed the Passover lamb, Jesus' disciples said to him, "Where do you want us to go and prepare for you to eat the Passover?" He sent two of his disciples and said to them, "Go into the city and a man will meet you, carrying a jar of water. Follow him. Wherever he enters, say to the master of the house, 'The Teacher says, "Where is my guest room where I may eat the Passover with my disciples?"' Then he will show you a large upper room furnished and ready. Make the preparations for us there." The disciples then went off, entered the city, and found it just as he had told them; and they prepared the Passover.

While they were eating, he took bread, said the blessing, broke it, gave it to them, and said, "Take it; this is my body." Then he took a cup, gave thanks, and gave it to them, and they all drank from it. He said to them, "This is my blood of the covenant, which will be shed for many. Amen, I say to you, I shall not drink again the fruit of the vine until the day when I drink it new in the kingdom of God." Then, after singing a hymn, they went out to the Mount of Olives.

It is desirable that a procession take place after the Mass in which the Host to be carried in the procession is consecrated. This may be done even after a public and lengthy period of adoration following the Mass. If a procession takes place after Mass, when Communion is over, the monstrance in which the consecrated Host has been placed is set on the altar. After the Prayer after Communion is said, the Concluding Rites are omitted and the procession forms.

927 THE MOST HOLY BODY AND BLOOD OF CHRIST (CORPUS CHRISTI) — C

FIRST READING *Genesis 14:18–20*

In those days, Melchizedek, king of Salem, brought out bread and wine, and being a priest of God Most High, he blessed Abram with these words:
"Blessed be Abram by God Most High,
the creator of heaven and earth; and blessed be God Most High, who delivered your foes into your hand."
Then Abram gave him a tenth of everything.

RESPONSORIAL PSALM *Psalm 110:1, 2, 3, 4*

℟. You are a priest for ev - er, in the line of Mel - chiz - e - dek.

▶ The LORD said to my Lord: "Sit at my right hand
  till I make your enemies your footstool." ℟.

▶ The scepter of your power the LORD will stretch forth from Zion:
  "Rule in the midst of your enemies." ℟.

▶ "Yours is princely power in the day of your birth, in holy splendor;
  before the daystar, like the dew, I have begotten you." ℟.

▶ The LORD has sworn, and he will not repent:
  "You are a priest forever, according to the order of Melchizedek." ℟.

SECOND READING *1 Corinthians 11:23–26*

Brothers and sisters: I received from the Lord what I also handed on to you, that the Lord Jesus, on the night he was handed over, took bread, and, after he had given thanks, broke it and said, "This is my body that is for you. Do this in remembrance of me."
In the same way also the cup, after supper, saying, "This cup is the new covenant in my blood. Do this, as often as you drink it, in remembrance of me." For as often as you eat this bread and drink the cup, you proclaim the death of the Lord until he comes.

SEQUENCE (Optional) *Lauda Sion*

The sequence Laud, O Zion (Lauda Sion), *or the shorter form beginning with the verse* Lo! the angel's food is given, *may be sung before the Gospel Acclamation. (For music, see #453.)*

Laud, O Zion, your salvation,
Laud with hymns of exultation,
  Christ, your king and shepherd true:

Bring him all the praise you know,
He is more than you bestow.
  Never can you reach his due.

Special theme for glad thanksgiving
Is the quick'ning and the living
  Bread today before you set:

From his hands of old partaken,
As we know, by faith unshaken,
  Where the Twelve at supper met.

Full and clear ring out your chanting,
Joy nor sweetest grace be wanting,
  From your heart let praises burst:

For today the feast is holden,
When the institution olden
  Of that supper was rehearsed.

Here the new law's new oblation,
By the new king's revelation,
 Ends the form of ancient rite:

Now the new the old effaces,
Truth away the shadow chases,
 Light dispels the gloom of night.

What he did at supper seated,
Christ ordained to be repeated,
 His memorial ne'er to cease:

And his rule for guidance taking,
Bread and wine we hallow, making
 Thus our sacrifice of peace.

This the truth each Christian learns,
Bread into his flesh he turns,
 To his precious blood the wine:

Sight has fail'd, nor thought conceives,
But a dauntless faith believes,
 Resting on a pow'r divine.

Here beneath these signs are hidden
Priceless things to sense forbidden;
 Signs, not things are all we see:

Blood is poured and flesh is broken,
Yet in either wondrous token
 Christ entire we know to be.

Whoso of this food partakes,
Does not rend the Lord nor breaks;
 Christ is whole to all that taste:

Thousands are, as one, receivers,
One, as thousands of believers,
 Eats of him who cannot waste.

Bad and good the feast are sharing,
Of what divers dooms preparing,
 Endless death, or endless life.

Life to these, to those damnation,
See how like participation
 Is with unlike issues rife.

When the sacrament is broken,
Doubt not, but believe 'tis spoken,
 That each sever'd outward token
 doth the very whole contain.

Nought the precious gift divides,
Breaking but the sign betides
 Jesus still the same abides,
 still unbroken does remain.

*The shorter form of the sequence
begins here.*

Lo! the angel's food is given
To the pilgrim who has striven;
 See the children's bread from heaven,
 which on dogs may not be spent.

Truth the ancient types fulfilling,
Isaac bound, a victim willing,
 Paschal lamb, its lifeblood spilling,
 manna to the fathers sent.

Very bread, good shepherd, tend us,
Jesu, of your love befriend us,
 You refresh us, you defend us,
 Your eternal goodness send us
In the land of life to see.

You who all things can and know,
Who on earth such food bestow,
 Grant us with your saints,
 though lowest,
 Where the heav'nly feast you show,
Fellow heirs and guests to be.
 Amen. Alleluia.

GOSPEL ACCLAMATION

John 6:51

℟. Al - le - lu - ia, al - le - lu - ia, al - le - lu - ia.

(Omit if not sung)

▶ I am the living bread that came down from heaven, says the Lord;
 whoever eats this bread will live forever. **℟.**

GOSPEL

Luke 9:11b–17

Jesus spoke to the crowds about the kingdom of God, and he healed those who needed to be cured. As the day was drawing to a close, the Twelve approached him and said, "Dismiss the crowd so that they can go to the surrounding villages and farms and find lodging and provisions; for we are in a deserted place here." He said to them, "Give them some food yourselves." They replied, "Five loaves and two fish are all we have, unless we ourselves go and buy food for all these people." Now the men there numbered about five thousand. Then he said to his disciples, "Have them sit down in groups of about fifty." They did so and made them all sit down. Then taking the five loaves and the two fish, and looking up to heaven, he said the blessing over them, broke them, and gave them to the disciples to set before the crowd. They all ate and were satisfied. And when the leftover fragments were picked up, they filled twelve wicker baskets.

It is desirable that a procession take place after the Mass in which the Host to be carried in the procession is consecrated. This may be done even after a public and lengthy period of adoration following the Mass. If a procession takes place after Mass, when Communion is over, the monstrance in which the consecrated Host has been placed is set on the altar. After the Prayer after Communion is said, the Concluding Rites are omitted and the procession forms.

928 THE MOST SACRED HEART OF JESUS — A

FIRST READING

Deuteronomy 7:6–11

Moses said to the people: "You are a people sacred to the LORD, your God; he has chosen you from all the nations on the face of the earth to be a people peculiarly his own. It was not because you are the largest of all nations that the LORD set his heart on you and chose you, for you are really the smallest of all nations. It was because the LORD loved you and because of his fidelity to the oath he had sworn to your fathers, that he brought you out with his strong hand from the place of slavery, and ransomed you from the hand of Pharaoh, king of Egypt. Understand, then, that the LORD, your God, is God indeed, the faithful God who keeps his merciful covenant down to the thousandth generation toward those who love him and keep his commandments, but who repays with destruction a person who hates him; he does not dally with such a one, but makes them personally pay for it. You shall therefore carefully observe the commandments, the statutes and the decrees that I enjoin on you today."

RESPONSORIAL PSALM

Psalm 103:1–2, 3–4, 8, 10

℟. The Lord's kind-ness is ev-er-last-ing to those who fear him.

▶ Bless the LORD, O my soul;
all my being, bless his holy name.
Bless the LORD, O my soul;
and forget not all his benefits. ℟.

▶ He pardons all your iniquities,
heals all your ills.
He redeems your life
from destruction,
crowns you with kindness
and compassion. ℟.

▶ Merciful and gracious is the LORD,
slow to anger and abounding
in kindness.
Not according to our sins does he
deal with us,
nor does he requite us according to
our crimes. ℟.

SECOND READING

1 John 4:7–16

Beloved, let us love one another, because love is of God; everyone who loves is begotten by God and knows God. Whoever is without love does not know God, for God is love. In this way the love of God was revealed to us: God sent his only Son into the world so that we might have life through him. In this is love: not that we have loved God, but that he loved us and sent his Son as expiation for our sins. Beloved, if God so loved us, we also must love one another. No one has ever seen God. Yet, if we love one another, God remains in us, and his love is brought to perfection in us.

This is how we know that we remain in him and he in us, that he has given us of his Spirit. Moreover, we have seen and testify that the Father sent his Son as savior of the world. Whoever acknowledges that Jesus is the Son of God, God remains in him and he in God. We have come to know and to believe in the love God has for us.

God is love, and whoever remains in love remains in God and God in him.

GOSPEL ACCLAMATION

Matthew 11:29ab

℟. Al - le - lu - ia, al - le - lu - ia, al - le - lu - ia.

Music: Owen Alstott, b. 1947, © 1977, 1990, OCP. All rights reserved. *(Omit if not sung)*

▶ Take my yoke upon you, says the Lord;
and learn from me, for I am meek and humble of heart. ℟.

GOSPEL

Matthew 11:25–30

At that time Jesus exclaimed: "I give praise to you, Father, Lord of heaven and earth, for although you have hidden these things from the wise and the learned you have revealed them to little ones. Yes, Father, such has been your gracious will. All things have been handed over to me by my Father. No one knows the Son except the Father, and no one knows the Father except the Son and anyone to whom the Son wishes to reveal him.

"Come to me, all you who labor and are burdened, and I will give you rest. Take my yoke upon you and learn from me, for I am meek and humble of heart; and you will find rest for yourselves. For my yoke is easy, and my burden light."

929   THE MOST SACRED HEART OF JESUS — B

FIRST READING   *Hosea 11:1, 3–4, 8c–9*

Thus says the LORD:
>When Israel was a child I loved him,
>>out of Egypt I called my son.
>
>Yet it was I who taught Ephraim
>>to walk,
>>who took them in my arms;
>
>I drew them with human cords,
>>with bands of love;
>
>I fostered them like one
>>who raises an infant to his cheeks;
>
>Yet, though I stooped to feed
>>my child,

they did not know that I was
>their healer.

My heart is overwhelmed,
>my pity is stirred.

I will not give vent to my
>blazing anger,
>I will not destroy Ephraim again;

For I am God and not a man,
>the Holy One present
>among you;

I will not let the flames
>consume you.

RESPONSORIAL PSALM   *Isaiah 12:2–3, 4, 5–6*

℟. You will draw wa - ter joy - ful - ly from the springs of sal - va - tion.

▸ God indeed is my savior;
>I am confident and unafraid.

My strength and my courage is
>the LORD,
>and he has been my savior.

With joy you will draw water
>at the fountain of salvation. ℟.

▸ Give thanks to the LORD, acclaim
>his name;
>among the nations make known
>his deeds,

proclaim how exalted is
>his name. ℟.

▸ Sing praise to the LORD for his
>glorious achievement;
>let this be known throughout all
>the earth.

Shout with exultation, O city of Zion,
>for great in your midst
>is the Holy One of Israel! ℟.

SECOND READING   *Ephesians 3:8–12, 14–19*

Brothers and sisters: To me, the very least of all the holy ones, this grace was given, to preach to the Gentiles the inscrutable riches of Christ, and to bring to light for all what is the plan of the mystery hidden from ages past in God who created all things, so that the manifold wisdom of God might now be made known through the church to the principalities and authorities in the heavens. This was according to the eternal purpose that he accomplished in Christ Jesus our Lord, in whom we have boldness of speech and confidence of access through faith in him.

For this reason I kneel before the Father, from whom every family in heaven and on earth is named, that he may grant you in accord with the riches of his glory to be strengthened with power through his Spirit in the inner self, and that Christ may dwell in your hearts through faith; that you, rooted and grounded in love, may have strength to comprehend with all the holy ones what is the breadth and length and height and depth, and to know the love of Christ which surpasses knowledge, so that you may be filled with all the fullness of God.

GOSPEL ACCLAMATION

Matthew 11:29ab

R. Al - le - lu - ia, al - le - lu - ia, al - le - lu - ia.

(Omit if not sung)

▶ Take my yoke upon you, says the Lord; and learn from me, for I am meek and humble of heart. R.

Or   *1 John 4:10b*

▶ God first loved us and sent his Son as expiation for our sins. R.

GOSPEL

John 19:31–37

Since it was preparation day, in order that the bodies might not remain on the cross on the sabbath, for the sabbath day of that week was a solemn one, the Jews asked Pilate that their legs be broken and they be taken down. So the soldiers came and broke the legs of the first and then of the other one who was crucified with Jesus. But when they came to Jesus and saw that he was already dead, they did not break his legs, but one soldier thrust his lance into his side, and immediately blood and water flowed out. An eyewitness has testified, and his testimony is true; he knows that he is speaking the truth, so that you also may come to believe. For this happened so that the Scripture passage might be fulfilled:
Not a bone of it will be broken.
And again another passage says:
They will look upon him whom they have pierced.

MOST SACRED HEART OF JESUS — C   930

FIRST READING

Ezekiel 34:11–16

Thus says the Lord GOD: I myself will look after and tend my sheep. As a shepherd tends his flock when he finds himself among his scattered sheep, so will I tend my sheep. I will rescue them from every place where they were scattered when it was cloudy and dark. I will lead them out from among the peoples and gather them from the foreign lands; I will bring them back to their own country and pasture them upon the mountains of Israel in the land's ravines and all its inhabited places. In good pastures will I pasture them, and on the mountain heights of Israel shall be their grazing ground. There they shall lie down on good grazing ground, and in rich pastures shall they be pastured on the mountains of Israel. I myself will pasture my sheep; I myself will give them rest, says the Lord GOD. The lost

I will seek out, the strayed I will bring
back, the injured I will bind up, the sick
I will heal, but the sleek and the strong
I will destroy, shepherding them rightly.

RESPONSORIAL PSALM

Psalm 23:1–3a, 3b–4, 5, 6

℟. The Lord is my shep-herd; there is noth-ing I shall want.

▶ The LORD is my shepherd; I shall
     not want.
   In verdant pastures he gives
     me repose;
   beside restful waters he leads me;
     he refreshes my soul. ℟.

▶ He guides me in right paths
     for his name's sake.
   Even though I walk in the dark valley
     I fear no evil; for you are at my side
   with your rod and your staff
     that give me courage. ℟.

▶ You spread the table before me
     in the sight of my foes;
   you anoint my head with oil;
     my cup overflows. ℟.

▶ Only goodness and kindness
     follow me
   all the days of my life;
   and I shall dwell in the house of
     the LORD
   for years to come. ℟.

SECOND READING

Romans 5:5b–11

Brothers and sisters: The love of God has been poured out into our hearts through the Holy Spirit that has been given to us. For Christ, while we were still helpless, died at the appointed time for the ungodly. Indeed, only with difficulty does one die for a just person, though perhaps for a good person one might even find courage to die. But God proves his love for us in that while we were still sinners Christ died for us. How much more then, since we are now justified by his blood, will we be saved through him from the wrath. Indeed, if, while we were enemies, we were reconciled to God through the death of his Son, how much more, once reconciled, will we be saved by his life. Not only that, but we also boast of God through our Lord Jesus Christ, through whom we have now received reconciliation.

GOSPEL ACCLAMATION

Matthew 11:29ab

℟. Al - le - lu - ia, al - le - lu - ia, al - le - lu - ia.

(Omit if not sung)

▶ Take my yoke upon you, says the Lord;
   and learn from me, for I am meek and humble of heart. ℟.

Or

John 10:14

▶ I am the good shepherd, says the Lord;
   I know my sheep, and mine know me. ℟.

GOSPEL

Luke 15:3–7

Jesus addressed this parable to the Pharisees and scribes: "What man among you having a hundred sheep and losing one of them would not leave the ninety-nine in the desert and go after the lost one until he finds it? And when he does find it, he sets it on his shoulders with great joy and, upon his arrival home, he calls together his friends and neighbors and says to them, 'Rejoice with me because I have found my lost sheep.' I tell you, in just the same way there will be more joy in heaven over one sinner who repents than over ninety-nine righteous people who have no need of repentance."

ORDINARY TIME

The First Sunday in Ordinary Time is the Feast of the Baptism of the Lord (see #879–881).

SECOND SUNDAY IN ORDINARY TIME — A   931

FIRST READING

Isaiah 49:3, 5–6

The LORD said to me: You are
   my servant,
  Israel, through whom I show
   my glory.
Now the LORD has spoken
  who formed me as his servant from
   the womb,
that Jacob may be brought back
   to him
  and Israel gathered to him;

and I am made glorious in the sight
   of the LORD,
  and my God is now my strength!
It is too little, the LORD says, for you
   to be my servant,
  to raise up the tribes of Jacob,
  and restore the survivors of Israel;
I will make you a light to the nations,
  that my salvation may reach to the
   ends of the earth.

RESPONSORIAL PSALM

Psalm 40:2, 4, 7–8, 8–9, 10

℟. Here am I, Lord; I come to do your will.

Music: Owen Alstott, b. 1947, © 1977, 1990, OCP. All rights reserved.

▶ I have waited, waited for the LORD,
  and he stooped toward me and
   heard my cry.
And he put a new song into
   my mouth,
  a hymn to our God. ℟.

▶ Sacrifice or offering you wished not,
  but ears open to obedience you
   gave me.
Holocausts or sin-offerings you
   sought not;
  then said I, "Behold I come." ℟.

▶ "In the written scroll it is prescribed
   for me,
  to do your will, O my God,
   is my delight,
  and your law is within my heart!" ℟.

▶ I announced your justice in the
   vast assembly;
  I did not restrain my lips, as you,
   O LORD, know. ℟.

SECOND READING
1 Corinthians 1:1–3

Paul, called to be an apostle of Christ Jesus by the will of God, and Sosthenes our brother, to the church of God that is in Corinth, to you who have been sanctified in Christ Jesus, called to be holy, with all those everywhere who call upon the name of our Lord Jesus Christ, their Lord and ours. Grace to you and peace from God our Father and the Lord Jesus Christ.

GOSPEL ACCLAMATION
John 1:14a, 12a

℟. Al - le - lu - ia, al - le - lu - ia, al - le - lu - ia.

(Omit if not sung)

▶ The Word of God became flesh and dwelt among us.
  To those who accepted him,
  he gave power to become children of God. ℟.

GOSPEL
John 1:29–34

John the Baptist saw Jesus coming toward him and said, "Behold, the Lamb of God, who takes away the sin of the world. He is the one of whom I said, 'A man is coming after me who ranks ahead of me because he existed before me.' I did not know him, but the reason why I came baptizing with water was that he might be made known to Israel." John testified further, saying, "I saw the Spirit come down like a dove from heaven and remain upon him. I did not know him, but the one who sent me to baptize with water told me, 'On whomever you see the Spirit come down and remain, he is the one who will baptize with the Holy Spirit.' Now I have seen and testified that he is the Son of God."

---

932   SECOND SUNDAY IN ORDINARY TIME — B

FIRST READING
1 Samuel 3:3b–10, 19

Samuel was sleeping in the temple of the LORD where the ark of God was. The LORD called to Samuel, who answered, "Here I am." Samuel ran to Eli and said, "Here I am. You called me." "I did not call you," Eli said. "Go back to sleep." So he went back to sleep. Again the LORD called Samuel, who rose and went to Eli. "Here I am," he said. "You called me." But Eli answered, "I did not call you, my son. Go back to sleep."

  At that time Samuel was not familiar with the LORD, because the LORD had not revealed anything to him as yet. The LORD called Samuel again, for the third time. Getting up and going to Eli, he said, "Here I am. You called me." Then Eli understood that the LORD was calling the youth. So he said to Samuel, "Go to sleep, and if you are called, reply, Speak, LORD, for your servant is listening." When Samuel went to sleep in his place, the LORD came and revealed his presence, calling out as before, "Samuel, Samuel!" Samuel answered, "Speak, for your servant is listening."

  Samuel grew up, and the LORD was with him, not permitting any word of his to be without effect.

RESPONSORIAL PSALM

Psalm 40:2, 4, 7–8, 8–9, 10

℟. Here am I, Lord; I come to do your will.

▸ I have waited, waited for the LORD,
  and he stooped toward me and
    heard my cry.
And he put a new song into
  my mouth,
  a hymn to our God. ℟.

▸ Sacrifice or offering you wished not,
  but ears open to obedience you
    gave me.
Holocausts or sin-offerings you
  sought not;
  then said I, "Behold I come." ℟.

▸ "In the written scroll it is prescribed
    for me,
  to do your will, O my God, is
    my delight,
  and your law is within my heart!" ℟.

▸ I announced your justice in the
    vast assembly;
  I did not restrain my lips, as you,
  O LORD, know. ℟.

SECOND READING

1 Corinthians 6:13c–15a, 17–20

Brothers and sisters: The body is not for immorality, but for the Lord, and the Lord is for the body; God raised the Lord and will also raise us by his power.

Do you not know that your bodies are members of Christ? But whoever is joined to the Lord becomes one Spirit with him. Avoid immorality. Every other sin a person commits is outside the body, but the immoral person sins against his own body. Do you not know that your body is a temple of the Holy Spirit within you, whom you have from God, and that you are not your own? For you have been purchased at a price. Therefore glorify God in your body.

GOSPEL ACCLAMATION

John 1:41, 17b

℟. Al - le - lu - ia, al - le - lu - ia, al - le - lu - ia.

(Omit if not sung)

▸ We have found the Messiah:
  Jesus Christ, who brings us truth and grace. ℟.

GOSPEL

John 1:35–42

John was standing with two of his disciples, and as he watched Jesus walk by, he said, "Behold, the Lamb of God." The two disciples heard what he said and followed Jesus. Jesus turned and saw them following him and said to them, "What are you looking for?" They said to him, "Rabbi"—which translated means Teacher—, "where are you staying?" He said to them, "Come, and you will see." So they went and saw where Jesus was staying, and they stayed with him that day. It was about four in the afternoon. Andrew, the brother of Simon Peter, was one of the two who heard John and followed Jesus. He first found his own brother Simon and told

him, "We have found the Messiah"—
which is translated Christ. Then he
brought him to Jesus. Jesus looked
at him and said, "You are Simon
the son of John; you will be called
Cephas"—which is translated Peter.

933   SECOND SUNDAY IN ORDINARY TIME — C

FIRST READING
Isaiah 62:1–5

For Zion's sake I will not be silent,
   for Jerusalem's sake I will not
     be quiet,
until her vindication shines forth like
   the dawn
   and her victory like a
     burning torch.

Nations shall behold
   your vindication,
   and all the kings your glory;
you shall be called by a new name
   pronounced by the mouth
     of the LORD.

You shall be a glorious crown in the
   hand of the LORD,
   a royal diadem held by your God.
No more shall people call
   you "Forsaken,"
   or your land "Desolate,"
but you shall be called "My Delight,"
   and your land "Espoused."
For the LORD delights in you
   and makes your land his spouse.
As a young man marries a virgin,
   your Builder shall marry you;
and as a bridegroom rejoices in
   his bride
   so shall your God rejoice in you.

RESPONSORIAL PSALM
Psalm 96:1–2, 2–3, 7–8, 9–10

℟. Pro-claim his mar-vel-ous deeds to all the na - tions.

Music: Owen Alstott, b. 1947, © 1977, 1990, OCP. All rights reserved.

▶ Sing to the LORD a new song;
   sing to the LORD, all you lands.
  Sing to the LORD; bless his name. ℟.

▶ Announce his salvation, day after day.
  Tell his glory among the nations;
   among all peoples, his
    wondrous deeds. ℟.

▶ Give to the LORD, you families
   of nations,

  give to the LORD glory and praise;
  give to the LORD the glory due
   his name! ℟.

▶ Worship the LORD in holy attire.
  Tremble before him, all the earth;
  say among the nations: The LORD
   is king.
  He governs the peoples
   with equity. ℟.

SECOND READING
1 Corinthians 12:4–11

Brothers and sisters: There are
different kinds of spiritual gifts but the
same Spirit; there are different forms
of service but the same Lord; there are
different workings but the same God
who produces all of them in everyone.
To each individual the manifestation
of the Spirit is given for some benefit.

To one is given through the Spirit the
expression of wisdom; to another, the
expression of knowledge according
to the same Spirit; to another, faith
by the same Spirit; to another, gifts of
healing by the one Spirit; to another,
mighty deeds; to another, prophecy;
to another, discernment of spirits;

to another, varieties of tongues; to another, interpretation of tongues. But one and the same Spirit produces all of these, distributing them individually to each person as he wishes.

GOSPEL ACCLAMATION

cf. 2 Thessalonians 2:14

℟. Al - le - lu - ia, al - le - lu - ia, al - le - lu - ia.

Music: Owen Alstott, b. 1947, © 1977, 1990, OCP. All rights reserved. *(Omit if not sung)*

▸ God has called us through the Gospel
to possess the glory of our Lord Jesus Christ. ℟.

GOSPEL

John 2:1–11

There was a wedding at Cana in Galilee, and the mother of Jesus was there. Jesus and his disciples were also invited to the wedding. When the wine ran short, the mother of Jesus said to him, "They have no wine." And Jesus said to her, "Woman, how does your concern affect me? My hour has not yet come." His mother said to the servers, "Do whatever he tells you." Now there were six stone water jars there for Jewish ceremonial washings, each holding twenty to thirty gallons. Jesus told them, "Fill the jars with water." So they filled them to the brim. Then he told them, "Draw some out now and take it to the headwaiter." So they took it. And when the headwaiter tasted the water that had become wine, without knowing where it came from— although the servers who had drawn the water knew—, the headwaiter called the bridegroom and said to him, "Everyone serves good wine first, and then when people have drunk freely, an inferior one; but you have kept the good wine until now." Jesus did this as the beginning of his signs at Cana in Galilee and so revealed his glory, and his disciples began to believe in him.

THIRD SUNDAY IN ORDINARY TIME — A   934

FIRST READING

Isaiah 8:23—9:3

First the LORD degraded the land of Zebulun and the land of Naphtali; but in the end he has glorified the seaward road, the land west of the Jordan, the District of the Gentiles.

Anguish has taken wing, dispelled
is darkness:
for there is no gloom where but
now there was distress.
The people who walked in darkness
have seen a great light;
upon those who dwelt in the land
of gloom
a light has shone.

You have brought them abundant joy
and great rejoicing,
as they rejoice before you as at
the harvest,
as people make merry when
dividing spoils.
For the yoke that burdened them,
the pole on their shoulder,
and the rod of their taskmaster
you have smashed, as on the day
of Midian.

RESPONSORIAL PSALM

Psalm 27:1, 4, 13–14

℟. The Lord is my light and my sal - va - tion.

▶ The LORD is my light and my salvation;
    whom should I fear?
 The LORD is my life's refuge;
    of whom should I be afraid? ℟.

▶ One thing I ask of the LORD;
    this I seek:
 to dwell in the house of the LORD
    all the days of my life,

that I may gaze on the loveliness
    of the LORD
and contemplate his temple. ℟.

▶ I believe that I shall see the bounty of
    the LORD
 in the land of the living.
Wait for the LORD with courage;
    be stouthearted, and wait for
    the LORD. ℟.

SECOND READING

1 Corinthians 1:10–13, 17

I urge you, brothers and sisters, in the name of our Lord Jesus Christ, that all of you agree in what you say, and that there be no divisions among you, but that you be united in the same mind and in the same purpose. For it has been reported to me about you, my brothers and sisters, by Chloe's people, that there are rivalries among you. I mean that each of you is saying, "I belong to Paul," or "I belong to Apollos," or "I belong to Cephas," or "I belong to Christ." Is Christ divided? Was Paul crucified for you? Or were you baptized in the name of Paul? For Christ did not send me to baptize but to preach the gospel, and not with the wisdom of human eloquence, so that the cross of Christ might not be emptied of its meaning.

GOSPEL ACCLAMATION

cf. Matthew 4:23

℟. Al - le - lu - ia, al - le - lu - ia, al - le - lu - ia.

(Omit if not sung)

▶ Jesus proclaimed the Gospel of the kingdom
  and cured every disease among the people. ℟.

GOSPEL

Matthew 4:12–23 or 4:12–17

(Include bracketed text for Long Form)

When Jesus heard that John had been arrested, he withdrew to Galilee. He left Nazareth and went to live in Capernaum by the sea, in the region of Zebulun and Naphtali, that what had been said through Isaiah the prophet might be fulfilled:
   *Land of Zebulun and land
    of Naphtali,*

   *the way to the sea, beyond
    the Jordan,
   Galilee of the Gentiles,
the people who sit in darkness have
    seen a great light,
on those dwelling in a land
    overshadowed by death
light has arisen.*

From that time on, Jesus began to preach and say, "Repent, for the kingdom of heaven is at hand."

[As he was walking by the Sea of Galilee, he saw two brothers, Simon who is called Peter, and his brother Andrew, casting a net into the sea; they were fishermen. He said to them, "Come after me, and I will make you fishers of men." At once they left their nets and followed him. He walked along from there and saw two other brothers, James, the son of Zebedee, and his brother John. They were in a boat, with their father Zebedee, mending their nets. He called them, and immediately they left their boat and their father and followed him.

He went around all of Galilee, teaching in their synagogues, proclaiming the gospel of the kingdom, and curing every disease and illness among the people.]

THIRD SUNDAY IN ORDINARY TIME — B   935

FIRST READING

Jonah 3:1–5, 10

The word of the LORD came to Jonah, saying: "Set out for the great city of Nineveh, and announce to it the message that I will tell you." So Jonah made ready and went to Nineveh, according to the LORD's bidding. Now Nineveh was an enormously large city; it took three days to go through it. Jonah began his journey through the city, and had gone but a single day's walk announcing, "Forty days more and Nineveh shall be destroyed," when the people of Nineveh believed God; they proclaimed a fast and all of them, great and small, put on sackcloth.

When God saw by their actions how they turned from their evil way, he repented of the evil that he had threatened to do to them; he did not carry it out.

RESPONSORIAL PSALM

Psalm 25:4–5, 6–7, 8–9

℟. Teach me your ways, O Lord.

Music: Owen Alstott, b. 1947, © 1977, 1990, OCP. All rights reserved.

▸ Your ways, O LORD, make known
    to me;
  teach me your paths,
  guide me in your truth and teach me,
    for you are God my savior. ℟.

▸ Remember that your compassion,
    O LORD,
  and your love are from of old.

In your kindness remember me,
  because of your goodness,
    O LORD. ℟.

▸ Good and upright is the LORD;
    thus he shows sinners the way.
He guides the humble to justice
    and teaches the humble his way. ℟.

SECOND READING

1 Corinthians 7:29–31

I tell you, brothers and sisters, the time is running out. From now on, let those having wives act as not having them, those weeping as not weeping, those rejoicing as not rejoicing, those buying as not owning, those using the world as not using it fully. For the world in its present form is passing away.

GOSPEL ACCLAMATION

Mark 1:15

R̶. Al - le - lu - ia, al - le - lu - ia, al - le - lu - ia.

(Omit if not sung)

▶ The kingdom of God is at hand.
  Repent and believe in the Gospel. **R̶.**

GOSPEL

Mark 1:14–20

After John had been arrested, Jesus came to Galilee proclaiming the gospel of God: "This is the time of fulfillment. The kingdom of God is at hand. Repent, and believe in the gospel."

As he passed by the Sea of Galilee, he saw Simon and his brother Andrew casting their nets into the sea; they were fishermen. Jesus said to them, "Come after me, and I will make you fishers of men." Then they abandoned their nets and followed him. He walked along a little farther and saw James, the son of Zebedee, and his brother John. They too were in a boat mending their nets. Then he called them. So they left their father Zebedee in the boat along with the hired men and followed him.

---

936   THIRD SUNDAY IN ORDINARY TIME — C

FIRST READING

Nehemiah 8:2–4a, 5–6, 8–10

Ezra the priest brought the law before the assembly, which consisted of men, women, and those children old enough to understand. Standing at one end of the open place that was before the Water Gate, he read out of the book from daybreak till midday, in the presence of the men, the women, and those children old enough to understand; and all the people listened attentively to the book of the law. Ezra the scribe stood on a wooden platform that had been made for the occasion. He opened the scroll so that all the people might see it—for he was standing higher up than any of the people—; and, as he opened it, all the people rose. Ezra blessed the LORD, the great God, and all the people, their hands raised high, answered, "Amen, amen!" Then they bowed down and prostrated themselves before the LORD, their faces to the ground. Ezra read plainly from the book of the law of God, interpreting it so that all could understand what was read. Then Nehemiah, that is, His Excellency, and Ezra the priest-scribe and the Levites who were instructing the people said to all the people: "Today is holy to the LORD your God. Do not be sad, and do not weep"—for all the people were weeping as they heard the words of the law. He said further: "Go, eat rich foods and drink sweet drinks, and allot portions to those who had nothing prepared; for today is holy to our LORD. Do not be saddened this day, for rejoicing in the LORD must be your strength!"

RESPONSORIAL PSALM
Psalm 19:8, 9, 10, 15

℟. Your words, Lord, are Spir - it and life.

▶ The law of the LORD is perfect,
refreshing the soul;
the decree of the LORD is trustworthy,
giving wisdom to the simple. ℟.

▶ The precepts of the LORD are right,
rejoicing the heart;
the command of the LORD is clear,
enlightening the eye. ℟.

▶ The fear of the LORD is pure,
enduring forever;
the ordinances of the LORD are true,
all of them just. ℟.

▶ Let the words of my mouth and the
thought of my heart
find favor before you,
O LORD, my rock and my redeemer. ℟.

SECOND READING
1 Corinthians 12:12–30 or 12:12–14, 27

(Include bracketed text for Long Form)

Brothers and sisters: As a body is one though it has many parts, and all the parts of the body, though many, are one body, so also Christ. For in one Spirit we were all baptized into one body, whether Jews or Greeks, slaves or free persons, and we were all given to drink of one Spirit.

Now the body is not a single part, but many. [If a foot should say, "Because I am not a hand I do not belong to the body," it does not for this reason belong any less to the body. Or if an ear should say, "Because I am not an eye I do not belong to the body," it does not for this reason belong any less to the body. If the whole body were an eye, where would the hearing be? If the whole body were hearing, where would the sense of smell be? But as it is, God placed the parts, each one of them, in the body as he intended. If they were all one part, where would the body be? But as it is, there are many parts, yet one body. The eye cannot say to the hand, "I do not need you," nor again the head to the feet, "I do not need you." Indeed, the parts of the body that seem to be weaker are all the more necessary, and those parts of the body that we consider less honorable we surround with greater honor, and our less presentable parts are treated with greater propriety, whereas our more presentable parts do not need this. But God has so constructed the body as to give greater honor to a part that is without it, so that there may be no division in the body, but that the parts may have the same concern for one another. If one part suffers, all the parts suffer with it; if one part is honored, all the parts share its joy.

Now] you are Christ's body, and individually parts of it. [Some people God has designated in the church to be, first, apostles; second, prophets; third, teachers; then, mighty deeds; then gifts of healing, assistance, administration, and varieties of tongues. Are all apostles? Are all prophets? Are all teachers? Do all work mighty deeds? Do all have gifts of healing? Do all speak in tongues? Do all interpret?]

GOSPEL ACCLAMATION

cf. Luke 4:18

℟. Al - le - lu - ia, al - le - lu - ia, al - le - lu - ia.

Music: Owen Alstott, b. 1947, © 1977, 1990, OCP. All rights reserved.

(Omit if not sung)

▶ The Lord sent me to bring glad tidings to the poor,
and to proclaim liberty to captives. ℟.

GOSPEL

Luke 1:1–4; 4:14–21

Since many have undertaken to compile a narrative of the events that have been fulfilled among us, just as those who were eyewitnesses from the beginning and ministers of the word have handed them down to us, I too have decided, after investigating everything accurately anew, to write it down in an orderly sequence for you, most excellent Theophilus, so that you may realize the certainty of the teachings you have received.

Jesus returned to Galilee in the power of the Spirit, and news of him spread throughout the whole region. He taught in their synagogues and was praised by all.

He came to Nazareth, where he had grown up, and went according to his custom into the synagogue on the sabbath day. He stood up to read and was handed a scroll of the prophet Isaiah. He unrolled the scroll and found the passage where it was written:

The Spirit of the Lord is upon me,
because he has anointed me
to bring glad tidings to the poor.
He has sent me to proclaim liberty
to captives
and recovery of sight to the blind,
to let the oppressed go free,
and to proclaim a year acceptable
to the Lord.

Rolling up the scroll, he handed it back to the attendant and sat down, and the eyes of all in the synagogue looked intently at him. He said to them, "Today this Scripture passage is fulfilled in your hearing."

---

937   FOURTH SUNDAY IN ORDINARY TIME — A

FIRST READING

Zephaniah 2:3; 3:12–13

Seek the LORD, all you humble
of the earth,
who have observed his law;
seek justice, seek humility;
perhaps you may be sheltered
on the day of the LORD's anger.

But I will leave as a remnant
in your midst
a people humble and lowly,
who shall take refuge in the name of
the LORD:
the remnant of Israel.

They shall do no wrong
and speak no lies;
nor shall there be found in
their mouths
a deceitful tongue;
they shall pasture and couch
their flocks
with none to disturb them.

RESPONSORIAL PSALM

Psalm 146:6–7, 8–9, 9–10

℟. Blessed are the poor in spir-it; the king-dom of heav-en is theirs!

Or ℟. Alleluia.

▶ The LORD keeps faith forever,
    secures justice for the oppressed,
    gives food to the hungry.
The LORD sets captives free. ℟.

▶ The LORD gives sight to the blind;
    the LORD raises up those who were
        bowed down.
The LORD loves the just;
    the LORD protects strangers. ℟.

▶ The fatherless and the widow the
        LORD sustains,
    but the way of the wicked
        he thwarts.
The LORD shall reign forever;
    your God, O Zion, through all
        generations. Alleluia. ℟.

SECOND READING

1 Corinthians 1:26–31

Consider your own calling, brothers and sisters. Not many of you were wise by human standards, not many were powerful, not many were of noble birth. Rather, God chose the foolish of the world to shame the wise, and God chose the weak of the world to shame the strong, and God chose the lowly and despised of the world, those who count for nothing, to reduce to nothing those who are something, so that no human being might boast before God. It is due to him that you are in Christ Jesus, who became for us wisdom from God, as well as righteousness, sanctification, and redemption, so that, as it is written, "Whoever boasts, should boast in the Lord."

GOSPEL ACCLAMATION

Matthew 5:12a

℟. Al - le - lu - ia, al - le - lu - ia, al - le - lu - ia.

(Omit if not sung)

▶ Rejoice and be glad;
    your reward will be great in heaven. ℟.

GOSPEL

Matthew 5:1–12a

When Jesus saw the crowds, he went up the mountain, and after he had sat down, his disciples came to him. He began to teach them, saying:
    "Blessed are the poor in spirit,
        for theirs is the kingdom
            of heaven.
    Blessed are they who mourn,
        for they will be comforted.
    Blessed are the meek,
        for they will inherit the land.
    Blessed are they who hunger and
        thirst for righteousness,
        for they will be satisfied.
    Blessed are the merciful,
        for they will be shown mercy.
    Blessed are the clean of heart,
        for they will see God.
    Blessed are the peacemakers,
        for they will be called children
            of God.

Blessed are they who are persecuted
for the sake of righteousness,
for theirs is the kingdom
of heaven.

Blessed are you when they insult you
and persecute you and utter every
kind of evil against you falsely because
of me. Rejoice and be glad, for your
reward will be great in heaven."

938   FOURTH SUNDAY IN ORDINARY TIME — B

FIRST READING   *Deuteronomy 18:15–20*

Moses spoke to all the people, saying:
"A prophet like me will the LORD, your
God, raise up for you from among
your own kin; to him you shall listen.
This is exactly what you requested
of the LORD, your God, at Horeb on
the day of the assembly, when you
said, 'Let us not again hear the voice
of the LORD, our God, nor see this
great fire any more, lest we die.' And
the LORD said to me, 'This was well

said. I will raise up for them a prophet
like you from among their kin, and
will put my words into his mouth;
he shall tell them all that I command
him. Whoever will not listen to my
words which he speaks in my name,
I myself will make him answer for it.
But if a prophet presumes to speak
in my name an oracle that I have not
commanded him to speak, or speaks in
the name of other gods, he shall die.'"

RESPONSORIAL PSALM   *Psalm 95:1–2, 6–7, 7–9*

℟. If to - day you hear his voice, hard - en not your hearts.

Music: Owen Alstott, b. 1947, © 1977, 1990, OCP. All rights reserved.

▸ Come, let us sing joyfully to the LORD;
let us acclaim the rock of
our salvation.
Let us come into his presence
with thanksgiving;
let us joyfully sing psalms to him. ℟.

▸ Come, let us bow down in worship;
let us kneel before the LORD who
made us.
For he is our God,
and we are the people he
shepherds, the flock he guides. ℟.

▸ Oh, that today you would hear
his voice:
"Harden not your hearts as
at Meribah,
as in the day of Massah in
the desert,
where your fathers tempted me;
they tested me though they had
seen my works." ℟.

SECOND READING   *1 Corinthians 7:32–35*

Brothers and sisters: I should like you
to be free of anxieties. An unmarried
man is anxious about the things of
the Lord, how he may please the
Lord. But a married man is anxious
about the things of the world, how
he may please his wife, and he is
divided. An unmarried woman or a
virgin is anxious about the things of

the Lord, so that she may be holy
in both body and spirit. A married
woman, on the other hand, is anxious
about the things of the world, how she
may please her husband. I am telling
you this for your own benefit, not to
impose a restraint upon you, but for
the sake of propriety and adherence
to the Lord without distraction.

GOSPEL ACCLAMATION

Matthew 4:16

℟. Al - le - lu - ia, al - le - lu - ia, al - le - lu - ia.

(Omit if not sung)

▸ The people who sit in darkness have seen a great light;
on those dwelling in a land overshadowed by death,
light has arisen. ℟.

GOSPEL

Mark 1:21–28

Then they came to Capernaum, and on the sabbath Jesus entered the synagogue and taught. The people were astonished at his teaching, for he taught them as one having authority and not as the scribes. In their synagogue was a man with an unclean spirit; he cried out, "What have you to do with us, Jesus of Nazareth? Have you come to destroy us? I know who you are—the Holy One of God!" Jesus rebuked him and said, "Quiet! Come out of him!" The unclean spirit convulsed him and with a loud cry came out of him. All were amazed and asked one another, "What is this? A new teaching with authority. He commands even the unclean spirits and they obey him." His fame spread everywhere throughout the whole region of Galilee.

FOURTH SUNDAY IN ORDINARY TIME — C 939

FIRST READING

Jeremiah 1:4–5, 17–19

The word of the LORD came to me, saying:
Before I formed you in the womb I knew you,
before you were born I dedicated you,
a prophet to the nations I appointed you.

But do you gird your loins;
stand up and tell them
all that I command you.
Be not crushed on their account,
as though I would leave you crushed before them;
for it is I this day
who have made you a fortified city,
a pillar of iron, a wall of brass,
against the whole land:
against Judah's kings and princes,
against its priests and people.
They will fight against you but not prevail over you,
for I am with you to deliver you,
says the LORD.

RESPONSORIAL PSALM

Psalm 71:1–2, 3–4, 5–6, 15, 17

℟. I will sing of your sal - va - tion.

▸ In you, O LORD, I take refuge;
let me never be put to shame.
In your justice rescue me, and
deliver me;
incline your ear to me, and
save me. ℟.

℟. **I will sing of your salvation.**

▸ Be my rock of refuge,
  a stronghold to give me safety,
  for you are my rock and
    my fortress.
O my God, rescue me from the hand
  of the wicked. ℟.

▸ For you are my hope, O Lord;
  my trust, O God, from my youth.

On you I depend from birth;
  from my mother's womb you are
    my strength. ℟.

▸ My mouth shall declare your justice,
  day by day your salvation.
O God, you have taught me from
  my youth,
  and till the present I proclaim your
    wondrous deeds. ℟.

SECOND READING

1 Corinthians 12:31—13:13 or 13:4–13

(Include bracketed text for Long Form)

Brothers and sisters: [Strive eagerly for the greatest spiritual gifts. But I shall show you a still more excellent way.

If I speak in human and angelic tongues, but do not have love, I am a resounding gong or a clashing cymbal. And if I have the gift of prophecy, and comprehend all mysteries and all knowledge; if I have all faith so as to move mountains, but do not have love, I am nothing. If I give away everything I own, and if I hand my body over so that I may boast, but do not have love, I gain nothing.]

Love is patient, love is kind. It is not jealous, it is not pompous, it is not inflated, it is not rude, it does not seek its own interests, it is not quick-tempered, it does not brood over injury, it does not rejoice over wrongdoing but rejoices with the truth. It bears all things, believes all things, hopes all things, endures all things.

Love never fails. If there are prophecies, they will be brought to nothing; if tongues, they will cease; if knowledge, it will be brought to nothing. For we know partially and we prophesy partially, but when the perfect comes, the partial will pass away. When I was a child, I used to talk as a child, think as a child, reason as a child; when I became a man, I put aside childish things. At present we see indistinctly, as in a mirror, but then face to face. At present I know partially; then I shall know fully, as I am fully known. So faith, hope, love remain, these three; but the greatest of these is love.

GOSPEL ACCLAMATION

Luke 4:18

℟. Al - le - lu - ia,   al - le - lu - ia,   al - le - lu - ia.

(Omit if not sung)

▸ The Lord sent me to bring glad tidings to the poor,
  to proclaim liberty to captives. ℟.

GOSPEL

Luke 4:21–30

Jesus began speaking in the synagogue, saying: "Today this Scripture passage is fulfilled in your hearing." And all spoke highly of him and were amazed at the gracious words that came from his mouth. They also asked, "Isn't this the son of Joseph?" He said to them, "Surely you will quote me this proverb, 'Physician, cure yourself,' and say, 'Do here in your native place the things that we heard were done in Capernaum.'" And he said, "Amen, I say to you, no prophet is accepted in his own native place. Indeed, I tell you, there were many widows in Israel in the days of Elijah when the sky was closed for three and a half years and a severe famine spread over the entire land. It was to none of these that Elijah was sent, but only to a widow in Zarephath in the land of Sidon. Again, there were many lepers in Israel during the time of Elisha the prophet; yet not one of them was cleansed, but only Naaman the Syrian." When the people in the synagogue heard this, they were all filled with fury. They rose up, drove him out of the town, and led him to the brow of the hill on which their town had been built, to hurl him down headlong. But Jesus passed through the midst of them and went away.

FIFTH SUNDAY IN ORDINARY TIME — A 940

FIRST READING *Isaiah 58:7–10*

Thus says the LORD:
　Share your bread with the hungry,
　　shelter the oppressed and
　　　the homeless;
　clothe the naked when you
　　see them,
　　and do not turn your back on
　　　your own.
　Then your light shall break forth like
　　the dawn,
　　and your wound shall quickly
　　　be healed;
　your vindication shall go before you,
　　and the glory of the LORD shall be
　　　your rear guard.

Then you shall call, and the LORD
　will answer,
　you shall cry for help, and he will
　　say: Here I am!
If you remove from your midst
　oppression, false accusation and
　　malicious speech;
if you bestow your bread on
　the hungry
　and satisfy the afflicted;
then light shall rise for you in
　the darkness,
　and the gloom shall become for
　　you like midday.

RESPONSORIAL PSALM *Psalm 112:4–5, 6–7, 8–9*

℟. The just man is a light in dark-ness to the up-right.

Music: Owen Alstott, b. 1947, © 1977, 1990, OCP. All rights reserved.

Or ℟. Alleluia.

▸ Light shines through the darkness for
　　the upright;
　he is gracious and merciful
　　and just.
　Well for the man who is gracious
　　and lends,
　who conducts his affairs
　　with justice. ℟.

▸ He shall never be moved;
　　the just one shall be in everlasting
　　　remembrance.
　An evil report he shall not fear;
　　his heart is firm, trusting in
　　　the LORD. ℟.

▸ His heart is steadfast; he shall
　　not fear.
　Lavishly he gives to the poor;
　his justice shall endure forever;
　　his horn shall be exalted in glory. ℟.

SECOND READING

1 Corinthians 2:1–5

When I came to you, brothers and sisters, proclaiming the mystery of God, I did not come with sublimity of words or of wisdom. For I resolved to know nothing while I was with you except Jesus Christ, and him crucified. I came to you in weakness and fear and much trembling, and my message and my proclamation were not with persuasive words of wisdom, but with a demonstration of Spirit and power, so that your faith might rest not on human wisdom but on the power of God.

GOSPEL ACCLAMATION

John 8:12

℟. Al - le - lu - ia, al - le - lu - ia, al - le - lu - ia.

(Omit if not sung)

▶ I am the light of the world, says the Lord;
whoever follows me will have the light of life. ℟.

GOSPEL

Matthew 5:13–16

Jesus said to his disciples: "You are the salt of the earth. But if salt loses its taste, with what can it be seasoned? It is no longer good for anything but to be thrown out and trampled underfoot. You are the light of the world. A city set on a mountain cannot be hidden. Nor do they light a lamp and then put it under a bushel basket; it is set on a lampstand, where it gives light to all in the house. Just so, your light must shine before others, that they may see your good deeds and glorify your heavenly Father."

---

941   FIFTH SUNDAY IN ORDINARY TIME — B

FIRST READING

Job 7:1–4, 6–7

Job spoke, saying:
Is not man's life on earth a drudgery?
Are not his days those of hirelings?
He is a slave who longs for
the shade,
a hireling who waits for his wages.
So I have been assigned months
of misery,
and troubled nights have been
allotted to me.

If in bed I say, "When shall I arise?"
then the night drags on;
I am filled with restlessness until
the dawn.
My days are swifter than a
weaver's shuttle;
they come to an end without hope.
Remember that my life is like the wind;
I shall not see happiness again.

RESPONSORIAL PSALM

Psalm 147:1–2, 3–4, 5–6

℟. Praise the Lord, who heals the bro - ken - heart - ed.

Or ℟. Alleluia.

▶ Praise the LORD, for he is good;
   sing praise to our God, for he
      is gracious;
   it is fitting to praise him.
   The LORD rebuilds Jerusalem;
      the dispersed of Israel he gathers. ℟.

▶ He heals the brokenhearted
   and binds up their wounds.

He tells the number of the stars;
   he calls each by name. ℟.

▶ Great is our Lord and mighty
      in power;
   to his wisdom there is no limit.
   The LORD sustains the lowly;
      the wicked he casts to
         the ground. ℟.

SECOND READING
1 Corinthians 9:16–19, 22–23

Brothers and sisters: If I preach the gospel, this is no reason for me to boast, for an obligation has been imposed on me, and woe to me if I do not preach it! If I do so willingly, I have a recompense, but if unwillingly, then I have been entrusted with a stewardship. What then is my recompense? That, when I preach, I offer the gospel free of charge so as not to make full use of my right in the gospel.

Although I am free in regard to all, I have made myself a slave to all so as to win over as many as possible. To the weak I became weak, to win over the weak. I have become all things to all, to save at least some. All this I do for the sake of the gospel, so that I too may have a share in it.

GOSPEL ACCLAMATION
Matthew 8:17

℟. Al - le - lu - ia, al - le - lu - ia, al - le - lu - ia.

(Omit if not sung)

▶ Christ took away our infirmities
   and bore our diseases. ℟.

GOSPEL
Mark 1:29–39

On leaving the synagogue Jesus entered the house of Simon and Andrew with James and John. Simon's mother-in-law lay sick with a fever. They immediately told him about her. He approached, grasped her hand, and helped her up. Then the fever left her and she waited on them.

When it was evening, after sunset, they brought to him all who were ill or possessed by demons. The whole town was gathered at the door. He cured many who were sick with various diseases, and he drove out many demons, not permitting them to speak because they knew him.

Rising very early before dawn, he left and went off to a deserted place, where he prayed. Simon and those who were with him pursued him and on finding him said, "Everyone is looking for you." He told them, "Let us go on to the nearby villages that I may preach there also. For this purpose have I come." So he went into their synagogues, preaching and driving out demons throughout the whole of Galilee.

942   FIFTH SUNDAY IN ORDINARY TIME — C

FIRST READING   *Isaiah 6:1–2a, 3–8*

In the year King Uzziah died, I saw the Lord seated on a high and lofty throne, with the train of his garment filling the temple. Seraphim were stationed above.

They cried one to the other, "Holy, holy, holy is the LORD of hosts! All the earth is filled with his glory!" At the sound of that cry, the frame of the door shook and the house was filled with smoke.

Then I said, "Woe is me, I am doomed! For I am a man of unclean lips, living among a people of unclean lips; yet my eyes have seen the King, the LORD of hosts!" Then one of the seraphim flew to me, holding an ember that he had taken with tongs from the altar.

He touched my mouth with it, and said, "See, now that this has touched your lips, your wickedness is removed, your sin purged."

Then I heard the voice of the Lord saying, "Whom shall I send? Who will go for us?" "Here I am," I said; "send me!"

RESPONSORIAL PSALM   *Psalm 138:1–2, 2–3, 4–5, 7–8*

℟. In the sight of the an-gels I will sing your prais-es, Lord.

Music: Owen Alstott, b. 1947, © 1977, 1990, OCP. All rights reserved.

▶ I will give thanks to you, O LORD, with
all my heart,
   for you have heard the words of
my mouth;
   in the presence of the angels I will
sing your praise;
I will worship at your holy temple
   and give thanks to your name. ℟.

▶ Because of your kindness and
your truth;
   for you have made great above
all things
your name and your promise.
When I called, you answered me;
   you built up strength within me. ℟.

▶ All the kings of the earth shall give
thanks to you, O LORD,
   when they hear the words of
your mouth;
and they shall sing of the ways of
the LORD:
   "Great is the glory of the LORD." ℟.

▶ Your right hand saves me.
   The LORD will complete what he
has done for me;
your kindness, O LORD,
   endures forever;
forsake not the work of
   your hands. ℟.

SECOND READING   *1 Corinthians 15:1–11 or 15:3–8, 11*

(Include bracketed text for Long Form)

[I am reminding you,] brothers and sisters, [of the gospel I preached to you, which you indeed received and in which you also stand. Through it you are also being saved, if you hold fast to the word I preached to you, unless you believed in vain. For] I handed on to you as of first importance what I also received: that Christ died for our sins in accordance with the Scriptures; that he was buried; that he was raised on the third day in accordance with the Scriptures; that he appeared to Cephas, then to the Twelve. After that, he appeared to more than five hundred brothers at once, most of whom are still living, though some have fallen asleep. After that he appeared to James, then to all the apostles. Last of all, as to one born abnormally, he appeared to me. [For I am the least of the apostles, not fit to be called an apostle, because I persecuted the church of God. But by the grace of God I am what I am, and his grace to me has not been ineffective. Indeed, I have toiled harder than all of them; not I, however, but the grace of God that is with me.] Therefore, whether it be I or they, so we preach and so you believed.

GOSPEL ACCLAMATION

Matthew 4:19

℟. Al - le - lu - ia, al - le - lu - ia, al - le - lu - ia.

Music: Owen Alstott, b. 1947, © 1977, 1990, OCP. All rights reserved.　　　*(Omit if not sung)*

▶ Come after me
and I will make you fishers of men. ℟.

GOSPEL

Luke 5:1–11

While the crowd was pressing in on Jesus and listening to the word of God, he was standing by the Lake of Gennesaret. He saw two boats there alongside the lake; the fishermen had disembarked and were washing their nets. Getting into one of the boats, the one belonging to Simon, he asked him to put out a short distance from the shore. Then he sat down and taught the crowds from the boat. After he had finished speaking, he said to Simon, "Put out into deep water and lower your nets for a catch." Simon said in reply, "Master, we have worked hard all night and have caught nothing, but at your command I will lower the nets." When they had done this, they caught a great number of fish and their nets were tearing. They signaled to their partners in the other boat to come to help them. They came and filled both boats so that the boats were in danger of sinking. When Simon Peter saw this, he fell at the knees of Jesus and said, "Depart from me, Lord, for I am a sinful man." For astonishment at the catch of fish they had made seized him and all those with him, and likewise James and John, the sons of Zebedee, who were partners of Simon. Jesus said to Simon, "Do not be afraid; from now on you will be catching men." When they brought their boats to the shore, they left everything and followed him.

SIXTH SUNDAY IN ORDINARY TIME — A　　943

FIRST READING

Sirach 15:15–20

If you choose you can keep the
　　commandments, they will
　　save you;
　if you trust in God, you too
　　shall live;
he has set before you fire and water;
　to whichever you choose, stretch
　　forth your hand.
Before man are life and death, good
　　and evil,
　whichever he chooses shall be
　　given him.
Immense is the wisdom of the Lord;
　he is mighty in power,
　　and all-seeing.

The eyes of God are on those who
    fear him;
    he understands man's every deed.

No one does he command to
    act unjustly,
    to none does he give license to sin.

RESPONSORIAL PSALM

Psalm 119:1–2, 4–5, 17–18, 33–34

℟. Bless-ed are they who fol-low the law of the Lord!

▸ Blessed are they whose way
    is blameless,
    who walk in the law of the LORD.
Blessed are they who observe
    his decrees,
    who seek him with all their heart. ℟.

▸ You have commanded that
    your precepts
    be diligently kept.
Oh, that I might be firm in the ways
    of keeping your statutes! ℟.

▸ Be good to your servant,
    that I may live
    and keep your words.
Open my eyes, that I may consider
    the wonders of your law. ℟.

▸ Instruct me, O LORD, in the way of
    your statutes,
    that I may exactly observe them.
Give me discernment, that I may
    observe your law
    and keep it with all my heart. ℟.

SECOND READING

1 Corinthians 2:6–10

Brothers and sisters: We speak a
wisdom to those who are mature,
not a wisdom of this age, nor of the
rulers of this age who are passing
away. Rather, we speak God's wisdom,
mysterious, hidden, which God
predetermined before the ages for our
glory, and which none of the rulers of
this age knew; for, if they had known
it, they would not have crucified the
Lord of glory. But as it is written:

*What eye has not seen, and ear has
    not heard,
    and what has not entered the
    human heart,
    what God has prepared for those
    who love him,*
this God has revealed to us through
the Spirit.
    For the Spirit scrutinizes everything,
even the depths of God.

GOSPEL ACCLAMATION

cf. Matthew 11:25

℟. Al-le-lu - ia, al-le-lu - ia, al - le - lu - ia.

(Omit if not sung)

▸ Blessed are you, Father, Lord of heaven and earth;
    you have revealed to little ones the mysteries of the kingdom. ℟.

GOSPEL

Matthew 5:17–37 or 5:20–22a, 27–28, 33–34a, 37

(Include bracketed text for Long Form)

Jesus said to his disciples: ["Do not
think that I have come to abolish the
law or the prophets. I have come not

to abolish but to fulfill. Amen, I say
to you, until heaven and earth pass
away, not the smallest letter or the

smallest part of a letter will pass from the law, until all things have taken place. Therefore, whoever breaks one of the least of these commandments and teaches others to do so will be called least in the kingdom of heaven. But whoever obeys and teaches these commandments will be called greatest in the kingdom of heaven.] I tell you, unless your righteousness surpasses that of the scribes and Pharisees, you will not enter the kingdom of heaven.

"You have heard that it was said to your ancestors, *You shall not kill; and whoever kills will be liable to judgment.* But I say to you, whoever is angry with his brother will be liable to judgment; [and whoever says to his brother, 'Raqa,' will be answerable to the Sanhedrin; and whoever says, 'You fool,' will be liable to fiery Gehenna. Therefore, if you bring your gift to the altar, and there recall that your brother has anything against you, leave your gift there at the altar, go first and be reconciled with your brother, and then come and offer your gift. Settle with your opponent quickly while on the way to court. Otherwise your opponent will hand you over to the judge, and the judge will hand you over to the guard, and you will be thrown into prison. Amen, I say to you, you will not be released until you have paid the last penny.]

"You have heard that it was said, *You shall not commit adultery.* But I say to you, everyone who looks at a woman with lust has already committed adultery with her in his heart. [If your right eye causes you to sin, tear it out and throw it away. It is better for you to lose one of your members than to have your whole body thrown into Gehenna. And if your right hand causes you to sin, cut it off and throw it away. It is better for you to lose one of your members than to have your whole body go into Gehenna.

"It was also said, *Whoever divorces his wife must give her a bill of divorce.* But I say to you, whoever divorces his wife—unless the marriage is unlawful—causes her to commit adultery, and whoever marries a divorced woman commits adultery.]

"Again you have heard that it was said to your ancestors, *Do not take a false oath, but make good to the Lord all that you vow.* But I say to you, do not swear at all; [not by heaven, for it is God's throne; nor by the earth, for it is his footstool; nor by Jerusalem, for it is the city of the great King. Do not swear by your head, for you cannot make a single hair white or black.] Let your 'Yes' mean 'Yes,' and your 'No' mean 'No.' Anything more is from the evil one."

SIXTH SUNDAY IN ORDINARY TIME — B 944

FIRST READING

Leviticus 13:1–2, 44–46

The LORD said to Moses and Aaron, "If someone has on his skin a scab or pustule or blotch which appears to be the sore of leprosy, he shall be brought to Aaron, the priest, or to one of the priests among his descendants. If the man is leprous and unclean, the priest shall declare him unclean by reason of the sore on his head.

"The one who bears the sore of leprosy shall keep his garments rent and his head bare, and shall muffle his beard; he shall cry out, 'Unclean, unclean!' As long as the sore is on him he shall declare himself unclean, since he is in fact unclean. He shall dwell apart, making his abode outside the camp."

RESPONSORIAL PSALM
Psalm 32:1–2, 5, 11

℟. I turn to you, Lord, in time of trou - ble, and you fill me with the joy of sal - va - tion.

▸ Blessed is he whose fault is
   taken away,
     whose sin is covered.
Blessed the man to whom the LORD
     imputes not guilt,
     in whose spirit there is no guile. **℟.**

▸ Then I acknowledged my sin to you,
   my guilt I covered not.

I said, "I confess my faults to
   the LORD,"
   and you took away the guilt of
   my sin. **℟.**

▸ Be glad in the LORD and rejoice,
   you just;
   exult, all you upright of heart. **℟.**

SECOND READING
1 Corinthians 10:31—11:1

Brothers and sisters, whether you
eat or drink, or whatever you do, do
everything for the glory of God. Avoid
giving offense, whether to the Jews or
Greeks or the church of God, just as

I try to please everyone in every way,
not seeking my own benefit but that
of the many, that they may be saved.
Be imitators of me, as I am of Christ.

GOSPEL ACCLAMATION
Luke 7:16

℟. Al - le - lu - ia, al - le - lu - ia, al - le - lu - ia.

(Omit if not sung)

▸ A great prophet has arisen in our midst,
   God has visited his people. **℟.**

GOSPEL
Mark 1:40–45

A leper came to Jesus and kneeling
down begged him and said, "If you
wish, you can make me clean." Moved
with pity, he stretched out his hand,
touched him, and said to him, "I do
will it. Be made clean." The leprosy
left him immediately, and he was
made clean. Then, warning him
sternly, he dismissed him at once.

   He said to him, "See that you
tell no one anything, but go, show

yourself to the priest and offer for
your cleansing what Moses prescribed;
that will be proof for them."

   The man went away and began
to publicize the whole matter. He
spread the report abroad so that it
was impossible for Jesus to enter a
town openly. He remained outside
in deserted places, and people kept
coming to him from everywhere.

SIXTH SUNDAY IN ORDINARY TIME — C   945

FIRST READING   *Jeremiah 17:5–8*

Thus says the LORD:
  Cursed is the one who trusts in
    human beings,
      who seeks his strength in flesh,
    whose heart turns away from
      the LORD.
  He is like a barren bush in the desert
    that enjoys no change of season,
  but stands in a lava waste,
    a salt and empty earth.

Blessed is the one who trusts in
  the LORD,
    whose hope is the LORD.
He is like a tree planted beside
  the waters
    that stretches out its roots to
    the stream:
it fears not the heat when it comes;
  its leaves stay green;
in the year of drought it shows
  no distress,
  but still bears fruit.

RESPONSORIAL PSALM   *Psalm 1:1–2, 3, 4&6*

℟. Bless - ed are they who hope in the Lord.

Music: Owen Alstott, b. 1947, © 1977, 1990, OCP. All rights reserved.

▶ Blessed the man who follows not
    the counsel of the wicked,
  nor walks in the way of sinners,
    nor sits in the company of
    the insolent,
  but delights in the law of the LORD
    and meditates on his law day
    and night. ℟.

▶ He is like a tree
    planted near running water,

that yields its fruit in due season,
    and whose leaves never fade.
Whatever he does, prospers. ℟.

▶ Not so the wicked, not so;
    they are like chaff which the wind
    drives away.
For the LORD watches over the way of
    the just,
  but the way of the wicked
    vanishes. ℟.

SECOND READING   *1 Corinthians 15:12, 16–20*

Brothers and sisters: If Christ is
preached as raised from the dead,
how can some among you say there
is no resurrection of the dead? If the
dead are not raised, neither has Christ
been raised, and if Christ has not been
raised, your faith is vain; you are still in

your sins. Then those who have fallen
asleep in Christ have perished. If for
this life only we have hoped in Christ,
we are the most pitiable people of all.
  But now Christ has been raised
from the dead, the firstfruits of
those who have fallen asleep.

GOSPEL ACCLAMATION   *Luke 6:23ab*

℟. Al - le - lu - ia, al - le - lu - ia, al - le - lu - ia.

Music: Owen Alstott, b. 1947, © 1977, 1990, OCP. All rights reserved.   *(Omit if not sung)*

▶ Rejoice and be glad;
  your reward will be great in heaven. ℟.

GOSPEL

Luke 6:17, 20–26

Jesus came down with the Twelve and stood on a stretch of level ground with a great crowd of his disciples and a large number of the people from all Judea and Jerusalem and the coastal region of Tyre and Sidon. And raising his eyes toward his disciples he said:

"Blessed are you who are poor,
for the kingdom of God is yours.
Blessed are you who are
now hungry,
for you will be satisfied.
Blessed are you who are
now weeping,
for you will laugh.
Blessed are you when people
hate you,
and when they exclude and
insult you,
and denounce your name as evil
on account of the Son of Man.
Rejoice and leap for joy on that day!
Behold, your reward will be great in heaven. For their ancestors treated the prophets in the same way.
But woe to you who are rich,
for you have received
your consolation.
Woe to you who are filled now,
for you will be hungry.
Woe to you who laugh now,
for you will grieve and weep.
Woe to you when all speak well
of you,
for their ancestors treated the false prophets in this way."

---

946   SEVENTH SUNDAY IN ORDINARY TIME — A

FIRST READING

Leviticus 19:1–2, 17–18

The LORD said to Moses, "Speak to the whole Israelite community and tell them: Be holy, for I, the LORD, your God, am holy.

"You shall not bear hatred for your brother or sister in your heart. Though you may have to reprove your fellow citizen, do not incur sin because of him. Take no revenge and cherish no grudge against any of your people. You shall love your neighbor as yourself. I am the LORD."

RESPONSORIAL PSALM

Psalm 103:1–2, 3–4, 8, 10, 12–13

℟. The Lord is kind and mer - ci - ful.

▸ Bless the LORD, O my soul;
and all my being, bless his
holy name.
Bless the LORD, O my soul,
and forget not all his benefits. ℟.

▸ He pardons all your iniquities,
heals all your ills.
He redeems your life
from destruction,
crowns you with kindness
and compassion. ℟.

▸ Merciful and gracious is the LORD,
slow to anger and abounding
in kindness.
Not according to our sins does he
deal with us,
nor does he requite us according to
our crimes. ℟.

▸ As far as the east is from the west,
so far has he put our transgressions
from us.

As a father has compassion on
his children,

so the LORD has compassion on
those who fear him. ℟.

SECOND READING

1 Corinthians 3:16–23

Brothers and sisters: Do you not know
that you are the temple of God, and
that the Spirit of God dwells in you?
If anyone destroys God's temple,
God will destroy that person; for the
temple of God, which you are, is holy.

Let no one deceive himself. If any
one among you considers himself wise
in this age, let him become a fool, so as
to become wise. For the wisdom
of this world is foolishness in the
eyes of God, for it is written:

*God catches the wise in their
    own ruses,*
and again:
    *The Lord knows the thoughts of
        the wise,
        that they are vain.*
So let no one boast about human
beings, for everything belongs to
you, Paul or Apollos or Cephas, or the
world or life or death, or the present
or the future: all belong to you, and
you to Christ, and Christ to God.

GOSPEL ACCLAMATION

1 John 2:5

℟. Al - le - lu - ia,   al - le - lu - ia,   al - le - lu - ia.

Music: Owen Alstott, b. 1947, © 1977, 1990, OCP. All rights reserved.   *(Omit if not sung)*

▶ Whoever keeps the word of Christ,
    the love of God is truly perfected in him. ℟.

GOSPEL

Matthew 5:38–48

Jesus said to his disciples: "You have
heard that it was said, *An eye for an
eye and a tooth for a tooth.* But I say
to you, offer no resistance to one who
is evil. When someone strikes you on
your right cheek, turn the other one
as well. If anyone wants to go to law
with you over your tunic, hand over
your cloak as well. Should anyone
press you into service for one mile, go
for two miles. Give to the one who
asks of you, and do not turn your
back on one who wants to borrow.

"You have heard that it was said,
You shall love your neighbor and hate

your enemy. But I say to you, love
your enemies and pray for those
who persecute you, that you may be
children of your heavenly Father, for
he makes his sun rise on the bad
and the good, and causes rain to
fall on the just and the unjust. For if
you love those who love you, what
recompense will you have? Do not
the tax collectors do the same? And if
you greet your brothers only, what is
unusual about that? Do not the pagans
do the same? So be perfect, just as
your heavenly Father is perfect."

SEVENTH SUNDAY IN ORDINARY TIME — B   947

FIRST READING

Isaiah 43:18–19, 21–22, 24b–25

Thus says the LORD:
    Remember not the events of the past,
        the things of long ago consider not;

see, I am doing something new!
    Now it springs forth, do you not
        perceive it?

In the desert I make a way,
   in the wasteland, rivers.
The people I formed for myself,
   that they might announce
      my praise.
Yet you did not call upon me,
   O Jacob,

for you grew weary of me, O Israel.
You burdened me with your sins,
   and wearied me with your crimes.
It is I, I, who wipe out,
   for my own sake, your offenses;
   your sins I remember no more.

RESPONSORIAL PSALM

Psalm 41:2–3, 4–5, 13–14

℟. Lord, heal my soul, for I have sinned a - gainst you.

▸ Blessed is the one who has regard for
   the lowly and the poor;
   in the day of misfortune the LORD
   will deliver him.
The LORD will keep and preserve him;
   and make him blessed on earth,
   and not give him over to the will of
   his enemies. ℟.

▸ The LORD will help him on
   his sickbed,
   he will take away all his ailment
   when he is ill.

Once I said, "O LORD, have pity
   on me;
   heal me, though I have sinned
   against you." ℟.

▸ But because of my integrity you
   sustain me
   and let me stand before
   you forever.
Blessed be the LORD, the God
   of Israel,
   from all eternity. Amen. Amen. ℟.

SECOND READING

2 Corinthians 1:18–22

Brothers and sisters: As God is faithful, our word to you is not "yes" and "no." For the Son of God, Jesus Christ, who was proclaimed to you by us, Silvanus and Timothy and me, was not "yes" and "no," but "yes" has been in him. For however many are the promises of God, their Yes is in him; therefore, the Amen from us also goes through him to God for glory. But the one who gives us security with you in Christ and who anointed us is God; he has also put his seal upon us and given the Spirit in our hearts as a first installment.

GOSPEL ACCLAMATION

cf. Luke 4:18

℟. Al - le - lu - ia, al - le - lu - ia, al - le - lu - ia.

(Omit if not sung)

▸ The Lord sent me to bring glad tidings to the poor,
   and to proclaim liberty to captives. ℟.

GOSPEL

Mark 2:1–12

When Jesus returned to Capernaum after some days, it became known that he was at home. Many gathered together so that there was no longer room for them, not even around the door, and he preached the word to them. They came bringing to him a paralytic carried by four men. Unable to get near Jesus because of the crowd, they opened up the roof above him. After they had broken through, they let down the mat on which the paralytic was lying. When Jesus saw their faith, he said to the paralytic, "Child, your sins are forgiven." Now some of the scribes were sitting there asking themselves, "Why does this man speak that way? He is blaspheming. Who but God alone can forgive sins?" Jesus immediately knew in his mind what they were thinking to themselves,

so he said, "Why are you thinking such things in your hearts? Which is easier, to say to the paralytic, 'Your sins are forgiven,' or to say, 'Rise, pick up your mat and walk'? But that you may know that the Son of Man has authority to forgive sins on earth"—he said to the paralytic, "I say to you, rise, pick up your mat, and go home." He rose, picked up his mat at once, and went away in the sight of everyone. They were all astounded and glorified God, saying, "We have never seen anything like this."

SEVENTH SUNDAY IN ORDINARY TIME — C 948

FIRST READING

1 Samuel 26:2, 7–9, 12–13, 22–23

In those days, Saul went down to the desert of Ziph with three thousand picked men of Israel, to search for David in the desert of Ziph. So David and Abishai went among Saul's soldiers by night and found Saul lying asleep within the barricade, with his spear thrust into the ground at his head and Abner and his men sleeping around him.

Abishai whispered to David: "God has delivered your enemy into your grasp this day. Let me nail him to the ground with one thrust of the spear; I will not need a second thrust!" But David said to Abishai, "Do not harm him, for who can lay hands on the LORD's anointed and

remain unpunished?" So David took the spear and the water jug from their place at Saul's head, and they got away without anyone's seeing or knowing or awakening. All remained asleep, because the LORD had put them into a deep slumber.

Going across to an opposite slope, David stood on a remote hilltop at a great distance from Abner, son of Ner, and the troops. He said: "Here is the king's spear. Let an attendant come over to get it. The LORD will reward each man for his justice and faithfulness. Today, though the LORD delivered you into my grasp, I would not harm the LORD's anointed."

RESPONSORIAL PSALM

Psalm 103:1–2, 3–4, 8, 10, 12–13

℟. The Lord is kind and mer - ci - ful.

Music: Owen Alstott, b. 1947, © 1977, 1990, OCP. All rights reserved.

▶ Bless the LORD, O my soul;
　　and all my being, bless his
　　　　holy name.
　Bless the LORD, O my soul,
　　and forget not all his benefits. ℟.

▶ He pardons all your iniquities,
　　heals all your ills.
　He redeems your life
　　　　from destruction,
　　crowns you with kindness
　　　　and compassion. ℟.

℟. The Lord is kind and merciful.

▶ Merciful and gracious is the LORD,
slow to anger and abounding
in kindness.
Not according to our sins does he
deal with us,
nor does he requite us according to
our crimes. ℟.

▶ As far as the east is from the west,
so far has he put our transgressions
from us.
As a father has compassion on
his children,
so the LORD has compassion on
those who fear him. ℟.

SECOND READING
1 Corinthians 15:45–49

Brothers and sisters: It is written, *The first man, Adam, became a living being,* the last Adam a life-giving spirit. But the spiritual was not first; rather the natural and then the spiritual. The first man was from the earth, earthly; the second man, from heaven. As was the earthly one, so also are the earthly, and as is the heavenly one, so also are the heavenly. Just as we have borne the image of the earthly one, we shall also bear the image of the heavenly one.

GOSPEL ACCLAMATION
John 13:34

℟. Al - le - lu - ia, al - le - lu - ia, al - le - lu - ia.

Music: Owen Alstott, b. 1947, © 1977, 1990, OCP. All rights reserved.   *(Omit if not sung)*

▶ I give you a new commandment, says the Lord:
love one another as I have loved you. ℟.

GOSPEL
Luke 6:27–38

Jesus said to his disciples: "To you who hear I say, love your enemies, do good to those who hate you, bless those who curse you, pray for those who mistreat you. To the person who strikes you on one cheek, offer the other one as well, and from the person who takes your cloak, do not withhold even your tunic. Give to everyone who asks of you, and from the one who takes what is yours do not demand it back. Do to others as you would have them do to you. For if you love those who love you, what credit is that to you? Even sinners love those who love them. And if you do good to those who do good to you, what credit is that to you? Even sinners do the same. If you lend money to those from whom you expect repayment, what credit is that to you? Even sinners lend to sinners, and get back the same amount. But rather, love your enemies and do good to them, and lend expecting nothing back; then your reward will be great and you will be children of the Most High, for he himself is kind to the ungrateful and the wicked. Be merciful, just as your Father is merciful.

"Stop judging and you will not be judged. Stop condemning and you will not be condemned. Forgive and you will be forgiven. Give, and gifts will be given to you; a good measure, packed together, shaken down, and overflowing, will be poured into your lap. For the measure with which you measure will in return be measured out to you."

Eighth Sunday in Ordinary Time — A   949

First Reading
Isaiah 49:14–15

Zion said, "The LORD has
  forsaken me;
  my LORD has forgotten me."
Can a mother forget her infant,
be without tenderness for the child
  of her womb?
Even should she forget,
  I will never forget you.

Responsorial Psalm
Psalm 62:2–3, 6–7, 8–9

℟. Rest in God a - lone, my soul.

▶ Only in God is my soul at rest;
  from him comes my salvation.
He only is my rock and my salvation,
  my stronghold; I shall not be
    disturbed at all. ℟.

▶ Only in God be at rest, my soul,
  for from him comes my hope.
He only is my rock and my salvation,
  my stronghold; I shall not
    be disturbed. ℟.

▶ With God is my safety and my glory,
  he is the rock of my strength; my
    refuge is in God.
Trust in him at all times,
  O my people!
  Pour out your hearts before him. ℟.

Second Reading
1 Corinthians 4:1–5

Brothers and sisters: Thus should one
regard us: as servants of Christ and
stewards of the mysteries of God. Now
it is of course required of stewards
that they be found trustworthy. It
does not concern me in the least that
I be judged by you or any human
tribunal; I do not even pass judgment
on myself; I am not conscious of
anything against me, but I do not
thereby stand acquitted; the one
who judges me is the Lord. Therefore
do not make any judgment before
the appointed time, until the Lord
comes, for he will bring to light what is
hidden in darkness and will manifest
the motives of our hearts, and then
everyone will receive praise from God.

Gospel Acclamation
Hebrews 4:12

℟. Al - le - lu - ia, al - le - lu - ia, al - le - lu - ia.

(Omit if not sung)

▶ The word of God is living and effective;
  discerning reflections and thoughts of the heart. ℟.

Gospel
Matthew 6:24–34

Jesus said to his disciples: "No one
can serve two masters. He will either
hate one and love the other, or be
devoted to one and despise the other.

You cannot serve God and mammon.

"Therefore I tell you, do not worry about your life, what you will eat or drink, or about your body, what you will wear. Is not life more than food and the body more than clothing? Look at the birds in the sky; they do not sow or reap, they gather nothing into barns, yet your heavenly Father feeds them. Are not you more important than they? Can any of you by worrying add a single moment to your life-span? Why are you anxious about clothes? Learn from the way the wild flowers grow. They do not work or spin. But I tell you that not even Solomon in all his splendor was clothed like one of them. If God so clothes the grass of the field, which grows today and is thrown into the oven tomorrow, will he not much more provide for you, O you of little faith? So do not worry and say, 'What are we to eat?' or 'What are we to drink?' or 'What are we to wear?' All these things the pagans seek. Your heavenly Father knows that you need them all. But seek first the kingdom of God and his righteousness, and all these things will be given you besides. Do not worry about tomorrow; tomorrow will take care of itself. Sufficient for a day is its own evil."

950   EIGHTH SUNDAY IN ORDINARY TIME — B

FIRST READING

Hosea 2:16b, 17b, 21–22

Thus says the LORD:
  I will lead her into the desert
    and speak to her heart.
  She shall respond there as in the
      days of her youth,
    when she came up from the land
      of Egypt.

I will espouse you to me forever:
  I will espouse you in right and
      in justice,
    in love and in mercy;
  I will espouse you in fidelity,
    and you shall know the LORD.

RESPONSORIAL PSALM

Psalm 103:1–2, 3–4, 8, 10, 12–13

℟. The Lord is kind and mer - ci - ful.

Music: Owen Alstott, b. 1947, © 1977, 1990, OCP. All rights reserved.

▶ Bless the LORD, O my soul;
    and all my being, bless his
      holy name.
  Bless the LORD, O my soul,
    and forget not all his benefits. ℟.

▶ He pardons all your iniquities,
    heals all your ills.
  He redeems your life
      from destruction,
    crowns you with kindness
      and compassion. ℟.

▶ Merciful and gracious is the LORD,
    slow to anger and abounding
      in kindness.
  Not according to our sins does he
      deal with us,
    nor does he requite us according to
      our crimes. ℟.

▶ As far as the east is from the west,
    so far has he put our transgressions
      from us.
  As a father has compassion on
      his children,
    so the LORD has compassion on
      those who fear him. ℟.

SECOND READING

2 Corinthians 3:1b–6

Brothers and sisters: Do we need, as some do, letters of recommendation to you or from you? You are our letter, written on our hearts, known and read by all, shown to be a letter of Christ ministered by us, written not in ink but by the Spirit of the living God, not on tablets of stone but on tablets that are hearts of flesh.

Such confidence we have through Christ toward God. Not that of ourselves we are qualified to take credit for anything as coming from us; rather, our qualification comes from God, who has indeed qualified us as ministers of a new covenant, not of letter but of spirit; for the letter brings death, but the Spirit gives life.

GOSPEL ACCLAMATION

James 1:18

℟. Al - le - lu - ia, al - le - lu - ia, al - le - lu - ia.

(Omit if not sung)

▸ The Father willed to give us birth by the word of truth that we may be a kind of firstfruits of his creatures. ℟.

GOSPEL

Mark 2:18–22

The disciples of John and of the Pharisees were accustomed to fast. People came to him and objected, "Why do the disciples of John and the disciples of the Pharisees fast, but your disciples do not fast?" Jesus answered them, "Can the wedding guests fast while the bridegroom is with them? As long as they have the bridegroom with them they cannot fast. But the days will come when the bridegroom is taken

away from them, and then they will fast on that day. No one sews a piece of unshrunken cloth on an old cloak. If he does, its fullness pulls away, the new from the old, and the tear gets worse. Likewise, no one pours new wine into old wineskins. Otherwise, the wine will burst the skins, and both the wine and the skins are ruined. Rather, new wine is poured into fresh wineskins."

EIGHTH SUNDAY IN ORDINARY TIME — C 951

FIRST READING

Sirach 27:4–7

When a sieve is shaken,
  the husks appear;
   so do one's faults when one speaks.
As the test of what the potter molds
  is in the furnace,
   so in tribulation is the test of
    the just.

The fruit of a tree shows the care it
  has had;
   so too does one's speech disclose
    the bent of one's mind.
Praise no one before he speaks,
  for it is then that people are tested.

RESPONSORIAL PSALM

Psalm 92:2–3, 13–14, 15–16

▶ It is good to give thanks to the LORD,
　　to sing praise to your name,
　　　　Most High,
　to proclaim your kindness at dawn
　　and your faithfulness throughout
　　　　the night. ℟.

▶ The just one shall flourish like the
　　palm tree,
　　like a cedar of Lebanon shall
　　　　he grow.

They that are planted in the house of
　　the LORD
　　shall flourish in the courts of
　　　　our God. ℟.

▶ They shall bear fruit even in old age;
　　vigorous and sturdy shall they be,
　declaring how just is the LORD,
　　my rock, in whom there is
　　　　no wrong. ℟.

SECOND READING

1 Corinthians 15:54–58

Brothers and sisters: When this which is corruptible clothes itself with incorruptibility and this which is mortal clothes itself with immortality, then the word that is written shall come about:
Death is swallowed up in victory.
　Where, O death, is your victory?
　Where, O death, is your sting?

The sting of death is sin, and the power of sin is the law. But thanks be to God who gives us the victory through our Lord Jesus Christ.

Therefore, my beloved brothers and sisters, be firm, steadfast, always fully devoted to the work of the Lord, knowing that in the Lord your labor is not in vain.

GOSPEL ACCLAMATION

Philippians 2:15d, 16a

(Omit if not sung)

▶ Shine like lights in the world
　as you hold on to the word of life. ℟.

GOSPEL

Luke 6:39–45

Jesus told his disciples a parable, "Can a blind person guide a blind person? Will not both fall into a pit? No disciple is superior to the teacher; but when fully trained, every disciple will be like his teacher. Why do you notice the splinter in your brother's eye, but do not perceive the wooden beam in your own? How can you say to your brother, 'Brother, let me remove that splinter in your eye,' when you do not

even notice the wooden beam in your own eye? You hypocrite! Remove the wooden beam from your eye first; then you will see clearly to remove the splinter in your brother's eye.

"A good tree does not bear rotten fruit, nor does a rotten tree bear good fruit. For every tree is known by its own fruit. For people do not pick figs from thornbushes, nor do they gather grapes from brambles. A good person out of the store of goodness in his heart produces good, but an evil person out of a store of evil produces evil; for from the fullness of the heart the mouth speaks."

NINTH SUNDAY IN ORDINARY TIME — A 952

FIRST READING
Deuteronomy 11:18, 26–28, 32

Moses told the people, "Take these words of mine into your heart and soul. Bind them at your wrist as a sign, and let them be a pendant on your forehead.

"I set before you here, this day, a blessing and a curse: a blessing for obeying the commandments of the LORD, your God, which I enjoin on you today; a curse if you do not obey the commandments of the LORD, your God, but turn aside from the way I ordain for you today, to follow other gods, whom you have not known. Be careful to observe all the statutes and decrees that I set before you today."

RESPONSORIAL PSALM
Psalm 31:2–3, 3–4, 17, 25

℟. Lord, be my rock of safe - ty.

▶ In you, O LORD, I take refuge;
   let me never be put to shame.
 In your justice rescue me,
    incline your ear to me,
    make haste to deliver me! ℟.

▶ Be my rock of refuge,
    a stronghold to give me safety.

You are my rock and my fortress;
   for your name's sake you will lead
      and guide me. ℟.

▶ Let your face shine upon your
      servant;
   save me in your kindness.
 Take courage and be stouthearted,
    all you who hope in the LORD. ℟.

SECOND READING
Romans 3:21–25, 28

Brothers and sisters: Now the righteousness of God has been manifested apart from the law, though testified to by the law and the prophets, the righteousness of God through faith in Jesus Christ for all who believe. For there is no distinction; all have sinned and are deprived of the glory of God. They are justified freely by his grace through the redemption in Christ Jesus, whom God set forth as an expiation, through faith, by his blood. For we consider that a person is justified by faith apart from works of the law.

GOSPEL ACCLAMATION
John 15:5

℟. Al - le - lu - ia, al - le - lu - ia, al - le - lu - ia.

(Omit if not sung)

▶ I am the vine, you are the branches, says the Lord;
   whoever remains in me and I in him will bear much fruit. ℟.

GOSPEL
Matthew 7:21–27

Jesus said to his disciples: "Not everyone who says to me, 'Lord, Lord,' will enter the kingdom of heaven, but only the one who does the will of my Father in heaven. Many will say to me on that day, 'Lord, Lord, did we not prophesy in your name? Did we not drive out demons in your name? Did we not do mighty deeds in your name?' Then I will declare to them solemnly, 'I never knew you. Depart from me, you evildoers.'

"Everyone who listens to these words of mine and acts on them will be like a wise man who built his house on rock. The rain fell, the floods came, and the winds blew and buffeted the house. But it did not collapse; it had been set solidly on rock. And everyone who listens to these words of mine but does not act on them will be like a fool who built his house on sand. The rain fell, the floods came, and the winds blew and buffeted the house. And it collapsed and was completely ruined."

---

953 NINTH SUNDAY IN ORDINARY TIME — B

FIRST READING
Deuteronomy 5:12–15

Thus says the LORD: "Take care to keep holy the sabbath day as the LORD, your God, commanded you. Six days you may labor and do all your work; but the seventh day is the sabbath of the LORD, your God. No work may be done then, whether by you, or your son or daughter, or your male or female slave, or your ox or ass or any

of your beasts, or the alien who lives with you. Your male and female slave should rest as you do. For remember that you too were once a slave in Egypt, and the LORD, your God, brought you from there with his strong hand and outstretched arm. That is why the LORD, your God, has commanded you to observe the sabbath day."

RESPONSORIAL PSALM
Psalm 81:3–4, 5–6, 6–8, 10–11

℟. Sing with joy to God our help.

Music: Owen Alstott, b. 1947, © 1977, 1990, OCP. All rights reserved.

▸ Take up a melody, and sound
    the timbrel,
  the pleasant harp and the lyre.
Blow the trumpet at the new moon,
  at the full moon, on our
    solemn feast. ℟.

▸ For it is a statute in Israel,
    an ordinance of the God of Jacob,
  who made it a decree for Joseph
    when he came forth from the land
    of Egypt. ℟.

▸ An unfamiliar speech I hear:
    "I relieved his shoulder of
      the burden;
    his hands were freed from
      the basket.
  In distress you called, and I
    rescued you." ℟.

▸ "There shall be no strange god
    among you
  nor shall you worship any
    alien god.
I, the LORD, am your God
  who led you forth from the land
    of Egypt." ℟.

SECOND READING

2 Corinthians 4:6–11

Brothers and sisters: God who said, *Let light shine out of darkness,* has shone in our hearts to bring to light the knowledge of the glory of God on the face of Jesus Christ. But we hold this treasure in earthen vessels, that the surpassing power may be of God and not from us. We are afflicted in every way, but not constrained; perplexed, but not driven to despair; persecuted, but not abandoned; struck down, but not destroyed; always carrying about in the body the dying of Jesus, so that the life of Jesus may also be manifested in our body. For we who live are constantly being given up to death for the sake of Jesus, so that the life of Jesus may be manifested in our mortal flesh.

GOSPEL ACCLAMATION

cf. John 17:17b, 17a

℟. Al - le - lu - ia, al - le - lu - ia, al - le - lu - ia.

(Omit if not sung)

▶ Your word, O Lord, is truth; consecrate us in the truth. ℟.

GOSPEL

Mark 2:23—3:6 or 2:23–28

(Include bracketed text for Long Form)

As Jesus was passing through a field of grain on the sabbath, his disciples began to make a path while picking the heads of grain. At this the Pharisees said to him, "Look, why are they doing what is unlawful on the sabbath?" He said to them, "Have you never read what David did when he was in need and he and his companions were hungry? How he went into the house of God when Abiathar was high priest and ate the bread of offering that only the priests could lawfully eat, and shared it with his companions?" Then he said to them, "The sabbath was made for man, not man for the sabbath. That is why the Son of Man is lord even of the sabbath."

[Again he entered the synagogue. There was a man there who had a withered hand. They watched him closely to see if he would cure him on the sabbath so that they might accuse him. He said to the man with the withered hand, "Come up here before us." Then he said to them, "Is it lawful to do good on the sabbath rather than to do evil, to save life rather than to destroy it?" But they remained silent. Looking around at them with anger and grieved at their hardness of heart, he said to the man, "Stretch out your hand." He stretched it out and his hand was restored. The Pharisees went out and immediately took counsel with the Herodians against him to put him to death.]

NINTH SUNDAY IN ORDINARY TIME — C   954

FIRST READING

1 Kings 8:41–43

In those days, Solomon prayed in the temple, saying, "To the foreigner, who is not of your people Israel, but comes from a distant land to honor you—since they will learn of your great name and your mighty hand and your outstretched arm—, when he comes and prays toward this temple, listen from your heavenly dwelling. Do all that foreigner asks of you, that all the peoples of the earth may know your name, may fear you as do your people Israel, and may acknowledge that this temple which I have built is dedicated to your honor."

RESPONSORIAL PSALM

Psalm 117:1, 2

℟. Go out to all the world and tell the Good News.

Or ℟. **Alleluia.**

▶ Praise the LORD, all you nations;
  glorify him, all you peoples! ℟.

▶ For steadfast is his kindness
    toward us,
  and the fidelity of the LORD
    endures forever. ℟.

SECOND READING

Galatians 1:1–2, 6–10

Paul, an apostle not from human beings nor through a human being but through Jesus Christ and God the Father who raised him from the dead, and all the brothers who are with me, to the churches of Galatia.

  I am amazed that you are so quickly forsaking the one who called you by the grace of Christ for a different gospel—not that there is another. But there are some who are disturbing you and wish to pervert the gospel of Christ. But even if we or an angel from heaven should preach to you a gospel other than the one that we preached to you, let that one be accursed! As we have said before, and now I say again, if anyone preaches to you a gospel other than what you have received, let that one be accursed!

  Am I now currying favor with humans or with God? Or am I seeking to please people? If I were still trying to please people, I would not be a slave of Christ.

GOSPEL ACCLAMATION

John 3:16

℟. Al - le - lu - ia, al - le - lu - ia, al - le - lu - ia.

(Omit if not sung)

▶ God so loved the world that he gave his only Son,
  so that everyone who believes in him might have eternal life. ℟.

GOSPEL

Luke 7:1–10

When Jesus had finished all his words to the people, he entered Capernaum. A centurion there had a slave who was ill and about to die, and he was valuable to him. When he heard about Jesus, he sent elders of the Jews to him, asking him to come and save the life of his slave. They approached Jesus and strongly urged him to come, saying, "He deserves to have you do this for him, for he loves our nation and built the synagogue for us." And Jesus went with them, but when he was only a short distance from the house, the centurion sent friends to tell him, "Lord, do not trouble yourself, for I am not worthy to have you enter under my roof. Therefore, I did not consider myself worthy to come to you; but say the word and let my servant be healed. For I too am a person subject to authority, with soldiers subject to me. And I say to one, 'Go,' and he goes; and to another, 'Come here,' and he comes; and to my slave, 'Do this,' and he does it." When Jesus heard this he was amazed at him and, turning, said to the crowd following him, "I tell you, not even in Israel have I found such faith." When the messengers returned to the house, they found the slave in good health.

TENTH SUNDAY IN ORDINARY TIME — A 955

FIRST READING
Hosea 6:3–6

In their affliction, people will say:
"Let us know, let us strive to know
   the LORD;
   as certain as the dawn is
      his coming,
   and his judgment shines forth like
      the light of day!
He will come to us like the rain,
   like spring rain that waters
      the earth."

What can I do with you, Ephraim?
   What can I do with you, Judah?

Your piety is like a morning cloud,
   like the dew that early passes away.
For this reason I smote them through
   the prophets,
   I slew them by the words of
      my mouth;
for it is love that I desire,
   not sacrifice,
   and knowledge of God rather
      than holocausts.

RESPONSORIAL PSALM
Psalm 50:1, 8, 12–13, 14–15

℟. To the up-right I will show the sav-ing pow-er of God.

▶ God the LORD has spoken and
      summoned the earth,
   from the rising of the sun to
      its setting.
"Not for your sacrifices do I
      rebuke you,
   for your holocausts are before
      me always." ℟.

▶ "If I were hungry, I would not
      tell you,
   for mine are the world and
      its fullness.

Do I eat the flesh of strong bulls,
   or is the blood of goats
      my drink?" ℟.

▶ "Offer to God praise as your sacrifice
   and fulfill your vows to the
      Most High;
   then call upon me in time of distress;
   I will rescue you, and you shall
      glorify me." ℟.

SECOND READING
Romans 4:18–25

Brothers and sisters: Abraham believed, hoping against hope, that he would become "the father of many nations," according to what was said, "Thus shall your descendants be." He did not weaken in faith when he considered his own body as already dead—for he was almost a hundred years old—and the dead womb of Sarah. He did not doubt God's promise in unbelief; rather, he was strengthened by faith and gave glory to God and was fully convinced that what he had promised he was also able to do. That is why *it was credited to him as righteousness*. But it was not for him alone that it was written that *it was credited to him*; it was also for us, to whom it will be credited, who believe in the one who raised Jesus our Lord from the dead, who was handed over for our transgressions and was raised for our justification.

GOSPEL ACCLAMATION
cf. Luke 4:18

℟. Al - le - lu - ia, al - le - lu - ia, al - le - lu - ia.

Music: Owen Alstott, b. 1947, © 1977, 1990, OCP. All rights reserved.
(Omit if not sung)

▶ The Lord sent me to bring glad tidings to the poor, and to proclaim liberty to captives. ℟.

GOSPEL
Matthew 9:9–13

As Jesus passed on from there, he saw a man named Matthew sitting at the customs post. He said to him, "Follow me." And he got up and followed him. While he was at table in his house, many tax collectors and sinners came and sat with Jesus and his disciples. The Pharisees saw this and said to his disciples, "Why does your teacher eat with tax collectors and sinners?" He heard this and said, "Those who are well do not need a physician, but the sick do. Go and learn the meaning of the words, 'I desire mercy, not sacrifice.' I did not come to call the righteous but sinners."

---

956   TENTH SUNDAY IN ORDINARY TIME — B

FIRST READING
Genesis 3:9–15

After the man, Adam, had eaten of the tree, the LORD God called to the man and asked him, "Where are you?" He answered, "I heard you in the garden; but I was afraid, because I was naked, so I hid myself." Then he asked, "Who told you that you were naked? You have eaten, then, from the tree of which I had forbidden you to eat!" The man replied, "The woman whom you put here with me—she gave me fruit from the tree, and so I ate it." The LORD God then asked the woman, "Why did you do such a thing?" The woman answered, "The serpent tricked me into it, so I ate it."

Then the LORD God said to
the serpent:
"Because you have done this, you
shall be banned
from all the animals
and from all the wild creatures;
on your belly shall you crawl,
and dirt shall you eat
all the days of your life.

I will put enmity between you and
the woman,
and between your offspring
and hers;

he will strike at your head,
while you strike at his heel."

RESPONSORIAL PSALM

Psalm 130:1–2, 3–4, 5–6, 7–8

℟. With the Lord there is mer-cy and full-ness of re-demp-tion.

▶ Out of the depths I cry to you,
O LORD;
LORD, hear my voice!
Let your ears be attentive
to my voice in supplication. ℟.

▶ If you, O LORD, mark iniquities,
LORD, who can stand?
But with you is forgiveness,
that you may be revered. ℟.

▶ I trust in the LORD;
my soul trusts in his word.
More than sentinels wait for
the dawn,
let Israel wait for the LORD. ℟.

▶ For with the LORD is kindness
and with him is plenteous
redemption;
and he will redeem Israel
from all their iniquities. ℟.

SECOND READING

2 Corinthians 4:13 — 5:1

Brothers and sisters: Since we have the same spirit of faith, according to what is written, *I believed, therefore I spoke*, we too believe and therefore we speak, knowing that the one who raised the Lord Jesus will raise us also with Jesus and place us with you in his presence. Everything indeed is for you, so that the grace bestowed in abundance on more and more people may cause the thanksgiving to overflow for the glory of God. Therefore, we are not discouraged; rather, although our outer self is wasting away, our inner self is being renewed day by day. For this momentary light affliction is producing for us an eternal weight of glory beyond all comparison, as we look not to what is seen but to what is unseen; for what is seen is transitory, but what is unseen is eternal. For we know that if our earthly dwelling, a tent, should be destroyed, we have a building from God, a dwelling not made with hands, eternal in heaven.

GOSPEL ACCLAMATION

John 12:31b–32

℟. Al - le - lu - ia, al - le - lu - ia, al - le - lu - ia.

(Omit if not sung)

▶ Now the ruler of this world will be driven out, says the Lord;
and when I am lifted up from the earth, I will draw everyone to myself. ℟.

GOSPEL

Mark 3:20–35

Jesus came home with his disciples. Again the crowd gathered, making it impossible for them even to eat. When his relatives heard of this they set out to seize him, for they said, "He is out of his mind." The scribes who had come from Jerusalem said, "He is possessed by Beelzebul," and "By the prince of demons he drives out demons."

Summoning them, he began to speak to them in parables, "How can Satan drive out Satan? If a kingdom is divided against itself, that kingdom cannot stand. And if a house is divided against itself, that house will not be able to stand. And if Satan has risen up against himself and is divided, he cannot stand; that is the end of him. But no one can enter a strong man's house to plunder his property unless he first ties up the strong man. Then he can plunder the house. Amen, I say to you, all sins and all blasphemies that people utter will be forgiven them. But whoever blasphemes against the Holy Spirit will never have forgiveness, but is guilty of an everlasting sin." For they had said, "He has an unclean spirit."

His mother and his brothers arrived. Standing outside they sent word to him and called him. A crowd seated around him told him, "Your mother and your brothers and your sisters are outside asking for you." But he said to them in reply, "Who are my mother and my brothers?" And looking around at those seated in the circle he said, "Here are my mother and my brothers. For whoever does the will of God is my brother and sister and mother."

---

957 TENTH SUNDAY IN ORDINARY TIME — C

FIRST READING

1 Kings 17:17–24

Elijah went to Zarephath of Sidon to the house of a widow. The son of the mistress of the house fell sick, and his sickness grew more severe until he stopped breathing. So she said to Elijah, "Why have you done this to me, O man of God? Have you come to me to call attention to my guilt and to kill my son?" Elijah said to her, "Give me your son." Taking him from her lap, he carried the son to the upper room where he was staying, and put him on his bed. Elijah called out to the LORD: "O LORD, my God, will you afflict even the widow with whom I am staying by killing her son?" Then he stretched himself out upon the child three times and called out to the LORD: "O LORD, my God, let the life breath return to the body of this child." The LORD heard the prayer of Elijah; the life breath returned to the child's body and he revived. Taking the child, Elijah brought him down into the house from the upper room and gave him to his mother. Elijah said to her, "See! Your son is alive." The woman replied to Elijah, "Now indeed I know that you are a man of God. The word of the LORD comes truly from your mouth."

RESPONSORIAL PSALM

Psalm 30:2, 4, 5–6, 11, 12, 13

℟. I will praise you, Lord, for you have res-cued me.

▶ I will extol you, O LORD, for you drew
  me clear
  and did not let my enemies rejoice
  over me.
O LORD, you brought me up from the
  nether world;
  you preserved me from among
  those going down into the pit. ℟.

▶ Sing praise to the LORD, you his
  faithful ones,

and give thanks to his holy name.
For his anger lasts but a moment;
  a lifetime, his good will.
At nightfall, weeping enters in,
  but with the dawn, rejoicing. ℟.

▶ Hear, O LORD, and have pity on me;
  O LORD, be my helper.
You changed my mourning
  into dancing;
  O LORD, my God, forever will I give
  you thanks. ℟.

SECOND READING
Galatians 1:11–19

I want you to know, brothers and
sisters, that the gospel preached
by me is not of human origin. For
I did not receive it from a human
being, nor was I taught it, but it came
through a revelation of Jesus Christ.

For you heard of my former way of
life in Judaism, how I persecuted the
church of God beyond measure and
tried to destroy it, and progressed
in Judaism beyond many of my
contemporaries among my race, since
I was even more a zealot for my
ancestral traditions. But when God,

who from my mother's womb had set
me apart and called me through his
grace, was pleased to reveal his Son
to me, so that I might proclaim him
to the Gentiles, I did not immediately
consult flesh and blood, nor did I go
up to Jerusalem to those who were
apostles before me; rather, I went into
Arabia and then returned to Damascus.

Then after three years I went up to
Jerusalem to confer with Cephas and
remained with him for fifteen days. But
I did not see any other of the apostles,
only James the brother of the Lord.

GOSPEL ACCLAMATION
Luke 7:16

℟. Al - le - lu - ia,   al - le - lu - ia,   al - le - lu - ia.

Music: Owen Alstott, b. 1947, © 1977, 1990, OCP. All rights reserved.   *(Omit if not sung)*

▶ A great prophet has risen in our midst.
  God has visited his people. ℟.

GOSPEL
Luke 7:11–17

Jesus journeyed to a city called Nain,
and his disciples and a large crowd
accompanied him. As he drew near
to the gate of the city, a man who
had died was being carried out, the
only son of his mother, and she was a
widow. A large crowd from the city was
with her. When the Lord saw her, he
was moved with pity for her and said
to her, "Do not weep." He stepped
forward and touched the coffin; at

this the bearers halted, and he said,
"Young man, I tell you, arise!" The dead
man sat up and began to speak, and
Jesus gave him to his mother. Fear
seized them all, and they glorified
God, exclaiming, "A great prophet has
arisen in our midst," and "God has
visited his people." This report about
him spread through the whole of Judea
and in all the surrounding region.

958 11TH SUNDAY IN ORDINARY TIME — A

FIRST READING

Exodus 19:2–6a

In those days, the Israelites came to the desert of Sinai and pitched camp. While Israel was encamped here in front of the mountain, Moses went up the mountain to God. Then the LORD called to him and said, "Thus shall you say to the house of Jacob; tell the Israelites: You have seen for yourselves how I treated the Egyptians and how I bore you up on eagle wings and brought you here to myself. Therefore, if you hearken to my voice and keep my covenant, you shall be my special possession, dearer to me than all other people, though all the earth is mine. You shall be to me a kingdom of priests, a holy nation."

RESPONSORIAL PSALM

Psalm 100:1–2, 3, 5

℟. We are his peo - ple, the sheep of his flock.

Music: Owen Alstott, b. 1947, © 1977, 1990, OCP. All rights reserved.

▸ Sing joyfully to the LORD,
  all you lands;
    serve the LORD with gladness;
    come before him with
      joyful song. ℟.

▸ Know that the LORD is God;
  he made us, his we are;
    his people, the flock he tends. ℟.

▸ The LORD is good:
    his kindness endures forever,
    and his faithfulness to all
      generations. ℟.

SECOND READING

Romans 5:6–11

Brothers and sisters: Christ, while we were still helpless, yet died at the appointed time for the ungodly. Indeed, only with difficulty does one die for a just person, though perhaps for a good person one might even find courage to die. But God proves his love for us in that while we were still sinners Christ died for us. How much more then, since we are now justified by his blood, will we be saved through him from the wrath. Indeed, if, while we were enemies, we were reconciled to God through the death of his Son, how much more, once reconciled, will we be saved by his life. Not only that, but we also boast of God through our Lord Jesus Christ, through whom we have now received reconciliation.

GOSPEL ACCLAMATION

Mark 1:15

℟. Al - le - lu - ia, al - le - lu - ia, al - le - lu - ia.

Music: Owen Alstott, b. 1947, © 1977, 1990, OCP. All rights reserved.   *(Omit if not sung)*

▸ The kingdom of God is at hand.
  Repent and believe in the Gospel. ℟.

GOSPEL

Matthew 9:36—10:8

At the sight of the crowds, Jesus' heart was moved with pity for them because they were troubled and abandoned, like sheep without a shepherd. Then he said to his disciples, "The harvest is abundant but the laborers are few; so ask the master of the harvest to send out laborers for his harvest."

Then he summoned his twelve disciples and gave them authority over unclean spirits to drive them out and to cure every disease and every illness. The names of the twelve apostles are these: first, Simon called Peter, and his brother Andrew; James, the son of Zebedee, and his brother John;

Philip and Bartholomew, Thomas and Matthew the tax collector; James, the son of Alphaeus, and Thaddeus; Simon from Cana, and Judas Iscariot who betrayed him.

Jesus sent out these twelve after instructing them thus, "Do not go into pagan territory or enter a Samaritan town. Go rather to the lost sheep of the house of Israel. As you go, make this proclamation: 'The kingdom of heaven is at hand.' Cure the sick, raise the dead, cleanse lepers, drive out demons. Without cost you have received; without cost you are to give."

11TH SUNDAY IN ORDINARY TIME — B 959

FIRST READING

Ezekiel 17:22–24

Thus says the Lord GOD:
I, too, will take from the crest of
the cedar,
from its topmost branches tear off
a tender shoot,
and plant it on a high and
lofty mountain;
on the mountain heights of Israel
I will plant it.
It shall put forth branches and
bear fruit,
and become a majestic cedar.

Birds of every kind shall dwell
beneath it,
every winged thing in the shade
of its boughs.
And all the trees of the field
shall know
that I, the Lord,
bring low the high tree,
lift high the lowly tree,
wither up the green tree,
and make the withered tree bloom.
As I, the LORD, have spoken, so will
I do.

RESPONSORIAL PSALM

Psalm 92:2–3, 13–14, 15–16

℟. Lord, it is good to give thanks to you.

Music: Owen Alstott, b. 1947, © 1977, 1990, OCP. All rights reserved.

▶ It is good to give thanks to the LORD,
to sing praise to your name,
Most High,
to proclaim your kindness at dawn
and your faithfulness throughout
the night. ℟.

▶ The just one shall flourish like the
palm tree,
like a cedar of Lebanon shall
he grow.
They that are planted in the house of
the LORD
shall flourish in the courts of
our God. ℟.

℟. Lord, it is good to give thanks to you.

▶ They shall bear fruit even in old age;
vigorous and sturdy shall they be,
declaring how just is the LORD,

my rock, in whom there is
no wrong. ℟.

SECOND READING

2 Corinthians 5:6–10

Brothers and sisters: We are always courageous, although we know that while we are at home in the body we are away from the Lord, for we walk by faith, not by sight. Yet we are courageous, and we would rather leave the body and go home to the Lord. Therefore, we aspire to please him, whether we are at home or away. For we must all appear before the judgment seat of Christ, so that each may receive recompense, according to what he did in the body, whether good or evil.

GOSPEL ACCLAMATION

℟. Al - le - lu - ia, al - le - lu - ia, al - le - lu - ia.

Music: Owen Alstott, b. 1947, © 1977, 1990, OCP. All rights reserved. *(Omit if not sung)*

▶ The seed is the word of God, Christ is the sower.
All who come to him will live for ever. ℟.

GOSPEL

Mark 4:26–34

Jesus said to the crowds: "This is how it is with the kingdom of God; it is as if a man were to scatter seed on the land and would sleep and rise night and day and through it all the seed would sprout and grow, he knows not how. Of its own accord the land yields fruit, first the blade, then the ear, then the full grain in the ear. And when the grain is ripe, he wields the sickle at once, for the harvest has come."

He said, "To what shall we compare the kingdom of God, or what parable can we use for it? It is like a mustard seed that, when it is sown in the ground, is the smallest of all the seeds on the earth. But once it is sown, it springs up and becomes the largest of plants and puts forth large branches, so that the birds of the sky can dwell in its shade." With many such parables he spoke the word to them as they were able to understand it. Without parables he did not speak to them, but to his own disciples he explained everything in private.

---

960   11TH SUNDAY IN ORDINARY TIME — C

FIRST READING

2 Samuel 12:7–10, 13

Nathan said to David: "Thus says the LORD God of Israel: 'I anointed you king of Israel. I rescued you from the hand of Saul. I gave you your lord's house and your lord's wives for your own. I gave you the house of Israel and of Judah. And if this were not enough, I could count up for you still more. Why have you spurned the LORD and done evil in his sight? You have cut down Uriah the Hittite with the sword; you took his wife as your own, and him you killed with the sword of the Ammonites. Now, therefore, the sword shall never depart from your house, because you have despised me and have taken the wife of Uriah to be your wife.'"

Then David said to Nathan, "I have sinned against the LORD." Nathan answered David: "The LORD on his part has forgiven your sin: you shall not die."

RESPONSORIAL PSALM
Psalm 32:1–2, 5, 7, 11

℟. Lord, for-give the wrong I have done.

▶ Blessed is the one whose fault is
    taken away,
  whose sin is covered.
Blessed the man to whom the LORD
    imputes not guilt,
  in whose spirit there is no guile. ℟.

▶ I acknowledged my sin to you,
  my guilt I covered not.
I said, "I confess my faults to
  the LORD,"

and you took away the guilt
  of my sin. ℟.

▶ You are my shelter; from distress you
  will preserve me;
with glad cries of freedom you will
  ring me round. ℟.

▶ Be glad in the LORD and rejoice,
  you just;
exult, all you upright of heart. ℟.

SECOND READING
Galatians 2:16, 19–21

Brothers and sisters: We who know that a person is not justified by works of the law but through faith in Jesus Christ, even we have believed in Christ Jesus that we may be justified by faith in Christ and not by works of the law, because by works of the law no one will be justified. For through the law I died to the law, that I might live for

God. I have been crucified with Christ; yet I live, no longer I, but Christ lives in me; insofar as I now live in the flesh, I live by faith in the Son of God who has loved me and given himself up for me. I do not nullify the grace of God; for if justification comes through the law, then Christ died for nothing.

GOSPEL ACCLAMATION
1 John 4:10b

℟. Al-le-lu-ia, al-le-lu-ia, al-le-lu-ia.

(Omit if not sung)

▶ God loved us and sent his Son
  as expiation for our sins. ℟.

GOSPEL
Luke 7:36—8:3 or 7:36–50

(Include bracketed text for Long Form)

A Pharisee invited Jesus to dine with him, and he entered the Pharisee's house and reclined at table. Now there was a sinful woman in the city who learned that he was at table in

the house of the Pharisee. Bringing an alabaster flask of ointment, she stood behind him at his feet weeping and began to bathe his feet with her tears. Then she wiped them with her hair, kissed them, and anointed them with the ointment. When the Pharisee who had invited him saw this he said to himself, "If this man were a prophet, he would know who and what sort of woman this is who is touching him, that she is a sinner." Jesus said to him in reply, "Simon, I have something to say to you." "Tell me, teacher," he said. "Two people were in debt to a certain creditor; one owed five hundred days' wages and the other owed fifty. Since they were unable to repay the debt, he forgave it for both. Which of them will love him more?" Simon said in reply, "The one, I suppose, whose larger debt was forgiven." He said to him, "You have judged rightly."

Then he turned to the woman and said to Simon, "Do you see this woman? When I entered your house, you did not give me water for my feet, but she has bathed them with her tears and wiped them with her hair. You did not give me a kiss, but she has not ceased kissing my feet since the time I entered. You did not anoint my head with oil, but she anointed my feet with ointment. So I tell you, her many sins have been forgiven because she has shown great love. But the one to whom little is forgiven, loves little." He said to her, "Your sins are forgiven." The others at table said to themselves, "Who is this who even forgives sins?" But he said to the woman, "Your faith has saved you; go in peace."

[Afterward he journeyed from one town and village to another, preaching and proclaiming the good news of the kingdom of God. Accompanying him were the Twelve and some women who had been cured of evil spirits and infirmities, Mary, called Magdalene, from whom seven demons had gone out, Joanna, the wife of Herod's steward Chuza, Susanna, and many others who provided for them out of their resources.]

---

961   12TH SUNDAY IN ORDINARY TIME — A

FIRST READING   *Jeremiah 20:10–13*

Jeremiah said:
  "I hear the whisperings of many:
    'Terror on every side!
    Denounce! let us denounce him!'
  All those who were my friends
    are on the watch for any misstep
      of mine.
  'Perhaps he will be trapped; then we
      can prevail,
    and take our vengeance on him.'
  But the LORD is with me, like a
      mighty champion:
    my persecutors will stumble, they
      will not triumph.

In their failure they will be put to
    utter shame,
  to lasting, unforgettable confusion.
O LORD of hosts, you who test
    the just,
  who probe mind and heart,
  let me witness the vengeance you
    take on them,
    for to you I have entrusted
      my cause.
Sing to the LORD,
  praise the LORD,
for he has rescued the life of
    the poor
    from the power of the wicked!"

RESPONSORIAL PSALM   *Psalm 69:8–10, 14, 17, 33–35*

℟. Lord, in your great love, an - swer me.

▶ For your sake I bear insult,
 and shame covers my face.
I have become an outcast to
 my brothers,
 a stranger to my mother's children,
because zeal for your house
 consumes me,
 and the insults of those who
 blaspheme you fall upon me. ℟.

▶ I pray to you, O LORD,
 for the time of your favor, O God!
In your great kindness answer me
 with your constant help.

Answer me, O LORD, for bounteous is
 your kindness;
 in your great mercy turn
 toward me. ℟.

▶ "See, you lowly ones, and be glad;
 you who seek God, may your
 hearts revive!
For the LORD hears the poor,
 and his own who are in bonds he
 spurns not.
Let the heavens and the earth
 praise him,
 the seas and whatever moves
 in them!" ℟.

SECOND READING

Romans 5:12–15

Brothers and sisters: Through one man sin entered the world, and through sin, death, and thus death came to all men, inasmuch as all sinned—for up to the time of the law, sin was in the world, though sin is not accounted when there is no law. But death reigned from Adam to Moses, even over those who did not sin after the pattern of the trespass of Adam, who is the type of the one who was to come.

But the gift is not like the transgression. For if by the transgression of the one the many died, how much more did the grace of God and the gracious gift of the one man Jesus Christ overflow for the many.

GOSPEL ACCLAMATION

John 15:26b, 27a

℟. Al - le - lu - ia, al - le - lu - ia, al - le - lu - ia.

(Omit if not sung)

▶ The Spirit of truth will testify to me, says the Lord;
 and you also will testify. ℟.

GOSPEL

Matthew 10:26–33

Jesus said to the Twelve: "Fear no one. Nothing is concealed that will not be revealed, nor secret that will not be known. What I say to you in the darkness, speak in the light; what you hear whispered, proclaim on the housetops. And do not be afraid of those who kill the body but cannot kill the soul; rather, be afraid of the one who can destroy both soul and body in Gehenna. Are not two sparrows sold for a small coin? Yet not one of them falls to the ground without your Father's knowledge. Even all the hairs of your head are counted. So do not be afraid; you are worth more than many sparrows. Everyone who acknowledges me before others I will acknowledge before my heavenly Father. But whoever denies me before others, I will deny before my heavenly Father."

962   12TH SUNDAY IN ORDINARY TIME — B

FIRST READING   *Job 38:1, 8–11*

The LORD addressed Job out
of the storm and said:
  Who shut within doors the sea,
    when it burst forth from the womb;
  when I made the clouds its garment
    and thick darkness its
      swaddling bands?

When I set limits for it
  and fastened the bar of its door,
and said: Thus far shall you come but
  no farther,
  and here shall your proud waves
    be stilled!

RESPONSORIAL PSALM   *Psalm 107:23–24, 25–26, 28–29, 30–31*

℟. **Give thanks to the Lord,**   his love   is   ev - er - last - ing.

Or ℟. **Alleluia.**

▶ They who sailed the sea in ships,
  trading on the deep waters,
these saw the works of the LORD
  and his wonders in the abyss. ℟.

▶ His command raised up a storm wind
  which tossed its waves on high.
They mounted up to heaven; they
  sank to the depths;
  their hearts melted away in
  their plight. ℟.

▶ They cried to the LORD in
  their distress;
  from their straits he rescued them,

he hushed the storm to a
  gentle breeze,
and the billows of the sea
  were stilled. ℟.

▶ They rejoiced that they were calmed,
  and he brought them to their
  desired haven.
Let them give thanks to the LORD for
  his kindness
  and his wondrous deeds to the
  children of men. ℟.

SECOND READING   *2 Corinthians 5:14–17*

Brothers and sisters: The love of
Christ impels us, once we have come
to the conviction that one died
for all; therefore, all have died. He
indeed died for all, so that those
who live might no longer live for
themselves but for him who for
their sake died and was raised.

Consequently, from now on we
regard no one according to the
flesh; even if we once knew Christ
according to the flesh, yet now we
know him so no longer. So whoever
is in Christ is a new creation: the
old things have passed away;
behold, new things have come.

GOSPEL ACCLAMATION   *Luke 7:16*

℟. **Al - le - lu - ia,**   al - le - lu - ia,   al - le - lu - ia.

     (Omit if not sung)

▶ A great prophet has risen in our midst.
God has visited his people. ℟.

GOSPEL

Mark 4:35–41

On that day, as evening drew on, Jesus said to his disciples: "Let us cross to the other side." Leaving the crowd, they took Jesus with them in the boat just as he was. And other boats were with him. A violent squall came up and waves were breaking over the boat, so that it was already filling up. Jesus was in the stern, asleep on a cushion. They woke him and said to him, "Teacher, do you not care that we are perishing?" He woke up, rebuked the wind, and said to the sea, "Quiet! Be still!" The wind ceased and there was great calm. Then he asked them, "Why are you terrified? Do you not yet have faith?" They were filled with great awe and said to one another, "Who then is this whom even wind and sea obey?"

12TH SUNDAY IN ORDINARY TIME — C   963

FIRST READING

Zechariah 12:10–11; 13:1

Thus says the LORD: I will pour out on the house of David and on the inhabitants of Jerusalem a spirit of grace and petition; and they shall look on him whom they have pierced, and they shall mourn for him as one mourns for an only son, and they shall grieve over him as one grieves over a firstborn.

On that day the mourning in Jerusalem shall be as great as the mourning of Hadadrimmon in the plain of Megiddo.

On that day there shall be open to the house of David and to the inhabitants of Jerusalem, a fountain to purify from sin and uncleanness.

RESPONSORIAL PSALM

Psalm 63:2, 3–4, 5–6, 8–9

℟. My soul is thirst-ing for you, O Lord my God.

▶ O God, you are my God whom I seek;
for you my flesh pines and my
soul thirsts
like the earth, parched, lifeless and
without water. ℟.

▶ Thus have I gazed toward you in
the sanctuary
to see your power and your glory,
for your kindness is a greater good
than life;
my lips shall glorify you. ℟.

▶ Thus will I bless you while I live;
lifting up my hands, I will call upon
your name.
As with the riches of a banquet shall
my soul be satisfied,
and with exultant lips my mouth
shall praise you. ℟.

▶ You are my help,
and in the shadow of your wings
I shout for joy.
My soul clings fast to you;
your right hand upholds me. ℟.

SECOND READING
Galatians 3:26–29

Brothers and sisters: Through faith you are all children of God in Christ Jesus. For all of you who were baptized into Christ have clothed yourselves with Christ. There is neither Jew nor Greek, there is neither slave nor free person, there is not male and female; for you are all one in Christ Jesus. And if you belong to Christ, then you are Abraham's descendant, heirs according to the promise.

GOSPEL ACCLAMATION
John 10:27

℟. Al - le - lu - ia, al - le - lu - ia, al - le - lu - ia.

(Omit if not sung)

▶ My sheep hear my voice, says the Lord;
I know them, and they follow me. ℟.

GOSPEL
Luke 9:18–24

Once when Jesus was praying in solitude, and the disciples were with him, he asked them, "Who do the crowds say that I am?" They said in reply, "John the Baptist; others, Elijah; still others, 'One of the ancient prophets has arisen.'" Then he said to them, "But who do you say that I am?" Peter said in reply, "The Christ of God." He rebuked them and directed them not to tell this to anyone.

He said, "The Son of Man must suffer greatly and be rejected by the elders, the chief priests, and the scribes, and be killed and on the third day be raised." Then he said to all, "If anyone wishes to come after me, he must deny himself and take up his cross daily and follow me. For whoever wishes to save his life will lose it, but whoever loses his life for my sake will save it."

---

964   13TH SUNDAY IN ORDINARY TIME — A

FIRST READING
2 Kings 4:8–11, 14–16a

One day Elisha came to Shunem, where there was a woman of influence, who urged him to dine with her. Afterward, whenever he passed by, he used to stop there to dine. So she said to her husband, "I know that Elisha is a holy man of God. Since he visits us often, let us arrange a little room on the roof and furnish it for him with a bed, table, chair, and lamp, so that when he comes to us he can stay there." Sometime later Elisha arrived and stayed in the room overnight.

Later Elisha asked, "Can something be done for her?" His servant Gehazi answered, "Yes! She has no son, and her husband is getting on in years." Elisha said, "Call her." When the woman had been called and stood at the door, Elisha promised, "This time next year you will be fondling a baby son."

RESPONSORIAL PSALM
Psalm 89:2–3, 16–17, 18–19

R. For - ev - er I will sing the good - ness of the Lord.

▶ The promises of the LORD I will
    sing forever,
  through all generations my mouth
    shall proclaim your faithfulness.
For you have said, "My kindness is
    established forever";
  in heaven you have confirmed
    your faithfulness. R.

▶ Blessed the people who know the
    joyful shout;

in the light of your countenance,
  O LORD, they walk.
At your name they rejoice all the day,
  and through your justice they
    are exalted. R.

▶ You are the splendor of their strength,
  and by your favor our horn
    is exalted.
For to the LORD belongs our shield,
  and to the Holy One of Israel,
    our king. R.

SECOND READING
Romans 6:3–4, 8–11

Brothers and sisters: Are you unaware that we who were baptized into Christ Jesus were baptized into his death? We were indeed buried with him through baptism into death, so that, just as Christ was raised from the dead by the glory of the Father, we too might live in newness of life.

If, then, we have died with Christ, we believe that we shall also live with him. We know that Christ, raised from the dead, dies no more; death no longer has power over him. As to his death, he died to sin once and for all; as to his life, he lives for God. Consequently, you too must think of yourselves as dead to sin and living for God in Christ Jesus.

GOSPEL ACCLAMATION
1 Peter 2:9

R. Al - le - lu - ia, al - le - lu - ia, al - le - lu - ia.

(Omit if not sung)

▶ You are a chosen race, a royal priesthood, a holy nation;
  announce the praises of him who called you out of darkness into his
    wonderful light. R.

GOSPEL
Matthew 10:37–42

Jesus said to his apostles: "Whoever loves father or mother more than me is not worthy of me, and whoever loves son or daughter more than me is not worthy of me; and whoever does not take up his cross and follow after me is not worthy of me. Whoever finds his life will lose it, and whoever loses his life for my sake will find it.

"Whoever receives you receives me, and whoever receives me receives the one who sent me. Whoever receives a prophet because he is a prophet will receive a prophet's reward, and whoever receives a righteous man because he is a righteous man will receive a righteous man's reward. And whoever gives only a cup of

cold water to one of these little ones
to drink because the little one is
a disciple—amen, I say to you, he
will surely not lose his reward."

965 13TH SUNDAY IN ORDINARY TIME — B

FIRST READING

Wisdom 1:13–15; 2:23–24

God did not make death,
  nor does he rejoice in the
    destruction of the living.
For he fashioned all things that they
    might have being;
  and the creatures of the world
    are wholesome,
and there is not a destructive drug
    among them
  nor any domain of the netherworld
    on earth,
  for justice is undying.

For God formed man to be
  imperishable;
  the image of his own nature he
    made him.
But by the envy of the devil, death
  entered the world,
  and they who belong to his
    company experience it.

RESPONSORIAL PSALM

Psalm 30:2, 4, 5–6, 11, 12, 13

℟. I will praise you, Lord, for you have res-cued me.

Music: Owen Alstott, b. 1947, © 1977, 1990, OCP. All rights reserved.

▶ I will extol you, O LORD, for you drew
    me clear
  and did not let my enemies rejoice
    over me.
O LORD, you brought me up from
    the netherworld;
  you preserved me from among
    those going down into the pit. ℟.

▶ Sing praise to the LORD, you his
    faithful ones,
  and give thanks to his holy name.

For his anger lasts but a moment;
  a lifetime, his good will.
At nightfall, weeping enters in,
  but with the dawn, rejoicing. ℟.

▶ Hear, O LORD, and have pity on me;
  O LORD, be my helper.
You changed my mourning
    into dancing;
  O LORD, my God, forever will I give
    you thanks. ℟.

SECOND READING

2 Corinthians 8:7, 9, 13–15

Brothers and sisters: As you excel
in every respect, in faith, discourse,
knowledge, all earnestness, and in
the love we have for you, may you
excel in this gracious act also.
  For you know the gracious act of our
Lord Jesus Christ, that though he was
rich, for your sake he became poor, so
that by his poverty you might become
rich. Not that others should have relief
while you are burdened, but that as a
matter of equality your abundance at
the present time should supply their
needs, so that their abundance may
also supply your needs, that there
may be equality. As it is written:
  Whoever had much did not
    have more,
  and whoever had little did not
    have less.

GOSPEL ACCLAMATION *cf. 2 Timothy 1:10*

℟. Al - le - lu - ia, al - le - lu - ia, al - le - lu - ia.

Music: Owen Alstott, b. 1947, © 1977, 1990, OCP. All rights reserved. *(Omit if not sung)*

▸ Our Savior Jesus Christ destroyed death
and brought life to light through the Gospel. ℟.

GOSPEL *Mark 5:21–43 or 5:21–24, 35b–43*

(Include bracketed text for Long Form)

When Jesus had crossed again in the boat to the other side, a large crowd gathered around him, and he stayed close to the sea. One of the synagogue officials, named Jairus, came forward. Seeing him he fell at his feet and pleaded earnestly with him, saying, "My daughter is at the point of death. Please, come lay your hands on her that she may get well and live." He went off with him, and a large crowd followed him and pressed upon him.

[There was a woman afflicted with hemorrhages for twelve years. She had suffered greatly at the hands of many doctors and had spent all that she had. Yet she was not helped but only grew worse. She had heard about Jesus and came up behind him in the crowd and touched his cloak. She said, "If I but touch his clothes, I shall be cured." Immediately her flow of blood dried up. She felt in her body that she was healed of her affliction. Jesus, aware at once that power had gone out from him, turned around in the crowd and asked, "Who has touched my clothes?" But his disciples said to Jesus, "You see how the crowd is pressing upon you, and yet you ask, 'Who touched me?'" And he looked around to see who had done it. The woman, realizing what had happened to her, approached in fear and trembling. She fell down before Jesus and told him the whole truth. He said to her, "Daughter, your faith has saved you. Go in peace and be cured of your affliction."]

While he was still speaking, people from the synagogue official's house arrived and said, "Your daughter has died; why trouble the teacher any longer?" Disregarding the message that was reported, Jesus said to the synagogue official, "Do not be afraid; just have faith." He did not allow anyone to accompany him inside except Peter, James, and John, the brother of James. When they arrived at the house of the synagogue official, he caught sight of a commotion, people weeping and wailing loudly. So he went in and said to them, "Why this commotion and weeping? The child is not dead but asleep." And they ridiculed him. Then he put them all out. He took along the child's father and mother and those who were with him and entered the room where the child was. He took the child by the hand and said to her, *"Talitha koum,"* which means, "Little girl, I say to you, arise!" The girl, a child of twelve, arose immediately and walked around. At that they were utterly astounded. He gave strict orders that no one should know this and said that she should be given something to eat.

966 13TH SUNDAY IN ORDINARY TIME — C

FIRST READING

1 Kings 19:16b, 19–21

The LORD said to Elijah: "You shall anoint Elisha, son of Shaphat of Abel-meholah, as prophet to succeed you."

Elijah set out and came upon Elisha, son of Shaphat, as he was plowing with twelve yoke of oxen; he was following the twelfth. Elijah went over to him and threw his cloak over him. Elisha left the oxen, ran after Elijah, and said, "Please, let me kiss my father and mother goodbye, and I will follow you." Elijah answered, "Go back! Have I done anything to you?" Elisha left him and, taking the yoke of oxen, slaughtered them; he used the plowing equipment for fuel to boil their flesh, and gave it to his people to eat. Then Elisha left and followed Elijah as his attendant.

RESPONSORIAL PSALM

Psalm 16:1–2, 5, 7–8, 9–10, 11

℟. You are my in - her - i - tance, O Lord.

Music: Owen Alstott, b. 1947, © 1977, 1990, OCP. All rights reserved.

▸ Keep me, O God, for in you
　　I take refuge;
　I say to the LORD, "My Lord are you.
　O LORD, my allotted portion and
　　my cup,
　　you it is who hold fast my lot." ℟.

▸ I bless the LORD who counsels me;
　　even in the night my heart
　　exhorts me.
　I set the LORD ever before me;
　　with him at my right hand I shall
　　not be disturbed. ℟.

▸ Therefore my heart is glad and my
　　soul rejoices,
　　my body, too, abides in confidence
　because you will not abandon my
　　soul to the netherworld,
　　nor will you suffer your faithful one
　　to undergo corruption. ℟.

▸ You will show me the path to life,
　　fullness of joys in your presence,
　　the delights at your right hand
　　forever. ℟.

SECOND READING

Galatians 5:1, 13–18

Brothers and sisters: For freedom Christ set us free; so stand firm and do not submit again to the yoke of slavery.

For you were called for freedom, brothers and sisters. But do not use this freedom as an opportunity for the flesh; rather, serve one another through love. For the whole law is fulfilled in one statement, namely, *You shall love your neighbor as yourself.* But if you go on biting and devouring one another, beware that you are not consumed by one another.

I say, then: live by the Spirit and you will certainly not gratify the desire of the flesh. For the flesh has desires against the Spirit, and the Spirit against the flesh; these are opposed to each other, so that you may not do what you want. But if you are guided by the Spirit, you are not under the law.

GOSPEL ACCLAMATION   *1 Samuel 3:9; John 6:68c*

℟. Al - le - lu - ia,   al - le - lu - ia,   al - le - lu - ia.

(Omit if not sung)

▶ Speak, Lord, your servant is listening;
  you have the words of everlasting life. ℟.

GOSPEL   *Luke 9:51–62*

When the days for Jesus' being
taken up were fulfilled, he resolutely
determined to journey to Jerusalem,
and he sent messengers ahead of him.
On the way they entered a Samaritan
village to prepare for his reception
there, but they would not welcome
him because the destination of his
journey was Jerusalem. When the
disciples James and John saw this they
asked, "Lord, do you want us to call
down fire from heaven to consume
them?" Jesus turned and rebuked them,
and they journeyed to another village.

As they were proceeding on their
journey someone said to him, "I will
follow you wherever you go." Jesus
answered him, "Foxes have dens and
birds of the sky have nests, but the Son
of Man has nowhere to rest his head."

And to another he said, "Follow me."
But he replied, "Lord, let me go first
and bury my father." But he answered
him, "Let the dead bury their dead. But
you, go and proclaim the kingdom of
God." And another said, "I will follow
you, Lord, but first let me say farewell
to my family at home." To him Jesus
said, "No one who sets a hand to
the plow and looks to what was left
behind is fit for the kingdom of God."

14TH SUNDAY IN ORDINARY TIME — A   967

FIRST READING   *Zechariah 9:9–10*

Thus says the LORD:
  Rejoice heartily, O daughter Zion,
    shout for joy, O daughter
      Jerusalem!
  See, your king shall come to you;
    a just savior is he,
  meek, and riding on an ass,
    on a colt, the foal of an ass.
  He shall banish the chariot
from Ephraim,
  and the horse from Jerusalem;
the warrior's bow shall be banished,
  and he shall proclaim peace to
    the nations.
His dominion shall be from sea to sea,
  and from the River to the ends of
    the earth.

RESPONSORIAL PSALM

Psalm 145:1–2, 8–9, 10–11, 13–14

℟. I will praise your name for ev-er, my king and my God.

Or ℟. **Alleluia.**

▶ I will extol you, O my God and King,
    and I will bless your name forever
     and ever.
  Every day will I bless you,
    and I will praise your name forever
    and ever. ℟.

▶ The LORD is gracious and merciful,
    slow to anger and of great kindness.
  The LORD is good to all
    and compassionate toward all
    his works. ℟.

▶ Let all your works give you thanks,
    O LORD,
    and let your faithful ones bless you.
  Let them discourse of the glory of
    your kingdom
    and speak of your might. ℟.

▶ The LORD is faithful in all his words
    and holy in all his works.
  The LORD lifts up all who are falling
    and raises up all who are
    bowed down. ℟.

SECOND READING

Romans 8:9, 11–13

Brothers and sisters: You are not in the flesh; on the contrary, you are in the spirit, if only the Spirit of God dwells in you. Whoever does not have the Spirit of Christ does not belong to him. If the Spirit of the one who raised Jesus from the dead dwells in you, the one who raised Christ from the dead will give life to your mortal bodies also, through his Spirit that dwells in you. Consequently, brothers and sisters, we are not debtors to the flesh, to live according to the flesh. For if you live according to the flesh, you will die, but if by the Spirit you put to death the deeds of the body, you will live.

GOSPEL ACCLAMATION

cf. Matthew 11:25

℟. Al-le-lu - ia, al-le-lu - ia, al - le - lu - ia.

(Omit if not sung)

▶ Blessed are you, Father, Lord of heaven and earth;
  you have revealed to little ones the mysteries of the kingdom. ℟.

GOSPEL

Matthew 11:25–30

At that time Jesus exclaimed: "I give praise to you, Father, Lord of heaven and earth, for although you have hidden these things from the wise and the learned you have revealed them to little ones. Yes, Father, such has been your gracious will. All things have been handed over to me by my Father. No one knows the Son except the Father, and no one knows the Father except the Son and anyone to whom the Son wishes to reveal him.

"Come to me, all you who labor and are burdened, and I will give you rest. Take my yoke upon you and learn from me, for I am meek and humble of heart; and you will find rest for yourselves. For my yoke is easy, and my burden light."

14TH SUNDAY IN ORDINARY TIME — B 968

FIRST READING

Ezekiel 2:2–5

As the LORD spoke to me, the spirit entered into me and set me on my feet, and I heard the one who was speaking say to me: Son of man, I am sending you to the Israelites, rebels who have rebelled against me; they and their ancestors have revolted against me to this very day. Hard of face and obstinate of heart are they to whom I am sending you. But you shall say to them: Thus says the Lord GOD! And whether they heed or resist—for they are a rebellious house—they shall know that a prophet has been among them.

RESPONSORIAL PSALM

Psalm 123:1–2, 2, 3–4

℟. Our eyes are fixed on the Lord, plead-ing for his mer-cy.

▸ To you I lift up my eyes
   who are enthroned in heaven—
as the eyes of servants
   are on the hands of their masters. ℟.

▸ As the eyes of a maid
   are on the hands of her mistress,
so are our eyes on the LORD, our God,
   till he have pity on us. ℟.

▸ Have pity on us, O LORD, have pity
   on us,
   for we are more than sated
      with contempt;
our souls are more than sated
   with the mockery of the arrogant,
   with the contempt of the proud. ℟.

SECOND READING

2 Corinthians 12:7–10

Brothers and sisters: That I, Paul, might not become too elated, because of the abundance of the revelations, a thorn in the flesh was given to me, an angel of Satan, to beat me, to keep me from being too elated. Three times I begged the Lord about this, that it might leave me, but he said to me, "My grace is sufficient for you, for power is made perfect in weakness." I will rather boast most gladly of my weaknesses, in order that the power of Christ may dwell with me. Therefore, I am content with weaknesses, insults, hardships, persecutions, and constraints, for the sake of Christ; for when I am weak, then I am strong.

GOSPEL ACCLAMATION

cf. Luke 4:18

℟. Al - le - lu - ia, al - le - lu - ia, al - le - lu - ia.

(Omit if not sung)

▸ The Spirit of the Lord is upon me
   for he sent me to bring glad tidings to the poor. ℟.

GOSPEL

Mark 6:1–6

Jesus departed from there and came to his native place, accompanied by his disciples. When the sabbath came he began to teach in the synagogue, and many who heard him were astonished. They said, "Where did this man get all this? What kind of wisdom has been given him? What mighty deeds are wrought by his hands! Is he not the carpenter, the son of Mary, and the brother of James and Joses and Judas and Simon? And are not his sisters here with us?" And they took offense at him. Jesus said to them, "A prophet is not without honor except in his native place and among his own kin and in his own house." So he was not able to perform any mighty deed there, apart from curing a few sick people by laying his hands on them. He was amazed at their lack of faith.

---

969   14TH SUNDAY IN ORDINARY TIME — C

FIRST READING

Isaiah 66:10–14c

Thus says the LORD:
  Rejoice with Jerusalem and be glad
      because of her,
    all you who love her;
  exult, exult with her,
    all you who were mourning
        over her!
Oh, that you may suck fully
    of the milk of her comfort,
that you may nurse with delight
    at her abundant breasts!
    For thus says the LORD:
  Lo, I will spread prosperity over
      Jerusalem like a river,
    and the wealth of the nations like
        an overflowing torrent.

As nurslings, you shall be carried in
      her arms,
    and fondled in her lap;
as a mother comforts her child,
    so will I comfort you;
    in Jerusalem you shall find
        your comfort.

When you see this, your heart
      shall rejoice
    and your bodies flourish like
        the grass;
  the LORD's power shall be known to
      his servants.

RESPONSORIAL PSALM

Psalm 66:1–3, 4–5, 6–7, 16, 20

℟. Let all the earth cry out to God with joy.

Music: Owen Alstott, b. 1947, © 1977, 1990, OCP. All rights reserved.

▶ Shout joyfully to God, all the earth,
    sing praise to the glory of his name;
    proclaim his glorious praise.
  Say to God, "How tremendous are
      your deeds!" ℟.

▶ "Let all on earth worship and sing
      praise to you,
    sing praise to your name!"

Come and see the works of God,
    his tremendous deeds among the
      children of Adam. ℟.

▶ He has changed the sea into dry land;
    through the river they passed
      on foot;
    therefore let us rejoice in him.
  He rules by his might forever. ℟.

▸ Hear now, all you who fear God,
while I declare what he has done
for me.

Blessed be God who refused me not
my prayer or his kindness! ℟.

SECOND READING
Galatians 6:14–18

Brothers and sisters: May I never
boast except in the cross of our
Lord Jesus Christ, through which
the world has been crucified to me,
and I to the world. For neither does
circumcision mean anything, nor
does uncircumcision, but only a new
creation. Peace and mercy be to all
who follow this rule and to the Israel
of God.

From now on, let no one make
troubles for me; for I bear the marks of
Jesus on my body.

The grace of our Lord Jesus Christ be
with your spirit, brothers and sisters.
Amen.

GOSPEL ACCLAMATION
Colossians 3:15a, 16a

℟. Al - le - lu - ia, al - le - lu - ia, al - le - lu - ia.

Music: Owen Alstott, b. 1947, © 1977, 1990, OCP. All rights reserved.

(Omit if not sung)

▸ Let the peace of Christ control your hearts;
let the word of Christ dwell in you richly. ℟.

GOSPEL
Luke 10:1–12, 17–20 or 10:1–9

(Include bracketed text for Long Form)

At that time the Lord appointed
seventy-two others whom he sent
ahead of him in pairs to every town
and place he intended to visit. He said
to them, "The harvest is abundant
but the laborers are few; so ask the
master of the harvest to send out
laborers for his harvest. Go on your
way; behold, I am sending you like
lambs among wolves. Carry no money
bag, no sack, no sandals; and greet
no one along the way. Into whatever
house you enter, first say, 'Peace to
this household.' If a peaceful person
lives there, your peace will rest on him;
but if not, it will return to you. Stay
in the same house and eat and drink
what is offered to you, for the laborer
deserves his payment. Do not move
about from one house to another.
Whatever town you enter and they
welcome you, eat what is set before
you, cure the sick in it and say to them,
'The kingdom of God is at hand for
you.' [Whatever town you enter and
they do not receive you, go out into
the streets and say, 'The dust of your
town that clings to our feet, even that
we shake off against you.' Yet know
this: the kingdom of God is at hand. I
tell you, it will be more tolerable for
Sodom on that day than for that town."

The seventy-two returned rejoicing,
and said, "Lord, even the demons are
subject to us because of your name."
Jesus said, "I have observed Satan fall
like lightning from the sky. Behold, I
have given you the power to 'tread
upon serpents' and scorpions and
upon the full force of the enemy and
nothing will harm you. Nevertheless,
do not rejoice because the spirits are
subject to you, but rejoice because
your names are written in heaven."]

970 15TH SUNDAY IN ORDINARY TIME — A

FIRST READING

Isaiah 55:10–11

Thus says the LORD:
Just as from the heavens
the rain and snow come down
and do not return there
till they have watered the earth,
making it fertile and fruitful,
giving seed to the one who sows

and bread to the one who eats,
so shall my word be
that goes forth from my mouth;
my word shall not return to me void,
but shall do my will,
achieving the end for which I
sent it.

RESPONSORIAL PSALM

Psalm 65:10, 11, 12–13, 14

℟. The seed that falls on good ground will yield a fruit - ful har - vest.

Music: Owen Alstott, b. 1947, © 1977, 1990, OCP. All rights reserved.

▶ You have visited the land and
watered it;
greatly have you enriched it.
God's watercourses are filled;
you have prepared the grain. ℟.

▶ Thus have you prepared the land:
drenching its furrows,
breaking up its clods,
softening it with showers,
blessing its yield. ℟.

▶ You have crowned the year with
your bounty,
and your paths overflow with a
rich harvest;
the untilled meadows overflow
with it,
and rejoicing clothes the hills. ℟.

▶ The fields are garmented with flocks
and the valleys blanketed
with grain.
They shout and sing for joy. ℟.

SECOND READING

Romans 8:18–23

Brothers and sisters: I consider that
the sufferings of this present time are
as nothing compared with the glory
to be revealed for us. For creation
awaits with eager expectation the
revelation of the children of God;
for creation was made subject to
futility, not of its own accord but
because of the one who subjected
it, in hope that creation itself would

be set free from slavery to corruption
and share in the glorious freedom of
the children of God. We know that
all creation is groaning in labor pains
even until now; and not only that, but
we ourselves, who have the firstfruits
of the Spirit, we also groan within
ourselves as we wait for adoption,
the redemption of our bodies.

GOSPEL ACCLAMATION

℟. Al - le - lu - ia, al - le - lu - ia, al - le - lu - ia.

Music: Owen Alstott, b. 1947, © 1977, 1990, OCP. All rights reserved. *(Omit if not sung)*

▶ The seed is the word of God, Christ is the sower.
All who come to him will have life forever. ℟.

GOSPEL   *Matthew 13:1–23 or 13:1–9*

(Include bracketed text for Long Form)

On that day, Jesus went out of the house and sat down by the sea. Such large crowds gathered around him that he got into a boat and sat down, and the whole crowd stood along the shore. And he spoke to them at length in parables, saying: "A sower went out to sow. And as he sowed, some seed fell on the path, and birds came and ate it up. Some fell on rocky ground, where it had little soil. It sprang up at once because the soil was not deep, and when the sun rose it was scorched, and it withered for lack of roots. Some seed fell among thorns, and the thorns grew up and choked it. But some seed fell on rich soil, and produced fruit, a hundred or sixty or thirtyfold. Whoever has ears ought to hear."

[The disciples approached him and said, "Why do you speak to them in parables?" He said to them in reply, "Because knowledge of the mysteries of the kingdom of heaven has been granted to you, but to them it has not been granted. To anyone who has, more will be given and he will grow rich; from anyone who has not, even what he has will be taken away. This is why I speak to them in parables, because *they look but do not see and hear but do not listen or understand.* Isaiah's prophecy is fulfilled in them, which says:

You shall indeed hear but
    not understand,

you shall indeed look but
    never see.
Gross is the heart of this people,
    they will hardly hear with their ears,
    they have closed their eyes,
    lest they see with their eyes
    and hear with their ears
and understand with their hearts and
    be converted,
    and I heal them.

"But blessed are your eyes, because they see, and your ears, because they hear. Amen, I say to you, many prophets and righteous people longed to see what you see but did not see it, and to hear what you hear but did not hear it.

"Hear then the parable of the sower. The seed sown on the path is the one who hears the word of the kingdom without understanding it, and the evil one comes and steals away what was sown in his heart. The seed sown on rocky ground is the one who hears the word and receives it at once with joy. But he has no root and lasts only for a time. When some tribulation or persecution comes because of the word, he immediately falls away. The seed sown among thorns is the one who hears the word, but then worldly anxiety and the lure of riches choke the word and it bears no fruit. But the seed sown on rich soil is the one who hears the word and understands it, who indeed bears fruit and yields a hundred or sixty or thirtyfold."]

15TH SUNDAY IN ORDINARY TIME — B   971

FIRST READING   *Amos 7:12–15*

Amaziah, priest of Bethel, said to Amos, "Off with you, visionary, flee to the land of Judah! There earn your bread by prophesying, but never again prophesy in Bethel; for it is the king's sanctuary and a royal temple." Amos answered Amaziah, "I was no prophet, nor have I belonged to a company of prophets; I was a shepherd and a dresser of sycamores. The LORD took me from following the flock, and said to me, Go, prophesy to my people Israel."

RESPONSORIAL PSALM
Psalm 85:9–10, 11–12, 13–14

℟. Lord, let us see your kind - ness, and grant us your sal - va - tion.

▸ I will hear what God proclaims;
 the LORD—for he proclaims peace.
 Near indeed is his salvation to those
 who fear him,
 glory dwelling in our land. ℟.

▸ Kindness and truth shall meet;
 justice and peace shall kiss.

Truth shall spring out of the earth,
 and justice shall look down
 from heaven. ℟.

▸ The LORD himself will give
 his benefits;
 our land shall yield its increase.
 Justice shall walk before him,
 and prepare the way of his steps. ℟.

SECOND READING
Ephesians 1:3–14 or 1:3–10

(Include bracketed text for Long Form)

Blessed be the God and Father of our Lord Jesus Christ, who has blessed us in Christ with every spiritual blessing in the heavens, as he chose us in him, before the foundation of the world, to be holy and without blemish before him. In love he destined us for adoption to himself through Jesus Christ, in accord with the favor of his will, for the praise of the glory of his grace that he granted us in the beloved. In him we have redemption by his blood, the forgiveness of transgressions, in accord with the riches of his grace that he lavished upon us. In all wisdom and insight, he has made known to us the mystery of his will in accord with his favor that he set forth in him as a plan for the fullness of times, to sum up all things in Christ, in heaven and on earth.

[In him we were also chosen, destined in accord with the purpose of the One who accomplishes all things according to the intention of his will, so that we might exist for the praise of his glory, we who first hoped in Christ. In him you also, who have heard the word of truth, the gospel of your salvation, and have believed in him, were sealed with the promised Holy Spirit, which is the first installment of our inheritance toward redemption as God's possession, to the praise of his glory.]

GOSPEL ACCLAMATION
cf. Ephesians 1:17–18

℟. Al - le - lu - ia, al - le - lu - ia, al - le - lu - ia.

(Omit if not sung)

▸ May the Father of our Lord Jesus Christ
 enlighten the eyes of our hearts,
 that we may know what is the hope
 that belongs to our call. ℟.

GOSPEL

Mark 6:7–13

Jesus summoned the Twelve and began to send them out two by two and gave them authority over unclean spirits. He instructed them to take nothing for the journey but a walking stick—no food, no sack, no money in their belts. They were, however, to wear sandals but not a second tunic. He said to them, "Wherever you enter a house, stay there until you leave. Whatever place does not welcome you or listen to you, leave there and shake the dust off your feet in testimony against them." So they went off and preached repentance. The Twelve drove out many demons, and they anointed with oil many who were sick and cured them.

15TH SUNDAY IN ORDINARY TIME — C 972

FIRST READING

Deuteronomy 30:10–14

Moses said to the people: "If only you would heed the voice of the LORD, your God, and keep his commandments and statutes that are written in this book of the law, when you return to the LORD, your God, with all your heart and all your soul.

"For this command that I enjoin on you today is not too mysterious and remote for you. It is not up in the sky, that you should say, 'Who will go up in the sky to get it for us and tell us of it, that we may carry it out?' Nor is it across the sea, that you should say, 'Who will cross the sea to get it for us and tell us of it, that we may carry it out?' No, it is something very near to you, already in your mouths and in your hearts; you have only to carry it out."

RESPONSORIAL PSALM

Psalm 69:14, 17, 30–31, 33–34, 36, 37

℟. Turn to the Lord in your need, and you will live.

Music: Owen Alstott, b. 1947, © 1977, 1990, OCP. All rights reserved.

▶ I pray to you, O LORD,
　　for the time of your favor, O God!
In your great kindness answer me
　　with your constant help.
Answer me, O LORD, for bounteous is
　　your kindness:
　　in your great mercy turn
　　toward me. ℟.

▶ I am afflicted and in pain;
　　let your saving help, O God,
　　protect me.
I will praise the name of God in song,
　　and I will glorify him with
　　thanksgiving. ℟.

▶ "See, you lowly ones, and be glad;
　　you who seek God, may your
　　hearts revive!
For the LORD hears the poor,
　　and his own who are in bonds he
　　spurns not." ℟.

▶ For God will save Zion
　　and rebuild the cities of Judah.
The descendants of his servants shall
　　inherit it,
　　and those who love his name shall
　　inhabit it. ℟.

Or

RESPONSORIAL PSALM

Psalm 19:8, 9, 10, 11

℟. Your words, Lord, are Spir - it and life.

▶ The law of the LORD is perfect,
  refreshing the soul;
  the decree of the LORD is trustworthy,
  giving wisdom to the simple. ℟.

▶ The precepts of the LORD are right,
  rejoicing the heart;
  the command of the LORD is clear,
  enlightening the eye. ℟.

▶ The fear of the LORD is pure,
  enduring forever;
  the ordinances of the LORD are true,
  all of them just. ℟.

▶ They are more precious than gold,
  than a heap of purest gold;
  sweeter also than syrup
  or honey from the comb. ℟.

SECOND READING

Colossians 1:15–20

Christ Jesus is the image of the
    invisible God,
  the firstborn of all creation.
For in him were created all things in
    heaven and on earth,
  the visible and the invisible,
  whether thrones or dominions or
    principalities or powers;
  all things were created through him
    and for him.
He is before all things,
  and in him all things hold together.
He is the head of the body, the church.

He is the beginning, the firstborn
    from the dead,
  that in all things he himself might
    be preeminent.
For in him all the fullness was
    pleased to dwell,
  and through him to reconcile all
    things for him,
  making peace by the blood of
    his cross
  through him, whether those on
    earth or those in heaven.

GOSPEL ACCLAMATION

cf. John 6:63c, 68c

℟. Al - le - lu - ia, al - le - lu - ia, al - le - lu - ia.

(Omit if not sung)

▶ Your words, Lord, are Spirit and life;
  you have the words of everlasting life. ℟.

GOSPEL

Luke 10:25–37

There was a scholar of the law who
stood up to test Jesus and said,
"Teacher, what must I do to inherit
eternal life?" Jesus said to him, "What
is written in the law? How do you
read it?" He said in reply, *"You shall
love the Lord, your God, with all your
heart, with all your being, with all*
*your strength, and with all your mind,
and your neighbor as yourself."* He
replied to him, "You have answered
correctly; do this and you will live."
    But because he wished to justify
himself, he said to Jesus, "And who
is my neighbor?" Jesus replied, "A
man fell victim to robbers as he went

down from Jerusalem to Jericho. They stripped and beat him and went off leaving him half-dead. A priest happened to be going down that road, but when he saw him, he passed by on the opposite side. Likewise a Levite came to the place, and when he saw him, he passed by on the opposite side. But a Samaritan traveler who came upon him was moved with compassion at the sight. He approached the victim, poured oil and wine over his wounds and bandaged them. Then he lifted him up on his own animal, took him to an inn, and cared for him. The next day he took out two silver coins and gave them to the innkeeper with the instruction, 'Take care of him. If you spend more than what I have given you, I shall repay you on my way back.' Which of these three, in your opinion, was neighbor to the robbers' victim?" He answered, "The one who treated him with mercy." Jesus said to him, "Go and do likewise."

16TH SUNDAY IN ORDINARY TIME — A　　973

FIRST READING
Wisdom 12:13, 16–19

There is no god besides you who
　　have the care of all,
　　that you need show you have not
　　unjustly condemned.
For your might is the source
　　of justice;
　　your mastery over all things makes
　　you lenient to all.
For you show your might when the
　　perfection of your power
　　is disbelieved;
　　and in those who know you, you
　　rebuke temerity.

But though you are master of might,
　　you judge with clemency,
　　and with much lenience you
　　govern us;
　　for power, whenever you will,
　　attends you.
And you taught your people,
　　by these deeds,
　　that those who are just must
　　be kind;
　　and you gave your children good
　　ground for hope
　　that you would permit repentance
　　for their sins.

RESPONSORIAL PSALM
Psalm 86:5–6, 9–10, 15–16

℟. Lord, you are good and for - giv - ing.

Music: Owen Alstott, b. 1947, © 1977, 1990, OCP. All rights reserved.

▶ You, O LORD, are good and forgiving,
　　abounding in kindness to all who
　　call upon you.
　　Hearken, O LORD, to my prayer
　　and attend to the sound of
　　my pleading. ℟.

▶ All the nations you have made
　　shall come
　　and worship you, O LORD,
　　and glorify your name.

For you are great, and you do
　　wondrous deeds;
　　you alone are God. ℟.

▶ You, O LORD, are a God merciful
　　and gracious,
　　slow to anger, abounding in
　　kindness and fidelity.
　　Turn toward me, and have pity on me;
　　give your strength to your
　　servant. ℟.

SECOND READING
Romans 8:26–27

Brothers and sisters: The Spirit comes to the aid of our weakness; for we do not know how to pray as we ought, but the Spirit himself intercedes with inexpressible groanings. And the one who searches hearts knows what is the intention of the Spirit, because he intercedes for the holy ones according to God's will.

GOSPEL ACCLAMATION
cf. Matthew 11:25

℟. Al - le - lu - ia, al - le - lu - ia, al - le - lu - ia.

(Omit if not sung)

▶ Blessed are you, Father, Lord of heaven and earth;
  you have revealed to little ones the mysteries of the kingdom. ℟.

GOSPEL
Matthew 13:24–43 or 13:24–30

(Include bracketed text for Long Form)

Jesus proposed another parable to the crowds, saying: "The kingdom of heaven may be likened to a man who sowed good seed in his field. While everyone was asleep his enemy came and sowed weeds all through the wheat, and then went off. When the crop grew and bore fruit, the weeds appeared as well. The slaves of the householder came to him and said, 'Master, did you not sow good seed in your field? Where have the weeds come from?' He answered, 'An enemy has done this.' His slaves said to him, 'Do you want us to go and pull them up?' He replied, 'No, if you pull up the weeds you might uproot the wheat along with them. Let them grow together until harvest; then at harvest time I will say to the harvesters, "First collect the weeds and tie them in bundles for burning; but gather the wheat into my barn."'"

[He proposed another parable to them. "The kingdom of heaven is like a mustard seed that a person took and sowed in a field. It is the smallest of all the seeds, yet when full-grown it is the largest of plants. It becomes a large bush, and the 'birds of the sky come and dwell in its branches.'"

He spoke to them another parable. "The kingdom of heaven is like yeast that a woman took and mixed with three measures of wheat flour until the whole batch was leavened."

All these things Jesus spoke to the crowds in parables. He spoke to them only in parables, to fulfill what had been said through the prophet:
I will open my mouth in parables,
  I will announce what has lain
    hidden from the foundation of
    the world.

Then, dismissing the crowds, he went into the house. His disciples approached him and said, "Explain to us the parable of the weeds in the field." He said in reply, "He who sows good seed is the Son of Man, the field is the world, the good seed the children of the kingdom. The weeds are the children of the evil one, and the enemy who sows them is the devil. The harvest is the end of the age, and the harvesters are angels. Just as weeds are collected and burned up with fire, so will it be at the end of the age. The Son of Man will send his angels, and they will collect out of his kingdom all who cause others to sin and all evildoers. They will throw them into the fiery furnace, where there will be wailing and grinding of teeth. Then the righteous will shine like the sun in the kingdom of their Father. Whoever has ears ought to hear."]

16TH SUNDAY IN ORDINARY TIME — B 974

FIRST READING

Jeremiah 23:1–6

Woe to the shepherds who mislead and scatter the flock of my pasture, says the LORD. Therefore, thus says the LORD, the God of Israel, against the shepherds who shepherd my people: You have scattered my sheep and driven them away. You have not cared for them, but I will take care to punish your evil deeds. I myself will gather the remnant of my flock from all the lands to which I have driven them and bring them back to their meadow; there they shall increase and multiply. I will appoint shepherds for them who will shepherd them so that they need no longer fear and tremble; and none shall be missing, says the LORD.

> Behold, the days are coming, says
> the LORD,
> when I will raise up a righteous
> shoot to David;
> as king he shall reign and
> govern wisely,
> he shall do what is just and right in
> the land.
> In his days Judah shall be saved,
> Israel shall dwell in security.
> This is the name they give him:
> "The LORD our justice."

RESPONSORIAL PSALM

Psalm 23:1–3, 3–4, 5, 6

℟. The Lord is my shep-herd; there is noth-ing I shall want.

Music: Owen Alstott, b. 1947, © 1977, 1990, OCP. All rights reserved.

▸ The LORD is my shepherd; I shall
> not want.
> In verdant pastures he gives
> me repose;
> beside restful waters he leads me;
> he refreshes my soul. ℟.

▸ He guides me in right paths
> for his name's sake.
> Even though I walk in the dark valley
> I fear no evil; for you are at my side
> with your rod and your staff
> that give me courage. ℟.

▸ You spread the table before me
> in the sight of my foes;
> you anoint my head with oil;
> my cup overflows. ℟.

▸ Only goodness and kindness
> follow me
> all the days of my life;
> and I shall dwell in the house
> of the LORD
> for years to come. ℟.

SECOND READING

Ephesians 2:13–18

Brothers and sisters: In Christ Jesus you who once were far off have become near by the blood of Christ.

For he is our peace, he who made both one and broke down the dividing wall of enmity, through his flesh, abolishing the law with its commandments and legal claims, that he might create in himself one new person in place of the two, thus establishing peace, and might reconcile both with God, in one body, through the cross, putting that enmity to death by it. He came and preached peace to you who were far off and peace to those who were near, for through him we both have access in one Spirit to the Father.

GOSPEL ACCLAMATION
John 10:27

℟. Al - le - lu - ia, al - le - lu - ia, al - le - lu - ia.

Music: Owen Alstott, b. 1947, © 1977, 1990, OCP. All rights reserved. *(Omit if not sung)*

▸ My sheep hear my voice, says the Lord; I know them, and they follow me. ℟.

GOSPEL
Mark 6:30–34

The apostles gathered together with Jesus and reported all they had done and taught. He said to them, "Come away by yourselves to a deserted place and rest a while." People were coming and going in great numbers, and they had no opportunity even to eat. So they went off in the boat by themselves to a deserted place.

People saw them leaving and many came to know about it. They hastened there on foot from all the towns and arrived at the place before them.

When he disembarked and saw the vast crowd, his heart was moved with pity for them, for they were like sheep without a shepherd; and he began to teach them many things.

---

975   16TH SUNDAY IN ORDINARY TIME — C

FIRST READING
Genesis 18:1–10a

The LORD appeared to Abraham by the terebinth of Mamre, as he sat in the entrance of his tent, while the day was growing hot. Looking up, Abraham saw three men standing nearby. When he saw them, he ran from the entrance of the tent to greet them; and bowing to the ground, he said: "Sir, if I may ask you this favor, please do not go on past your servant. Let some water be brought, that you may bathe your feet, and then rest yourselves under the tree. Now that you have come this close to your servant, let me bring you a little food, that you may refresh yourselves; and afterward you may go on your way." The men replied,

"Very well, do as you have said."

Abraham hastened into the tent and told Sarah, "Quick, three measures of fine flour! Knead it and make rolls." He ran to the herd, picked out a tender, choice steer, and gave it to a servant, who quickly prepared it. Then Abraham got some curds and milk, as well as the steer that had been prepared, and set these before the three men; and he waited on them under the tree while they ate.

They asked Abraham, "Where is your wife Sarah?" He replied, "There in the tent." One of them said, "I will surely return to you about this time next year, and Sarah will then have a son."

RESPONSORIAL PSALM

Psalm 15:2–3, 3–4, 5

℟. He who does jus-tice will live in the pres-ence of the Lord.

▶ One who walks blamelessly and
    does justice;
  who thinks the truth in his heart
  and slanders not with his tongue. ℟.

▶ Who harms not his fellow man,
  nor takes up a reproach against
    his neighbor;

by whom the reprobate is despised,
  while he honors those who fear
    the LORD. ℟.

▶ Who lends not his money at usury
  and accepts no bribe against
    the innocent.
One who does these things
  shall never be disturbed. ℟.

SECOND READING

Colossians 1:24–28

Brothers and sisters: Now I rejoice in my sufferings for your sake, and in my flesh I am filling up what is lacking in the afflictions of Christ on behalf of his body, which is the church, of which I am a minister in accordance with God's stewardship given to me to bring to completion for you the word of God, the mystery hidden from ages and from generations past.

But now it has been manifested to his holy ones, to whom God chose to make known the riches of the glory of this mystery among the Gentiles; it is Christ in you, the hope for glory. It is he whom we proclaim, admonishing everyone and teaching everyone with all wisdom, that we may present everyone perfect in Christ.

GOSPEL ACCLAMATION

cf. Luke 8:15

℟. Al - le - lu - ia, al - le - lu - ia, al - le - lu - ia.

(Omit if not sung)

▶ Blessed are they who have kept the word with a generous heart
  and yield a harvest through perseverance. ℟.

GOSPEL

Luke 10:38–42

Jesus entered a village where a woman whose name was Martha welcomed him. She had a sister named Mary who sat beside the Lord at his feet listening to him speak. Martha, burdened with much serving, came to him and said, "Lord, do you not care that my sister has left me by myself to do the serving? Tell her to help me." The Lord said to her in reply, "Martha, Martha, you are anxious and worried about many things. There is need of only one thing. Mary has chosen the better part and it will not be taken from her."

976 17TH SUNDAY IN ORDINARY TIME — A

FIRST READING

1 Kings 3:5, 7–12

The LORD appeared to Solomon in a dream at night. God said, "Ask something of me and I will give it to you." Solomon answered: "O LORD, my God, you have made me, your servant, king to succeed my father David; but I am a mere youth, not knowing at all how to act. I serve you in the midst of the people whom you have chosen, a people so vast that it cannot be numbered or counted. Give your servant, therefore, an understanding heart to judge your people and to distinguish right from wrong. For who is able to govern this vast people of yours?"

The LORD was pleased that Solomon made this request. So God said to him: "Because you have asked for this—not for a long life for yourself, nor for riches, nor for the life of your enemies, but for understanding so that you may know what is right—I do as you requested. I give you a heart so wise and understanding that there has never been anyone like you up to now, and after you there will come no one to equal you."

RESPONSORIAL PSALM

Psalm 119:57, 72, 76–77, 127–128, 129–130

℟. Lord, I love your com - mands.

Music: Owen Alstott, b. 1947, © 1977, 1990, OCP. All rights reserved.

▶ I have said, O LORD, that my part
  is to keep your words.
The law of your mouth is to me
    more precious
  than thousands of gold and
    silver pieces. ℟.

▶ Let your kindness comfort me
  according to your promise to
  your servants.
Let your compassion come to me that
  I may live,
  for your law is my delight. ℟.

▶ For I love your commands
  more than gold, however fine.
For in all your precepts I go forward;
  every false way I hate. ℟.

▶ Wonderful are your decrees;
  therefore I observe them.
The revelation of your words
    sheds light,
  giving understanding to the
    simple. ℟.

SECOND READING

Romans 8:28–30

Brothers and sisters: We know that all things work for good for those who love God, who are called according to his purpose. For those he foreknew he also predestined to be conformed to the image of his Son, so that he might be the firstborn among many brothers and sisters. And those he predestined he also called; and those he called he also justified; and those he justified he also glorified.

GOSPEL ACCLAMATION

cf. Matthew 11:25

℟. Al - le - lu - ia, al - le - lu - ia, al - le - lu - ia.

(Omit if not sung)

▶ Blessed are you, Father, Lord of heaven and earth;
for you have revealed to little ones the mysteries of the kingdom. ℟.

GOSPEL

Matthew 13:44–52 or 13:44–46

(Include bracketed text for Long Form)

Jesus said to his disciples: "The kingdom of heaven is like a treasure buried in a field, which a person finds and hides again, and out of joy goes and sells all that he has and buys that field. Again, the kingdom of heaven is like a merchant searching for fine pearls. When he finds a pearl of great price, he goes and sells all that he has and buys it. [Again, the kingdom of heaven is like a net thrown into the sea, which collects fish of every kind. When it is full they haul it ashore and sit down to put what is good into buckets. What is bad they throw away. Thus it will be at the end of the age. The angels will go out and separate the wicked from the righteous and throw them into the fiery furnace, where there will be wailing and grinding of teeth.

"Do you understand all these things?" They answered, "Yes." And he replied, "Then every scribe who has been instructed in the kingdom of heaven is like the head of a household who brings from his storeroom both the new and the old."]

17TH SUNDAY IN ORDINARY TIME — B   977

FIRST READING

2 Kings 4:42–44

A man came from Baal-shalishah bringing to Elisha, the man of God, twenty barley loaves made from the firstfruits, and fresh grain in the ear. Elisha said, "Give it to the people to eat." But his servant objected, "How can I set this before a hundred people?" Elisha insisted, "Give it to the people to eat. For thus says the LORD, 'They shall eat and there shall be some left over.'" And when they had eaten, there was some left over, as the LORD had said.

RESPONSORIAL PSALM

Psalm 145:10–11, 15–16, 17–18

℟. The hand of the Lord feeds us; he an-swers all our needs.

▶ Let all your works give you thanks,
O LORD,
and let your faithful ones bless you.
Let them discourse of the glory of
your kingdom
and speak of your might. ℟.

▶ The eyes of all look hopefully to you,
and you give them their food in
due season;
you open your hand
and satisfy the desire of every
living thing. ℟.

℟. **The hand of the Lord feeds us; he answers all our needs.**

▶ The LORD is just in all his ways
    and holy in all his works.
The LORD is near to all who call
      upon him,
    to all who call upon him in truth. ℟.

SECOND READING

Ephesians 4:1–6

Brothers and sisters: I, a prisoner
for the Lord, urge you to live in
a manner worthy of the call you
have received, with all humility and
gentleness, with patience, bearing
with one another through love,
striving to preserve the unity of the
spirit through the bond of peace: one
body and one Spirit, as you were also
called to the one hope of your call;
one Lord, one faith, one baptism;
one God and Father of all, who is
over all and through all and in all.

GOSPEL ACCLAMATION

Luke 7:16

℟. Al - le - lu - ia,   al - le - lu - ia,   al - le - lu - ia.

(Omit if not sung)

▶ A great prophet has risen in our midst.
  God has visited his people. ℟.

GOSPEL

John 6:1–15

Jesus went across the Sea of Galilee.
A large crowd followed him, because
they saw the signs he was performing
on the sick. Jesus went up on the
mountain, and there he sat down
with his disciples. The Jewish feast of
Passover was near. When Jesus raised
his eyes and saw that a large crowd
was coming to him, he said to Philip,
"Where can we buy enough food
for them to eat?" He said this to test
him, because he himself knew what
he was going to do. Philip answered
him, "Two hundred days' wages worth
of food would not be enough for
each of them to have a little." One of
his disciples, Andrew, the brother of
Simon Peter, said to him, "There is a
boy here who has five barley loaves
and two fish; but what good are these
for so many?" Jesus said, "Have the
people recline." Now there was a
great deal of grass in that place. So
the men reclined, about five thousand
in number. Then Jesus took the
loaves, gave thanks, and distributed
them to those who were reclining,
and also as much of the fish as they
wanted. When they had had their fill,
he said to his disciples, "Gather the
fragments left over, so that nothing
will be wasted." So they collected
them, and filled twelve wicker baskets
with fragments from the five barley
loaves that had been more than they
could eat. When the people saw the
sign he had done, they said, "This
is truly the Prophet, the one who is
to come into the world." Since Jesus
knew that they were going to come
and carry him off to make him king, he
withdrew again to the mountain alone.

17th Sunday in Ordinary Time — C   978

First Reading
Genesis 18:20–32

In those days, the LORD said: "The outcry against Sodom and Gomorrah is so great, and their sin so grave, that I must go down and see whether or not their actions fully correspond to the cry against them that comes to me. I mean to find out."

While Abraham's visitors walked on farther toward Sodom, the LORD remained standing before Abraham. Then Abraham drew nearer and said: "Will you sweep away the innocent with the guilty? Suppose there were fifty innocent people in the city; would you wipe out the place, rather than spare it for the sake of the fifty innocent people within it? Far be it from you to do such a thing, to make the innocent die with the guilty so that the innocent and the guilty would be treated alike! Should not the judge of all the world act with justice?" The LORD replied, "If I find fifty innocent people in the city of Sodom, I will spare the whole place for their sake." Abraham spoke up again: "See how I am presuming to speak to my Lord, though I am but dust and ashes! What if there are five less than fifty innocent people? Will you destroy the whole city because of those five?" He answered, "I will not destroy it, if I find forty-five there." But Abraham persisted, saying, "What if only forty are found there?" He replied, "I will forbear doing it for the sake of the forty." Then Abraham said, "Let not my Lord grow impatient if I go on. What if only thirty are found there?" He replied, "I will forbear doing it if I can find but thirty there." Still Abraham went on, "Since I have thus dared to speak to my Lord, what if there are no more than twenty?" The LORD answered, "I will not destroy it, for the sake of the twenty." But he still persisted: "Please, let not my Lord grow angry if I speak up this last time. What if there are at least ten there?" He replied, "For the sake of those ten, I will not destroy it."

Responsorial Psalm
Psalm 138:1–2, 2–3, 6–7, 7–8

℟. Lord, on the day I called for help, you answered me.

Music: Owen Alstott, b. 1947, © 1977, 1990, OCP. All rights reserved.

▶ I will give thanks to you, O LORD, with
　　all my heart,
　　for you have heard the words of
　　my mouth;
　　in the presence of the angels I will
　　sing your praise;
I will worship at your holy temple
　　and give thanks to your name. ℟.

▶ Because of your kindness and
　　your truth;
　　for you have made great above
　　all things
　　your name and your promise.
When I called you answered me;
　　you built up strength within me. ℟.

▶ The LORD is exalted, yet the lowly
　　he sees,
　　and the proud he knows from afar.
Though I walk amid distress, you
　　preserve me;
　　against the anger of my enemies
　　you raise your hand. ℟.

▶ Your right hand saves me.
　　The LORD will complete what he
　　has done for me;
your kindness, O LORD,
　　endures forever;
　　forsake not the work of
　　your hands. ℟.

SECOND READING

Colossians 2:12–14

Brothers and sisters: You were buried with him in baptism, in which you were also raised with him through faith in the power of God, who raised him from the dead. And even when you were dead in transgressions and the uncircumcision of your flesh, he brought you to life along with him, having forgiven us all our transgressions; obliterating the bond against us, with its legal claims, which was opposed to us, he also removed it from our midst, nailing it to the cross.

GOSPEL ACCLAMATION

Romans 8:15bc

℟. Al - le - lu - ia,   al - le - lu - ia,   al - le - lu - ia.

Music: Owen Alstott, b. 1947, © 1977, 1990, OCP. All rights reserved.   *(Omit if not sung)*

▶ You have received a Spirit of adoption, through which we cry, Abba, Father. ℟.

GOSPEL

Luke 11:1–13

Jesus was praying in a certain place, and when he had finished, one of his disciples said to him, "Lord, teach us to pray just as John taught his disciples." He said to them, "When you pray, say:

Father, hallowed be your name,
   your kingdom come.
    Give us each day our daily bread
    and forgive us our sins
     for we ourselves forgive everyone
      in debt to us,
     and do not subject us to the
      final test."

And he said to them, "Suppose one of you has a friend to whom he goes at midnight and says, 'Friend, lend me three loaves of bread, for a friend of mine has arrived at my house from a journey and I have nothing to offer him,' and he says in reply from within, 'Do not bother me; the door has already been locked and my children and I are already in bed. I cannot get up to give you anything.' I tell you, if he does not get up to give the visitor the loaves because of their friendship, he will get up to give him whatever he needs because of his persistence.

"And I tell you, ask and you will receive; seek and you will find; knock and the door will be opened to you. For everyone who asks, receives; and the one who seeks, finds; and to the one who knocks, the door will be opened. What father among you would hand his son a snake when he asks for a fish? Or hand him a scorpion when he asks for an egg? If you then, who are wicked, know how to give good gifts to your children, how much more will the Father in heaven give the Holy Spirit to those who ask him?"

---

979   18TH SUNDAY IN ORDINARY TIME — A

FIRST READING

Isaiah 55:1–3

Thus says the LORD:
  All you who are thirsty,
   come to the water!
  You who have no money,
   come, receive grain and eat;

Come, without paying and
   without cost,
  drink wine and milk!
Why spend your money for what is
   not bread;

your wages for what fails to satisfy?
Heed me, and you shall eat well,
  you shall delight in rich fare.
Come to me heedfully,

listen, that you may have life.
I will renew with you the
  everlasting covenant,
the benefits assured to David.

RESPONSORIAL PSALM
Psalm 145:8–9, 15–16, 17–18

℟. The hand of the Lord feeds us; he an-swers all our needs.

Music: Owen Alstott, b. 1947, © 1977, 1990, OCP. All rights reserved.

▶ The LORD is gracious and merciful,
    slow to anger and of
    great kindness.
  The LORD is good to all
    and compassionate toward all
    his works. ℟.

▶ The eyes of all look hopefully to you,
    and you give them their food in
    due season;

you open your hand
  and satisfy the desire of every
  living thing. ℟.

▶ The LORD is just in all his ways
    and holy in all his works.
  The LORD is near to all who call
    upon him,
  to all who call upon him in truth. ℟.

SECOND READING
Romans 8:35, 37–39

Brothers and sisters: What will separate
us from the love of Christ? Will anguish,
or distress, or persecution, or famine,
or nakedness, or peril, or the sword?
No, in all these things we conquer
overwhelmingly through him who
loved us. For I am convinced that

neither death, nor life, nor angels, nor
principalities, nor present things, nor
future things, nor powers, nor height,
nor depth, nor any other creature
will be able to separate us from the
love of God in Christ Jesus our Lord.

GOSPEL ACCLAMATION
Matthew 4:4b

℟. Al - le - lu - ia, al - le - lu - ia, al - le - lu - ia.

Music: Owen Alstott, b. 1947, © 1977, 1990, OCP. All rights reserved.
(Omit if not sung)

▶ One does not live on bread alone,
  but on every word that comes forth from the mouth of God. ℟.

GOSPEL
Matthew 14:13–21

When Jesus heard of the death of John
the Baptist, he withdrew in a boat
to a deserted place by himself. The
crowds heard of this and followed him
on foot from their towns. When he
disembarked and saw the vast crowd,
his heart was moved with pity for them,
and he cured their sick. When it was
evening, the disciples approached him

and said, "This is a deserted place and
it is already late; dismiss the crowds
so that they can go to the villages and
buy food for themselves." Jesus said
to them, "There is no need for them
to go away; give them some food
yourselves." But they said to him, "Five
loaves and two fish are all we have
here." Then he said, "Bring them here

to me," and he ordered the crowds to sit down on the grass. Taking the five loaves and the two fish, and looking up to heaven, he said the blessing, broke the loaves, and gave them to the disciples, who in turn gave them to the crowds. They all ate and were satisfied, and they picked up the fragments left over—twelve wicker baskets full. Those who ate were about five thousand men, not counting women and children.

980   18TH SUNDAY IN ORDINARY TIME — B

FIRST READING   Exodus 16:2–4, 12–15

The whole Israelite community grumbled against Moses and Aaron. The Israelites said to them, "Would that we had died at the LORD's hand in the land of Egypt, as we sat by our fleshpots and ate our fill of bread! But you had to lead us into this desert to make the whole community die of famine!"

Then the LORD said to Moses, "I will now rain down bread from heaven for you. Each day the people are to go out and gather their daily portion; thus will I test them, to see whether they follow my instructions or not.

"I have heard the grumbling of the Israelites. Tell them: In the evening twilight you shall eat flesh, and in the morning you shall have your fill of bread, so that you may know that I, the LORD, am your God."

In the evening quail came up and covered the camp. In the morning a dew lay all about the camp, and when the dew evaporated, there on the surface of the desert were fine flakes like hoarfrost on the ground. On seeing it, the Israelites asked one another, "What is this?" for they did not know what it was. But Moses told them, "This is the bread that the LORD has given you to eat."

RESPONSORIAL PSALM   Psalm 78:3–4, 23–24, 25, 54

℟. The Lord gave them [bread,] bread from heav - en.

Music: Owen Alstott, b. 1947, © 1977, 1990, OCP. All rights reserved.

▶ What we have heard and know,
  and what our fathers have declared
    to us,
  we will declare to the generation
    to come,
    the glorious deeds of the LORD and
      his strength
    and the wonders that he
      wrought. ℟.

▶ He commanded the skies above
  and opened the doors of heaven;
  he rained manna upon them for food
  and gave them heavenly bread. ℟.

▶ Man ate the bread of angels,
  food he sent them in abundance.
  And he brought them to his
    holy land,
    to the mountains his right hand
      had won. ℟.

SECOND READING

Ephesians 4:17, 20–24

Brothers and sisters: I declare and testify in the Lord that you must no longer live as the Gentiles do, in the futility of their minds; that is not how you learned Christ, assuming that you have heard of him and were taught in him, as truth is in Jesus, that you should put away the old self of your former way of life, corrupted through deceitful desires, and be renewed in the spirit of your minds, and put on the new self, created in God's way in righteousness and holiness of truth.

GOSPEL ACCLAMATION

Matthew 4:4b

℟. Al - le - lu - ia, al - le - lu - ia, al - le - lu - ia.

Music: Owen Alstott, b. 1947, © 1977, 1990, OCP. All rights reserved.   *(Omit if not sung)*

▶ One does not live on bread alone,
but on every word that comes forth from the mouth of God. ℟.

GOSPEL

John 6:24–35

When the crowd saw that neither Jesus nor his disciples were there, they themselves got into boats and came to Capernaum looking for Jesus. And when they found him across the sea they said to him, "Rabbi, when did you get here?" Jesus answered them and said, "Amen, amen, I say to you, you are looking for me not because you saw signs but because you ate the loaves and were filled. Do not work for food that perishes but for the food that endures for eternal life, which the Son of Man will give you. For on him the Father, God, has set his seal." So they said to him, "What can we do to accomplish the works of God?" Jesus answered and said to them, "This is the work of God, that you believe in the one he sent." So they said to him, "What sign can you do, that we may see and believe in you? What can you do? Our ancestors ate manna in the desert, as it is written:

*He gave them bread from heaven
to eat."*

So Jesus said to them, "Amen, amen, I say to you, it was not Moses who gave the bread from heaven; my Father gives you the true bread from heaven. For the bread of God is that which comes down from heaven and gives life to the world."

So they said to him, "Sir, give us this bread always." Jesus said to them, "I am the bread of life; whoever comes to me will never hunger, and whoever believes in me will never thirst."

18TH SUNDAY IN ORDINARY TIME — C   981

FIRST READING

Ecclesiastes 1:2; 2:21–23

Vanity of vanities, says Qoheleth, vanity of vanities! All things are vanity!

Here is one who has labored with wisdom and knowledge and skill, and yet to another who has not labored over it, he must leave property. This also is vanity and a great misfortune. For what profit comes to man from all the toil and anxiety of heart with which he has labored under the sun? All his days sorrow and grief are his occupation; even at night his mind is not at rest. This also is vanity.

RESPONSORIAL PSALM

Psalm 90:3–4, 5–6, 12–13, 14 & 17

℟. If to-day you hear his voice, hard-en not your hearts.

▸ You turn man back to dust,
  saying, "Return, O children
  of men."
For a thousand years in your sight
  are as yesterday, now that it is past,
  or as a watch of the night. ℟.

▸ You make an end of them in
  their sleep;
  the next morning they are like the
  changing grass,
which at dawn springs up anew,
  but by evening wilts and fades. ℟.

▸ Teach us to number our days aright,
  that we may gain wisdom of heart.
Return, O LORD! How long?
  Have pity on your servants! ℟.

▸ Fill us at daybreak with your kindness,
  that we may shout for joy and
  gladness all our days.
And may the gracious care of the
  LORD our God be ours;
  prosper the work of our hands
  for us!
  Prosper the work of our hands! ℟.

SECOND READING

Colossians 3:1–5, 9–11

Brothers and sisters: If you were raised with Christ, seek what is above, where Christ is seated at the right hand of God. Think of what is above, not of what is on earth. For you have died, and your life is hidden with Christ in God. When Christ your life appears, then you too will appear with him in glory.

Put to death, then, the parts of you that are earthly: immorality, impurity, passion, evil desire, and the greed that is idolatry. Stop lying to one another, since you have taken off the old self with its practices and have put on the new self, which is being renewed, for knowledge, in the image of its creator. Here there is not Greek and Jew, circumcision and uncircumcision, barbarian, Scythian, slave, free; but Christ is all and in all.

GOSPEL ACCLAMATION

Matthew 5:3

℟. Al-le-lu - ia, al-le-lu - ia, al-le-lu - ia.

(Omit if not sung)

▸ Blessed are the poor in spirit,
  for theirs is the kingdom of heaven. ℟.

GOSPEL

Luke 12:13–21

Someone in the crowd said to Jesus, "Teacher, tell my brother to share the inheritance with me." He replied to him, "Friend, who appointed me as your judge and arbitrator?" Then he said to the crowd, "Take care to guard against all greed, for though one may be rich, one's life does not consist of possessions."

Then he told them a parable. "There was a rich man whose land produced a bountiful harvest. He asked himself, 'What shall I do, for I do not have space to store my harvest?' And he said, 'This is what I shall do: I shall tear down my barns and build larger ones. There I shall store all my grain and other goods and I shall say to myself, "Now as for you, you have so many good things stored up for many years, rest, eat, drink, be merry!"' But God said to him, 'You fool, this night your life will be demanded of you; and the things you have prepared, to whom will they belong?' Thus will it be for all who store up treasure for themselves but are not rich in what matters to God."

19TH SUNDAY IN ORDINARY TIME — A   982

FIRST READING
1 Kings 19:9a, 11–13a

At the mountain of God, Horeb, Elijah came to a cave where he took shelter. Then the LORD said to him, "Go outside and stand on the mountain before the LORD; the LORD will be passing by." A strong and heavy wind was rending the mountains and crushing rocks before the LORD—but the LORD was not in the wind. After the wind there was an earthquake—but the LORD was not in the earthquake. After the earthquake there was fire— but the LORD was not in the fire. After the fire there was a tiny whispering sound. When he heard this, Elijah hid his face in his cloak and went and stood at the entrance of the cave.

RESPONSORIAL PSALM
Psalm 85:9, 10, 11–12, 13–14

℟. Lord, let us see your kind - ness, and grant us your sal - va - tion.

Music: Owen Alstott, b. 1947, © 1977, 1990, OCP. All rights reserved.

▶ I will hear what God proclaims;
   the LORD—for he proclaims peace.
Near indeed is his salvation to those
      who fear him,
   glory dwelling in our land. ℟.

▶ Kindness and truth shall meet;
   justice and peace shall kiss.

Truth shall spring out of the earth,
   and justice shall look down from
      heaven. ℟.

▶ The LORD himself will give
      his benefits;
   our land shall yield its increase.
Justice shall walk before him,
   and prepare the way of his steps. ℟.

SECOND READING
Romans 9:1–5

Brothers and sisters: I speak the truth in Christ, I do not lie; my conscience joins with the Holy Spirit in bearing me witness that I have great sorrow and constant anguish in my heart. For I could wish that I myself were accursed and cut off from Christ for the sake of my own people, my kindred according to the flesh. They are Israelites; theirs the adoption, the glory, the covenants, the giving of the law, the worship, and the promises; theirs the patriarchs, and from them, according to the flesh, is the Christ, who is over all, God blessed forever. Amen.

GOSPEL ACCLAMATION

cf. Psalm 130:5

℟. Al - le - lu - ia, al - le - lu - ia, al - le - lu - ia.

Music: Owen Alstott, b. 1947, © 1977, 1990, OCP. All rights reserved.   *(Omit if not sung)*

▶ I wait for the Lord;
my soul waits for his word. ℟.

GOSPEL

Matthew 14:22–33

After he had fed the people, Jesus made the disciples get into a boat and precede him to the other side, while he dismissed the crowds. After doing so, he went up on the mountain by himself to pray. When it was evening he was there alone. Meanwhile the boat, already a few miles offshore, was being tossed about by the waves, for the wind was against it. During the fourth watch of the night, he came toward them walking on the sea. When the disciples saw him walking on the sea they were terrified. "It is a ghost," they said, and they cried out in fear. At once Jesus spoke to them, "Take courage, it is I; do not be afraid." Peter said to him in reply, "Lord, if it is you, command me to come to you on the water." He said, "Come." Peter got out of the boat and began to walk on the water toward Jesus. But when he saw how strong the wind was he became frightened; and, beginning to sink, he cried out, "Lord, save me!" Immediately Jesus stretched out his hand and caught Peter, and said to him, "O you of little faith, why did you doubt?" After they got into the boat, the wind died down. Those who were in the boat did him homage, saying, "Truly, you are the Son of God."

---

983   19TH SUNDAY IN ORDINARY TIME — B

FIRST READING

1 Kings 19:4–8

Elijah went a day's journey into the desert, until he came to a broom tree and sat beneath it. He prayed for death, saying: "This is enough, O LORD! Take my life, for I am no better than my fathers." He lay down and fell asleep under the broom tree, but then an angel touched him and ordered him to get up and eat. Elijah looked and there at his head was a hearth cake and a jug of water. After he ate and drank, he lay down again, but the angel of the LORD came back a second time, touched him, and ordered, "Get up and eat, else the journey will be too long for you!" He got up, ate, and drank; then strengthened by that food, he walked forty days and forty nights to the mountain of God, Horeb.

RESPONSORIAL PSALM

Psalm 34:2–3, 4–5, 6–7, 8–9

℟. Taste and see the good - ness of the Lord.

Music: Owen Alstott, b. 1947, © 1977, 1990, OCP. All rights reserved.

▶ I will bless the LORD at all times;
   his praise shall be ever in
     my mouth.
Let my soul glory in the LORD;
   the lowly will hear me and
     be glad. ℟.

▶ Glorify the LORD with me,
   let us together extol his name.
I sought the LORD, and he
     answered me
   and delivered me from all
     my fears. ℟.

▶ Look to him that you may be radiant
   with joy,
   and your faces may not blush
     with shame.
When the afflicted man called out,
     the LORD heard,
   and from all his distress he
     saved him. ℟.

▶ The angel of the LORD encamps
   around those who fear him and
   delivers them.
Taste and see how good the LORD is;
   blessed the man who takes refuge
   in him. ℟.

SECOND READING
Ephesians 4:30—5:2

Brothers and sisters: Do not grieve the Holy Spirit of God, with which you were sealed for the day of redemption. All bitterness, fury, anger, shouting, and reviling must be removed from you, along with all malice. And be kind to one another, compassionate, forgiving one another as God has forgiven you in Christ.

   So be imitators of God, as beloved children, and live in love, as Christ loved us and handed himself over for us as a sacrificial offering to God for a fragrant aroma.

GOSPEL ACCLAMATION
John 6:51

℟. Al - le - lu - ia, al - le - lu - ia, al - le - lu - ia.

Music: Owen Alstott, b. 1947, © 1977, 1990, OCP. All rights reserved.   *(Omit if not sung)*

▶ I am the living bread that came down from heaven, says the Lord;
   whoever eats this bread will live forever. ℟.

GOSPEL
John 6:41–51

The Jews murmured about Jesus because he said, "I am the bread that came down from heaven," and they said, "Is this not Jesus, the son of Joseph? Do we not know his father and mother? Then how can he say, 'I have come down from heaven'?" Jesus answered and said to them, "Stop murmuring among yourselves. No one can come to me unless the Father who sent me draw him, and I will raise him on the last day. It is written in the prophets:

   They shall all be taught by God.
Everyone who listens to my Father and learns from him comes to me. Not that anyone has seen the Father except the one who is from God; he has seen the Father. Amen, amen, I say to you, whoever believes has eternal life. I am the bread of life. Your ancestors ate the manna in the desert, but they died; this is the bread that comes down from heaven so that one may eat it and not die. I am the living bread that came down from heaven; whoever eats this bread will live forever; and the bread that I will give is my flesh for the life of the world."

984 19TH SUNDAY IN ORDINARY TIME — C

FIRST READING *Wisdom 18:6–9*

The night of the passover was known
    beforehand to our fathers,
  that, with sure knowledge of the
    oaths in which they put their
    faith,
  they might have courage.
Your people awaited the salvation of
    the just
  and the destruction of their foes.

For when you punished our
    adversaries,
  in this you glorified us whom you
    had summoned.
For in secret the holy children of the
    good were offering sacrifice
  and putting into effect with one
    accord the divine institution.

RESPONSORIAL PSALM *Psalm 33:1, 12, 18–19, 20–22*

℟. Bless-ed the peo-ple the Lord has [cho-sen,] cho-sen to be his own.

Music: Owen Alstott, b. 1947, © 1977, 1990, OCP. All rights reserved.

▸ Exult, you just, in the LORD;
  praise from the upright is fitting.
Blessed the nation whose God is
    the LORD,
  the people he has chosen for his
    own inheritance. ℟.

▸ See, the eyes of the LORD are upon
    those who fear him,
  upon those who hope for
    his kindness,

to deliver them from death
  and preserve them in spite
    of famine. ℟.

▸ Our soul waits for the LORD,
  who is our help and our shield.
May your kindness, O LORD, be
    upon us
  who have put our hope in you. ℟.

SECOND READING *Hebrews 11:1–2, 8–19 or 11:1–2, 8–12*

(Include bracketed text for Long Form)

Brothers and sisters: Faith is the
realization of what is hoped for and
evidence of things not seen. Because
of it the ancients were well attested.

  By faith Abraham obeyed when he
was called to go out to a place that
he was to receive as an inheritance;
he went out, not knowing where he
was to go. By faith he sojourned in
the promised land as in a foreign
country, dwelling in tents with Isaac
and Jacob, heirs of the same promise;
for he was looking forward to the city
with foundations, whose architect and
maker is God. By faith he received
power to generate, even though he

was past the normal age—and Sarah
herself was sterile—for he thought that
the one who had made the promise
was trustworthy. So it was that there
came forth from one man, himself
as good as dead, descendants as
numerous as the stars in the sky and as
countless as the sands on the seashore.
  [All these died in faith. They did
not receive what had been promised
but saw it and greeted it from afar
and acknowledged themselves to
be strangers and aliens on earth, for
those who speak thus show that
they are seeking a homeland. If they
had been thinking of the land from

which they had come, they would have had opportunity to return. But now they desire a better homeland, a heavenly one. Therefore, God is not ashamed to be called their God, for he has prepared a city for them.

By faith Abraham, when put to the test, offered up Isaac, and he who had received the promises was ready to offer his only son, of whom it was said, "Through Isaac descendants shall bear your name." He reasoned that God was able to raise even from the dead, and he received Isaac back as a symbol.]

GOSPEL ACCLAMATION
Matthew 24:42a, 44

℟. Al - le - lu - ia, al - le - lu - ia, al - le - lu - ia.

Music: Owen Alstott, b. 1947, © 1977, 1990, OCP. All rights reserved.
(Omit if not sung)

▸ Stay awake and be ready!
For you do not know on what day your Lord will come. **℟.**

GOSPEL
Luke 12:32–48 or 12:35–40

(Include bracketed text for Long Form)

Jesus said to his disciples: ["Do not be afraid any longer, little flock, for your Father is pleased to give you the kingdom. Sell your belongings and give alms. Provide money bags for yourselves that do not wear out, an inexhaustible treasure in heaven that no thief can reach nor moth destroy. For where your treasure is, there also will your heart be.]

"Gird your loins and light your lamps and be like servants who await their master's return from a wedding, ready to open immediately when he comes and knocks. Blessed are those servants whom the master finds vigilant on his arrival. Amen, I say to you, he will gird himself, have them recline at table, and proceed to wait on them. And should he come in the second or third watch and find them prepared in this way, blessed are those servants. Be sure of this: if the master of the house had known the hour when the thief was coming, he would not have let his house be broken into. You also must be prepared, for at an hour you do not expect, the Son of Man will come."

[Then Peter said, "Lord, is this parable meant for us or for everyone?"

And the Lord replied, "Who, then, is the faithful and prudent steward whom the master will put in charge of his servants to distribute the food allowance at the proper time? Blessed is that servant whom his master on arrival finds doing so. Truly, I say to you, the master will put the servant in charge of all his property. But if that servant says to himself, 'My master is delayed in coming,' and begins to beat the menservants and the maidservants, to eat and drink and get drunk, then that servant's master will come on an unexpected day and at an unknown hour and will punish the servant severely and assign him a place with the unfaithful. That servant who knew his master's will but did not make preparations nor act in accord with his will shall be beaten severely; and the servant who was ignorant of his master's will but acted in a way deserving of a severe beating shall be beaten only lightly. Much will be required of the person entrusted with much, and still more will be demanded of the person entrusted with more."]

985   20TH SUNDAY IN ORDINARY TIME — A

FIRST READING
Isaiah 56:1, 6–7

Thus says the LORD:
  Observe what is right, do what is just;
    for my salvation is about to come,
    my justice, about to be revealed.

  The foreigners who join themselves
    to the LORD,
    ministering to him,
  loving the name of the LORD,
    and becoming his servants—
  all who keep the sabbath free
    from profanation

and hold to my covenant,
  them I will bring to my holy
    mountain
  and make joyful in my house
    of prayer;
  their burnt offerings and sacrifices
    will be acceptable on my altar,
  for my house shall be called
    a house of prayer for all peoples.

RESPONSORIAL PSALM
Psalm 67:2–3, 5, 6, 8

R. O God, let all the na - tions praise you!

▶ May God have pity on us and
    bless us;
  may he let his face shine upon us.
  So may your way be known
    upon earth;
    among all nations, your salvation. R.

▶ May the nations be glad and exult
    because you rule the peoples
    in equity;

the nations on the earth
  you guide. R.

▶ May the peoples praise you, O God;
  may all the peoples praise you!
May God bless us,
  and may all the ends of the earth
    fear him! R.

SECOND READING
Romans 11:13–15, 29–32

Brothers and sisters: I am speaking
to you Gentiles. Inasmuch as I
am the apostle to the Gentiles, I
glory in my ministry in order to
make my race jealous and thus
save some of them. For if their
rejection is the reconciliation of the
world, what will their acceptance
be but life from the dead?

For the gifts and the call of God
are irrevocable. Just as you once
disobeyed God but have now received
mercy because of their disobedience,
so they have now disobeyed in order
that, by virtue of the mercy shown to
you, they too may now receive mercy.
For God delivered all to disobedience,
that he might have mercy upon all.

GOSPEL ACCLAMATION
cf. Matthew 4:23

R. Al - le - lu - ia, al - le - lu - ia, al - le - lu - ia.

(Omit if not sung)

▸ Jesus proclaimed the Gospel of the kingdom
and cured every disease among the people. ℟.

GOSPEL

Matthew 15:21–28

At that time, Jesus withdrew to the region of Tyre and Sidon. And behold, a Canaanite woman of that district came and called out, "Have pity on me, Lord, Son of David! My daughter is tormented by a demon." But Jesus did not say a word in answer to her. Jesus' disciples came and asked him, "Send her away, for she keeps calling out after us." He said in reply, "I was sent only to the lost sheep of the house of Israel." But the woman came and did Jesus homage, saying, "Lord, help me." He said in reply, "It is not right to take the food of the children and throw it to the dogs." She said, "Please, Lord, for even the dogs eat the scraps that fall from the table of their masters." Then Jesus said to her in reply, "O woman, great is your faith! Let it be done for you as you wish." And the woman's daughter was healed from that hour.

20TH SUNDAY IN ORDINARY TIME — B 986

FIRST READING

Proverbs 9:1–6

Wisdom has built her house,
   she has set up her seven columns;
she has dressed her meat, mixed
   her wine,
   yes, she has spread her table.
She has sent out her maidens;
   she calls
   from the heights out over the city:

"Let whoever is simple turn in here";
   to the one who lacks
   understanding, she says,
"Come, eat of my food,
   and drink of the wine I have mixed!
Forsake foolishness that you may live;
   advance in the way of
   understanding."

RESPONSORIAL PSALM

Psalm 34:2–3, 4–5, 6–7

℟. Taste and see the good-ness of the Lord.

Music: Owen Alstott, b. 1947, © 1977, 1990, OCP. All rights reserved.

▸ I will bless the LORD at all times;
   his praise shall be ever in
   my mouth.
Let my soul glory in the LORD;
   the lowly will hear me and
   be glad. ℟.

▸ Glorify the LORD with me,
   let us together extol his name.
I sought the LORD, and he
   answered me

and delivered me from all
   my fears. ℟.

▸ Look to him that you may be radiant
   with joy,
   and your faces may not blush
   with shame.
When the poor one called out,
   the LORD heard,
   and from all his distress he
   saved him. ℟.

SECOND READING

Ephesians 5:15–20

Brothers and sisters: Watch carefully how you live, not as foolish persons but as wise, making the most of the opportunity, because the days are evil. Therefore, do not continue in ignorance, but try to understand what is the will of the Lord. And do not get drunk on wine, in which lies debauchery, but be filled with the Spirit, addressing one another in psalms and hymns and spiritual songs, singing and playing to the Lord in your hearts, giving thanks always and for everything in the name of our Lord Jesus Christ to God the Father.

GOSPEL ACCLAMATION
John 6:56

R. Al - le - lu - ia, al - le - lu - ia, al - le - lu - ia.

Music: Owen Alstott, b. 1947, © 1977, 1990, OCP. All rights reserved. *(Omit if not sung)*

▶ Whoever eats my flesh and drinks my blood remains in me and I in him, says the Lord. R.

GOSPEL
John 6:51–58

Jesus said to the crowds: "I am the living bread that came down from heaven; whoever eats this bread will live forever; and the bread that I will give is my flesh for the life of the world."

The Jews quarreled among themselves, saying, "How can this man give us his flesh to eat?" Jesus said to them, "Amen, amen, I say to you, unless you eat the flesh of the Son of Man and drink his blood, you do not have life within you. Whoever eats my flesh and drinks my blood has eternal life, and I will raise him on the last day. For my flesh is true food, and my blood is true drink. Whoever eats my flesh and drinks my blood remains in me and I in him. Just as the living Father sent me and I have life because of the Father, so also the one who feeds on me will have life because of me. This is the bread that came down from heaven. Unlike your ancestors who ate and still died, whoever eats this bread will live forever."

---

987 20TH SUNDAY IN ORDINARY TIME — C

FIRST READING
Jeremiah 38:4–6, 8–10

In those days, the princes said to the king: "Jeremiah ought to be put to death; he is demoralizing the soldiers who are left in this city, and all the people, by speaking such things to them; he is not interested in the welfare of our people, but in their ruin." King Zedekiah answered: "He is in your power"; for the king could do nothing with them. And so they took Jeremiah and threw him into the cistern of Prince Malchiah, which was in the quarters of the guard, letting him down with ropes. There was no water in the cistern, only mud, and Jeremiah sank into the mud.

Ebed-melech, a court official, went there from the palace and said to him: "My lord king, these men have been at fault in all they have done to the prophet Jeremiah, casting him into the cistern. He will die of famine on the spot, for there is no more food in the city." Then the king ordered Ebed-melech the Cushite to take three men along with him, and draw the prophet Jeremiah out of the cistern before he should die.

RESPONSORIAL PSALM

Psalm 40:2, 3, 4, 18

℟. Lord, come to my aid!

▶ I have waited, waited for the LORD,
and he stooped toward me. ℟.

▶ The LORD heard my cry.
He drew me out of the pit
of destruction,
out of the mud of the swamp;
he set my feet upon a crag;
he made firm my steps. ℟.

▶ And he put a new song into
my mouth,
a hymn to our God.
Many shall look on in awe
and trust in the LORD. ℟.

▶ Though I am afflicted and poor,
yet the LORD thinks of me.
You are my help and my deliverer;
O my God, hold not back! ℟.

SECOND READING

Hebrews 12:1–4

Brothers and sisters: Since we are surrounded by so great a cloud of witnesses, let us rid ourselves of every burden and sin that clings to us and persevere in running the race that lies before us while keeping our eyes fixed on Jesus, the leader and perfecter of faith. For the sake of the joy that lay before him he endured the cross, despising its shame, and has taken his seat at the right of the throne of God. Consider how he endured such opposition from sinners, in order that you may not grow weary and lose heart. In your struggle against sin you have not yet resisted to the point of shedding blood.

GOSPEL ACCLAMATION

John 10:27

℟. Al - le - lu - ia, al - le - lu - ia, al - le - lu - ia.

(Omit if not sung)

▶ My sheep hear my voice, says the Lord;
I know them, and they follow me. ℟.

GOSPEL

Luke 12:49–53

Jesus said to his disciples: "I have come to set the earth on fire, and how I wish it were already blazing! There is a baptism with which I must be baptized, and how great is my anguish until it is accomplished! Do you think that I have come to establish peace on the earth? No, I tell you, but rather division. From now on a household of five will be divided, three against two and two against three; a father will be divided against his son and a son against his father, a mother against her daughter and a daughter against her mother, a mother-in-law against her daughter-in-law and a daughter-in-law against her mother-in-law."

988 21ST SUNDAY IN ORDINARY TIME — A

FIRST READING *Isaiah 22:19–23*

Thus says the LORD to Shebna, master
   of the palace:
"I will thrust you from your office
   and pull you down from
      your station.
On that day I will summon
   my servant
   Eliakim, son of Hilkiah;
I will clothe him with your robe,
   and gird him with your sash,
   and give over to him your authority.

He shall be a father to the inhabitants
   of Jerusalem,
   and to the house of Judah.
I will place the key of the House of
   David on Eliakim's shoulder;
   when he opens, no one shall shut,
   when he shuts, no one shall open.
I will fix him like a peg in a sure spot,
   to be a place of honor for
      his family."

RESPONSORIAL PSALM *Psalm 138:1–2, 2–3, 6, 8*

℟. Lord, your love is e-ter-nal; do not for-sake the work of your hands.

Music: Owen Alstott, b. 1947, © 1977, 1990, OCP. All rights reserved.

▶ I will give thanks to you, O LORD, with
   all my heart,
   for you have heard the words of
      my mouth;
in the presence of the angels I will
   sing your praise;
   I will worship at your
      holy temple. ℟.

▶ I will give thanks to your name,
   because of your kindness and
   your truth:

when I called, you answered me;
   you built up strength within me. ℟.

▶ The LORD is exalted, yet the lowly
   he sees,
   and the proud he knows from afar.
Your kindness, O LORD, endures
   forever;
   forsake not the work of
   your hands. ℟.

SECOND READING *Romans 11:33–36*

Oh, the depth of the riches and
wisdom and knowledge of God!
How inscrutable are his judgments
and how unsearchable his ways!
*For who has known the mind of
   the Lord*

*or who has been his counselor?
Or who has given the Lord anything
   that he may be repaid?*
For from him and through him
and for him are all things. To
him be glory forever. Amen.

GOSPEL ACCLAMATION

Matthew 16:18

℟. Al - le - lu - ia, al - le - lu - ia, al - le - lu - ia.

(Omit if not sung)

▸ You are Peter and upon this rock I will build my Church
and the gates of the netherworld shall not prevail against it. **℟.**

GOSPEL

Matthew 16:13–20

Jesus went into the region of Caesarea Philippi and he asked his disciples, "Who do people say that the Son of Man is?" They replied, "Some say John the Baptist, others Elijah, still others Jeremiah or one of the prophets." He said to them, "But who do you say that I am?" Simon Peter said in reply, "You are the Christ, the Son of the living God." Jesus said to him in reply, "Blessed are you, Simon son of Jonah. For flesh and blood has not revealed this to you, but my heavenly Father. And so I say to you, you are Peter, and upon this rock I will build my church, and the gates of the netherworld shall not prevail against it. I will give you the keys to the kingdom of heaven. Whatever you bind on earth shall be bound in heaven; and whatever you loose on earth shall be loosed in heaven." Then he strictly ordered his disciples to tell no one that he was the Christ.

21ST SUNDAY IN ORDINARY TIME — B   989

FIRST READING

Joshua 24:1–2a, 15–17, 18b

Joshua gathered together all the tribes of Israel at Shechem, summoning their elders, their leaders, their judges, and their officers. When they stood in ranks before God, Joshua addressed all the people: "If it does not please you to serve the LORD, decide today whom you will serve, the gods your fathers served beyond the River or the gods of the Amorites in whose country you are now dwelling. As for me and my household, we will serve the LORD."

But the people answered, "Far be it from us to forsake the LORD for the service of other gods. For it was the LORD, our God, who brought us and our fathers up out of the land of Egypt, out of a state of slavery. He performed those great miracles before our very eyes and protected us along our entire journey and among the peoples through whom we passed. Therefore we also will serve the LORD, for he is our God."

RESPONSORIAL PSALM

Psalm 34:2–3, 16–17, 18–19, 20–21

℟. Taste and see the good - ness of the Lord.

▸ I will bless the LORD at all times;
his praise shall be ever in
my mouth.

Let my soul glory in the LORD;
the lowly will hear me and
be glad. **℟.**

℟. **Taste and see the goodness of the Lord.**

▸ The LORD has eyes for the just,
  and ears for their cry.
The LORD confronts the evildoers,
  to destroy remembrance of them
    from the earth. ℟.

▸ When the just cry out, the LORD
  hears them,
  and from all their distress he
    rescues them.

The LORD is close to the
  brokenhearted;
  and those who are crushed in spirit
    he saves. ℟.

▸ Many are the troubles of the just one,
  but out of them all the LORD
    delivers him;
  he watches over all his bones;
    not one of them shall be broken. ℟.

SECOND READING
Ephesians 5:21–32 or 5:2a, 25–32

(Include bracketed text for Long Form and text in parentheses for Short Form)

Brothers and sisters: [Be subordinate to one another out of reverence for Christ. Wives should be subordinate to their husbands as to the Lord. For the husband is head of his wife just as Christ is head of the church, he himself the savior of the body. As the church is subordinate to Christ, so wives should be subordinate to their husbands in everything.] (Live in love, as Christ loved us.) Husbands, love your wives, even as Christ loved the church and handed himself over for her to sanctify her, cleansing her by the bath of water with the word, that he might present to himself the church in splendor, without spot or wrinkle or any such thing, that she might be holy and without blemish. So also husbands should love their wives as their own bodies. He who loves his wife loves himself. For no one hates his own flesh but rather nourishes and cherishes it, even as Christ does the church, because we are members of his body.
For this reason a man shall leave his
   father and his mother
   and be joined to his wife,
   and the two shall become one flesh.
This is a great mystery, but I speak in reference to Christ and the church.

GOSPEL ACCLAMATION
John 6:63c, 68c

℟. Al - le - lu - ia, al - le - lu - ia, al - le - lu - ia.

Music: Owen Alstott, b. 1947, © 1977, 1990, OCP. All rights reserved.　　　*(Omit if not sung)*

▸ Your words, Lord, are Spirit and life;
  you have the words of everlasting life. ℟.

GOSPEL
John 6:60–69

Many of Jesus' disciples who were listening said, "This saying is hard; who can accept it?" Since Jesus knew that his disciples were murmuring about this, he said to them, "Does this shock you? What if you were to see the Son of Man ascending to where he was before? It is the spirit that gives life, while the flesh is of no avail. The words I have spoken to you are Spirit and life. But there are some of you who do not believe." Jesus knew from the beginning the ones who would not believe and the one who would betray him. And he said, "For this reason I have told you that no one can come to me unless it is granted him by my Father."

As a result of this, many of his disciples returned to their former way of life and no longer accompanied him. Jesus then said to the Twelve, "Do you also want to leave?" Simon Peter answered him, "Master, to whom shall we go? You have the words of eternal life. We have come to believe and are convinced that you are the Holy One of God."

21ST SUNDAY IN ORDINARY TIME — C 990

FIRST READING

Isaiah 66:18–21

Thus says the LORD: I know their works and their thoughts, and I come to gather nations of every language; they shall come and see my glory. I will set a sign among them; from them I will send fugitives to the nations: to Tarshish, Put and Lud, Mosoch, Tubal and Javan, to the distant coastlands that have never heard of my fame, or seen my glory; and they shall proclaim my glory among the nations. They shall bring all your brothers and sisters from all the nations as an offering to the LORD, on horses and in chariots, in carts, upon mules and dromedaries, to Jerusalem, my holy mountain, says the LORD, just as the Israelites bring their offering to the house of the LORD in clean vessels. Some of these I will take as priests and Levites, says the LORD.

RESPONSORIAL PSALM

Psalm 117:1, 2

℟. Go out to all the world and tell the Good News.

Music: Owen Alstott, b. 1947, © 1977, 1990, OCP. All rights reserved.

Or ℟. **Alleluia.**

▶ Praise the LORD, all you nations; glorify him, all you peoples! ℟.

▶ For steadfast is his kindness toward us, and the fidelity of the LORD endures forever. ℟.

SECOND READING

Hebrews 12:5–7, 11–13

Brothers and sisters, You have forgotten the exhortation addressed to you as children:
"My son, do not disdain the discipline of the Lord
or lose heart when reproved by him;
for whom the Lord loves, he disciplines;
he scourges every son he acknowledges."
Endure your trials as "discipline"; God treats you as sons. For what "son" is there whom his father does not discipline? At the time, all discipline seems a cause not for joy but for pain, yet later it brings the peaceful fruit of righteousness to those who are trained by it.

So strengthen your drooping hands and your weak knees. Make straight paths for your feet, that what is lame may not be disjointed but healed.

GOSPEL ACCLAMATION

John 14:6

℟. Al - le - lu - ia, al - le - lu - ia, al - le - lu - ia.

Music: Owen Alstott, b. 1947, © 1977, 1990, OCP. All rights reserved. *(Omit if not sung)*

▸ I am the way, the truth and the life, says the Lord;
no one comes to the Father, except through me. **℟.**

GOSPEL

Luke 13:22–30

Jesus passed through towns and villages, teaching as he went and making his way to Jerusalem. Someone asked him, "Lord, will only a few people be saved?" He answered them, "Strive to enter through the narrow gate, for many, I tell you, will attempt to enter but will not be strong enough. After the master of the house has arisen and locked the door, then will you stand outside knocking and saying, 'Lord, open the door for us.' He will say to you in reply, 'I do not know where you are from.' And you will say, 'We ate and drank in your company and you taught in our streets.' Then he will say to you, 'I do not know where you are from. Depart from me, all you evildoers!' And there will be wailing and grinding of teeth when you see Abraham, Isaac, and Jacob and all the prophets in the kingdom of God and you yourselves cast out. And people will come from the east and the west and from the north and the south and will recline at table in the kingdom of God. For behold, some are last who will be first, and some are first who will be last."

---

991   22ND SUNDAY IN ORDINARY TIME — A

FIRST READING

Jeremiah 20:7–9

You duped me, O LORD, and I let
    myself be duped;
  you were too strong for me, and
    you triumphed.
All the day I am an object of laughter;
  everyone mocks me.

Whenever I speak, I must cry out,
  violence and outrage is
    my message;
the word of the LORD has brought me
  derision and reproach all the day.

I say to myself, I will not
    mention him,
  I will speak in his name no more.
But then it becomes like fire burning
    in my heart,
  imprisoned in my bones;
I grow weary holding it in, I cannot
    endure it.

RESPONSORIAL PSALM

Psalm 63:2, 3–4, 5–6, 8–9

℟. My soul is thirst - ing for you, O Lord my God.

Music: Owen Alstott, b. 1947, © 1977, 1990, OCP. All rights reserved.

▶ O God, you are my God whom I seek;
　for you my flesh pines and my
　　soul thirsts
　like the earth, parched, lifeless and
　　without water. ℟.

▶ Thus have I gazed toward you in
　　the sanctuary
　to see your power and your glory,
　for your kindness is a greater good
　　than life;
　my lips shall glorify you. ℟.

▶ Thus will I bless you while I live;
　lifting up my hands, I will call upon
　　your name.
As with the riches of a banquet shall
　　my soul be satisfied,
　and with exultant lips my mouth
　　shall praise you. ℟.

▶ You are my help,
　and in the shadow of your wings
　　I shout for joy.
My soul clings fast to you;
　your right hand upholds me. ℟.

SECOND READING
Romans 12:1–2

I urge you, brothers and sisters, by
the mercies of God, to offer your
bodies as a living sacrifice, holy
and pleasing to God, your spiritual
worship. Do not conform yourselves
to this age but be transformed by the
renewal of your mind, that you may
discern what is the will of God, what
is good and pleasing and perfect.

GOSPEL ACCLAMATION
cf. Ephesians 1:17–18

℟. Al - le - lu - ia,　al - le - lu - ia,　al - le - lu - ia.

　　(Omit if not sung)

▶ May the Father of our Lord Jesus Christ
　enlighten the eyes of our hearts,
　that we may know what is the hope
　that belongs to our call. ℟.

GOSPEL
Matthew 16:21–27

Jesus began to show his disciples that
he must go to Jerusalem and suffer
greatly from the elders, the chief
priests, and the scribes, and be killed
and on the third day be raised. Then
Peter took Jesus aside and began to
rebuke him, "God forbid, Lord! No
such thing shall ever happen to you."
He turned and said to Peter, "Get
behind me, Satan! You are an obstacle
to me. You are thinking not as God
does, but as human beings do."

Then Jesus said to his disciples,
"Whoever wishes to come after me
must deny himself, take up his cross,
and follow me. For whoever wishes to
save his life will lose it, but whoever
loses his life for my sake will find it.
What profit would there be for one
to gain the whole world and forfeit
his life? Or what can one give in
exchange for his life? For the Son
of Man will come with his angels in
his Father's glory, and then he will
repay all according to his conduct."

992 22ND SUNDAY IN ORDINARY TIME — B

FIRST READING

Deuteronomy 4:1–2, 6–8

Moses said to the people: "Now, Israel, hear the statutes and decrees which I am teaching you to observe, that you may live, and may enter in and take possession of the land which the LORD, the God of your fathers, is giving you. In your observance of the commandments of the LORD, your God, which I enjoin upon you, you shall not add to what I command you nor subtract from it. Observe them carefully, for thus will you give evidence of your wisdom and intelligence to the nations, who will hear of all these statutes and say, 'This great nation is truly a wise and intelligent people.' For what great nation is there that has gods so close to it as the LORD, our God, is to us whenever we call upon him? Or what great nation has statutes and decrees that are as just as this whole law which I am setting before you today?"

RESPONSORIAL PSALM

Psalm 15:2–3, 3–4, 4–5

℟. The one who does jus-tice will live in the pres-ence of the Lord.

▸ Whoever walks blamelessly and
    does justice;
  who thinks the truth in his heart
  and slanders not with his tongue. ℟.

▸ Who harms not his fellow man,
  nor takes up a reproach against
    his neighbor;

by whom the reprobate is despised,
  while he honors those who fear
    the LORD. ℟.

▸ Who lends not his money at usury
  and accepts no bribe against
    the innocent.
  Whoever does these things
    shall never be disturbed. ℟.

SECOND READING

James 1:17–18, 21b–22, 27

Dearest brothers and sisters: All good giving and every perfect gift is from above, coming down from the Father of lights, with whom there is no alteration or shadow caused by change. He willed to give us birth by the word of truth that we may be a kind of firstfruits of his creatures.

Humbly welcome the word that has been planted in you and is able to save your souls.

Be doers of the word and not hearers only, deluding yourselves.

Religion that is pure and undefiled before God and the Father is this: to care for orphans and widows in their affliction and to keep oneself unstained by the world.

GOSPEL ACCLAMATION

James 1:18

℟. Al - le - lu-ia, al - le - lu - ia, al - le - lu - ia.

(Omit if not sung)

▶ The Father willed to give us birth by the word of truth
that we may be a kind of firstfruits of his creatures. ℟.

GOSPEL
Mark 7:1–8, 14–15, 21–23

When the Pharisees with some scribes who had come from Jerusalem gathered around Jesus, they observed that some of his disciples ate their meals with unclean, that is, unwashed, hands.—For the Pharisees and, in fact, all Jews, do not eat without carefully washing their hands, keeping the tradition of the elders. And on coming from the marketplace they do not eat without purifying themselves. And there are many other things that they have traditionally observed, the purification of cups and jugs and kettles and beds.—So the Pharisees and scribes questioned him, "Why do your disciples not follow the tradition of the elders but instead eat a meal with unclean hands?" He responded, "Well did Isaiah prophesy about you hypocrites, as it is written:

This people honors me with
their lips,
but their hearts are far from me;
in vain do they worship me,
teaching as doctrines
human precepts.
You disregard God's commandment but cling to human tradition."

He summoned the crowd again and said to them, "Hear me, all of you, and understand. Nothing that enters one from outside can defile that person; but the things that come out from within are what defile.

"From within people, from their hearts, come evil thoughts, unchastity, theft, murder, adultery, greed, malice, deceit, licentiousness, envy, blasphemy, arrogance, folly. All these evils come from within and they defile."

22ND SUNDAY IN ORDINARY TIME — C 993

FIRST READING
Sirach 3:17–18, 20, 28–29

My child, conduct your affairs
with humility,
and you will be loved more than a
giver of gifts.
Humble yourself the more, the
greater you are,
and you will find favor with God.
What is too sublime for you,
seek not,

into things beyond your strength
search not.
The mind of a sage appreciates
proverbs,
and an attentive ear is the joy of
the wise.
Water quenches a flaming fire,
and alms atone for sins.

RESPONSORIAL PSALM
Psalm 68:4–5, 6–7, 10–11

℟. God, in your good-ness, you have made [a home,] a home for the poor.

▶ The just rejoice and exult before God;
they are glad and rejoice.

Sing to God, chant praise to his name,
whose name is the LORD. ℟.

℞. God, in your goodness, you have made a home for the poor.

▶ The father of orphans and the
defender of widows
is God in his holy dwelling.
God gives a home to the forsaken;
he leads forth prisoners
to prosperity. ℞.

▶ A bountiful rain you showered down,
O God, upon your inheritance;
you restored the land when
it languished;
your flock settled in it;
in your goodness, O God, you
provided it for the needy. ℞.

SECOND READING
Hebrews 12:18–19, 22–24a

Brothers and sisters: You have not approached that which could be touched and a blazing fire and gloomy darkness and storm and a trumpet blast and a voice speaking words such that those who heard begged that no message be further addressed to them. No, you have approached Mount Zion and the city of the living God, the heavenly Jerusalem, and countless angels in festal gathering, and the assembly of the firstborn enrolled in heaven, and God the judge of all, and the spirits of the just made perfect, and Jesus, the mediator of a new covenant, and the sprinkled blood that speaks more eloquently than that of Abel.

GOSPEL ACCLAMATION
Matthew 11:29ab

℞. Al - le - lu - ia, al - le - lu - ia, al - le - lu - ia.

Music: Owen Alstott, b. 1947, © 1977, 1990, OCP. All rights reserved.   *(Omit if not sung)*

▶ Take my yoke upon you, says the Lord,
and learn from me, for I am meek and humble of heart. ℞.

GOSPEL
Luke 14:1, 7–14

On a sabbath Jesus went to dine at the home of one of the leading Pharisees, and the people there were observing him carefully.

He told a parable to those who had been invited, noticing how they were choosing the places of honor at the table. "When you are invited by someone to a wedding banquet, do not recline at table in the place of honor. A more distinguished guest than you may have been invited by him, and the host who invited both of you may approach you and say, 'Give your place to this man,' and then you would proceed with embarrassment to take the lowest place. Rather, when you are invited, go and take the lowest place so that when the host comes to you he may say, 'My friend, move up to a higher position.' Then you will enjoy the esteem of your companions at the table. For everyone who exalts himself will be humbled, but the one who humbles himself will be exalted." Then he said to the host who invited him, "When you hold a lunch or a dinner, do not invite your friends or your brothers or your relatives or your wealthy neighbors, in case they may invite you back and you have repayment. Rather, when you hold a banquet, invite the poor, the crippled, the lame, the blind; blessed indeed will you be because of their inability to repay you. For you will be repaid at the resurrection of the righteous."

23RD SUNDAY IN ORDINARY TIME — A 994

FIRST READING
Ezekiel 33:7–9

Thus says the LORD: You, son of man, I have appointed watchman for the house of Israel; when you hear me say anything, you shall warn them for me. If I tell the wicked, "O wicked one, you shall surely die," and you do not speak out to dissuade the wicked from his way, the wicked shall die for his guilt, but I will hold you responsible for his death. But if you warn the wicked, trying to turn him from his way, and he refuses to turn from his way, he shall die for his guilt, but you shall save yourself.

RESPONSORIAL PSALM
Psalm 95:1–2, 6–7, 8–9

℟. If to-day you hear his voice, hard-en not your hearts.

▶ Come, let us sing joyfully to the LORD;
    let us acclaim the rock of
        our salvation.
Let us come into his presence with
        thanksgiving;
    let us joyfully sing psalms
        to him. ℟.

▶ Come, let us bow down in worship;
    let us kneel before the LORD who
        made us.
For he is our God,

and we are the people he
    shepherds, the flock
    he guides. ℟.

▶ Oh, that today you would hear
        his voice:
    "Harden not your hearts as
        at Meribah,
    as in the day of Massah in
        the desert,
where your fathers tempted me;
    they tested me though they had
        seen my works." ℟.

SECOND READING
Romans 13:8–10

Brothers and sisters: Owe nothing to anyone, except to love one another; for the one who loves another has fulfilled the law. The commandments, "You shall not commit adultery; you shall not kill; you shall not steal; you shall not covet," and whatever other commandment there may be, are summed up in this saying, namely, "You shall love your neighbor as yourself." Love does no evil to the neighbor; hence, love is the fulfillment of the law.

GOSPEL ACCLAMATION
2 Corinthians 5:19

℟. Al - le - lu - ia, al - le - lu - ia, al - le - lu - ia.

(Omit if not sung)

▶ God was reconciling the world to himself in Christ
    and entrusting to us the message of reconciliation. ℟.

GOSPEL

Matthew 18:15–20

Jesus said to his disciples: "If your brother sins against you, go and tell him his fault between you and him alone. If he listens to you, you have won over your brother. If he does not listen, take one or two others along with you, so that 'every fact may be established on the testimony of two or three witnesses.' If he refuses to listen to them, tell the church. If he refuses to listen even to the church, then treat him as you would a Gentile or a tax collector. Amen, I say to you, whatever you bind on earth shall be bound in heaven, and whatever you loose on earth shall be loosed in heaven. Again, amen, I say to you, if two of you agree on earth about anything for which they are to pray, it shall be granted to them by my heavenly Father. For where two or three are gathered together in my name, there am I in the midst of them."

---

995   23RD SUNDAY IN ORDINARY TIME — B

FIRST READING

Isaiah 35:4–7a

Thus says the LORD:
    Say to those whose hearts
        are frightened:
        Be strong, fear not!
Here is your God,
    he comes with vindication;
with divine recompense
    he comes to save you.
Then will the eyes of the blind
        be opened,
    the ears of the deaf be cleared;
then will the lame leap like a stag,
    then the tongue of the mute
        will sing.
Streams will burst forth in
        the desert,
    and rivers in the steppe.
The burning sands will
        become pools,
    and the thirsty ground, springs
        of water.

RESPONSORIAL PSALM

Psalm 146:6–7, 8–9, 9–10

℟. Praise   the   Lord,   my   soul!

Music: Owen Alstott, b. 1947, © 1977, 1990, OCP. All rights reserved.

Or ℟. **Alleluia.**

▸ The God of Jacob keeps faith forever,
    secures justice for the oppressed,
    gives food to the hungry.
The LORD sets captives free. ℟.

▸ The LORD gives sight to the blind;
    the LORD raises up those who were
        bowed down.
The LORD loves the just;
    the LORD protects strangers. ℟.

▸ The fatherless and the widow the
        LORD sustains,
    but the way of the wicked
        he thwarts.
The LORD shall reign forever;
    your God, O Zion, through all
        generations. Alleluia. ℟.

SECOND READING
James 2:1–5

My brothers and sisters, show no partiality as you adhere to the faith in our glorious Lord Jesus Christ. For if a man with gold rings and fine clothes comes into your assembly, and a poor person in shabby clothes also comes in, and you pay attention to the one wearing the fine clothes and say, "Sit here, please," while you say to the poor one, "Stand there," or "Sit at my feet," have you not made distinctions among yourselves and become judges with evil designs?

Listen, my beloved brothers and sisters. Did not God choose those who are poor in the world to be rich in faith and heirs of the kingdom that he promised to those who love him?

GOSPEL ACCLAMATION
cf. Matthew 4:23

℟. Al - le - lu - ia, al - le - lu - ia, al - le - lu - ia.

(Omit if not sung)

▸ Jesus proclaimed the Gospel of the kingdom and cured every disease among the people. ℟.

GOSPEL
Mark 7:31–37

Again Jesus left the district of Tyre and went by way of Sidon to the Sea of Galilee, into the district of the Decapolis. And people brought to him a deaf man who had a speech impediment and begged him to lay his hand on him. He took him off by himself away from the crowd. He put his finger into the man's ears and, spitting, touched his tongue; then he looked up to heaven and groaned, and said to him, *"Ephphatha!"*—that is, "Be opened!"—And immediately the man's ears were opened, his speech impediment was removed, and he spoke plainly. He ordered them not to tell anyone. But the more he ordered them not to, the more they proclaimed it. They were exceedingly astonished and they said, "He has done all things well. He makes the deaf hear and the mute speak."

23RD SUNDAY IN ORDINARY TIME — C   996

FIRST READING
Wisdom 9:13–18b

Who can know God's counsel,
  or who can conceive what the
    LORD intends?
For the deliberations of mortals
    are timid,
  and unsure are our plans.
For the corruptible body burdens
    the soul
  and the earthen shelter weighs
    down the mind that has
    many concerns.
And scarce do we guess the things
    on earth,
  and what is within our grasp we
    find with difficulty;
  but when things are in heaven,
    who can search them out?
Or who ever knew your counsel,
    except you had given wisdom
  and sent your holy spirit from
    on high?
And thus were the paths of those on
    earth made straight.

RESPONSORIAL PSALM

Psalm 90:3–4, 5–6, 12–13, 14, 17

℟. In ev - 'ry age, O Lord, you have been our ref - uge.

▶ You turn man back to dust,
    saying, "Return, O children
        of men."
For a thousand years in your sight
    are as yesterday, now that it is past,
    or as a watch of the night. ℟.

▶ You make an end of them in
        their sleep;
    the next morning they are like the
        changing grass,
which at dawn springs up anew,
    but by evening wilts and fades. ℟.

▶ Teach us to number our days aright,
    that we may gain wisdom of heart.
Return, O LORD! How long?
    Have pity on your servants! ℟.

▶ Fill us at daybreak with your kindness,
    that we may shout for joy and
        gladness all our days.
And may the gracious care of the
    LORD our God be ours;
    prosper the work of our hands
        for us!
Prosper the work of our hands! ℟.

SECOND READING

Philemon 9–10, 12–17

I, Paul, an old man, and now also a prisoner for Christ Jesus, urge you on behalf of my child Onesimus, whose father I have become in my imprisonment; I am sending him, that is, my own heart, back to you. I should have liked to retain him for myself, so that he might serve me on your behalf in my imprisonment for the gospel, but I did not want to do anything without your consent, so that the good you do might not be forced but voluntary. Perhaps this is why he was away from you for a while, that you might have him back forever, no longer as a slave but more than a slave, a brother, beloved especially to me, but even more so to you, as a man and in the Lord. So if you regard me as a partner, welcome him as you would me.

GOSPEL ACCLAMATION

Psalm 119:135

℟. Al - le - lu - ia, al - le - lu - ia, al - le - lu - ia.

(Omit if not sung)

▶ Let your face shine upon your servant;
    and teach me your laws. ℟.

GOSPEL

Luke 14:25–33

Great crowds were traveling with Jesus, and he turned and addressed them, "If anyone comes to me without hating his father and mother, wife and children, brothers and sisters, and even his own life, he cannot be my disciple. Whoever does not carry his own cross and come after me cannot be my disciple. Which of you wishing to construct a tower does not first sit down and calculate the cost to see if there is enough for its completion? Otherwise, after laying the foundation and finding himself unable to finish the work the onlookers should laugh at him and say, 'This one began to build but did not have the resources to finish.' Or what king marching into battle would not first sit down and decide whether with ten thousand troops he can successfully oppose another king advancing upon him with twenty thousand troops? But if not, while he is still far away, he will send a delegation to ask for peace terms. In the same way, anyone of you who does not renounce all his possessions cannot be my disciple."

24TH SUNDAY IN ORDINARY TIME — A   997

FIRST READING

Sirach 27:30—28:7

Wrath and anger are hateful things,
  yet the sinner hugs them tight.
The vengeful will suffer the
    LORD's vengeance,
  for he remembers their sins
    in detail.
Forgive your neighbor's injustice;
  then when you pray, your own sins
    will be forgiven.
Could anyone nourish anger
  against another
and expect healing from the LORD?
Could anyone refuse mercy to
  another like himself,
can he seek pardon for his
  own sins?
If one who is but flesh
  cherishes wrath,
who will forgive his sins?
Remember your last days, set
  enmity aside;
remember death and decay, and
  cease from sin!
Think of the commandments, hate
  not your neighbor;
remember the Most High's
  covenant, and overlook faults.

RESPONSORIAL PSALM

Psalm 103:1–2, 3–4, 9–10, 11–12

Music: Owen Alstott, b. 1947, © 1977, 1990, OCP. All rights reserved.

▸ Bless the LORD, O my soul;
  and all my being, bless his
    holy name.
Bless the LORD, O my soul,
  and forget not all his benefits. ℟.

▸ He pardons all your iniquities,
  heals all your ills.
He redeems your life from
    destruction,
  crowns you with kindness
    and compassion. ℟.

▸ He will not always chide,
  nor does he keep his wrath forever.
Not according to our sins does he
    deal with us,
  nor does he requite us according to
    our crimes. ℟.

▸ For as the heavens are high above
    the earth,
  so surpassing is his kindness
    toward those who fear him.
As far as the east is from the west,
  so far has he put our transgressions
    from us. ℟.

SECOND READING

Romans 14:7–9

Brothers and sisters: None of us lives for oneself, and no one dies for oneself. For if we live, we live for the Lord, and if we die, we die for the Lord; so then, whether we live or die, we are the Lord's. For this is why Christ died and came to life, that he might be Lord of both the dead and the living.

GOSPEL ACCLAMATION

John 13:34

R. Al - le - lu - ia, al - le - lu - ia, al - le - lu - ia.

Music: Owen Alstott, b. 1947, © 1977, 1990, OCP. All rights reserved. *(Omit if not sung)*

▶ I give you a new commandment, says the Lord; love one another as I have loved you. R.

GOSPEL

Matthew 18:21–35

Peter approached Jesus and asked him, "Lord, if my brother sins against me, how often must I forgive? As many as seven times?" Jesus answered, "I say to you, not seven times but seventy-seven times. That is why the kingdom of heaven may be likened to a king who decided to settle accounts with his servants. When he began the accounting, a debtor was brought before him who owed him a huge amount. Since he had no way of paying it back, his master ordered him to be sold, along with his wife, his children, and all his property, in payment of the debt. At that, the servant fell down, did him homage, and said, 'Be patient with me, and I will pay you back in full.' Moved with compassion the master of that servant let him go and forgave him the loan. When that servant had left, he found one of his fellow servants who owed him a much smaller amount.

He seized him and started to choke him, demanding, 'Pay back what you owe.' Falling to his knees, his fellow servant begged him, 'Be patient with me, and I will pay you back.' But he refused. Instead, he had the fellow servant put in prison until he paid back the debt. Now when his fellow servants saw what had happened, they were deeply disturbed, and went to their master and reported the whole affair. His master summoned him and said to him, 'You wicked servant! I forgave you your entire debt because you begged me to. Should you not have had pity on your fellow servant, as I had pity on you?' Then in anger his master handed him over to the torturers until he should pay back the whole debt. So will my heavenly Father do to you, unless each of you forgives your brother from your heart."

---

998   ## 24TH SUNDAY IN ORDINARY TIME — B

FIRST READING

Isaiah 50:4c–9a

The Lord GOD opens my ear that
   I may hear;
and I have not rebelled,
   have not turned back.

I gave my back to those who beat me,
   my cheeks to those who plucked
     my beard;
my face I did not shield
   from buffets and spitting.

The Lord GOD is my help,
therefore I am not disgraced;
I have set my face like flint,
knowing that I shall not be put
to shame.
He is near who upholds my right;

if anyone wishes to oppose me,
let us appear together.
Who disputes my right?
Let that man confront me.
See, the Lord GOD is my help;
who will prove me wrong?

RESPONSORIAL PSALM

Psalm 116:1–2, 3–4, 5–6, 8–9

℞. I will walk be - fore the Lord, in the land of the liv - ing.

Or ℞. **Alleluia.**

▸ I love the LORD because he has heard
my voice in supplication,
because he has inclined his ear to me
the day I called. ℞.

▸ The cords of death encompassed me;
the snares of the netherworld
seized upon me;
I fell into distress and sorrow,
and I called upon the name of
the LORD,
"O LORD, save my life!" ℞.

▸ Gracious is the LORD and just;
yes, our God is merciful.
The LORD keeps the little ones;
I was brought low, and he
saved me. ℞.

▸ For he has freed my soul from death,
my eyes from tears, my feet
from stumbling.
I shall walk before the LORD
in the land of the living. ℞.

SECOND READING

James 2:14–18

What good is it, my brothers and
sisters, if someone says he has faith
but does not have works? Can that
faith save him? If a brother or sister
has nothing to wear and has no food
for the day, and one of you says to
them, "Go in peace, keep warm, and
eat well," but you do not give them
the necessities of the body, what
good is it? So also faith of itself, if
it does not have works, is dead.

Indeed someone might say, "You
have faith and I have works."
Demonstrate your faith to me without
works, and I will demonstrate my
faith to you from my works.

GOSPEL ACCLAMATION

Galatians 6:14

℞. Al - le - lu - ia, al - le - lu - ia, al - le - lu - ia.

(Omit if not sung)

▸ May I never boast except in the cross of our Lord
through which the world has been crucified to me and I to the world. ℞.

GOSPEL

Mark 8:27–35

Jesus and his disciples set out for the
villages of Caesarea Philippi. Along the
way he asked his disciples, "Who do
people say that I am?" They said
in reply, "John the Baptist, others Elijah,
still others one of the prophets."

And he asked them, "But who do you say that I am?" Peter said to him in reply, "You are the Christ." Then he warned them not to tell anyone about him.

He began to teach them that the Son of Man must suffer greatly and be rejected by the elders, the chief priests, and the scribes, and be killed, and rise after three days. He spoke this openly. Then Peter took him aside and began to rebuke him. At this he turned around and, looking at his disciples, rebuked Peter and said, "Get behind me, Satan. You are thinking not as God does, but as human beings do."

He summoned the crowd with his disciples and said to them, "Whoever wishes to come after me must deny himself, take up his cross, and follow me. For whoever wishes to save his life will lose it, but whoever loses his life for my sake and that of the gospel will save it."

---

999   24TH SUNDAY IN ORDINARY TIME — C

FIRST READING
Exodus 32:7–11, 13–14

The LORD said to Moses, "Go down at once to your people, whom you brought out of the land of Egypt, for they have become depraved. They have soon turned aside from the way I pointed out to them, making for themselves a molten calf and worshiping it, sacrificing to it and crying out, 'This is your God, O Israel, who brought you out of the land of Egypt!' I see how stiff-necked this people is," continued the LORD to Moses. "Let me alone, then, that my wrath may blaze up against them to consume them. Then I will make of you a great nation."

But Moses implored the LORD, his God, saying, "Why, O LORD, should your wrath blaze up against your own people, whom you brought out of the land of Egypt with such great power and with so strong a hand? Remember your servants Abraham, Isaac, and Israel, and how you swore to them by your own self, saying, 'I will make your descendants as numerous as the stars in the sky; and all this land that I promised, I will give your descendants as their perpetual heritage.'" So the LORD relented in the punishment he had threatened to inflict on his people.

RESPONSORIAL PSALM
Psalm 51:3–4, 12–13, 17, 19

R. I will rise and go to my fa - ther.

Music: Owen Alstott, b. 1947, © 1977, 1990, OCP. All rights reserved.

▸ Have mercy on me, O God, in
    your goodness;
  in the greatness of your
    compassion wipe out
    my offense.
Thoroughly wash me from my guilt
  and of my sin cleanse me. R.

▸ A clean heart create for me, O God,
  and a steadfast spirit renew
    within me.

Cast me not out from your presence,
  and your Holy Spirit take not
    from me. R.

▸ O Lord, open my lips,
  and my mouth shall proclaim
    your praise.
My sacrifice, O God, is a
    contrite spirit;
  a heart contrite and humbled,
    O God, you will not spurn. R.

SECOND READING

1 Timothy 1:12–17

Beloved: I am grateful to him who has strengthened me, Christ Jesus our Lord, because he considered me trustworthy in appointing me to the ministry. I was once a blasphemer and a persecutor and arrogant, but I have been mercifully treated because I acted out of ignorance in my unbelief. Indeed, the grace of our Lord has been abundant, along with the faith and love that are in Christ Jesus. This saying is trustworthy and deserves full acceptance: Christ Jesus came into the world to save sinners. Of these I am the foremost. But for that reason I was mercifully treated, so that in me, as the foremost, Christ Jesus might display all his patience as an example for those who would come to believe in him for everlasting life. To the king of ages, incorruptible, invisible, the only God, honor and glory forever and ever. Amen.

GOSPEL ACCLAMATION

2 Corinthians 5:19

℟. Al - le - lu - ia, al - le - lu - ia, al - le - lu - ia.

Music: Owen Alstott, b. 1947, © 1977, 1990, OCP. All rights reserved.

(Omit if not sung)

▸ God was reconciling the world to himself in Christ
and entrusting to us the message of reconciliation. ℟.

GOSPEL

Luke 15:1–32 or 15:1–10

(Include bracketed text for Long Form)

Tax collectors and sinners were all drawing near to listen to Jesus, but the Pharisees and scribes began to complain, saying, "This man welcomes sinners and eats with them." So to them he addressed this parable. "What man among you having a hundred sheep and losing one of them would not leave the ninety-nine in the desert and go after the lost one until he finds it? And when he does find it, he sets it on his shoulders with great joy and, upon his arrival home, he calls together his friends and neighbors and says to them, 'Rejoice with me because I have found my lost sheep.' I tell you, in just the same way there will be more joy in heaven over one sinner who repents than over ninety-nine righteous people who have no need of repentance.

"Or what woman having ten coins and losing one would not light a lamp and sweep the house, searching carefully until she finds it? And when she does find it, she calls together her friends and neighbors and says to them, 'Rejoice with me because I have found the coin that I lost.' In just the same way, I tell you, there will be rejoicing among the angels of God over one sinner who repents."

[Then he said, "A man had two sons, and the younger son said to his father, 'Father give me the share of your estate that should come to me.' So the father divided the property between them. After a few days, the younger son collected all his belongings and set off to a distant country where he squandered his inheritance on a life of dissipation. When he had freely spent everything, a severe famine struck that country, and he found himself in dire need. So he hired himself out to one of the local citizens who sent him to his farm to tend the swine. And he longed to eat his fill of the pods on which the swine fed, but nobody gave him any. Coming to his senses he thought, 'How many of my father's hired workers have more than enough food to eat, but here am I, dying from hunger. I shall get up and go to my father and I shall say to him, "Father, I have sinned against heaven and against you. I no longer deserve to be called your son; treat me as you would treat one of your hired workers."' So he got up and went back to his father. While he was still a long way off, his father caught sight of him, and was filled with compassion. He ran to his son, embraced him and kissed him. His son said to him, 'Father, I have sinned against heaven and against you; I no longer deserve to be called your son.' But his father ordered his servants, 'Quickly bring the finest robe and put it on him; put a ring on his finger and sandals on his feet. Take the fattened calf and slaughter it. Then let us celebrate with a feast, because this son of mine was dead, and has come to life again; he was lost, and has been found.' Then the celebration began. Now the older son had been out in the field and, on his way back, as he neared the house, he heard the sound of music and dancing. He called one of the servants and asked what this might mean. The servant said to him, 'Your brother has returned and your father has slaughtered the fattened calf because he has him back safe and sound.' He became angry, and when he refused to enter the house, his father came out and pleaded with him. He said to his father in reply, 'Look, all these years I served you and not once did I disobey your orders; yet you never gave me even a young goat to feast on with my friends. But when your son returns, who swallowed up your property with prostitutes, for him you slaughter the fattened calf.' He said to him, 'My son, you are here with me always; everything I have is yours. But now we must celebrate and rejoice, because your brother was dead and has come to life again; he was lost and has been found.'"]

1000   25TH SUNDAY IN ORDINARY TIME — A

FIRST READING

Isaiah 55:6–9

Seek the LORD while he may
    be found,
  call him while he is near.
Let the scoundrel forsake his way,
    and the wicked his thoughts;
  let him turn to the LORD for mercy;
    to our God, who is generous
      in forgiving.

For my thoughts are not
    your thoughts,
  nor are your ways my ways, says
    the LORD.
As high as the heavens are above
    the earth,
  so high are my ways above
    your ways
  and my thoughts above
    your thoughts.

RESPONSORIAL PSALM

Psalm 145:2–3, 8–9, 17–18

℟. The Lord is near to all who call up-on him.

▶ Every day will I bless you,
and I will praise your name forever
and ever.
Great is the LORD and highly to
be praised;
his greatness is unsearchable. ℟.

▶ The LORD is gracious and merciful,
slow to anger and of
great kindness.

The LORD is good to all
and compassionate toward all
his works. ℟.

▶ The LORD is just in all his ways
and holy in all his works.
The LORD is near to all who call
upon him,
to all who call upon him in truth. ℟.

SECOND READING
Philippians 1:20c–24, 27a

Brothers and sisters: Christ will be magnified in my body, whether by life or by death. For to me life is Christ, and death is gain. If I go on living in the flesh, that means fruitful labor for me. And I do not know which I shall choose. I am caught between the two. I long to depart this life and be with Christ, for that is far better. Yet that I remain in the flesh is more necessary for your benefit.

Only, conduct yourselves in a way worthy of the gospel of Christ.

GOSPEL ACCLAMATION
cf. Acts of the Apostles 16:14b

℟. Al - le - lu - ia, al - le - lu - ia, al - le - lu - ia.

Music: Owen Alstott, b. 1947, © 1977, 1990, OCP. All rights reserved.　　　　*(Omit if not sung)*

▶ Open our hearts, O Lord,
to listen to the words of your Son. ℟.

GOSPEL
Matthew 20:1–16a

Jesus told his disciples this parable: "The kingdom of heaven is like a landowner who went out at dawn to hire laborers for his vineyard. After agreeing with them for the usual daily wage, he sent them into his vineyard. Going out about nine o'clock, the landowner saw others standing idle in the marketplace, and he said to them, 'You too go into my vineyard, and I will give you what is just.' So they went off. And he went out again around noon, and around three o'clock, and did likewise. Going out about five o'clock, the landowner found others standing around, and said to them, 'Why do you stand here idle all day?' They answered, 'Because no one has hired us.' He said to them, 'You too go into my vineyard.' When it was evening the owner of the vineyard said to his foreman, 'Summon the laborers and give them their pay, beginning with the last and ending with the first.' When those who had started about five o'clock came, each received the usual daily wage. So when the first came, they thought that they would receive more, but each of them also got the usual wage. And on receiving it they grumbled against the landowner, saying, 'These last ones worked only one hour, and you have made them equal to us, who bore the day's burden and the heat.' He said to one of them in reply, 'My friend, I am not cheating you. Did you not agree with me for the usual daily wage? Take what is yours and go. What if I wish to give this last one the same as you? Or am I not free to do as I wish with my own money? Are you envious because I am generous?' Thus, the last will be first, and the first will be last."

1001 25TH SUNDAY IN ORDINARY TIME — B

FIRST READING

Wisdom 2:12, 17–20

The wicked say:
  Let us beset the just one, because he
    is obnoxious to us;
  he sets himself against our doings,
reproaches us for transgressions of
    the law
  and charges us with violations of
    our training.
Let us see whether his words be
    true;
  let us find out what will happen
    to him.

For if the just one be the son of God,
  God will defend him
  and deliver him from the hand of
    his foes.
With revilement and torture let us
    put the just one to the test
  that we may have proof of his
    gentleness
  and try his patience.
Let us condemn him to a
    shameful death;
  for according to his own words,
    God will take care of him.

RESPONSORIAL PSALM

Psalm 54:3–4, 5, 6 & 8

℟. The Lord up - holds my life.

▸ O God, by your name save me,
  and by your might defend
    my cause.
O God, hear my prayer;
  hearken to the words of
    my mouth. ℟.

▸ For the haughty have risen up
  against me,

the ruthless seek my life;
they set not God before
  their eyes. ℟.

▸ Behold, God is my helper;
  the Lord sustains my life.
Freely will I offer you sacrifice;
  I will praise your name, O LORD,
    for its goodness. ℟.

SECOND READING

James 3:16 — 4:3

Beloved: Where jealousy and selfish ambition exist, there is disorder and every foul practice. But the wisdom from above is first of all pure, then peaceable, gentle, compliant, full of mercy and good fruits, without inconstancy or insincerity. And the fruit of righteousness is sown in peace for those who cultivate peace.

Where do the wars and where do the conflicts among you come from? Is it not from your passions that make war within your members? You covet but do not possess. You kill and envy but you cannot obtain; you fight and wage war. You do not possess because you do not ask. You ask but do not receive, because you ask wrongly, to spend it on your passions.

GOSPEL ACCLAMATION

cf. 2 Thessalonians 2:14

℟. Al - le - lu - ia, al - le - lu - ia, al - le - lu - ia.

(Omit if not sung)

▸God has called us through the Gospel
to possess the glory of our Lord Jesus Christ. ℟.

GOSPEL *Mark 9:30–37*

Jesus and his disciples left from there and began a journey through Galilee, but he did not wish anyone to know about it. He was teaching his disciples and telling them, "The Son of Man is to be handed over to men and they will kill him, and three days after his death the Son of Man will rise." But they did not understand the saying, and they were afraid to question him.

They came to Capernaum and, once inside the house, he began to ask them, "What were you arguing about on the way?" But they remained silent. They had been discussing among themselves on the way who was the greatest. Then he sat down, called the Twelve, and said to them, "If anyone wishes to be first, he shall be the last of all and the servant of all." Taking a child, he placed it in their midst, and putting his arms around it, he said to them, "Whoever receives one child such as this in my name, receives me; and whoever receives me, receives not me but the One who sent me."

25TH SUNDAY IN ORDINARY TIME — C 1002

FIRST READING *Amos 8:4–7*

Hear this, you who trample upon
   the needy
  and destroy the poor of the land!
"When will the new moon be over,"
   you ask,
  "that we may sell our grain,
  and the sabbath, that we may
   display the wheat?
We will diminish the ephah,
  add to the shekel,
  and fix our scales for cheating!

We will buy the lowly for silver,
  and the poor for a pair of sandals;
  even the refuse of the wheat we
   will sell!"
The LORD has sworn by the pride
  of Jacob:
  Never will I forget a thing they
   have done!

RESPONSORIAL PSALM *Psalm 113:1–2, 4–6, 7–8*

℟. Praise the Lord who lifts up the poor.

Or ℟. **Alleluia.**

▸Praise, you servants of the LORD,
  praise the name of the LORD.
Blessed be the name of the LORD
  both now and forever. ℟.

▸High above all nations is the LORD;
  above the heavens is his glory.
Who is like the LORD, our God, who is
  enthroned on high

and looks upon the heavens and
  the earth below? ℟.

▸He raises up the lowly from the dust;
  from the dunghill he lifts up
   the poor
to seat them with princes,
  with the princes of his
   own people. ℟.

SECOND READING
1 Timothy 2:1–8

Beloved: First of all, I ask that supplications, prayers, petitions, and thanksgivings be offered for everyone, for kings and for all in authority, that we may lead a quiet and tranquil life in all devotion and dignity. This is good and pleasing to God our savior, who wills everyone to be saved and to come to knowledge of the truth.

For there is one God.

There is also one mediator between God and men,

the man Christ Jesus, who gave himself as ransom for all. This was the testimony at the proper time. For this I was appointed preacher and apostle—I am speaking the truth, I am not lying—, teacher of the Gentiles in faith and truth.

It is my wish, then, that in every place the men should pray, lifting up holy hands, without anger or argument.

GOSPEL ACCLAMATION
cf. 2 Corinthians 8:9

℟. Al - le - lu - ia, al - le - lu - ia, al - le - lu - ia.

Music: Owen Alstott, b. 1947, © 1977, 1990, OCP. All rights reserved.　　　　*(Omit if not sung)*

▶ Though our Lord Jesus Christ was rich, he became poor, so that by his poverty you might become rich. ℟.

GOSPEL
Luke 16:1–13 or 16:10–13

(Include bracketed text for Long Form)

Jesus said to his disciples, **[**"A rich man had a steward who was reported to him for squandering his property. He summoned him and said, 'What is this I hear about you? Prepare a full account of your stewardship, because you can no longer be my steward.' The steward said to himself, 'What shall I do, now that my master is taking the position of steward away from me? I am not strong enough to dig and I am ashamed to beg. I know what I shall do so that, when I am removed from the stewardship, they may welcome me into their homes.' He called in his master's debtors one by one. To the first he said, 'How much do you owe my master?' He replied, 'One hundred measures of olive oil.' He said to him, 'Here is your promissory note. Sit down and quickly write one for fifty.' Then to another the steward said, 'And you, how much do you owe?' He replied, 'One hundred kors of wheat.' The steward said to him, 'Here is your

promissory note; write one for eighty.' And the master commended that dishonest steward for acting prudently.

"For the children of this world are more prudent in dealing with their own generation than are the children of light. I tell you, make friends for yourselves with dishonest wealth, so that when it fails, you will be welcomed into eternal dwellings.**]** The person who is trustworthy in very small matters is also trustworthy in great ones; and the person who is dishonest in very small matters is also dishonest in great ones. If, therefore, you are not trustworthy with dishonest wealth, who will trust you with true wealth? If you are not trustworthy with what belongs to another, who will give you what is yours? No servant can serve two masters. He will either hate one and love the other, or be devoted to one and despise the other. You cannot serve both God and mammon."

26TH SUNDAY IN ORDINARY TIME — A   1003

FIRST READING
Ezekiel 18:25–28

Thus says the LORD: You say, "The LORD's way is not fair!" Hear now, house of Israel: Is it my way that is unfair, or rather, are not your ways unfair? When someone virtuous turns away from virtue to commit iniquity, and dies, it is because of the iniquity he committed that he must die. But if he turns from the wickedness he has committed, and does what is right and just, he shall preserve his life; since he has turned away from all the sins that he has committed, he shall surely live, he shall not die.

RESPONSORIAL PSALM
Psalm 25:4–5, 6–7, 8–9

℟. Re - mem - ber your mer - cies, O Lord.

▸ Your ways, O LORD, make known
    to me;
  teach me your paths,
  guide me in your truth and teach me,
    for you are God my savior. ℟.

▸ Remember that your compassion,
    O LORD,
  and your love are from of old.
  The sins of my youth and my frailties
    remember not;

in your kindness remember me,
  because of your goodness,
    O LORD. ℟.

▸ Good and upright is the LORD;
    thus he shows sinners the way.
  He guides the humble to justice,
    and teaches the humble
      his way. ℟.

SECOND READING
Philippians 2:1–11 or 2:1–5

(Include bracketed text for Long Form)

Brothers and sisters: If there is any encouragement in Christ, any solace in love, any participation in the Spirit, any compassion and mercy, complete my joy by being of the same mind, with the same love, united in heart, thinking one thing. Do nothing out of selfishness or out of vainglory; rather, humbly regard others as more important than yourselves, each looking out not for his own interests, but also for those of others.
  Have in you the same attitude that is also in Christ Jesus,
  [Who, though he was in the form of God,
    did not regard equality with God something to be grasped.

Rather, he emptied himself,
    taking the form of a slave,
    coming in human likeness;
    and found human in appearance,
    he humbled himself,
    becoming obedient to the point
      of death,
    even death on a cross.
Because of this, God greatly
      exalted him
    and bestowed on him the name
    which is above every name,
    that at the name of Jesus
    every knee should bend,
    of those in heaven and on earth
      and under the earth,
    and every tongue confess that
    Jesus Christ is Lord,
    to the glory of God the Father.]

GOSPEL ACCLAMATION

John 10:27

℟. Al - le - lu - ia, al - le - lu - ia, al - le - lu - ia.

Music: Owen Alstott, b. 1947, © 1977, 1990, OCP. All rights reserved. *(Omit if not sung)*

▸ My sheep hear my voice, says the Lord;
I know them, and they follow me. ℟.

GOSPEL

Matthew 21:28–32

Jesus said to the chief priests and elders of the people: "What is your opinion? A man had two sons. He came to the first and said, 'Son, go out and work in the vineyard today.' He said in reply, 'I will not,' but afterwards changed his mind and went. The man came to the other son and gave the same order. He said in reply, 'Yes, sir,' but did not go. Which of the two did his father's will?" They answered, "The first." Jesus said to them, "Amen, I say to you, tax collectors and prostitutes are entering the kingdom of God before you. When John came to you in the way of righteousness, you did not believe him; but tax collectors and prostitutes did. Yet even when you saw that, you did not later change your minds and believe him."

1004   26TH SUNDAY IN ORDINARY TIME — B

FIRST READING

Numbers 11:25–29

The LORD came down in the cloud and spoke to Moses. Taking some of the spirit that was on Moses, the LORD bestowed it on the seventy elders; and as the spirit came to rest on them, they prophesied.

Now two men, one named Eldad and the other Medad, were not in the gathering but had been left in the camp. They too had been on the list, but had not gone out to the tent; yet the spirit came to rest on them also, and they prophesied in the camp. So, when a young man quickly told Moses, "Eldad and Medad are prophesying in the camp," Joshua, son of Nun, who from his youth had been Moses' aide, said, "Moses, my lord, stop them." But Moses answered him, "Are you jealous for my sake? Would that all the people of the LORD were prophets! Would that the LORD might bestow his spirit on them all!"

RESPONSORIAL PSALM

Psalm 19:8, 10, 12–13, 14

℟. The pre-cepts of the Lord give joy to the heart.

Music: Owen Alstott, b. 1947, © 1977, 1990, OCP. All rights reserved.

▸ The law of the LORD is perfect,
refreshing the soul;
the decree of the LORD is trustworthy,
giving wisdom to the simple. ℟.

▸ The fear of the LORD is pure,
enduring forever;
the ordinances of the LORD are true,
all of them just. ℟.

▶ Though your servant is careful
    of them,
  very diligent in keeping them,
  yet who can detect failings?
    Cleanse me from my
      unknown faults! ℟.

▶ From wanton sin especially, restrain
    your servant;
  let it not rule over me.
  Then shall I be blameless
    and innocent
  of serious sin. ℟.

SECOND READING

James 5:1–6

Come now, you rich, weep and wail over your impending miseries. Your wealth has rotted away, your clothes have become moth-eaten, your gold and silver have corroded, and that corrosion will be a testimony against you; it will devour your flesh like a fire. You have stored up treasure for the last days. Behold, the wages you withheld from the workers who harvested your fields are crying aloud; and the cries of the harvesters have reached the ears of the Lord of hosts. You have lived on earth in luxury and pleasure; you have fattened your hearts for the day of slaughter. You have condemned; you have murdered the righteous one; he offers you no resistance.

GOSPEL ACCLAMATION

cf. John 17:17b, 17a

℟. Al - le - lu - ia, al - le - lu - ia, al - le - lu - ia.

(Omit if not sung)

▶ Your word, O Lord, is truth;
  consecrate us in the truth. ℟.

GOSPEL

Mark 9:38–43, 45, 47–48

At that time, John said to Jesus, "Teacher, we saw someone driving out demons in your name, and we tried to prevent him because he does not follow us." Jesus replied, "Do not prevent him. There is no one who performs a mighty deed in my name who can at the same time speak ill of me. For whoever is not against us is for us. Anyone who gives you a cup of water to drink because you belong to Christ, amen, I say to you, will surely not lose his reward.

  "Whoever causes one of these little ones who believe in me to sin, it would be better for him if a great millstone were put around his neck and he were thrown into the sea. If your hand causes you to sin, cut it off. It is better for you to enter into life maimed than with two hands to go into Gehenna, into the unquenchable fire. And if your foot causes you to sin, cut if off. It is better for you to enter into life crippled than with two feet to be thrown into Gehenna. And if your eye causes you to sin, pluck it out. Better for you to enter into the kingdom of God with one eye than with two eyes to be thrown into Gehenna, where 'their worm does not die, and the fire is not quenched.'"

1005 26TH SUNDAY IN ORDINARY TIME — C

FIRST READING
Amos 6:1a, 4–7

Thus says the LORD the God of hosts:
 Woe to the complacent in Zion!
 Lying upon beds of ivory,
  stretched comfortably on
   their couches,
 they eat lambs taken from the flock,
  and calves from the stall!
 Improvising to the music of the harp,
  like David, they devise their own
   accompaniment.

They drink wine from bowls
 and anoint themselves with the
  best oils;
 yet they are not made ill by the
  collapse of Joseph!
Therefore, now they shall be the first
 to go into exile,
 and their wanton revelry shall be
  done away with.

RESPONSORIAL PSALM
Psalm 146:7, 8–9, 9–10

℟. Praise the Lord, my soul!

Or ℟. **Alleluia.**

▸ Blessed is he who keeps faith forever,
  secures justice for the oppressed,
  gives food to the hungry.
 The LORD sets captives free. ℟.

▸ The LORD gives sight to the blind;
  the LORD raises up those who were
   bowed down.
 The LORD loves the just;
  the LORD protects strangers. ℟.

▸ The fatherless and the widow
  he sustains,
  but the way of the wicked
   he thwarts.
 The LORD shall reign forever;
  your God, O Zion, through all
   generations. Alleluia. ℟.

SECOND READING
1 Timothy 6:11–16

But you, man of God, pursue righteousness, devotion, faith, love, patience, and gentleness. Compete well for the faith. Lay hold of eternal life, to which you were called when you made the noble confession in the presence of many witnesses. I charge you before God, who gives life to all things, and before Christ Jesus, who gave testimony under Pontius Pilate for the noble confession, to keep the commandment without stain or reproach until the appearance of our Lord Jesus Christ that the blessed and only ruler will make manifest at the proper time, the King of kings and Lord of lords, who alone has immortality, who dwells in unapproachable light, and whom no human being has seen or can see. To him be honor and eternal power. Amen.

GOSPEL ACCLAMATION
cf. 2 Corinthians 8:9

℟. Al - le - lu - ia, al - le - lu - ia, al - le - lu - ia.

(Omit if not sung)

▶ Though our Lord Jesus Christ was rich, he became poor,
so that by his poverty you might become rich. ℟.

GOSPEL

Luke 16:19–31

Jesus said to the Pharisees: "There was a rich man who dressed in purple garments and fine linen and dined sumptuously each day. And lying at his door was a poor man named Lazarus, covered with sores, who would gladly have eaten his fill of the scraps that fell from the rich man's table. Dogs even used to come and lick his sores. When the poor man died, he was carried away by angels to the bosom of Abraham. The rich man also died and was buried, and from the netherworld, where he was in torment, he raised his eyes and saw Abraham far off and Lazarus at his side. And he cried out, 'Father Abraham, have pity on me. Send Lazarus to dip the tip of his finger in water and cool my tongue, for I am suffering torment in these flames.' Abraham replied, 'My child, remember that you received what was good during your lifetime while Lazarus likewise received what was bad; but now he is comforted here, whereas you are tormented. Moreover, between us and you a great chasm is established to prevent anyone from crossing who might wish to go from our side to yours or from your side to ours.' He said, 'Then I beg you, father, send him to my father's house, for I have five brothers, so that he may warn them, lest they too come to this place of torment.' But Abraham replied, 'They have Moses and the prophets. Let them listen to them.' He said, 'Oh no, father Abraham, but if someone from the dead goes to them, they will repent.' Then Abraham said, 'If they will not listen to Moses and the prophets, neither will they be persuaded if someone should rise from the dead.'"

27TH SUNDAY IN ORDINARY TIME — A   1006

FIRST READING

Isaiah 5:1–7

Let me now sing of my friend,
  my friend's song concerning
    his vineyard.
My friend had a vineyard
  on a fertile hillside;
he spaded it, cleared it of stones,
  and planted the choicest vines;
within it he built a watchtower,
  and hewed out a wine press.
Then he looked for the crop
    of grapes,
  but what it yielded was
    wild grapes.

Now, inhabitants of Jerusalem and
    people of Judah,
  judge between me and
    my vineyard:

What more was there to do for
    my vineyard
  that I had not done?
Why, when I looked for the crop
    of grapes,
  did it bring forth wild grapes?
Now, I will let you know
  what I mean to do with
    my vineyard:
take away its hedge, give it to grazing,
  break through its wall, let it
    be trampled!
Yes, I will make it a ruin:
  it shall not be pruned or hoed,
  but overgrown with thorns
    and briers;
I will command the clouds
  not to send rain upon it.

The vineyard of the LORD of hosts is
the house of Israel,
and the people of Judah are his
cherished plant;

he looked for judgment, but
see, bloodshed!
for justice, but hark, the outcry!

RESPONSORIAL PSALM

Psalm 80:9, 12, 13–14, 15–16, 19–20

℟. The vine-yard of the Lord is the house of Is-ra-el.

▶ A vine from Egypt you transplanted;
you drove away the nations and
planted it.
It put forth its foliage to the Sea,
its shoots as far as the River. ℟.

▶ Why have you broken down its walls,
so that every passer-by plucks
its fruit,
the boar from the forest lays it waste,
and the beasts of the field feed
upon it? ℟.

▶ Once again, O LORD of hosts,
look down from heaven, and see;
take care of this vine,
and protect what your right hand
has planted,
the son of man whom you yourself
made strong. ℟.

▶ Then we will no more withdraw
from you;
give us new life, and we will call
upon your name.
O LORD, God of hosts, restore us;
if your face shine upon us, then we
shall be saved. ℟.

SECOND READING

Philippians 4:6–9

Brothers and sisters: Have no anxiety
at all, but in everything, by prayer
and petition, with thanksgiving, make
your requests known to God. Then
the peace of God that surpasses
all understanding will guard your
hearts and minds in Christ Jesus.
    Finally, brothers and sisters, whatever
is true, whatever is honorable,

whatever is just, whatever is pure,
whatever is lovely, whatever is gracious,
if there is any excellence and if there
is anything worthy of praise, think
about these things. Keep on doing
what you have learned and received
and heard and seen in me. Then
the God of peace will be with you.

GOSPEL ACCLAMATION

cf. John 15:16

℟. Al-le-lu - ia, al-le-lu - ia, al-le-lu - ia.

(Omit if not sung)

▶ I have chosen you from the world, says the Lord,
to go and bear fruit that will remain. ℟.

GOSPEL

Matthew 21:33–43

Jesus said to the chief priests and the
elders of the people: "Hear another

parable. There was a landowner who
planted a vineyard, put a hedge around

it, dug a wine press in it, and built a tower. Then he leased it to tenants and went on a journey. When vintage time drew near, he sent his servants to the tenants to obtain his produce. But the tenants seized the servants and one they beat, another they killed, and a third they stoned. Again he sent other servants, more numerous than the first ones, but they treated them in the same way. Finally, he sent his son to them, thinking, 'They will respect my son.' But when the tenants saw the son, they said to one another, 'This is the heir. Come, let us kill him and acquire his inheritance.' They seized him, threw him out of the vineyard, and killed him. What will the owner of the vineyard do to those tenants when he comes?" They answered him, "He will put those wretched men to a wretched death and lease his vineyard to other tenants who will give him the produce at the proper times." Jesus said to them, "Did you never read in the Scriptures:

The stone that the builders rejected
has become the cornerstone;
by the Lord has this been done,
and it is wonderful in our eyes?

Therefore, I say to you, the kingdom of God will be taken away from you and given to a people that will produce its fruit."

27TH SUNDAY IN ORDINARY TIME — B 1007

FIRST READING   *Genesis 2:18–24*

The LORD God said: "It is not good for the man to be alone. I will make a suitable partner for him." So the LORD God formed out of the ground various wild animals and various birds of the air, and he brought them to the man to see what he would call them; whatever the man called each of them would be its name. The man gave names to all the cattle, all the birds of the air, and all wild animals; but none proved to be the suitable partner for the man.

So the LORD God cast a deep sleep on the man, and while he was asleep, he took out one of his ribs and closed up its place with flesh. The LORD God then built up into a woman the rib that he had taken from the man. When he brought her to the man, the man said:

"This one, at last, is bone of my
   bones and flesh of my flesh;
this one shall be called 'woman,'
   for out of 'her man' this one has
   been taken."

That is why a man leaves his father and mother and clings to his wife, and the two of them become one flesh.

RESPONSORIAL PSALM   *Psalm 128:1–2, 3, 4–5, 6*

℟. **May the Lord bless us all the days of our lives.**

Music: Owen Alstott, b. 1947, © 1977, 1990, OCP. All rights reserved.

▸ Blessed are you who fear the LORD,
   who walk in his ways!
For you shall eat the fruit of
   your handiwork;
blessed shall you be, and favored. ℟.

▸ Your wife shall be like a fruitful vine
   in the recesses of your home,
your children like olive plants
   around your table. ℟.

℟. **May the Lord bless us all the days of our lives.**

▸ Behold, thus is the man blessed
  who fears the LORD.
The LORD bless you from Zion:
  may you see the prosperity
    of Jerusalem
  all the days of your life. ℟.

▸ May you see your children's children.
  Peace be upon Israel! ℟.

SECOND READING
Hebrews 2:9–11

Brothers and sisters: He "for a little while" was made "lower than the angels," that by the grace of God he might taste death for everyone.

For it was fitting that he, for whom and through whom all things exist, in bringing many children to glory, should make the leader to their salvation perfect through suffering. He who consecrates and those who are being consecrated all have one origin. Therefore, he is not ashamed to call them "brothers."

GOSPEL ACCLAMATION
1 John 4:12

℟. **Al - le - lu - ia, al - le - lu - ia, al - le - lu - ia.**

Music: Owen Alstott, b. 1947, © 1977, 1990, OCP. All rights reserved.   *(Omit if not sung)*

▸ If we love one another, God remains in us
  and his love is brought to perfection in us. ℟.

GOSPEL
Mark 10:2–16 or 10:2–12

(Include bracketed text for Long Form)

The Pharisees approached Jesus and asked, "Is it lawful for a husband to divorce his wife?" They were testing him. He said to them in reply, "What did Moses command you?" They replied, "Moses permitted a husband to write a bill of divorce and dismiss her." But Jesus told them, "Because of the hardness of your hearts he wrote you this commandment. But from the beginning of creation, *God made them male and female. For this reason a man shall leave his father and mother and be joined to his wife, and the two shall become one flesh.* So they are no longer two but one flesh. Therefore what God has joined together, no human being must separate." In the house the disciples again questioned Jesus about this. He said to them, "Whoever divorces his wife and marries another commits adultery against her; and if she divorces her husband and marries another, she commits adultery."

[And people were bringing children to him that he might touch them, but the disciples rebuked them. When Jesus saw this he became indignant and said to them, "Let the children come to me; do not prevent them, for the kingdom of God belongs to such as these. Amen, I say to you, whoever does not accept the kingdom of God like a child will not enter it." Then he embraced them and blessed them, placing his hands on them.]

27TH SUNDAY IN ORDINARY TIME — C **1008**

FIRST READING
Habakkuk 1:2–3; 2:2–4

How long, O LORD? I cry for help
 but you do not listen!
I cry out to you, "Violence!"
 but you do not intervene.
Why do you let me see ruin;
 why must I look at misery?
Destruction and violence are
  before me;
 there is strife, and clamorous
  discord.
Then the LORD answered me
 and said:

Write down the vision clearly upon
  the tablets,
 so that one can read it readily.
For the vision still has its time,
 presses on to fulfillment, and will
  not disappoint;
if it delays, wait for it,
 it will surely come, it will not
  be late.
The rash one has no integrity;
 but the just one, because of his
  faith, shall live.

RESPONSORIAL PSALM
Psalm 95:1–2, 6–7, 8–9

℟. If to - day you hear his voice, hard - en not your hearts.

Music: Owen Alstott, b. 1947, © 1977, 1990, OCP. All rights reserved.

▶ Come, let us sing joyfully to the LORD;
 let us acclaim the Rock of
  our salvation.
Let us come into his presence
 with thanksgiving;
 let us joyfully sing psalms to him. ℟.

▶ Come, let us bow down in worship;
 let us kneel before the LORD who
  made us.
For he is our God,
 and we are the people he
  shepherds, the flock he guides. ℟.

▶ Oh, that today you would hear
  his voice:
 "Harden not your hearts as
  at Meribah,
 as in the day of Massah in
  the desert,
where your fathers tempted me;
 they tested me though they had
  seen my works." ℟.

SECOND READING
2 Timothy 1:6–8, 13–14

Beloved: I remind you to stir into flame
the gift of God that you have through
the imposition of my hands. For God
did not give us a spirit of cowardice
but rather of power and love and self-
control. So do not be ashamed of your
testimony to our Lord, nor of me, a
prisoner for his sake; but bear your
share of hardship for the gospel with
the strength that comes from God.

Take as your norm the sound words
that you heard from me, in the faith
and love that are in Christ Jesus. Guard
this rich trust with the help of the
Holy Spirit that dwells within us.

GOSPEL ACCLAMATION

1 Peter 1:25

℟. Al - le - lu - ia, al - le - lu - ia, al - le - lu - ia.

(Omit if not sung)

▶ The word of the Lord remains for ever.
This is the word that has been proclaimed to you. ℟.

GOSPEL

Luke 17:5–10

The apostles said to the Lord, "Increase our faith." The Lord replied, "If you have faith the size of a mustard seed, you would say to this mulberry tree, 'Be uprooted and planted in the sea, 'and it would obey you.

"Who among you would say to your servant who has just come in from plowing or tending sheep in the field, 'Come here immediately and take your place at table'? Would he not rather say to him, 'Prepare something for me to eat. Put on your apron and wait on me while I eat and drink. You may eat and drink when I am finished'? Is he grateful to that servant because he did what was commanded? So should it be with you. When you have done all you have been commanded, say, 'We are unprofitable servants; we have done what we were obliged to do.'"

1009   28TH SUNDAY IN ORDINARY TIME — A

FIRST READING

Isaiah 25:6–10a

On this mountain the LORD of hosts
　　will provide for all peoples
a feast of rich food and choice wines,
　　juicy, rich food and pure,
　　　　choice wines.
On this mountain he will destroy
　　the veil that veils all peoples,
the web that is woven over
　　all nations;
　　he will destroy death forever.
The Lord GOD will wipe away
　　the tears from every face;

the reproach of his people he
　　will remove
　　from the whole earth; for the LORD
　　　　has spoken.
　　On that day it will be said:
"Behold our God, to whom we looked
　　to save us!
This is the LORD for whom
　　we looked;
　　let us rejoice and be glad that he
　　　　has saved us!"
For the hand of the LORD will rest on
　　this mountain.

RESPONSORIAL PSALM

Psalm 23:1–3a, 3b–4, 5, 6

℟. I shall live in the house of the Lord all the days of my life.

▶ The LORD is my shepherd; I shall
　　not want.
In verdant pastures he gives
　　me repose;

beside restful waters he leads me;
he refreshes my soul. ℟.

He guides me in right paths
   for his name's sake.
Even though I walk in the dark valley
   I fear no evil; for you are at my side
with your rod and your staff
   that give me courage. ℟.

You spread the table before me
   in the sight of my foes;

you anoint my head with oil;
   my cup overflows. ℟.

Only goodness and kindness
   follow me
   all the days of my life;
and I shall dwell in the house of
   the LORD
   for years to come. ℟.

SECOND READING

Philippians 4:12–14, 19–20

Brothers and sisters: I know how to live in humble circumstances; I know also how to live with abundance. In every circumstance and in all things I have learned the secret of being well fed and of going hungry, of living in abundance and of being in need. I can do all things in him who strengthens me. Still, it was kind of you to share in my distress.

My God will fully supply whatever you need, in accord with his glorious riches in Christ Jesus. To our God and Father, glory forever and ever. Amen.

GOSPEL ACCLAMATION

cf. Ephesians 1:17–18

℟. Al - le - lu - ia, al - le - lu - ia, al - le - lu - ia.

Music: Owen Alstott, b. 1947, © 1977, 1990, OCP. All rights reserved.   *(Omit if not sung)*

May the Father of our Lord Jesus Christ
   enlighten the eyes of our hearts,
   so that we may know what is the hope
   that belongs to our call. ℟.

GOSPEL

Matthew 22:1–14 or 22:1–10

(Include bracketed text for Long Form)

Jesus again in reply spoke to the chief priests and elders of the people in parables, saying, "The kingdom of heaven may be likened to a king who gave a wedding feast for his son. He dispatched his servants to summon the invited guests to the feast, but they refused to come. A second time he sent other servants, saying, 'Tell those invited: "Behold, I have prepared my banquet, my calves and fattened cattle are killed, and everything is ready; come to the feast."' Some ignored the invitation and went away, one to his farm, another to his business. The rest laid hold of his servants, mistreated them, and killed them. The king was enraged and sent his troops, destroyed those murderers, and burned their city. Then he said to his servants, 'The feast is ready, but those who were invited were not worthy to come. Go out, therefore, into the main roads and invite to the feast whomever you find.' The servants went out into the streets and gathered all they found, bad and good alike, and the hall was filled with guests. [But when the king came in to meet the guests, he saw a man there not dressed in a wedding garment. The king said to him, 'My friend, how is it that you came in here without a wedding garment?' But he was reduced to silence. Then the king said to his attendants, 'Bind his hands and feet, and cast him into the darkness outside, where there will be wailing and grinding of teeth.' Many are invited, but few are chosen."]

1010   28TH SUNDAY IN ORDINARY TIME — B

FIRST READING *Wisdom 7:7–11*

I prayed, and prudence was
  given me;
 I pleaded, and the spirit of wisdom
  came to me.
I preferred her to scepter and throne,
and deemed riches nothing in
  comparison with her,
 nor did I liken any priceless gem
  to her;
because all gold, in view of her, is a
  little sand,
 and before her, silver is to be
accounted mire.
Beyond health and comeliness I
  loved her,
and I chose to have her rather than
  the light,
 because the splendor of her never
  yields to sleep.
Yet all good things together came to
  me in her company,
 and countless riches at her hands.

RESPONSORIAL PSALM *Psalm 90:12–13, 14–15, 16–17*

℟. Fill us with your love, O Lord, and we will sing for joy!

Music: Owen Alstott, b. 1947, © 1977, 1990, OCP. All rights reserved.

▸ Teach us to number our days aright,
  that we may gain wisdom of heart.
 Return, O LORD! How long?
  Have pity on your servants! ℟.

▸ Fill us at daybreak with your kindness,
  that we may shout for joy and
  gladness all our days.
 Make us glad, for the days when you
  afflicted us,
  for the years when we saw evil. ℟.

▸ Let your work be seen by
  your servants
 and your glory by their children;
 and may the gracious care of the Lord
  our God be ours;
 prosper the work of our hands
  for us!
 Prosper the work of our hands! ℟.

SECOND READING *Hebrews 4:12–13*

Brothers and sisters: Indeed the word of God is living and effective, sharper than any two-edged sword, penetrating even between soul and spirit, joints and marrow, and able to discern reflections and thoughts of the heart. No creature is concealed from him, but everything is naked and exposed to the eyes of him to whom we must render an account.

GOSPEL ACCLAMATION

Matthew 5:3

℟. Al - le - lu - ia, al - le - lu - ia, al - le - lu - ia.

(Omit if not sung)

▸ Blessed are the poor in spirit,
  for theirs is the kingdom of heaven. ℟.

GOSPEL

Mark 10:17–30 or 10:17–27

(Include bracketed text for Long Form)

As Jesus was setting out on a journey, a man ran up, knelt down before him, and asked him, "Good teacher, what must I do to inherit eternal life?" Jesus answered him, "Why do you call me good? No one is good but God alone. You know the commandments: *You shall not kill; you shall not commit adultery; you shall not steal; you shall not bear false witness; you shall not defraud; honor your father and your mother.*" He replied and said to him, "Teacher, all of these I have observed from my youth." Jesus, looking at him, loved him and said to him, "You are lacking in one thing. Go, sell what you have, and give to the poor and you will have treasure in heaven; then come, follow me." At that statement his face fell, and he went away sad, for he had many possessions.

Jesus looked around and said to his disciples, "How hard it is for those who have wealth to enter the kingdom of God!" The disciples were amazed at his words. So Jesus again said to them in reply, "Children, how hard it is to enter the kingdom of God! It is easier for a camel to pass through the eye of a needle than for one who is rich to enter the kingdom of God." They were exceedingly astonished and said among themselves, "Then who can be saved?" Jesus looked at them and said, "For human beings it is impossible, but not for God. All things are possible for God." [Peter began to say to him, "We have given up everything and followed you." Jesus said, "Amen, I say to you, there is no one who has given up house or brothers or sisters or mother or father or children or lands for my sake and for the sake of the gospel who will not receive a hundred times more now in this present age: houses and brothers and sisters and mothers and children and lands, with persecutions, and eternal life in the age to come."]

28TH SUNDAY IN ORDINARY TIME — C   1011

FIRST READING

2 Kings 5:14–17

Naaman went down and plunged into the Jordan seven times at the word of Elisha, the man of God. His flesh became again like the flesh of a little child, and he was clean of his leprosy.

Naaman returned with his whole retinue to the man of God. On his arrival he stood before Elisha and said, "Now I know that there is no God in all the earth, except in Israel. Please accept a gift from your servant."

Elisha replied, "As the LORD lives whom I serve, I will not take it"; and despite Naaman's urging, he still refused. Naaman said: "If you will not accept, please let me, your servant, have two mule-loads of earth, for I will no longer offer holocaust or sacrifice to any other god except to the LORD."

RESPONSORIAL PSALM

Psalm 98:1, 2–3, 3–4

℟. The Lord has re-vealed to the na-tions his sav - ing pow'r.

▶ Sing to the LORD a new song,
    for he has done wondrous deeds;
his right hand has won victory
    for him,
    his holy arm. ℟.

▶ The LORD has made his
    salvation known:
in the sight of the nations he has
    revealed his justice.

He has remembered his kindness and
    his faithfulness
toward the house of Israel. ℟.

▶ All the ends of the earth have seen
    the salvation by our God.
Sing joyfully to the LORD,
    all you lands:
    break into song; sing praise. ℟.

SECOND READING

2 Timothy 2:8–13

Beloved: Remember Jesus Christ, raised from the dead, a descendant of David: such is my gospel, for which I am suffering, even to the point of chains, like a criminal. But the word of God is not chained. Therefore, I bear with everything for the sake of those who are chosen, so that they too may obtain the salvation that is in Christ Jesus, together with eternal glory. This saying is trustworthy:

If we have died with him
    we shall also live with him;
if we persevere
    we shall also reign with him.
But if we deny him
    he will deny us.
If we are unfaithful
    he remains faithful,
    for he cannot deny himself.

GOSPEL ACCLAMATION

1 Thessalonians 5:18

℟. Al - le - lu - ia, al - le - lu - ia, al - le - lu - ia.

(Omit if not sung)

▶ In all circumstances, give thanks,
    for this is the will of God for you in Christ Jesus. ℟.

GOSPEL

Luke 17:11–19

As Jesus continued his journey to Jerusalem, he traveled through Samaria and Galilee. As he was entering a village, ten lepers met him. They stood at a distance from him and raised their voices, saying, "Jesus, Master! Have pity on us!" And when he saw them, he said, "Go show yourselves to the priests." As they were going they were cleansed. And one of them, realizing he had been healed, returned, glorifying God in a loud voice; and he fell at the feet of Jesus and thanked him. He was a Samaritan. Jesus said in reply, "Ten were cleansed, were they not? Where are the other nine? Has none but this foreigner returned to give thanks to God?" Then he said to him, "Stand up and go; your faith has saved you."

29TH SUNDAY IN ORDINARY TIME — A   1012

FIRST READING   *Isaiah 45:1, 4–6*

Thus says the LORD to his
  anointed, Cyrus,
  whose right hand I grasp,
subduing nations before him,
  and making kings run in
   his service,
opening doors before him
  and leaving the gates unbarred:
For the sake of Jacob, my servant,
  of Israel, my chosen one,
I have called you by your name,
giving you a title, though you
  knew me not.
I am the LORD and there is no other,
  there is no God besides me.
It is I who arm you, though you know
  me not,
so that toward the rising and the
  setting of the sun
people may know that there is
  none besides me.
I am the LORD, there is no other.

RESPONSORIAL PSALM   *Psalm 96:1, 3, 4–5, 7–8, 9–10*

℟. Give the Lord glo - ry and hon - or.

Music: Owen Alstott, b. 1947, © 1977, 1990, OCP. All rights reserved.

▶ Sing to the LORD a new song;
  sing to the LORD, all you lands.
Tell his glory among the nations;
  among all peoples, his wondrous
   deeds. ℟.

▶ For great is the LORD and highly to
   be praised;
  awesome is he, beyond all gods.
For all the gods of the nations are
   things of nought,
  but the LORD made the heavens. ℟.

▶ Give to the LORD, you families
  of nations,
  give to the LORD glory and praise;
  give to the LORD the glory due
   his name!
Bring gifts, and enter his courts. ℟.

▶ Worship the LORD, in holy attire.
  Tremble before him, all the earth;
say among the nations: The LORD
  is king,
  he governs the peoples
   with equity. ℟.

SECOND READING   *1 Thessalonians 1:1–5b*

Paul, Silvanus, and Timothy to the church of the Thessalonians in God the Father and the Lord Jesus Christ: grace to you and peace.

  We give thanks to God always for all of you, remembering you in our prayers, unceasingly calling to mind your work of faith and labor of love and endurance in hope of our Lord Jesus Christ, before our God and Father, knowing, brothers and sisters loved by God, how you were chosen. For our gospel did not come to you in word alone, but also in power and in the Holy Spirit and with much conviction.

GOSPEL ACCLAMATION

Philippians 2:15d, 16a

℟. Al - le - lu - ia,   al - le - lu - ia,   al - le - lu - ia.

(Omit if not sung)

▶ Shine like lights in the world
   as you hold on to the word of life. ℟.

GOSPEL

Matthew 22:15–21

The Pharisees went off and plotted how they might entrap Jesus in speech. They sent their disciples to him, with the Herodians, saying, "Teacher, we know that you are a truthful man and that you teach the way of God in accordance with the truth. And you are not concerned with anyone's opinion, for you do not regard a person's status. Tell us, then, what is your opinion: Is it lawful to pay the census tax to Caesar or not?" Knowing their malice, Jesus said, "Why are you testing me, you hypocrites? Show me the coin that pays the census tax." Then they handed him the Roman coin. He said to them, "Whose image is this and whose inscription?" They replied, "Caesar's." At that he said to them, "Then repay to Caesar what belongs to Caesar and to God what belongs to God."

1013   29TH SUNDAY IN ORDINARY TIME — B

FIRST READING

Isaiah 53:10–11

The LORD was pleased
   to crush him in infirmity.

If he gives his life as an offering
      for sin,
   he shall see his descendants
      in a long life,
   and the will of the LORD shall be
      accomplished through him.

Because of his affliction
   he shall see the light in fullness
      of days;
through his suffering, my servant
   shall justify many,
   and their guilt he shall bear.

RESPONSORIAL PSALM

Psalm 33:4–5, 18–19, 20, 22

℟. Lord, let your mer - cy be on us,   as we place our trust in you.

▶ Upright is the word of the LORD,
   and all his works are trustworthy.
He loves justice and right;
   of the kindness of the LORD the
      earth is full. ℟.

▶ See, the eyes of the LORD are upon
      those who fear him,
   upon those who hope for
      his kindness,

to deliver them from death
   and preserve them in spite
      of famine. ℟.

▶ Our soul waits for the LORD,
   who is our help and our shield.
May your kindness, O LORD,
      be upon us
   who have put our hope in you. ℟.

SECOND READING

Hebrews 4:14–16

Brothers and sisters: Since we have a great high priest who has passed through the heavens, Jesus, the Son of God, let us hold fast to our confession. For we do not have a high priest who is unable to sympathize with our weaknesses, but one who has similarly been tested in every way, yet without sin. So let us confidently approach the throne of grace to receive mercy and to find grace for timely help.

GOSPEL ACCLAMATION

Mark 10:45

℟. Al - le - lu - ia, al - le - lu - ia, al - le - lu - ia.

Music: Owen Alstott, b. 1947, © 1977, 1990, OCP. All rights reserved.   *(Omit if not sung)*

▸ The Son of Man came to serve
  and to give his life as a ransom for many. ℟.

GOSPEL

Mark 10:35–45 or 10:42–45

(Include bracketed text for Long Form and text in parentheses for Short Form)

[James and John, the sons of Zebedee, came to Jesus and said to him, "Teacher, we want you to do for us whatever we ask of you." He replied, "What do you wish me to do for you?" They answered him, "Grant that in your glory we may sit one at your right and the other at your left." Jesus said to them, "You do not know what you are asking. Can you drink the cup that I drink or be baptized with the baptism with which I am baptized?" They said to him, "We can." Jesus said to them, "The cup that I drink, you will drink, and with the baptism with which I am baptized, you will be baptized; but to sit at my right or at my left is not mine to give but is for those for whom it has been prepared." When the ten heard this, they became indignant at James and John.] Jesus summoned [them] (the Twelve) and said to them, "You know that those who are recognized as rulers over the Gentiles lord it over them, and their great ones make their authority over them felt. But it shall not be so among you. Rather, whoever wishes to be great among you will be your servant; whoever wishes to be first among you will be the slave of all. For the Son of Man did not come to be served but to serve and to give his life as a ransom for many."

29TH SUNDAY IN ORDINARY TIME — C   1014

FIRST READING

Exodus 17:8–13

In those days, Amalek came and waged war against Israel. Moses, therefore, said to Joshua, "Pick out certain men, and tomorrow go out and engage Amalek in battle. I will be standing on top of the hill with the staff of God in my hand." So Joshua did as Moses told him: he engaged Amalek in battle after Moses had climbed to the top of the hill with Aaron and Hur. As long as Moses kept his hands raised up, Israel had the better of the fight, but when he let his hands rest, Amalek had the better of the fight. Moses' hands, however, grew tired; so they put a rock in place for him to sit on. Meanwhile Aaron and Hur supported his hands, one on one side and one on the other, so that his hands remained steady till sunset. And Joshua mowed down Amalek and his people with the edge of the sword.

RESPONSORIAL PSALM

Psalm 121:1–2, 3–4, 5–6, 7–8

℟. Our help is from the Lord, who made heaven and earth.

▶ I lift up my eyes toward
  the mountains;
    whence shall help come to me?
My help is from the LORD,
  who made heaven and earth. ℟.

▶ May he not suffer your foot to slip;
  may he slumber not who
    guards you:
indeed he neither slumbers
  nor sleeps,
    the guardian of Israel. ℟.

▶ The LORD is your guardian; the LORD
  is your shade;
    he is beside you at your right hand.
The sun shall not harm you by day,
  nor the moon by night. ℟.

▶ The LORD will guard you from all evil;
  he will guard your life.
The LORD will guard your coming and
  your going,
    both now and forever. ℟.

SECOND READING

2 Timothy 3:14—4:2

Beloved: Remain faithful to what you have learned and believed, because you know from whom you learned it, and that from infancy you have known the sacred Scriptures, which are capable of giving you wisdom for salvation through faith in Christ Jesus. All Scripture is inspired by God and is useful for teaching, for refutation, for correction, and for training in righteousness, so that one who belongs to God may be competent, equipped for every good work.

I charge you in the presence of God and of Christ Jesus, who will judge the living and the dead, and by his appearing and his kingly power: proclaim the word; be persistent whether it is convenient or inconvenient; convince, reprimand, encourage through all patience and teaching.

GOSPEL ACCLAMATION

Hebrews 4:12

℟. Al - le - lu - ia, al - le - lu - ia, al - le - lu - ia.

(Omit if not sung)

▶ The word of God is living and effective,
  discerning reflections and thoughts of the heart. ℟.

GOSPEL

Luke 18:1–8

Jesus told his disciples a parable about the necessity for them to pray always without becoming weary. He said, "There was a judge in a certain town who neither feared God nor respected any human being. And a widow in that town used to come to him and say, 'Render a just decision for me against my adversary.' For a long time the judge was unwilling, but eventually he thought, 'While it is true that I neither fear God nor respect any human being, because this widow keeps bothering me I shall deliver a just decision for her lest she finally come and strike me.'" The Lord said,

"Pay attention to what the dishonest judge says. Will not God then secure the rights of his chosen ones who call out to him day and night? Will he be slow to answer them? I tell you, he will see to it that justice is done for them speedily. But when the Son of Man comes, will he find faith on earth?"

30TH SUNDAY IN ORDINARY TIME — A   1015

FIRST READING
Exodus 22:20–26

Thus says the LORD: "You shall not molest or oppress an alien, for you were once aliens yourselves in the land of Egypt. You shall not wrong any widow or orphan. If ever you wrong them and they cry out to me, I will surely hear their cry. My wrath will flare up, and I will kill you with the sword; then your own wives will be widows, and your children orphans.

"If you lend money to one of your poor neighbors among my people, you shall not act like an extortioner toward him by demanding interest from him. If you take your neighbor's cloak as a pledge, you shall return it to him before sunset; for this cloak of his is the only covering he has for his body. What else has he to sleep in? If he cries out to me, I will hear him; for I am compassionate."

RESPONSORIAL PSALM
Psalm 18:2–3, 3–4, 47, 51

℟. I love you, Lord, my strength.

Music: Owen Alstott, b. 1947, © 1977, 1990, OCP. All rights reserved.

▶ I love you, O LORD, my strength,
    O LORD, my rock, my fortress,
        my deliverer. ℟.

▶ My God, my rock of refuge,
    my shield, the horn of my salvation,
        my stronghold!
    Praised be the LORD, I exclaim,
        and I am safe from my enemies. ℟.

▶ The LORD lives and blessed be
        my rock!
    Extolled be God my savior.
    You who gave great victories to
        your king
    and showed kindness to
        your anointed. ℟.

SECOND READING
1 Thessalonians 1:5c–10

Brothers and sisters: You know what sort of people we were among you for your sake. And you became imitators of us and of the Lord, receiving the word in great affliction, with joy from the Holy Spirit, so that you became a model for all the believers in Macedonia and in Achaia. For from

you the word of the Lord has sounded forth not only in Macedonia and in Achaia, but in every place your faith in God has gone forth, so that we have no need to say anything. For they themselves openly declare about us what sort of reception we had among you, and how you turned to God from

idols to serve the living and true God
and to await his Son from heaven,

whom he raised from the dead, Jesus,
who delivers us from the coming wrath.

GOSPEL ACCLAMATION

John 14:23

℟. Al - le - lu - ia, al - le - lu - ia, al - le - lu - ia.

(Omit if not sung)

▸ Whoever loves me will keep my word, says the Lord,
   and my Father will love him and we will come to him. ℟.

GOSPEL

Matthew 22:34–40

When the Pharisees heard that Jesus
had silenced the Sadducees, they
gathered together, and one of them,
a scholar of the law, tested him by
asking, "Teacher, which commandment
in the law is the greatest?" He said to
him, "You shall love the Lord, your
God, with all your heart, with all your
soul, and with all your mind. This is the
greatest and the first commandment.
The second is like it: You shall love
your neighbor as yourself. The
whole law and the prophets depend
on these two commandments."

1016 30TH SUNDAY IN ORDINARY TIME — B

FIRST READING

Jeremiah 31:7–9

Thus says the LORD:
   Shout with joy for Jacob,
      exult at the head of the nations;
      proclaim your praise and say:
   The LORD has delivered his people,
      the remnant of Israel.
   Behold, I will bring them back
      from the land of the north;
   I will gather them from the ends of
         the world,
      with the blind and the lame in
         their midst,

the mothers and those with child;
      they shall return as an
         immense throng.
They departed in tears,
   but I will console them and
      guide them;
I will lead them to brooks of water,
   on a level road, so that none
      shall stumble.
For I am a father to Israel,
   Ephraim is my first-born.

RESPONSORIAL PSALM

Psalm 126:1–2, 2–3, 4–5, 6

℟. The Lord has done great things for us; we are filled with joy.

▸ When the LORD brought back the
      captives of Zion,
   we were like men dreaming.
   Then our mouth was filled
      with laughter,
   and our tongue with rejoicing. ℟.

▸ Then they said among the nations,
      "The LORD has done great things
      for them."
   The LORD has done great things
      for us;
   we are glad indeed. ℟.

▶ Restore our fortunes, O LORD,
  like the torrents in the
    southern desert.
  Those that sow in tears
    shall reap rejoicing. ℟.

▶ Although they go forth weeping,
  carrying the seed to be sown,
  they shall come back rejoicing,
  carrying their sheaves. ℟.

SECOND READING
Hebrews 5:1–6

Brothers and sisters: Every high priest is taken from among men and made their representative before God, to offer gifts and sacrifices for sins. He is able to deal patiently with the ignorant and erring, for he himself is beset by weakness and so, for this reason, must make sin offerings for himself as well as for the people. No one takes this honor upon himself but only when called by God, just as Aaron was. In the same way, it was not Christ who glorified himself in becoming high priest, but rather the one who said to him:
You are my son:
  this day I have begotten you;
just as he says in another place:
You are a priest forever
  according to the order
  of Melchizedek.

GOSPEL ACCLAMATION
cf. 2 Timothy 1:10

℟. Al - le - lu - ia, al - le - lu - ia, al - le - lu - ia.

(Omit if not sung)

▶ Our Savior Jesus Christ destroyed death
  and brought life to light through the Gospel. ℟.

GOSPEL
Mark 10:46–52

As Jesus was leaving Jericho with his disciples and a sizable crowd, Bartimaeus, a blind man, the son of Timaeus, sat by the roadside begging. On hearing that it was Jesus of Nazareth, he began to cry out and say, "Jesus, son of David, have pity on me." And many rebuked him, telling him to be silent. But he kept calling out all the more, "Son of David, have pity on me." Jesus stopped and said, "Call him." So they called the blind man, saying to him, "Take courage; get up, Jesus is calling you." He threw aside his cloak, sprang up, and came to Jesus. Jesus said to him in reply, "What do you want me to do for you?" The blind man replied to him, "Master, I want to see." Jesus told him, "Go your way; your faith has saved you." Immediately he received his sight and followed him on the way.

30TH SUNDAY IN ORDINARY TIME — C   1017

FIRST READING
Sirach 35:12–14, 16–18

The LORD is a God of justice,
  who knows no favorites.
Though not unduly partial toward
    the weak,
  yet he hears the cry of
the oppressed.
The Lord is not deaf to the wail of
    the orphan,
  nor to the widow when she pours
    out her complaint.

The one who serves God willingly
    is heard;
  his petition reaches the heavens.
The prayer of the lowly pierces
    the clouds;
  it does not rest till it reaches
    its goal,

nor will it withdraw till the Most High
    responds,
  judges justly and affirms the right,
and the Lord will not delay.

RESPONSORIAL PSALM

Psalm 34:2–3, 17–18, 19, 23

℟. The Lord hears the cry of the poor.

▶ I will bless the LORD at all times;
  his praise shall be ever in
    my mouth.
Let my soul glory in the LORD;
  the lowly will hear me and
    be glad. ℟.

▶ The LORD confronts the evildoers,
  to destroy remembrance of them
    from the earth.
When the just cry out, the LORD
  hears them,

and from all their distress he
  rescues them. ℟.

▶ The LORD is close to the
    brokenhearted;
  and those who are crushed in spirit
    he saves.
The LORD redeems the lives of
  his servants;
  no one incurs guilt who takes
    refuge in him. ℟.

SECOND READING

2 Timothy 4:6–8, 16–18

Beloved: I am already being poured out like a libation, and the time of my departure is at hand. I have competed well; I have finished the race; I have kept the faith. From now on the crown of righteousness awaits me, which the Lord, the just judge, will award to me on that day, and not only to me, but to all who have longed for his appearance.

  At my first defense no one appeared on my behalf, but everyone deserted me. May it not be held against them! But the Lord stood by me and gave me strength, so that through me the proclamation might be completed and all the Gentiles might hear it. And I was rescued from the lion's mouth. The Lord will rescue me from every evil threat and will bring me safe to his heavenly kingdom. To him be glory forever and ever. Amen.

GOSPEL ACCLAMATION

2 Corinthians 5:19

℟. Al - le - lu - ia, al - le - lu - ia, al - le - lu - ia.

(Omit if not sung)

▶ God was reconciling the world to himself in Christ,
  and entrusting to us the message of salvation. ℟.

GOSPEL

Luke 18:9–14

Jesus addressed this parable to those who were convinced of their own righteousness and despised everyone else. "Two people went up to the temple area to pray; one was a Pharisee and the other was a tax collector. The Pharisee took up his position and spoke this prayer to himself, 'O God, I thank you that I am not like the rest of humanity—greedy, dishonest, adulterous—or even like this tax collector. I fast twice a week, and I pay tithes on my whole income.' But the tax collector stood off at a distance and would not even raise his eyes to heaven but beat his breast and prayed, 'O God, be merciful to me a sinner.' I tell you, the latter went home justified, not the former; for whoever exalts himself will be humbled, and the one who humbles himself will be exalted."

31ST SUNDAY IN ORDINARY TIME — A   1018

FIRST READING

Malachi 1:14b–2:2b, 8–10

A great King am I, says the LORD
    of hosts,
    and my name will be feared among
    the nations.
And now, O priests, this
    commandment is for you:
    If you do not listen,
    if you do not lay it to heart,
        to give glory to my name, says the
        LORD of hosts,
    I will send a curse upon you
        and of your blessing I will make
        a curse.
You have turned aside from the way,
    and have caused many to falter by
    your instruction;
you have made void the covenant
    of Levi,
    says the LORD of hosts.
I, therefore, have made you
    contemptible
    and base before all the people,
since you do not keep my ways,
    but show partiality in
    your decisions.
Have we not all the one father?
    Has not the one God created us?
Why then do we break faith with
    one another,
    violating the covenant of
    our fathers?

RESPONSORIAL PSALM

Psalm 131:1, 2, 3

℟. In you, Lord, I have found my peace.

▶ O LORD, my heart is not proud,
    nor are my eyes haughty;
I busy not myself with great things,
    nor with things too sublime
        for me. ℟.

▶ Nay rather, I have stilled and quieted
    my soul like a weaned child.
Like a weaned child on its
        mother's lap,
    so is my soul within me. ℟.

▶ O Israel, hope in the LORD,
    both now and forever. ℟.

SECOND READING
1 Thessalonians 2:7b–9, 13

Brothers and sisters: We were gentle among you, as a nursing mother cares for her children. With such affection for you, we were determined to share with you not only the gospel of God, but our very selves as well, so dearly beloved had you become to us. You recall, brothers and sisters, our toil and drudgery. Working night and day in order not to burden any of you, we proclaimed to you the gospel of God.

And for this reason we too give thanks to God unceasingly, that, in receiving the word of God from hearing us, you received not a human word but, as it truly is, the word of God, which is now at work in you who believe.

GOSPEL ACCLAMATION
Matthew 23:9b, 10b

℟. Al - le - lu - ia, al - le - lu - ia, al - le - lu - ia.

Music: Owen Alstott, b. 1947, © 1977, 1990, OCP. All rights reserved.

(Omit if not sung)

▶ You have but one Father in heaven and one master, the Christ. ℟.

GOSPEL
Matthew 23:1–12

Jesus spoke to the crowds and to his disciples, saying, "The scribes and the Pharisees have taken their seat on the chair of Moses. Therefore, do and observe all things whatsoever they tell you, but do not follow their example. For they preach but they do not practice. They tie up heavy burdens hard to carry and lay them on people's shoulders, but they will not lift a finger to move them. All their works are performed to be seen. They widen their phylacteries and lengthen their tassels. They love places of honor at banquets, seats of honor in synagogues, greetings in marketplaces, and the salutation 'Rabbi.' As for you, do not be called 'Rabbi.' You have but one teacher, and you are all brothers. Call no one on earth your father; you have but one Father in heaven. Do not be called 'Master'; you have but one master, the Christ. The greatest among you must be your servant. Whoever exalts himself will be humbled; but whoever humbles himself will be exalted."

1019   31ST SUNDAY IN ORDINARY TIME — B

FIRST READING
Deuteronomy 6:2–6

Moses spoke to the people, saying: "Fear the LORD, your God, and keep, throughout the days of your lives, all his statutes and commandments which I enjoin on you, and thus have long life. Hear then, Israel, and be careful to observe them, that you may grow and prosper the more, in keeping with the promise of the LORD, the God of your fathers, to give you a land flowing with milk and honey.

"Hear, O Israel! The LORD is our God, the LORD alone! Therefore, you shall love the LORD, your God, with all your heart, and with all your soul, and with all your strength. Take to heart these words which I enjoin on you today."

RESPONSORIAL PSALM

Psalm 18:2–3, 3–4, 47, 51

℟. I love you, Lord, my strength.

▶ I love you, O LORD, my strength,
    O LORD, my rock, my fortress, my
        deliverer. ℟.

▶ My God, my rock of refuge,
    my shield, the horn of my salvation,
        my stronghold!
    Praised be the LORD, I exclaim,
        and I am safe from my enemies. ℟.

▶ The LORD lives! And blessed be
    my rock!
    Extolled be God my savior,
    you who gave great victories
        to your king
    and showed kindness to
        your anointed. ℟.

SECOND READING

Hebrews 7:23–28

Brothers and sisters: The levitical priests were many because they were prevented by death from remaining in office, but Jesus, because he remains forever, has a priesthood that does not pass away. Therefore, he is always able to save those who approach God through him, since he lives forever to make intercession for them.

It was fitting that we should have such a high priest: holy, innocent, undefiled, separated from sinners, higher than the heavens. He has no need, as did the high priests, to offer sacrifice day after day, first for his own sins and then for those of the people; he did that once for all when he offered himself. For the law appoints men subject to weakness to be high priests, but the word of the oath, which was taken after the law, appoints a son, who has been made perfect forever.

GOSPEL ACCLAMATION

John 14:23

℟. Al - le - lu - ia, al - le - lu - ia, al - le - lu - ia.

(Omit if not sung)

▶ Whoever loves me will keep my word, says the Lord;
    and my Father will love him and we will come to him. ℟.

GOSPEL

Mark 12:28b–34

One of the scribes came to Jesus and asked him, "Which is the first of all the commandments?" Jesus replied, "The first is this: *Hear, O Israel! The Lord our God is Lord alone! You shall love the Lord your God with all your heart, with all your soul, with all your mind, and with all your strength.* The second is this: *You shall love your neighbor as yourself.* There is no other commandment greater than these." The scribe said to him, "Well said, teacher. You are right in saying, 'He is One and there is no other than he.' And 'to love him with all your heart, with all your understanding, with all your strength, and to love your neighbor as yourself' is worth more than all burnt offerings and sacrifices." And when Jesus saw that he answered with understanding, he said to him, "You are not far from the kingdom of God." And no one dared to ask him any more questions.

1020   31st Sunday in Ordinary Time — C

First Reading

Wisdom 11:22—12:2

Before the Lord the whole universe
    is as a grain from a balance
    or a drop of morning dew come
      down upon the earth.
But you have mercy on all, because
    you can do all things;
    and you overlook people's sins that
      they may repent.
For you love all things that are
    and loathe nothing that you
      have made;
    for what you hated, you would not
      have fashioned.
And how could a thing remain, unless
    you willed it;
or be preserved, had it not been
    called forth by you?
But you spare all things, because they
    are yours,
O Lord and lover of souls,
    for your imperishable spirit is
      in all things!
Therefore you rebuke offenders little
    by little,
    warn them and remind them of the
      sins they are committing,
    that they may abandon their
      wickedness and believe in you,
      O Lord!

Responsorial Psalm

Psalm 145:1–2, 8–9, 10–11, 13–14

℟. I will praise your name for ev-er, my king and my God.

Music: Owen Alstott, b. 1947, © 1977, 1990, OCP. All rights reserved.

▶ I will extol you, O my God and King,
    and I will bless your name forever
      and ever.
Every day will I bless you,
    and I will praise your name forever
      and ever. ℟.

▶ The Lord is gracious and merciful,
    slow to anger and of great kindness.
The Lord is good to all
    and compassionate toward all
      his works. ℟.

▶ Let all your works give you thanks,
    O Lord,
    and let your faithful ones bless you.
Let them discourse of the glory of
    your kingdom
    and speak of your might. ℟.

▶ The Lord is faithful in all his words
    and holy in all his works.
The Lord lifts up all who are falling
    and raises up all who are
      bowed down. ℟.

Second Reading

2 Thessalonians 1:11—2:2

Brothers and sisters: We always pray for you, that our God may make you worthy of his calling and powerfully bring to fulfillment every good purpose and every effort of faith, that the name of our Lord Jesus may be glorified in you, and you in him, in accord with the grace of our God and Lord Jesus Christ.

We ask you, brothers and sisters, with regard to the coming of our Lord Jesus Christ and our assembling with him, not to be shaken out of your minds suddenly, or to be alarmed either by a "spirit," or by an oral statement, or by a letter allegedly from us to the effect that the day of the Lord is at hand.

GOSPEL ACCLAMATION
John 3:16

℟. Al - le - lu - ia, al - le - lu - ia, al - le - lu - ia.

(Omit if not sung)

▶ God so loved the world that he gave his only Son, so that everyone who believes in him might have eternal life. ℟.

GOSPEL
Luke 19:1–10

At that time, Jesus came to Jericho and intended to pass through the town. Now a man there named Zacchaeus, who was a chief tax collector and also a wealthy man, was seeking to see who Jesus was; but he could not see him because of the crowd, for he was short in stature. So he ran ahead and climbed a sycamore tree in order to see Jesus, who was about to pass that way. When he reached the place, Jesus looked up and said, "Zacchaeus, come down quickly, for today I must stay at your house." And he came down quickly and received him with joy. When they all saw this, they began to grumble, saying, "He has gone to stay at the house of a sinner." But Zacchaeus stood there and said to the Lord, "Behold, half of my possessions, Lord, I shall give to the poor, and if I have extorted anything from anyone I shall repay it four times over." And Jesus said to him, "Today salvation has come to this house because this man too is a descendant of Abraham. For the Son of Man has come to seek and to save what was lost."

32ND SUNDAY IN ORDINARY TIME — A   1021

FIRST READING
Wisdom 6:12–16

Resplendent and unfading is wisdom,
and she is readily perceived by
those who love her,
and found by those who seek her.
She hastens to make herself known
in anticipation of their desire;
whoever watches for her at dawn
shall not be disappointed,
for he shall find her sitting by
his gate.

For taking thought of wisdom is the
perfection of prudence,
and whoever for her sake
keeps vigil
shall quickly be free from care;
because she makes her own rounds,
seeking those worthy of her,
and graciously appears to them in
the ways,
and meets them with all solicitude.

RESPONSORIAL PSALM
Psalm 63:2, 3–4, 5–6, 7–8

℟. My soul is thirst - ing for you, O Lord my God.

℟. My soul is thirsting for you, O Lord my God.

▶ O God, you are my God whom I seek;
  for you my flesh pines and my
    soul thirsts
  like the earth, parched, lifeless and
    without water. ℟.

▶ Thus have I gazed toward you in
    the sanctuary
  to see your power and your glory,
  for your kindness is a greater good
    than life;
  my lips shall glorify you. ℟.

▶ Thus will I bless you while I live;
  lifting up my hands, I will call upon
    your name.
  As with the riches of a banquet shall
    my soul be satisfied,
  and with exultant lips my mouth
    shall praise you. ℟.

▶ I will remember you upon my couch,
  and through the night-watches I
    will meditate on you:
  you are my help,
    and in the shadow of your wings
    I shout for joy. ℟.

SECOND READING

1 Thessalonians 4:13–18 or 4:13–14

(Include bracketed text for Long Form)

We do not want you to be unaware, brothers and sisters, about those who have fallen asleep, so that you may not grieve like the rest, who have no hope. For if we believe that Jesus died and rose, so too will God, through Jesus, bring with him those who have fallen asleep. [Indeed, we tell you this, on the word of the Lord, that we who are alive, who are left until the coming of the Lord, will surely not precede those who have fallen asleep. For the Lord himself, with a word of command, with the voice of an archangel and with the trumpet of God, will come down from heaven, and the dead in Christ will rise first. Then we who are alive, who are left, will be caught up together with them in the clouds to meet the Lord in the air. Thus we shall always be with the Lord. Therefore, console one another with these words.]

GOSPEL ACCLAMATION

Matthew 24:42a, 44

℟. Al - le - lu - ia, al - le - lu - ia, al - le - lu - ia.

Music: Owen Alstott, b. 1947, © 1977, 1990, OCP. All rights reserved.

(Omit if not sung)

▶ Stay awake and be ready!
  For you do not know on what day your Lord will come. ℟.

GOSPEL

Matthew 25:1–13

Jesus told his disciples this parable: "The kingdom of heaven will be like ten virgins who took their lamps and went out to meet the bridegroom. Five of them were foolish and five were wise. The foolish ones, when taking their lamps, brought no oil with them, but the wise brought flasks of oil with their lamps. Since the bridegroom was long delayed, they all became drowsy and fell asleep. At midnight, there was a cry, 'Behold, the bridegroom! Come out to meet him!' Then all those virgins got up and trimmed their lamps. The foolish ones said to the wise, 'Give us some of your oil, for our lamps are going out.' But the wise ones replied, 'No, for there may not be enough for us and you. Go instead to the merchants and buy some for yourselves.' While they went off to buy it, the bridegroom came and those who were ready went into the wedding feast with him. Then the door was locked. Afterwards the other virgins came and said, 'Lord, Lord, open the door for us!' But he said in reply, 'Amen, I say to you, I do not know you.' Therefore, stay awake, for you know neither the day nor the hour."

32ND SUNDAY IN ORDINARY TIME — B 1022

FIRST READING
1 Kings 17:10–16

In those days, Elijah the prophet went to Zarephath. As he arrived at the entrance of the city, a widow was gathering sticks there; he called out to her, "Please bring me a small cupful of water to drink." She left to get it, and he called out after her, "Please bring along a bit of bread." She answered, "As the LORD, your God, lives, I have nothing baked; there is only a handful of flour in my jar and a little oil in my jug. Just now I was collecting a couple of sticks, to go in and prepare something for myself and my son; when we have eaten it, we shall die." Elijah said to her, "Do not be afraid. Go and do as you propose. But first make me a little cake and bring it to me. Then you can prepare something for yourself and your son. For the LORD, the God of Israel, says, 'The jar of flour shall not go empty, nor the jug of oil run dry, until the day when the LORD sends rain upon the earth.'" She left and did as Elijah had said. She was able to eat for a year, and he and her son as well; the jar of flour did not go empty, nor the jug of oil run dry, as the LORD had foretold through Elijah.

RESPONSORIAL PSALM
Psalm 146:7, 8–9, 9–10

℟. Praise the Lord, my soul!

Music: Owen Alstott, b. 1947, © 1977, 1990, OCP. All rights reserved.

Or ℟. **Alleluia.**

▶ The LORD keeps faith forever,
  secures justice for the oppressed,
  gives food to the hungry.
The LORD sets captives free. ℟.

▶ The LORD gives sight to the blind;
  the LORD raises up those who were
  bowed down.
The LORD loves the just;
  the LORD protects strangers. ℟.

▶ The fatherless and the widow
  he sustains,
  but the way of the wicked
  he thwarts.
The LORD shall reign forever;
  your God, O Zion, through all
  generations. Alleluia. ℟.

SECOND READING
Hebrews 9:24–28

Christ did not enter into a sanctuary made by hands, a copy of the true one, but heaven itself, that he might now appear before God on our behalf. Not that he might offer himself repeatedly, as the high priest enters each year into the sanctuary with blood that is not his own; if that were so, he would have had to suffer repeatedly from the foundation of the world. But now once for all he has appeared at the end of the ages to take away sin by his sacrifice. Just as it is appointed that human beings die once, and after this the judgment, so also Christ, offered once to take away the sins of many, will appear a second time, not to take away sin but to bring salvation to those who eagerly await him.

GOSPEL ACCLAMATION

Matthew 5:3

℟. Al - le - lu - ia, al - le - lu - ia, al - le - lu - ia.

(Omit if not sung)

▸ Blessed are the poor in spirit,
  for theirs is the kingdom of heaven. ℟.

GOSPEL

Mark 12:38–44 or 12:41–44

(Include bracketed text for Long Form and text in parentheses for Short Form)

[In the course of his teaching Jesus said to the crowds, "Beware of the scribes, who like to go around in long robes and accept greetings in the marketplaces, seats of honor in synagogues, and places of honor at banquets. They devour the houses of widows and, as a pretext, recite lengthy prayers. They will receive a very severe condemnation."

He] (Jesus) sat down opposite the treasury and observed how the crowd put money into the treasury. Many rich people put in large sums. A poor widow also came and put in two small coins worth a few cents. Calling his disciples to himself, he said to them, "Amen, I say to you, this poor widow put in more than all the other contributors to the treasury. For they have all contributed from their surplus wealth, but she, from her poverty, has contributed all she had, her whole livelihood."

1023   32ND SUNDAY IN ORDINARY TIME — C

FIRST READING

2 Maccabees 7:1–2, 9–14

It happened that seven brothers with their mother were arrested and tortured with whips and scourges by the king, to force them to eat pork in violation of God's law. One of the brothers, speaking for the others, said: "What do you expect to achieve by questioning us? We are ready to die rather than transgress the laws of our ancestors."

At the point of death he said: "You accursed fiend, you are depriving us of this present life, but the King of the world will raise us up to live again forever. It is for his laws that we are dying."

After him the third suffered their cruel sport. He put out his tongue at once when told to do so, and bravely held out his hands, as he spoke these noble words: "It was from Heaven that I received these; for the sake of his laws I disdain them; from him I hope to receive them again." Even the king and his attendants marveled at the young man's courage, because he regarded his sufferings as nothing.

After he had died, they tortured and maltreated the fourth brother in the same way. When he was near death, he said, "It is my choice to die at the hands of men with the hope God gives of being raised up by him; but for you, there will be no resurrection to life."

RESPONSORIAL PSALM

Psalm 17:1, 5–6, 8, 15

℟. Lord, when your glo-ry ap-pears, my joy will be full.

▶ Hear, O LORD, a just suit;
attend to my outcry;
hearken to my prayer from lips
without deceit. ℟.

▶ My steps have been steadfast in
your paths,
my feet have not faltered.
I call upon you, for you will answer
me, O God;

incline your ear to me; hear
my word. ℟.

▶ Keep me as the apple of your eye,
hide me in the shadow of
your wings.
But I in justice shall behold your face;
on waking I shall be content in
your presence. ℟.

SECOND READING

2 Thessalonians 2:16 — 3:5

Brothers and sisters: May our Lord
Jesus Christ himself and God our
Father, who has loved us and given us
everlasting encouragement and good
hope through his grace, encourage
your hearts and strengthen them
in every good deed and word.

Finally, brothers and sisters, pray for
us, so that the word of the Lord may
speed forward and be glorified, as it

did among you, and that we may be
delivered from perverse and wicked
people, for not all have faith. But the
Lord is faithful; he will strengthen you
and guard you from the evil one. We
are confident of you in the Lord that
what we instruct you, you are doing
and will continue to do. May the Lord
direct your hearts to the love of God
and to the endurance of Christ.

GOSPEL ACCLAMATION

Revelation 1:5a, 6b

℟. Al-le-lu - ia, al-le-lu - ia, al-le-lu - ia.

(Omit if not sung)

▶ Jesus Christ is the firstborn of the dead;
to him be glory and power, forever and ever. ℟.

GOSPEL

Luke 20:27–38 or 20:27, 34–38

(Include bracketed text for Long Form)

Some Sadducees, those who deny
that there is a resurrection, came
forward [and put this question to Jesus,
saying, "Teacher, Moses wrote for
us, *If someone's brother dies leaving
a wife but no child, his brother must
take the wife and raise up descendants
for his brother.* Now there were
seven brothers; the first married a

woman but died childless. Then the
second and the third married her, and
likewise all the seven died childless.
Finally the woman also died. Now at
the resurrection whose wife will that
woman be? For all seven had been
married to her."] Jesus said to them,
"The children of this age marry and
remarry; but those who are deemed

worthy to attain to the coming age and to the resurrection of the dead neither marry nor are given in marriage. They can no longer die, for they are like angels; and they are the children of God because they are the ones who will rise. That the dead will rise even Moses made known in the passage about the bush, when he called out 'Lord,' the God of Abraham, the God of Isaac, and the God of Jacob; and he is not God of the dead, but of the living, for to him all are alive."

1024   33RD SUNDAY IN ORDINARY TIME — A

FIRST READING
Proverbs 31:10–13, 19–20, 30–31

When one finds a worthy wife,
  her value is far beyond pearls.
Her husband, entrusting his heart
    to her,
  has an unfailing prize.
She brings him good, and not evil,
  all the days of her life.
She obtains wool and flax
  and works with loving hands.
She puts her hands to the distaff,
  and her fingers ply the spindle.

She reaches out her hands to
    the poor,
  and extends her arms to the needy.
Charm is deceptive and
    beauty fleeting;
  the woman who fears the LORD is
    to be praised.
Give her a reward for her labors,
  and let her works praise her at the
    city gates.

RESPONSORIAL PSALM
Psalm 128:1–2, 3, 4–5

℟. Bless - ed are those who fear the Lord.

Music: Owen Alstott, b. 1947, © 1977, 1990, OCP. All rights reserved.

▶ Blessed are you who fear the LORD,
  who walk in his ways!
For you shall eat the fruit of
    your handiwork;
  blessed shall you be,
    and favored. ℟.

▶ Your wife shall be like a fruitful vine
  in the recesses of your home;

your children like olive plants
  around your table. ℟.

▶ Behold, thus is the man blessed
  who fears the LORD.
The LORD bless you from Zion:
  may you see the prosperity
    of Jerusalem
  all the days of your life. ℟.

SECOND READING
1 Thessalonians 5:1–6

Concerning times and seasons, brothers and sisters, you have no need for anything to be written to you. For you yourselves know very well that the day of the Lord will come like a thief at night. When people are saying, "Peace and security," then sudden disaster comes upon them, like labor pains upon a pregnant woman, and they will not escape.

But you, brothers and sisters, are not in darkness, for that day to overtake you like a thief. For all of you are children of the light and children of the day. We are not of the night or of darkness. Therefore, let us not sleep as the rest do, but let us stay alert and sober.

GOSPEL ACCLAMATION

John 15:4a, 5b

℟. Al - le - lu - ia, al - le - lu - ia, al - le - lu - ia.

Music: Owen Alstott, b. 1947, © 1977, 1990, OCP. All rights reserved. *(Omit if not sung)*

▶ Remain in me as I remain in you, says the Lord.
Whoever remains in me bears much fruit. ℟.

GOSPEL

Matthew 25:14–30 or 25:14–15, 19–21

(Include bracketed text for Long Form)

Jesus told his disciples this parable: "A man going on a journey called in his servants and entrusted his possessions to them. To one he gave five talents; to another, two; to a third, one—to each according to his ability. Then he went away. [Immediately the one who received five talents went and traded with them, and made another five. Likewise, the one who received two made another two. But the man who received one went off and dug a hole in the ground and buried his master's money.]

"After a long time the master of those servants came back and settled accounts with them. The one who had received five talents came forward bringing the additional five. He said, 'Master, you gave me five talents. See, I have made five more.' His master said to him, 'Well done, my good and faithful servant. Since you were faithful in small matters, I will give you great responsibilities. Come, share your master's joy.' [Then the one who had received two talents also came forward and said, 'Master, you gave me two talents. See, I have made two more.' His master said to him, 'Well done, my good and faithful servant. Since you were faithful in small matters, I will give you great responsibilities. Come, share your master's joy.' Then the one who had received the one talent came forward and said, 'Master, I knew you were a demanding person, harvesting where you did not plant and gathering where you did not scatter; so out of fear I went off and buried your talent in the ground. Here it is back.' His master said to him in reply, 'You wicked, lazy servant! So you knew that I harvest where I did not plant and gather where I did not scatter? Should you not then have put my money in the bank so that I could have got it back with interest on my return? Now then! Take the talent from him and give it to the one with ten. For to everyone who has, more will be given and he will grow rich; but from the one who has not, even what he has will be taken away. And throw this useless servant into the darkness outside, where there will be wailing and grinding of teeth.'"]

33RD SUNDAY IN ORDINARY TIME — B   1025

FIRST READING

Daniel 12:1–3

In those days, I, Daniel, heard
this word of the Lord:
  "At that time there shall arise
    Michael, the great prince,
      guardian of your people;
    it shall be a time unsurpassed
      in distress
    since nations began until that time.

At that time your people shall escape, everyone who is found written in the book.

"Many of those who sleep in the dust of the earth shall awake; some shall live forever,

others shall be an everlasting horror and disgrace.

"But the wise shall shine brightly like the splendor of the firmament, and those who lead the many to justice shall be like the stars forever."

RESPONSORIAL PSALM

Psalm 16:5, 8, 9–10, 11

℟. You are my in - her - i - tance, O Lord!

▸ O LORD, my allotted portion and my cup, you it is who hold fast my lot. I set the LORD ever before me; with him at my right hand I shall not be disturbed. ℟.

▸ Therefore my heart is glad and my soul rejoices, my body, too, abides in confidence;

because you will not abandon my soul to the netherworld, nor will you suffer your faithful one to undergo corruption. ℟.

▸ You will show me the path to life, fullness of joys in your presence, the delights at your right hand forever. ℟.

SECOND READING

Hebrews 10:11–14, 18

Brothers and sisters: Every priest stands daily at his ministry, offering frequently those same sacrifices that can never take away sins. But this one offered one sacrifice for sins, and took his seat forever at the right hand of God; now he waits until his enemies are made his footstool. For by one offering he has made perfect forever those who are being consecrated.

Where there is forgiveness of these, there is no longer offering for sin.

GOSPEL ACCLAMATION

Luke 21:36

℟. Al - le - lu - ia, al - le - lu - ia, al - le - lu - ia.

(Omit if not sung)

▸ Be vigilant at all times and pray that you have the strength to stand before the Son of Man. ℟.

GOSPEL

Mark 13:24–32

Jesus said to his disciples: "In those days after that tribulation the sun will be darkened, and the moon will not give its light, and the stars will be falling from the sky,

and the powers in the heavens will be shaken.

"And then they will see 'the Son of Man coming in the clouds' with great power and glory, and then he will send out the angels and gather his elect from the four winds, from the end of the earth to the end of the sky.

"Learn a lesson from the fig tree. When its branch becomes tender and sprouts leaves, you know that summer is near. In the same way, when you see these things happening, know that he is near, at the gates. Amen, I say to you, this generation will not pass away until all these things have taken place. Heaven and earth will pass away, but my words will not pass away.

"But of that day or hour, no one knows, neither the angels in heaven, nor the Son, but only the Father."

33RD SUNDAY IN ORDINARY TIME — C 1026

FIRST READING
Malachi 3:19–20a

Lo, the day is coming, blazing like
    an oven,
  when all the proud and all
    evildoers will be stubble,
and the day that is coming will set
    them on fire,
  leaving them neither root
    nor branch,

says the LORD of hosts.
But for you who fear my name, there
    will arise
the sun of justice with its
    healing rays.

RESPONSORIAL PSALM
Psalm 98:5–6, 7–8, 9

℟. The Lord comes to rule the earth with jus - tice.

Music: Owen Alstott, b. 1947, © 1977, 1990, OCP. All rights reserved.

▶ Sing praise to the LORD with the harp,
  with the harp and melodious song.
With trumpets and the sound of
    the horn
  sing joyfully before the King,
  the LORD. ℟.

▶ Let the sea and what fills it resound,
  the world and those who dwell
    in it;

let the rivers clap their hands,
  the mountains shout with them
    for joy. ℟.

▶ Before the LORD, for he comes,
  for he comes to rule the earth;
he will rule the world with justice
  and the peoples with equity. ℟.

SECOND READING
2 Thessalonians 3:7–12

Brothers and sisters: You know how one must imitate us. For we did not act in a disorderly way among you, nor did we eat food received free from anyone. On the contrary, in toil and drudgery, night and day we worked, so as not to burden any of you. Not that we do not have the right. Rather, we wanted to present ourselves as a model for you, so that you might imitate us. In fact, when we were with you, we instructed you that if anyone was unwilling to work, neither should that one eat. We hear that some are conducting themselves among you in a disorderly way, by not keeping busy but minding the business of others. Such people we instruct and urge in the Lord Jesus Christ to work quietly and to eat their own food.

GOSPEL ACCLAMATION

Luke 21:28

℟. Al - le - lu - ia, al - le - lu - ia, al - le - lu - ia.

(Omit if not sung)

▸ Stand erect and raise your heads
because your redemption is at hand. ℟.

GOSPEL

Luke 21:5–19

While some people were speaking about how the temple was adorned with costly stones and votive offerings, Jesus said, "All that you see here—the days will come when there will not be left a stone upon another stone that will not be thrown down."

Then they asked him, "Teacher, when will this happen? And what sign will there be when all these things are about to happen?" He answered, "See that you not be deceived, for many will come in my name, saying, 'I am he,' and 'The time has come.' Do not follow them! When you hear of wars and insurrections, do not be terrified; for such things must happen first, but it will not immediately be the end." Then he said to them, "Nation will rise against nation, and kingdom against kingdom. There will be powerful earthquakes, famines, and plagues from place to place; and awesome sights and mighty signs will come from the sky.

"Before all this happens, however, they will seize and persecute you, they will hand you over to the synagogues and to prisons, and they will have you led before kings and governors because of my name. It will lead to your giving testimony. Remember, you are not to prepare your defense beforehand, for I myself shall give you a wisdom in speaking that all your adversaries will be powerless to resist or refute. You will even be handed over by parents, brothers, relatives, and friends, and they will put some of you to death. You will be hated by all because of my name, but not a hair on your head will be destroyed. By your perseverance you will secure your lives."

1027   OUR LORD JESUS CHRIST, KING OF THE UNIVERSE — A

FIRST READING

Ezekiel 34:11–12, 15–17

Thus says the Lord GOD: I myself will look after and tend my sheep. As a shepherd tends his flock when he finds himself among his scattered sheep, so will I tend my sheep. I will rescue them from every place where they were scattered when it was cloudy and dark. I myself will pasture my sheep; I myself will give them rest, says the Lord GOD. The lost I will seek out, the strayed I will bring back, the injured I will bind up, the sick I will heal, but the sleek and the strong I will destroy, shepherding them rightly.

As for you, my sheep, says the Lord GOD, I will judge between one sheep and another, between rams and goats.

RESPONSORIAL PSALM

Psalm 23:1–2, 2–3, 5–6

℟. The Lord is my shep-herd; there is noth-ing I shall want.

▸ The LORD is my shepherd; I shall
    not want.
  In verdant pastures he gives
    me repose. ℟.

▸ Beside restful waters he leads me;
    he refreshes my soul.
  He guides me in right paths
    for his name's sake. ℟.

▸ You spread the table before me
    in the sight of my foes;
  you anoint my head with oil;
    my cup overflows. ℟.

▸ Only goodness and kindness
    follow me
  all the days of my life;
  and I shall dwell in the house of
    the LORD
    for years to come. ℟.

SECOND READING

1 Corinthians 15:20–26, 28

Brothers and sisters: Christ has been raised from the dead, the firstfruits of those who have fallen asleep. For since death came through man, the resurrection of the dead came also through man. For just as in Adam all die, so too in Christ shall all be brought to life, but each one in proper order: Christ the firstfruits; then, at his coming, those who belong to Christ; then comes the end, when he hands over the kingdom to his God and Father, when he has destroyed every sovereignty and every authority and power. For he must reign until he has put all his enemies under his feet. The last enemy to be destroyed is death. When everything is subjected to him, then the Son himself will also be subjected to the one who subjected everything to him, so that God may be all in all.

GOSPEL ACCLAMATION

Mark 11:9, 10

℟. Al - le - lu - ia, al - le - lu - ia, al - le - lu - ia.

(Omit if not sung)

▸ Blessed is he who comes in the name of the Lord!
  Blessed is the kingdom of our father David that is to come! ℟.

GOSPEL

Matthew 25:31–46

Jesus said to his disciples: "When the Son of Man comes in his glory, and all the angels with him, he will sit upon his glorious throne, and all the nations will be assembled before him. And he will separate them one from another, as a shepherd separates the sheep from the goats. He will place the sheep on his right and the goats on his left. Then the king will say to those on his right, 'Come, you who are blessed by my Father. Inherit the kingdom prepared for you from the foundation of the world. For I was hungry and you gave me food, I was thirsty and you gave me drink, a stranger and you welcomed me, naked and you clothed me, ill and you cared for me, in prison and you visited me.' Then the righteous will answer him and say, 'Lord, when did we see you hungry and feed you, or thirsty and give you drink? When did we see you a stranger and welcome you, or naked and clothe you? When did we see you ill or in prison, and visit you?' And the king will say to them in reply, 'Amen, I say to you, whatever you did for one of the least brothers of mine, you did for me.' Then he will say to those on his left, 'Depart from me, you accursed, into the eternal fire prepared for the devil and his angels. For I was hungry and you gave me no food, I was thirsty and you gave me no drink, a stranger and you gave me no welcome, naked and you gave me no clothing, ill and in prison, and you did not care for me.' Then they will answer and say, 'Lord, when did we see you hungry or thirsty or a stranger or naked or ill or in prison, and not minister to your needs?' He will answer them, 'Amen, I say to you, what you did not do for one of these least ones, you did not do for me.' And these will go off to eternal punishment, but the righteous to eternal life."

1028   OUR LORD JESUS CHRIST, KING OF THE UNIVERSE — B

FIRST READING

Daniel 7:13–14

As the visions during the night continued, I saw
    one like a Son of man coming,
      on the clouds of heaven;
    when he reached the Ancient One
      and was presented before him,
    the one like a Son of man received
      dominion, glory, and kingship;
all peoples, nations, and languages
    serve him.
His dominion is an everlasting dominion
    that shall not be taken away,
    his kingship shall not be destroyed.

RESPONSORIAL PSALM

Psalm 93:1, 1–2, 5

℟. The Lord is king; he is robed in maj - es - ty.

Music: Owen Alstott, b. 1947, © 1977, 1990, OCP. All rights reserved.

▸ The LORD is king, in splendor robed;
    robed is the LORD and girt about
      with strength. ℟.

▸ And he has made the world firm,
    not to be moved.
  Your throne stands firm from of old;
from everlasting you are,
    O LORD. ℟.

▸ Your decrees are worthy of
    trust indeed;
  holiness befits your house,
  O LORD, for length of days. ℟.

SECOND READING

Revelation 1:5–8

Jesus Christ is the faithful witness, the firstborn of the dead and ruler of the kings of the earth. To him who loves us and has freed us from our sins by his blood, who has made us into a kingdom, priests for his God and Father, to him be glory and power forever and ever. Amen.

Behold, he is coming amid the clouds,
and every eye will see him,
even those who pierced him.
All the peoples of the earth will
lament him.

Yes. Amen.
"I am the Alpha and the Omega,"
says the Lord God, "the one
who is and who was and who
is to come, the almighty."

GOSPEL ACCLAMATION

Mark 11:9, 10

℟. Al - le - lu - ia, al - le - lu - ia, al - le - lu - ia.

(Omit if not sung)

▸ Blessed is he who comes in the name of the Lord!
Blessed is the kingdom of our father David that is to come! ℟.

GOSPEL

John 18:33b–37

Pilate said to Jesus, "Are you the King
of the Jews?" Jesus answered, "Do you
say this on your own or have others
told you about me?" Pilate answered,
"I am not a Jew, am I? Your own nation
and the chief priests handed you over
to me. What have you done?" Jesus
answered, "My kingdom does not
belong to this world. If my kingdom
did belong to this world, my attendants
would be fighting to keep me from
being handed over to the Jews. But as
it is, my kingdom is not here." So
Pilate said to him, "Then you are a
king?" Jesus answered, "You say I
am a king. For this I was born and for
this I came into the world, to testify
to the truth. Everyone who belongs
to the truth listens to my voice."

OUR LORD JESUS CHRIST, 1029
KING OF THE UNIVERSE — C

FIRST READING

2 Samuel 5:1–3

In those days, all the tribes of Israel
came to David in Hebron and said:
"Here we are, your bone and your flesh.
In days past, when Saul was our king,
it was you who led the Israelites out
and brought them back. And the LORD
said to you, 'You shall shepherd my
people Israel and shall be commander
of Israel.'" When all the elders of
Israel came to David in Hebron, King
David made an agreement with
them there before the LORD, and
they anointed him king of Israel.

RESPONSORIAL PSALM

Psalm 122:1–2, 3–4, 4–5

℟. Let us go re - joic - ing to the house of the Lord.

▸ I rejoiced because they said to me,
"We will go up to the house of
the LORD."

And now we have set foot
within your gates, O Jerusalem. ℟.

℟. Let us go rejoicing to the house of the Lord.

▸ Jerusalem, built as a city
    with compact unity.
To it the tribes go up,
    the tribes of the LORD. ℟.

▸ According to the decree for Israel,
    to give thanks to the name of
    the LORD.
In it are set up judgment seats,
    seats for the house of David. ℟.

SECOND READING
Colossians 1:12–20

Brothers and sisters: Let us give
thanks to the Father, who has made
you fit to share in the inheritance of
the holy ones in light. He delivered
us from the power of darkness and
transferred us to the kingdom of
his beloved Son, in whom we have
redemption, the forgiveness of sins.
    He is the image of the invisible God,
      the firstborn of all creation.
    For in him were created all things in
      heaven and on earth,
      the visible and the invisible,
      whether thrones or dominions or
        principalities or powers;
    all things were created through
      him and for him.

He is before all things,
    and in him all things hold together.
He is the head of the body, the
    church.
He is the beginning, the firstborn
    from the dead,
    that in all things he himself might
    be preeminent.
For in him all the fullness was
    pleased to dwell,
    and through him to reconcile all
    things for him,
    making peace by the blood of
    his cross
through him, whether those on
    earth or those in heaven.

GOSPEL ACCLAMATION
Mark 11:9, 10

℟. Al - le - lu - ia, al - le - lu - ia, al - le - lu - ia.

Music: Owen Alstott, b. 1947, © 1977, 1990, OCP. All rights reserved.   *(Omit if not sung)*

▸ Blessed is he who comes in the name of the Lord!
  Blessed is the kingdom of our father David that is to come! ℟.

GOSPEL
Luke 23:35–43

The rulers sneered at Jesus and said,
"He saved others, let him save himself
if he is the chosen one, the Christ
of God." Even the soldiers jeered at
him. As they approached to offer him
wine they called out, "If you are King
of the Jews, save yourself." Above
him there was an inscription that
read, "This is the King of the Jews."
    Now one of the criminals hanging
there reviled Jesus, saying, "Are you
not the Christ? Save yourself and
us." The other, however, rebuking
him, said in reply, "Have you no fear
of God, for you are subject to the
same condemnation? And indeed, we
have been condemned justly, for the
sentence we received corresponds
to our crimes, but this man has
done nothing criminal." Then he
said, "Jesus, remember me when you
come into your kingdom." He replied
to him, "Amen, I say to you, today
you will be with me in Paradise."

THANKSGIVING DAY 1030

Other options for the readings are found in Volume IV of the Lectionary.

FIRST READING
Sirach 50:22–24

And now, bless the God of all,
who has done wondrous things
on earth;
Who fosters people's growth from
their mother's womb,
and fashions them according to
his will!

May he grant you joy of heart
and may peace abide among you;
May his goodness toward us endure
in Israel
to deliver us in our days.

RESPONSORIAL PSALM
Psalm 113:1–2, 3–4, 5–6, 7–8

℞. Bless - ed be the name of the Lord for ev - er.

Or ℞. **Alleluia.**

▸ Praise, you servants of the LORD,
praise the name of the LORD.
Blessed be the name of the LORD
both now and forever. ℞.

▸ From the rising to the setting of
the sun
is the name of the LORD to
be praised.
High above all nations is the LORD;
above the heavens is his glory. ℞.

▸ Who is like the LORD, our God, who is
enthroned on high
and looks upon the heavens and
the earth below? ℞.

▸ He raises up the lowly from the dust;
from the dunghill he lifts up
the poor,
To seat them with princes,
with the princes of his own
people. ℞.

SECOND READING
1 Corinthians 1:3–9

Brothers and sisters: Grace to you and peace from God our Father and the Lord Jesus Christ.

I give thanks to my God always on your account for the grace of God bestowed on you in Christ Jesus, that in him you were enriched in every way, with all discourse and all knowledge, as the testimony to Christ was confirmed among you, so that you are not lacking in any spiritual gift as you wait for the revelation of our Lord Jesus Christ. He will keep you firm to the end, irreproachable on the day of our Lord Jesus Christ. God is faithful, and by him you were called to fellowship with his Son, Jesus Christ our Lord.

GOSPEL ACCLAMATION
1 Thessalonians 5:18

℞. Al - le - lu - ia, al - le - lu - ia, al - le - lu - ia.

(Omit if not sung)

℟. **Alleluia, alleluia, alleluia.**

▶ In all circumstances, give thanks,
    for this is the will of God for you in Christ Jesus. ℟.

GOSPEL   *Luke 17:11–19*

As Jesus continued his journey to Jerusalem, he traveled through Samaria and Galilee. As he was entering a village, ten persons with leprosy met him. They stood at a distance from him and raised their voices, saying, "Jesus, Master! Have pity on us!" And when he saw them, he said, "Go show yourselves to the priests." As they were going they were cleansed. And one of them, realizing he had been healed, returned, glorifying God in a loud voice; and he fell at the feet of Jesus and thanked him. He was a Samaritan. Jesus said in reply, "Ten were cleansed, were they not? Where are the other nine? Has none but this foreigner returned to give thanks to God?" Then he said to him, "Stand up and go; your faith has saved you."

SOLEMNITIES AND FEASTS OF THE LORD AND THE SAINTS

1031   FEBRUARY 2 — THE PRESENTATION OF THE LORD

FIRST FORM: THE PROCESSION

The people gather in a chapel or other suitable place outside the church where the Mass will be celebrated. They carry unlighted candles. While the candles are being lighted, an appropriate hymn is sung (see #488, 630–635).

The Priest greets the people as usual, and after a short introduction blesses the candles.

He sprinkles the candles in silence. The Priest then takes the candle prepared for him, and the procession to the church begins. During the procession, an appropriate hymn is sung (see #124, 125). As the procession enters the church, the Entrance Antiphon of the Mass is sung.

When the Priest reaches the altar he venerates it, and may incense it. Then he goes to the chair. After the Gloria, he continues with the Collect and Mass proceeds as usual.

SECOND FORM: THE SOLEMN ENTRANCE

The people, carrying unlighted candles, assemble in the church. The Priest is accompanied by his ministers and by a representative group of the faithful. They go to a suitable place (either in front of the church door or in the church itself) where most of the assembly can easily take part. After the candles are blessed, they are lit, while the antiphon or another appropriate chant is sung. The ceremony then continues as described above.

FIRST READING   *Malachi 3:1–4*

Thus says the Lord GOD:
  Lo, I am sending my messenger
    to prepare the way before me;

And suddenly there will come to
    the temple
  the LORD whom you seek,

And the messenger of the covenant
whom you desire.
Yes, he is coming, says the LORD
of hosts.
But who will endure the day of
his coming?
And who can stand when
he appears?
For he is like the refiner's fire,
or like the fuller's lye.

He will sit refining and purifying silver,
and he will purify the sons of Levi,
Refining them like gold or like silver
that they may offer due sacrifice to
the LORD.
Then the sacrifice of Judah
and Jerusalem
will please the LORD,
as in the days of old, as in years
gone by.

RESPONSORIAL PSALM

Psalm 24:7, 8, 9, 10

℟. Who is this king of glo - ry? It is the Lord!

▶ Lift up, O gates, your lintels;
reach up, you ancient portals,
that the king of glory may
come in! ℟.

▶ Who is this king of glory?
The LORD, strong and mighty,
the LORD, mighty in battle. ℟.

▶ Lift up, O gates, your lintels;
reach up, you ancient portals,
that the king of glory may
come in! ℟.

▶ Who is this king of glory?
The LORD of hosts; he is the king
of glory. ℟.

SECOND READING

Hebrews 2:14–18

Since the children share in blood and flesh, Jesus likewise shared in them, that through death he might destroy the one who has the power of death, that is, the Devil, and free those who through fear of death had been subject to slavery all their life. Surely he did not help angels but rather the descendants of Abraham; therefore, he had to become like his brothers and sisters in every way, that he might be a merciful and faithful high priest before God to expiate the sins of the people. Because he himself was tested through what he suffered, he is able to help those who are being tested.

GOSPEL ACCLAMATION

Luke 2:32

℟. Al - le-lu - ia, al - le - lu - ia, al - le - lu - ia.

(Omit if not sung)

▶ A light of revelation to the Gentiles,
and glory for your people Israel. ℟.

GOSPEL

Luke 2:22–40 or 2:22–32

(Include bracketed text for Long Form)

When the days were completed for their purification according to the law of Moses, Mary and Joseph took Jesus up to Jerusalem to present him to the Lord, just as it is written in the law of the Lord, *Every male that opens the womb shall be consecrated to the Lord,* and to offer the sacrifice of *a pair of turtledoves or two young pigeons,* in accordance with the dictate in the law of the Lord.

Now there was a man in Jerusalem whose name was Simeon. This man was righteous and devout, awaiting the consolation of Israel, and the Holy Spirit was upon him. It had been revealed to him by the Holy Spirit that he should not see death before he had seen the Christ of the Lord. He came in the Spirit into the temple; and when the parents brought in the child Jesus to perform the custom of the law in regard to him, he took him into his arms and blessed God, saying:

"Now, Master, you may let your servant go
　in peace, according to your word,
for my eyes have seen your salvation,
　which you prepared in sight of all
　　the peoples:
a light for revelation to the Gentiles,
　and glory for your people Israel."
[The child's father and mother were amazed at what was said about him; and Simeon blessed them and said to Mary his mother, "Behold, this child is destined for the fall and rise of many in Israel, and to be a sign that will be contradicted—and you yourself a sword will pierce—so that the thoughts of many hearts may be revealed." There was also a prophetess, Anna, the daughter of Phanuel, of the tribe of Asher. She was advanced in years, having lived seven years with her husband after her marriage, and then as a widow until she was eighty-four. She never left the temple, but worshiped night and day with fasting and prayer. And coming forward at that very time, she gave thanks to God and spoke about the child to all who were awaiting the redemption of Jerusalem.

When they had fulfilled all the prescriptions of the law of the Lord, they returned to Galilee, to their own town of Nazareth. The child grew and became strong, filled with wisdom; and the favor of God was upon him.]

1032　MARCH 19 — SAINT JOSEPH, SPOUSE OF THE BLESSED VIRGIN MARY

FIRST READING　　　　　　　　　　2 Samuel 7:4–5a, 12–14a, 16

The LORD spoke to Nathan and said: "Go, tell my servant David, 'When your time comes and you rest with your ancestors, I will raise up your heir after you, sprung from your loins, and I will make his kingdom firm. It is he who shall build a house for my name. And I will make his royal throne firm forever. I will be a father to him, and he shall be a son to me. Your house and your kingdom shall endure forever before me; your throne shall stand firm forever.'"

RESPONSORIAL PSALM　　　　　　　Psalm 89:2–3, 4–5, 27 & 29

℟. The son of David will live for ev-er.

Music: Owen Alstott, b. 1947, © 1977, 1990, OCP. All rights reserved.

▸ The promises of the LORD I will
　sing forever,

through all generations my mouth
　shall proclaim your faithfulness,

For you have said, "My kindness is
established forever";
in heaven you have confirmed your
faithfulness. ℟.

▶ "I have made a covenant with my
chosen one;
I have sworn to David my servant:
forever will I confirm your posterity
and establish your throne for all
generations." ℟.

▶ "He shall say of me, 'You are
my father,
my God, the Rock, my savior.'
Forever I will maintain my kindness
toward him,
and my covenant with him
stands firm." ℟.

SECOND READING
Romans 4:13, 16–18, 22

Brothers and sisters: It was not through
the law that the promise was made to
Abraham and his descendants that he
would inherit the world, but through
the righteousness that comes from
faith. For this reason, it depends on
faith, so that it may be a gift, and the
promise may be guaranteed to all his
descendants, not to those who only
adhere to the law but to those who
follow the faith of Abraham, who is
the father of all of us, as it is written, *I
have made you father of many nations.*
He is our father in the sight of God,
in whom he believed, who gives life
to the dead and calls into being what
does not exist. He believed, hoping
against hope, that he would become
the father of many nations, according
to what was said, *Thus shall your
descendants be.* That is why *it was
credited to him as righteousness.*

GOSPEL ACCLAMATION
Psalm 84:5

℟. Praise to you, Lord Je-sus Christ, King of end-less glo - ry!

Music: Owen Alstott, b. 1947, © 1977, 1990, OCP. All rights reserved. *(Omit if not sung)*

Or (when transferred to the Easter Season)

℟. Al - le - lu - ia, al - le - lu - ia, al - le - lu - ia.

Music: Owen Alstott, b. 1947, © 1977, 1990, OCP. All rights reserved. *(Omit if not sung)*

▶ Blessed are those who dwell in your house, O Lord;
they never cease to praise you. ℟.

GOSPEL
Matthew 1:16, 18–21, 24a

Jacob was the father of Joseph, the
husband of Mary. Of her was born
Jesus who is called the Christ.
  Now this is how the birth of Jesus
Christ came about. When his mother
Mary was betrothed to Joseph, but
before they lived together, she was
found with child through the Holy
Spirit. Joseph her husband, since he
was a righteous man, yet unwilling
to expose her to shame, decided
to divorce her quietly. Such was
his intention when, behold, the
angel of the Lord appeared to him
in a dream and said, "Joseph, son
of David, do not be afraid to take
Mary your wife into your home. For
it is through the Holy Spirit that this

child has been conceived in her. She will bear a son and you are to name him Jesus, because he will save his people from their sins." When Joseph awoke, he did as the angel of the Lord had commanded him and took his wife into his home.

Or

GOSPEL

Luke 2:41–51a

Each year Jesus' parents went to Jerusalem for the feast of Passover, and when he was twelve years old, they went up according to festival custom. After they had completed its days, as they were returning, the boy Jesus remained behind in Jerusalem, but his parents did not know it. Thinking that he was in the caravan, they journeyed for a day and looked for him among their relatives and acquaintances, but not finding him, they returned to Jerusalem to look for him. After three days they found him in the temple, sitting in the midst of the teachers, listening to them and asking them questions, and all who heard him were astounded at his understanding and his answers. When his parents saw him, they were astonished, and his mother said to him, "Son, why have you done this to us? Your father and I have been looking for you with great anxiety." And he said to them, "Why were you looking for me? Did you not know that I must be in my Father's house?" But they did not understand what he said to them. He went down with them and came to Nazareth, and was obedient to them.

1033 MARCH 25 — THE ANNUNCIATION OF THE LORD

FIRST READING

Isaiah 7:10–14; 8:10

The LORD spoke to Ahaz, saying: Ask for a sign from the LORD, your God; let it be deep as the nether world, or high as the sky! But Ahaz answered, "I will not ask! I will not tempt the LORD!" Then Isaiah said: Listen, O house of David! Is it not enough for you to weary people, must you also weary my God? Therefore the Lord himself will give you this sign: the virgin shall be with child, and bear a son, and shall name him Emmanuel, which means "God is with us!"

RESPONSORIAL PSALM

Psalm 40:7–8a, 8b–9, 10, 11

℟. Here I am, Lord; I come to do your will.

▶ Sacrifice or oblation you wished not,
  but ears open to obedience you
    gave me.
  Holocausts and sin-offerings you
    sought not;
    then said I, "Behold I come." ℟.

▶ "In the written scroll it is prescribed
    for me,

To do your will, O God, is my delight,
  and your law is within my heart!" ℟.

▶ I announced your justice in the
    vast assembly;
  I did not restrain my lips, as you,
    O LORD, know. ℟.

▸ Your justice I kept not hid within
   my heart;
   your faithfulness and your salvation
   I have spoken of;

I have made no secret of your
kindness and your truth
in the vast assembly. ℟.

SECOND READING
Hebrews 10:4–10

Brothers and sisters: It is impossible
that the blood of bulls and goats
take away sins. For this reason, when
Christ came into the world, he said:
   "Sacrifice and offering you did
      not desire,
   but a body you prepared for me;
   in holocausts and sin offerings you
      took no delight.
   Then I said, 'As is written of me in
      the scroll,

behold, I come to do your will,
   O God.'"
First he says, "Sacrifices and
offerings, holocausts and sin
offerings, you neither desired nor
delighted in." These are offered
according to the law. Then he says,
"Behold, I come to do your will." He
takes away the first to establish the
second. By this "will," we have been
consecrated through the offering of
the Body of Jesus Christ once for all.

GOSPEL ACCLAMATION
John 1:14ab

℟. Praise to you, Lord Je-sus Christ, King of end-less glo - ry!

Music: Owen Alstott, b. 1947, © 1977, 1990, OCP. All rights reserved.   *(Omit if not sung)*

Or (when transferred to the Easter Season)

℟. Al - le - lu - ia, al - le - lu - ia, al - le - lu - ia.

Music: Owen Alstott, b. 1947, © 1977, 1990, OCP. All rights reserved.   *(Omit if not sung)*

▸ The Word of God became flesh and made his dwelling among us;
   and we saw his glory. ℟.

GOSPEL
Luke 1:26–38

The angel Gabriel was sent from God
to a town of Galilee called Nazareth,
to a virgin betrothed to a man named
Joseph, of the house of David, and
the virgin's name was Mary. And
coming to her, he said, "Hail, full of
grace! The Lord is with you." But she
was greatly troubled at what was said
and pondered what sort of greeting
this might be. Then the angel said to
her, "Do not be afraid, Mary, for you
have found favor with God. Behold,
you will conceive in your womb and
bear a son, and you shall name him

Jesus. He will be great and will be
called Son of the Most High, and the
Lord God will give him the throne of
David his father, and he will rule over
the house of Jacob forever, and of his
Kingdom there will be no end." But
Mary said to the angel, "How can this
be, since I have no relations with a
man?" And the angel said to her in
reply, "The Holy Spirit will come upon
you, and the power of the Most High
will overshadow you. Therefore the
child to be born will be called holy, the
Son of God. And behold, Elizabeth,

your relative, has also conceived a son in her old age, and this is the sixth month for her who was called barren; for nothing will be impossible for God." Mary said, "Behold, I am the handmaid of the Lord. May it be done to me according to your word." Then the angel departed from her.

1034   JUNE 23 — THE NATIVITY OF SAINT JOHN THE BAPTIST: AT THE VIGIL MASS

FIRST READING   *Jeremiah 1:4–10*

In the days of King Josiah, the word of the LORD came to me, saying:
> Before I formed you in the womb
>> I knew you,
>> before you were born I
>> dedicated you,
>> a prophet to the nations
>> I appointed you.

"Ah, Lord GOD!" I said,
> "I know not how to speak; I am
> too young."
But the LORD answered me,
> Say not, "I am too young."
> To whomever I send you,
>> you shall go;
>> whatever I command you,
>> you shall speak.
> Have no fear before them,
>> because I am with you to deliver
>> you, says the LORD.

Then the LORD extended his hand and touched my mouth, saying,
> See, I place my words in your mouth!
> This day I set you
>> over nations and over kingdoms,
> to root up and to tear down,
> to destroy and to demolish,
> to build and to plant.

RESPONSORIAL PSALM   *Psalm 71:1–2, 3–4a, 5–6ab, 15ab & 17*

℟. Since my moth-er's womb, you have been my strength.

Music: Owen Alstott, b. 1947, © 1977, 1990, OCP. All rights reserved.

▶ In you, O LORD, I take refuge;
  let me never be put to shame.
In your justice rescue me, and
    deliver me;
  incline your ear to me,
    and save me. ℟.

▶ Be my rock of refuge,
  a stronghold to give me safety,
  for you are my rock and my fortress.
O my God, rescue me from the hand
  of the wicked. ℟.

▶ For you are my hope, O LORD;
  my trust, O LORD, from my youth.
On you I depend from birth;
  from my mother's womb you are
    my strength. ℟.

▶ My mouth shall declare your justice,
  day by day your salvation.
O God, you have taught me from
  my youth,
  and till the present I proclaim your
    wondrous deeds. ℟.

SECOND READING   *1 Peter 1:8–12*

Beloved: Although you have not seen Jesus Christ you love him; even though you do not see him now yet believe in him, you rejoice with an indescribable and glorious joy, as you attain the goal of your faith, the salvation of your souls.

Concerning this salvation, prophets who prophesied about the grace that was to be yours searched and investigated it, investigating the time and circumstances that the Spirit of Christ within them indicated when he testified in advance to the sufferings destined for Christ and the glories to follow them. It was revealed to them that they were serving not themselves but you with regard to the things that have now been announced to you by those who preached the Good News to you through the Holy Spirit sent from heaven, things into which angels longed to look.

GOSPEL ACCLAMATION

cf. John 1:7; Luke 1:17

℟. Al - le - lu - ia, al - le - lu - ia, al - le - lu - ia.

(Omit if not sung)

▸ He came to testify to the light,
to prepare a people fit for the Lord. ℟.

GOSPEL

Luke 1:5–17

In the days of Herod, King of Judea, there was a priest named Zechariah of the priestly division of Abijah; his wife was from the daughters of Aaron, and her name was Elizabeth. Both were righteous in the eyes of God, observing all the commandments and ordinances of the Lord blamelessly. But they had no child, because Elizabeth was barren and both were advanced in years. Once when he was serving as priest in his division's turn before God, according to the practice of the priestly service, he was chosen by lot to enter the sanctuary of the Lord to burn incense. Then, when the whole assembly of the people was praying outside at the hour of the incense offering, the angel of the Lord appeared to him, standing at the right of the altar of incense. Zechariah was troubled by what he saw, and fear came upon him. But the angel said to him, "Do not be afraid, Zechariah, because your prayer has been heard. Your wife Elizabeth will bear you a son, and you shall name him John. And you will have joy and gladness, and many will rejoice at his birth, for he will be great in the sight of the Lord. John will drink neither wine nor strong drink. He will be filled with the Holy Spirit even from his mother's womb, and he will turn many of the children of Israel to the Lord their God. He will go before him in the spirit and power of Elijah to turn their hearts toward their children and the disobedient to the understanding of the righteous, to prepare a people fit for the Lord."

JUNE 24 — THE NATIVITY OF   1035
SAINT JOHN THE BAPTIST: AT THE MASS DURING THE DAY

FIRST READING

Isaiah 49:1–6

Hear me, O coastlands,
listen, O distant peoples.
The LORD called me from birth,
from my mother's womb he gave
me my name.

He made of me a sharp-edged sword
and concealed me in the shadow
of his arm.
He made me a polished arrow,
in his quiver he hid me.

You are my servant, he said to me,
Israel, through whom I show
my glory.

Though I thought I had toiled in vain,
and for nothing, uselessly, spent
my strength,
yet my reward is with the LORD,
my recompense is with my God.
For now the LORD has spoken
who formed me as his servant from
the womb,
that Jacob may be brought back
to him

and Israel gathered to him;
and I am made glorious in the sight
of the LORD,
and my God is now my strength!
It is too little, he says, for you to be
my servant,
to raise up the tribes of Jacob,
and restore the survivors of Israel;
I will make you a light to the nations,
that my salvation may reach to the
ends of the earth.

RESPONSORIAL PSALM
Psalm 139:1–3b, 13–14ab, 14c–15

℞. I praise you, for I am won-der-ful-ly made.

▶ O LORD, you have probed me and
you know me;
you know when I sit and when
I stand;
you understand my thoughts
from afar.
My journeys and my rest you
scrutinize,
with all my ways you are familiar. ℞.

▶ Truly you have formed my
inmost being;
you knit me in my mother's womb.
I give you thanks that I am fearfully,
wonderfully made;
wonderful are your works. ℞.

▶ My soul also you knew full well;
nor was my frame unknown to you
when I was made in secret,
when I was fashioned in the depths
of the earth. ℞.

SECOND READING
Acts of the Apostles 13:22–26

In those days, Paul said: "God raised up David as king; of him God testified, *I have found David, son of Jesse, a man after my own heart; he will carry out my every wish.* From this man's descendants God, according to his promise, has brought to Israel a savior, Jesus. John heralded his coming by proclaiming a baptism of repentance to all the people of Israel; and as John was completing his course, he would say, 'What do you suppose that I am? I am not he. Behold, one is coming after me; I am not worthy to unfasten the sandals of his feet.'

"My brothers, sons of the family of Abraham, and those others among you who are God-fearing, to us this word of salvation has been sent."

GOSPEL ACCLAMATION
cf. Luke 1:76

℞. Al-le-lu-ia, al-le-lu-ia, al-le-lu-ia.

(Omit if not sung)

▶ You, child, will be called prophet of the Most High,
for you will go before the Lord to prepare his way. ℟.

GOSPEL
Luke 1:57–66, 80

When the time arrived for Elizabeth to have her child she gave birth to a son. Her neighbors and relatives heard that the Lord had shown his great mercy toward her, and they rejoiced with her. When they came on the eighth day to circumcise the child, they were going to call him Zechariah after his father, but his mother said in reply, "No. He will be called John." But they answered her, "There is no one among your relatives who has this name." So they made signs, asking his father what he wished him to be called. He asked for a tablet and wrote, "John is his name," and all were amazed. Immediately his mouth was opened, his tongue freed, and he spoke blessing God. Then fear came upon all their neighbors, and all these matters were discussed throughout the hill country of Judea. All who heard these things took them to heart, saying, "What, then, will this child be?" For surely the hand of the Lord was with him.

The child grew and became strong in spirit, and he was in the desert until the day of his manifestation to Israel.

JUNE 28 — SAINTS PETER AND PAUL, APOSTLES: 1036 AT THE VIGIL MASS

For a votive Mass of Saint Peter the readings are taken from the Feast of the Chair of Saint Peter the Apostle, February 22, Lectionary number 535.

For a votive Mass of Saint Paul the readings are taken from the Feast of the Conversion of Saint Paul the Apostle, Lectionary number 519.

FIRST READING
Acts of the Apostles 3:1–10

Peter and John were going up to the temple area for the three o'clock hour of prayer. And a man crippled from birth was carried and placed at the gate of the temple called "the Beautiful Gate" every day to beg for alms from the people who entered the temple. When he saw Peter and John about to go into the temple, he asked for alms. But Peter looked intently at him, as did John, and said, "Look at us." He paid attention to them, expecting to receive something from them. Peter said, "I have neither silver nor gold, but what I do have I give you: in the name of Jesus Christ the Nazorean, rise and walk." Then Peter took him by the right hand and raised him up, and immediately his feet and ankles grew strong. He leaped up, stood, and walked around, and went into the temple with them, walking and jumping and praising God. When all the people saw the man walking and praising God, they recognized him as the one who used to sit begging at the Beautiful Gate of the temple, and they were filled with amazement and astonishment at what had happened to him.

RESPONSORIAL PSALM

Psalm 19:2–3, 4–5

℟. Their mes - sage goes out through all the earth.

▸ The heavens declare the glory
of God;
and the firmament proclaims
his handiwork.
Day pours out the word to day;
and night to night imparts
knowledge. ℟.

▸ Not a word nor a discourse
whose voice is not heard;
through all the earth their
voice resounds,
and to the ends of the world,
their message. ℟.

SECOND READING

Galatians 1:11–20

I want you to know, brothers and sisters, that the Gospel preached by me is not of human origin. For I did not receive it from a human being, nor was I taught it, but it came through a revelation of Jesus Christ.

For you heard of my former way of life in Judaism, how I persecuted the church of God beyond measure and tried to destroy it, and progressed in Judaism beyond many of my contemporaries among my race, since I was even more a zealot for my ancestral traditions. But when God, who from my mother's womb had set me apart and called me through his grace, was pleased to reveal his Son to me, so that I might proclaim him to the Gentiles, I did not immediately consult flesh and blood, nor did I go up to Jerusalem to those who were apostles before me; rather, I went into Arabia and then returned to Damascus.

Then after three years I went up to Jerusalem to confer with Cephas and remained with him for fifteen days. But I did not see any other of the Apostles, only James the brother of the Lord.—As to what I am writing to you, behold, before God, I am not lying.

GOSPEL ACCLAMATION

John 21:17

℟. Al - le - lu - ia, al - le - lu - ia, al - le - lu - ia.

(Omit if not sung)

▸ Lord, you know everything;
you know that I love you. ℟.

GOSPEL

John 21:15–19

Jesus had revealed himself to his disciples and, when they had finished breakfast, said to Simon Peter, "Simon, son of John, do you love me more than these?" Simon Peter answered him, "Yes, Lord, you know that I love you." Jesus said to him, "Feed my lambs." He then said to Simon Peter a second time, "Simon, son of John, do you love me?" Simon Peter answered him, "Yes, Lord, you know that I love you." He said to him, "Tend my sheep." He said to him the third time, "Simon, son of John, do you love me?" Peter was distressed that Jesus had said to him a third time, "Do you love me?" and he said to him, "Lord, you know everything; you know that I love you." Jesus said to him, "Feed my sheep. Amen, amen, I say to you, when you were younger, you used to dress yourself and go where you wanted; but when you grow old, you will stretch out your hands, and someone else will dress you and lead you where you do not want to go." He said this signifying by what kind of death he would glorify God. And when he had said this, he said to him, "Follow me."

JUNE 29 — SAINTS PETER AND PAUL, APOSTLES: 1037 AT THE MASS DURING THE DAY

FIRST READING

Acts of the Apostles 12:1–11

In those days, King Herod laid hands upon some members of the church to harm them. He had James, the brother of John, killed by the sword, and when he saw that this was pleasing to the Jews he proceeded to arrest Peter also.—It was the feast of Unleavened Bread.—He had him taken into custody and put in prison under the guard of four squads of four soldiers each. He intended to bring him before the people after Passover. Peter thus was being kept in prison, but prayer by the Church was fervently being made to God on his behalf.

On the very night before Herod was to bring him to trial, Peter, secured by double chains, was sleeping between two soldiers, while outside the door guards kept watch on the prison. Suddenly the angel of the Lord stood by him, and a light shone in the cell. He tapped Peter on the side and awakened him, saying, "Get up quickly." The chains fell from his wrists. The angel said to him, "Put on your belt and your sandals." He did so. Then he said to him, "Put on your cloak and follow me." So he followed him out, not realizing that what was happening through the angel was real; he thought he was seeing a vision. They passed the first guard, then the second, and came to the iron gate leading out to the city, which opened for them by itself. They emerged and made their way down an alley, and suddenly the angel left him. Then Peter recovered his senses and said, "Now I know for certain that the Lord sent his angel and rescued me from the hand of Herod and from all that the Jewish people had been expecting."

RESPONSORIAL PSALM

Psalm 34:2–3, 4–5, 6–7, 8–9

℟. The an-gel of the Lord will res-cue those who fear him.

Music: Owen Alstott, b. 1947, © 1977, 1990, OCP. All rights reserved.

▸ I will bless the LORD at all times;
  his praise shall be ever in
    my mouth.
Let my soul glory in the LORD;
  the lowly will hear me and
    be glad. ℟.

▸ Glorify the LORD with me,
    let us together extol his name.
I sought the LORD, and he
    answered me
  and delivered me from all
    my fears. ℟.

℟. **The angel of the Lord will rescue those who fear him.**

▶ Look to him that you may be radiant
    with joy,
   and your faces may not blush
    with shame.
  When the poor one called out, the
    LORD heard,
   and from all his distress he
    saved him. ℟.

▶ The angel of the LORD encamps
   around those who fear him, and
    delivers them.
  Taste and see how good the LORD is;
   blessed the man who takes refuge
    in him. ℟.

SECOND READING

2 Timothy 4:6–8, 17–18

I, Paul, am already being poured out like a libation, and the time of my departure is at hand. I have competed well; I have finished the race; I have kept the faith. From now on the crown of righteousness awaits me, which the Lord, the just judge, will award to me on that day, and not only to me, but to all who have longed for his appearance.

The Lord stood by me and gave me strength, so that through me the proclamation might be completed and all the Gentiles might hear it. And I was rescued from the lion's mouth. The Lord will rescue me from every evil threat and will bring me safe to his heavenly Kingdom. To him be glory forever and ever. Amen.

GOSPEL ACCLAMATION

Matthew 16:18

℟. Al - le - lu - ia, al - le - lu - ia, al - le - lu - ia.

Music: Owen Alstott, b. 1947, © 1977, 1990, OCP. All rights reserved.   *(Omit if not sung)*

▶ You are Peter and upon this rock I will build my Church,
  and the gates of the netherworld shall not prevail against it. ℟.

GOSPEL

Matthew 16:13–19

When Jesus went into the region of Caesarea Philippi he asked his disciples, "Who do people say that the Son of Man is?" They replied, "Some say John the Baptist, others Elijah, still others Jeremiah or one of the prophets." He said to them, "But who do you say that I am?" Simon Peter said in reply, "You are the Christ, the Son of the living God." Jesus said to him in reply, "Blessed are you, Simon son of Jonah. For flesh and blood has not revealed this to you, but my heavenly Father. And so I say to you, you are Peter, and upon this rock I will build my Church, and the gates of the netherworld shall not prevail against it. I will give you the keys to the Kingdom of heaven. Whatever you bind on earth shall be bound in heaven, and whatever you loose on earth shall be loosed in heaven."

1038   AUGUST 6 — THE TRANSFIGURATION OF THE LORD

FIRST READING

Daniel 7:9–10, 13–14

As I watched:
  Thrones were set up

and the Ancient One took
  his throne.

His clothing was bright as snow,
and the hair on his head as white
as wool;
His throne was flames of fire,
with wheels of burning fire.
A surging stream of fire
flowed out from where he sat;
Thousands upon thousands were
ministering to him,
and myriads upon myriads
attended him.
The court was convened, and the
books were opened. As the visions

during the night continued, I saw
One like a Son of man coming,
on the clouds of heaven;
When he reached the Ancient One
and was presented before him,
The one like a Son of man received
dominion, glory, and kingship;
all peoples, nations, and languages
serve him.
His dominion is an everlasting
dominion
that shall not be taken away,
his kingship shall not be destroyed.

RESPONSORIAL PSALM

Psalm 97:1–2, 5–6, 9

℟. The Lord is king, the Most High o - ver all the earth.

▸ The LORD is king; let the earth rejoice;
let the many islands be glad.
Clouds and darkness are round
about him,
justice and judgment are the
foundation of his throne. ℟.

▸ The mountains melt like wax before
the LORD,
before the LORD of all the earth.
The heavens proclaim his justice;
and all peoples see his glory. ℟.

▸ Because you, O LORD, are the Most
High over all the earth,
exalted far above all gods. ℟.

SECOND READING

2 Peter 1:16–19

Beloved: We did not follow cleverly
devised myths when we made known
to you the power and coming of our
Lord Jesus Christ, but we had been
eyewitnesses of his majesty. For
he received honor and glory from
God the Father when that unique
declaration came to him from the
majestic glory, "This is my Son, my

beloved, with whom I am well pleased."
We ourselves heard this voice come
from heaven while we were with him
on the holy mountain. Moreover, we
possess the prophetic message that is
altogether reliable. You will do well to
be attentive to it, as to a lamp shining
in a dark place, until day dawns and
the morning star rises in your hearts.

GOSPEL ACCLAMATION

Matthew 17:5c

℟. Al - le - lu - ia, al - le - lu - ia, al - le - lu - ia.

(Omit if not sung)

▸ This is my beloved Son, with whom I am well pleased;
listen to him. ℟.

GOSPEL — A

Matthew 17:1–9

Jesus took Peter, James, and his brother, John, and led them up a high mountain by themselves. And he was transfigured before them; his face shone like the sun and his clothes became white as light. And behold, Moses and Elijah appeared to them, conversing with him. Then Peter said to Jesus in reply, "Lord, it is good that we are here. If you wish, I will make three tents here, one for you, one for Moses, and one for Elijah." While he was still speaking, behold, a bright cloud cast a shadow over them, then from the cloud came a voice that said, "This is my beloved Son, with whom I am well pleased; listen to him." When the disciples heard this, they fell prostrate and were very much afraid. But Jesus came and touched them, saying, "Rise, and do not be afraid." And when the disciples raised their eyes, they saw no one else but Jesus alone.

As they were coming down from the mountain, Jesus charged them, "Do not tell the vision to anyone until the Son of Man has been raised from the dead."

GOSPEL — B

Mark 9:2–10

Jesus took Peter, James, and his brother John, and led them up a high mountain apart by themselves. And he was transfigured before them, and his clothes became dazzling white, such as no fuller on earth could bleach them. Then Elijah appeared to them along with Moses, and they were conversing with Jesus. Then Peter said to Jesus in reply, "Rabbi, it is good that we are here! Let us make three tents: one for you, one for Moses, and one for Elijah." He hardly knew what to say, they were so terrified. Then a cloud came, casting a shadow over them; from the cloud came a voice, "This is my beloved Son. Listen to him." Suddenly, looking around, they no longer saw anyone but Jesus alone with them.

As they were coming down from the mountain, he charged them not to relate what they had seen to anyone, except when the Son of Man had risen from the dead. So they kept the matter to themselves, questioning what rising from the dead meant.

GOSPEL — C

Luke 9:28b–36

Jesus took Peter, John, and James and went up a mountain to pray. While he was praying his face changed in appearance and his clothing became dazzling white. And behold, two men were conversing with him, Moses and Elijah, who appeared in glory and spoke of his exodus that he was going to accomplish in Jerusalem. Peter and his companions had been overcome by sleep, but becoming fully awake, they saw his glory and the two men standing with him. As they were about to part from him, Peter said to Jesus, "Master, it is good that we are here; let us make three tents, one for you, one for Moses, and one for Elijah." But he did not know what he was saying. While he was still speaking, a cloud came and cast a shadow over them, and they became frightened when they entered the cloud. Then from the cloud came a voice that said, "This is my chosen Son; listen to him." After the voice had spoken, Jesus was found alone. They fell silent and did not at that time tell anyone what they had seen.

AUGUST 14 — THE ASSUMPTION OF THE **1039** BLESSED VIRGIN MARY: AT THE VIGIL MASS

FIRST READING

1 Chronicles 15:3–4, 15–16; 16:1–2

David assembled all Israel in Jerusalem to bring the ark of the LORD to the place which he had prepared for it. David also called together the sons of Aaron and the Levites.

The Levites bore the ark of God on their shoulders with poles, as Moses had ordained according to the word of the LORD.

David commanded the chiefs of the Levites to appoint their kinsmen as chanters, to play on musical instruments, harps, lyres, and cymbals, to make a loud sound of rejoicing.

They brought in the ark of God and set it within the tent which David had pitched for it. Then they offered up burnt offerings and peace offerings to God. When David had finished offering up the burnt offerings and peace offerings, he blessed the people in the name of the LORD.

RESPONSORIAL PSALM

Psalm 132:6–7, 9–10, 13–14

℟. Lord, go up to the place of your rest, you and the ark of your ho-li-ness.

Music: Owen Alstott, b. 1947, © 1977, 1990, OCP. All rights reserved.

▶ Behold, we heard of it in Ephrathah;
  we found it in the fields of Jaar.
Let us enter his dwelling,
  let us worship at his footstool. ℟.

▶ May your priests be clothed
  with justice;
  let your faithful ones shout merrily
    for joy.

For the sake of David your servant,
  reject not the plea of
    your anointed. ℟.

▶ For the LORD has chosen Zion;
  he prefers her for his dwelling.
"Zion is my resting place forever;
  in her will I dwell,
    for I prefer her." ℟.

SECOND READING

1 Corinthians 15:54b–57

Brothers and sisters: When that which is mortal clothes itself with immortality, then the word that is written shall come about:
  Death is swallowed up in victory.
  Where, O death, is your victory?
Where, O death, is your sting?
The sting of death is sin, and the power of sin is the law. But thanks be to God who gives us the victory through our Lord Jesus Christ.

GOSPEL ACCLAMATION

Luke 11:28

℟. Al-le-lu - ia, al-le-lu - ia, al-le-lu - ia.

Music: Owen Alstott, b. 1947, © 1977, 1990, OCP. All rights reserved.   *(Omit if not sung)*

▶ Blessed are they who hear the word of God
  and observe it. ℟.

GOSPEL

Luke 11:27–28

While Jesus was speaking, a woman from the crowd called out and said to him, "Blessed is the womb that carried you and the breasts at which you nursed." He replied, "Rather, blessed are those who hear the word of God and observe it."

1040   AUGUST 15 — THE ASSUMPTION OF THE BLESSED VIRGIN MARY: AT THE MASS DURING THE DAY

FIRST READING

Revelation 11:19a; 12:1–6a, 10ab

God's temple in heaven was opened, and the ark of his covenant could be seen in the temple.

A great sign appeared in the sky, a woman clothed with the sun, with the moon under her feet, and on her head a crown of twelve stars. She was with child and wailed aloud in pain as she labored to give birth. Then another sign appeared in the sky; it was a huge red dragon, with seven heads and ten horns, and on its heads were seven diadems. Its tail swept away a third of the stars in the sky and hurled them down to the earth. Then the dragon stood before the woman about to give birth, to devour her child when she gave birth. She gave birth to a son, a male child, destined to rule all the nations with an iron rod. Her child was caught up to God and his throne. The woman herself fled into the desert where she had a place prepared by God.

Then I heard a loud voice in heaven say:

"Now have salvation and
     power come,
   and the Kingdom of our God
   and the authority of his
     Anointed One."

RESPONSORIAL PSALM

Psalm 45:10, 11, 12, 16

℟. The queen stands at your right hand, ar-rayed in gold.

▶ The queen takes her place at your right hand in gold of Ophir. ℟.

▶ Hear, O daughter, and see; turn your ear,
   forget your people and your father's house. ℟.

▶ So shall the king desire your beauty; for he is your lord. ℟.

▶ They are borne in with gladness and joy;
   they enter the palace of the king. ℟.

SECOND READING

1 Corinthians 15:20–27

Brothers and sisters: Christ has been raised from the dead, the firstfruits of those who have fallen asleep. For since death came through man, the resurrection of the dead came also through man. For just as in Adam all die, so too in Christ shall all be brought to life, but each one in proper order: Christ the firstfruits; then, at his coming, those who belong to Christ; then comes the end, when he hands over the Kingdom to his God and Father, when he has destroyed every sovereignty and every authority and power. For he must reign until he has put all his enemies under his feet. The last enemy to be destroyed is death, for "he subjected everything under his feet."

GOSPEL ACCLAMATION

℟. Al - le - lu - ia, al - le - lu - ia, al - le - lu - ia.

Music: Owen Alstott, b. 1947, © 1977, 1990, OCP. All rights reserved. *(Omit if not sung)*

▶ Mary is taken up to heaven;
a chorus of angels exults. ℟.

GOSPEL

Luke 1:39–56

Mary set out and traveled to the hill country in haste to a town of Judah, where she entered the house of Zechariah and greeted Elizabeth. When Elizabeth heard Mary's greeting, the infant leaped in her womb, and Elizabeth, filled with the Holy Spirit, cried out in a loud voice and said, "Blessed are you among women, and blessed is the fruit of your womb. And how does this happen to me, that the mother of my Lord should come to me? For at the moment the sound of your greeting reached my ears, the infant in my womb leaped for joy. Blessed are you who believed that what was spoken to you by the Lord would be fulfilled."

And Mary said:
"My soul proclaims the greatness of the Lord;
my spirit rejoices in God my Savior
for he has looked with favor on his lowly servant.
From this day all generations will call me blessed:
the Almighty has done great things for me

and holy is his Name.
He has mercy on those who fear him
in every generation.
He has shown the strength of his arm,
and has scattered the proud in their conceit.
He has cast down the mighty from their thrones,
and has lifted up the lowly.
He has filled the hungry with good things,
and the rich he has sent away empty.
He has come to the help of his servant Israel
for he has remembered his promise of mercy,
the promise he made to our fathers,
to Abraham and his children forever."
Mary remained with her about three months and then returned to her home.

SEPTEMBER 14 — THE EXALTATION OF THE HOLY CROSS   1041

FIRST READING

Numbers 21:4b–9

With their patience worn out by the journey, the people complained against God and Moses, "Why have you brought us up from Egypt to die in this desert, where there is no food or water? We are disgusted with this wretched food!"

In punishment the LORD sent among the people saraph serpents, which bit the people so that many of them died. Then the people came to Moses and said, "We have sinned in complaining against the LORD and you. Pray the LORD to take the serpents from us."

So Moses prayed for the people, and the LORD said to Moses, "Make a saraph and mount it on a pole, and if any who have been bitten look at it, they will live." Moses accordingly made a bronze serpent and mounted it on a pole, and whenever anyone who had been bitten by a serpent looked at the bronze serpent, he lived.

RESPONSORIAL PSALM

Psalm 78:1–2, 34–35, 36–37, 38

℟. **Do not forget the works of the Lord!**

▸ Hearken, my people, to my teaching;
  incline your ears to the words of
    my mouth.
I will open my mouth in a parable,
  I will utter mysteries from of old. ℟.

▸ While he slew them they sought him
  and inquired after God again,
Remembering that God was
    their rock
  and the Most High God,
    their redeemer. ℟.

▸ But they flattered him with
    their mouths
  and lied to him with their tongues,
Though their hearts were not
    steadfast toward him,
  nor were they faithful to
    his covenant. ℟.

▸ But he, being merciful,
    forgave their sin
  and destroyed them not;
Often he turned back his anger
  and let none of his wrath
    be roused. ℟.

SECOND READING

Philippians 2:6–11

Brothers and sisters:
  Christ Jesus, though he was in the
    form of God,
    did not regard equality with God
      something to be grasped.
  Rather, he emptied himself,
    taking the form of a slave,
    coming in human likeness;
  and found human in appearance,
    he humbled himself,
    becoming obedient to death,
      even death on a cross.

Because of this, God greatly
    exalted him
  and bestowed on him the name
    that is above every name,
    that at the name of Jesus
    every knee should bend,
    of those in heaven and on earth
      and under the earth,
    and every tongue confess that
    Jesus Christ is Lord,
    to the glory of God the Father.

GOSPEL ACCLAMATION

℟. **Al - le - lu - ia, al - le - lu - ia, al - le - lu - ia.**

(Omit if not sung)

▶ We adore you, O Christ, and we bless you,
because by your Cross you have redeemed the world. ℟.

GOSPEL
John 3:13–17

Jesus said to Nicodemus: "No one has gone up to heaven except the one who has come down from heaven, the Son of Man. And just as Moses lifted up the serpent in the desert, so must the Son of Man be lifted up, so that everyone who believes in him may have eternal life."

For God so loved the world that he gave his only Son, so that everyone who believes in him might not perish but might have eternal life. For God did not send his Son into the world to condemn the world, but that the world might be saved through him.

NOVEMBER 1 — ALL SAINTS   1042

FIRST READING
Revelation 7:2–4, 9–14

I, John, saw another angel come up from the East, holding the seal of the living God. He cried out in a loud voice to the four angels who were given power to damage the land and the sea, "Do not damage the land or the sea or the trees until we put the seal on the foreheads of the servants of our God." I heard the number of those who had been marked with the seal, one hundred and forty-four thousand marked from every tribe of the children of Israel.

After this I had a vision of a great multitude, which no one could count, from every nation, race, people, and tongue. They stood before the throne and before the Lamb, wearing white robes and holding palm branches in their hands. They cried out in a loud voice:

"Salvation comes from our God,
who is seated on the throne,
and from the Lamb."
All the angels stood around the throne and around the elders and the four living creatures. They prostrated themselves before the throne, worshiped God, and exclaimed:
"Amen. Blessing and glory, wisdom
and thanksgiving,
honor, power, and might
be to our God forever and ever.
Amen."
Then one of the elders spoke up and said to me, "Who are these wearing white robes, and where did they come from?" I said to him, "My lord, you are the one who knows." He said to me, "These are the ones who have survived the time of great distress; they have washed their robes and made them white in the Blood of the Lamb."

RESPONSORIAL PSALM
Psalm 24:1bc–2, 3–4ab, 5–6

℟. Lord, this is the peo - ple that longs to see your face.

Music: Owen Alstott, b. 1947, © 1977, 1990, OCP. All rights reserved.

▶ The LORD's are the earth and
its fullness;
the world and those who dwell in it.

For he founded it upon the seas
and established it upon
the rivers. ℟.

℟. **Lord, this is the people that longs to see your face.**

▶ Who can ascend the mountain of
     the LORD?
   or who may stand in his holy place?
   One whose hands are sinless, whose
     heart is clean,
   who desires not what is vain. ℟.

▶ He shall receive a blessing from
     the LORD,
   a reward from God his savior.
   Such is the race that seeks him,
     that seeks the face of the God
     of Jacob. ℟.

SECOND READING

1 John 3:1–3

Beloved: See what love the Father
has bestowed on us that we may be
called the children of God. Yet so we
are. The reason the world does not
know us is that it did not know him.
Beloved, we are God's children now;
what we shall be has not yet been
revealed. We do know that when it
is revealed we shall be like him, for
we shall see him as he is. Everyone
who has this hope based on him
makes himself pure, as he is pure.

GOSPEL ACCLAMATION

Matthew 11:28

℟. **Al - le - lu - ia,   al - le - lu - ia,   al - le - lu - ia.**

(Omit if not sung)

▶ Come to me, all you who labor and are burdened,
   and I will give you rest, says the Lord. ℟.

GOSPEL

Matthew 5:1–12a

When Jesus saw the crowds, he went
up the mountain, and after he had
sat down, his disciples came to him.
He began to teach them, saying:
   "Blessed are the poor in spirit,
     for theirs is the Kingdom
       of heaven.
   Blessed are they who mourn,
     for they will be comforted.
   Blessed are the meek,
     for they will inherit the land.
   Blessed are they who hunger and
       thirst for righteousness,
     for they will be satisfied.
   Blessed are the merciful,
     for they will be shown mercy.

Blessed are the clean of heart,
   for they will see God.
Blessed are the peacemakers,
   for they will be called children
     of God.
Blessed are they who are persecuted
     for the sake of righteousness,
   for theirs is the Kingdom
     of heaven.
Blessed are you when they insult you
and persecute you and utter every
kind of evil against you falsely because
of me. Rejoice and be glad, for your
reward will be great in heaven."

November 2 — The Commemoration of All the Faithful Departed (All Souls' Day)   1043

The following readings or those given in the Masses for the Dead, Lectionary numbers 1011–1016, may be used.

First Reading   *Isaiah 25:6, 7–9*

On this mountain the LORD of hosts
  will provide for all peoples.
On this mountain he will destroy
  the veil that veils all peoples,
The web that is woven over
  all nations;
he will destroy death forever.
The Lord GOD will wipe away
  the tears from all faces;
The reproach of his people he
  will remove

from the whole earth; for the LORD
  has spoken.
On that day it will be said:
"Behold our God, to whom we looked
  to save us!
This is the LORD for whom
  we looked;
let us rejoice and be glad that he
  has saved us!"

Responsorial Psalm   *Psalm 23:1–3a, 3b–4, 5, 6*

℟. The Lord is my shep-herd; there is noth-ing I shall want.

Or ℟. **Though I walk in the valley of darkness, I fear no evil, for you are with me.**

▸ The LORD is my shepherd; I shall
    not want.
  In verdant pastures he gives
    me repose;
  Beside restful waters he leads me;
    he refreshes my soul. ℟.

▸ He guides me in right paths
    for his name's sake.
  Even though I walk in the dark valley
    I fear no evil; for you are at my side
  With your rod and your staff
    that give me courage. ℟.

▸ You spread the table before me
    in the sight of my foes;
  You anoint my head with oil;
    my cup overflows. ℟.

▸ Only goodness and kindness
    follow me
  all the days of my life;
  And I shall dwell in the house of
    the LORD
    for years to come. ℟.

Second Reading   *Romans 6:3–9*

Brothers and sisters: Are you unaware
that we who were baptized into
Christ Jesus were baptized into his
death? We were indeed buried with
him through baptism into death, so
that, just as Christ was raised from
the dead by the glory of the Father,
we too might live in newness of life.

For if we have grown into union
with him through a death like his, we
shall also be united with him in the
resurrection. We know that our old
self was crucified with him, so that
our sinful body might be done away
with, that we might no longer be
in slavery to sin. For a dead person

has been absolved from sin. If, then, we have died with Christ, we believe that we shall also live with him. We know that Christ, raised from the dead, dies no more; death no longer has power over him.

GOSPEL ACCLAMATION

cf. John 6:40

℟. Al - le - lu - ia, al - le - lu - ia, al - le - lu - ia.

(Omit if not sung)

▸ This is the will of my Father, says the Lord.
  that everyone who sees the Son and believes in him
  may have eternal life. ℟.

GOSPEL

John 6:37–40

Jesus said to the crowds: "Everything that the Father gives me will come to me, and I will not reject anyone who comes to me, because I came down from heaven not to do my own will but the will of the one who sent me. And this is the will of the one who sent me, that I should not lose anything of what he gave me, but that I should raise it on the last day. For this is the will of my Father, that everyone who sees the Son and believes in him may have eternal life, and I shall raise him on the last day."

1044 NOVEMBER 9 — THE DEDICATION OF THE LATERAN BASILICA

FIRST READING

Ezekiel 47:1–2, 8–9, 12

The angel brought me back to the entrance of the temple, and I saw water flowing out from beneath the threshold of the temple toward the east, for the façade of the temple was toward the east; the water flowed down from the southern side of the temple, south of the altar. He led me outside by the north gate, and around to the outer gate facing the east, where I saw water trickling from the southern side. He said to me, "This water flows into the eastern district down upon the Arabah, and empties into the sea, the salt waters, which it makes fresh. Wherever the river flows, every sort of living creature that can multiply shall live, and there shall be abundant fish, for wherever this water comes the sea shall be made fresh. Along both banks of the river, fruit trees of every kind shall grow; their leaves shall not fade, nor their fruit fail. Every month they shall bear fresh fruit, for they shall be watered by the flow from the sanctuary. Their fruit shall serve for food, and their leaves for medicine."

RESPONSORIAL PSALM

Psalm 46:2–3, 5–6, 8–9

℞. The waters of the river gladden the ci - ty of God, the holy dwelling of the Most High!

▶ God is our refuge and our strength,
  an ever-present help in distress.
Therefore, we fear not, though the
  earth be shaken
  and mountains plunge into the
  depths of the sea. ℞.

▶ There is a stream whose runlets
  gladden the city of God,
  the holy dwelling of the Most High.

God is in its midst; it shall not
  be disturbed;
God will help it at the break
  of dawn. ℞.

▶ The LORD of hosts is with us;
  our stronghold is the God of Jacob.
Come! behold the deeds of the LORD,
  the astounding things he has
  wrought on earth. ℞.

SECOND READING

1 Corinthians 3:9c–11, 16–17

Brothers and sisters: You are God's building. According to the grace of God given to me, like a wise master builder I laid a foundation, and another is building upon it. But each one must be careful how he builds upon it, for no one can lay a foundation other than the one that is there, namely, Jesus Christ.

Do you not know that you are the temple of God, and that the Spirit of God dwells in you? If anyone destroys God's temple, God will destroy that person; for the temple of God, which you are, is holy.

GOSPEL ACCLAMATION

2 Chronicles 7:16

℞. Al - le - lu - ia, al - le - lu - ia, al - le - lu - ia.

(Omit if not sung)

▶ I have chosen and consecrated this house, says the Lord,
  that my name may be there forever. ℞.

GOSPEL

John 2:13–22

Since the Passover of the Jews was near, Jesus went up to Jerusalem. He found in the temple area those who sold oxen, sheep, and doves, as well as the money-changers seated there. He made a whip out of cords and drove them all out of the temple area, with the sheep and oxen, and spilled the coins of the money-changers and overturned their tables, and to those who sold doves he said, "Take these out of here, and stop making my Father's house a marketplace." His disciples recalled the words of Scripture,

Zeal for your house will consume me.

At this the Jews answered and said to him, "What sign can you show us for doing this?" Jesus answered and said to them, "Destroy this temple and in three days I will raise it up." The Jews said, "This temple has been under construction for forty-six years, and you will raise it up in three days?" But

he was speaking about the temple of his Body. Therefore, when he was raised from the dead, his disciples remembered that he had said this, and they came to believe the Scripture and the word Jesus had spoken.

1045 DECEMBER 8 — THE IMMACULATE CONCEPTION OF THE BLESSED VIRGIN MARY PATRONAL FEASTDAY OF THE UNITED STATES OF AMERICA

FIRST READING   *Genesis 3:9–15, 20*

After the man, Adam, had eaten of the tree, the LORD God called to the man and asked him, "Where are you?" He answered, "I heard you in the garden; but I was afraid, because I was naked, so I hid myself." Then he asked, "Who told you that you were naked? You have eaten, then, from the tree of which I had forbidden you to eat!" The man replied, "The woman whom you put here with me—she gave me fruit from the tree, and so I ate it." The LORD God then asked the woman, "Why did you do such a thing?" The woman answered, "The serpent tricked me into it, so I ate it."

Then the LORD God said to the serpent:
"Because you have done this, you
    shall be banned
  from all the animals
  and from all the wild creatures;
on your belly shall you crawl,
  and dirt shall you eat
  all the days of your life.
I will put enmity between you and
    the woman,
  and between your offspring
    and hers;
he will strike at your head,
  while you strike at his heel."
The man called his wife Eve, because she became the mother of all the living.

RESPONSORIAL PSALM   *Psalm 98:1, 2–3ab, 3cd–4*

℟. Sing to the Lord a new song, for he has done mar-vel-ous deeds.

▶ Sing to the LORD a new song,
  for he has done wondrous deeds;
His right hand has won victory
    for him,
  his holy arm. ℟.

▶ The LORD has made his
    salvation known:
  in the sight of the nations he has
    revealed his justice.

He has remembered his kindness and
  his faithfulness
  toward the house of Israel. ℟.

▶ All the ends of the earth have seen
  the salvation by our God.
Sing joyfully to the LORD,
  all you lands;
  break into song; sing praise. ℟.

SECOND READING

Ephesians 1:3–6, 11–12

Brothers and sisters: Blessed be the God and Father of our Lord Jesus Christ, who has blessed us in Christ with every spiritual blessing in the heavens, as he chose us in him, before the foundation of the world, to be holy and without blemish before him. In love he destined us for adoption to himself through Jesus Christ, in accord with the favor of his will, for the praise of the glory of his grace that he granted us in the beloved.

In him we were also chosen, destined in accord with the purpose of the One who accomplishes all things according to the intention of his will, so that we might exist for the praise of his glory, we who first hoped in Christ.

GOSPEL ACCLAMATION

cf. Luke 1:28

℟. Al - le - lu - ia, al - le - lu - ia, al - le - lu - ia.

(Omit if not sung)

▶ Hail, Mary, full of grace, the Lord is with you; blessed are you among women. ℟.

GOSPEL

Luke 1:26–38

The angel Gabriel was sent from God to a town of Galilee called Nazareth, to a virgin betrothed to a man named Joseph, of the house of David, and the virgin's name was Mary. And coming to her, he said, "Hail, full of grace! The Lord is with you." But she was greatly troubled at what was said and pondered what sort of greeting this might be. Then the angel said to her, "Do not be afraid, Mary, for you have found favor with God. Behold, you will conceive in your womb and bear a son, and you shall name him Jesus. He will be great and will be called Son of the Most High, and the Lord God will give him the throne of David his father, and he will rule over the house of Jacob forever, and of his Kingdom there will be no end." But Mary said to the angel, "How can this be, since I have no relations with a man?" And the angel said to her in reply, "The Holy Spirit will come upon you, and the power of the Most High will overshadow you. Therefore the child to be born will be called holy, the Son of God. And behold, Elizabeth, your relative, has also conceived a son in her old age, and this is the sixth month for her who was called barren; for nothing will be impossible for God." Mary said, "Behold, I am the handmaid of the Lord. May it be done to me according to your word." Then the angel departed from her.

DECEMBER 12 — OUR LADY OF GUADALUPE 1046

The following readings or any from the Common of the Blessed Virgin Mary, Lectionary numbers 707–712, may be used.

FIRST READING

Revelation 11:19a; 12:1–6a, 10ab

God's temple in heaven was opened, and the ark of his covenant could be seen in the temple.

A great sign appeared in the sky, a woman clothed with the sun, with the moon under her feet, and on her head a crown of twelve stars. She was with child and wailed aloud in pain as she labored to give birth. Then another sign appeared in the sky; it was a huge red dragon, with seven heads and ten horns, and on its heads were seven diadems. Its tail swept away a third of the stars in the sky and hurled them down to the earth. Then the dragon stood before the woman about to give birth, to devour her child when she gave birth.

She gave birth to a son, a male child, destined to rule all the nations with an iron rod. Her child was caught up to God and his throne. The woman herself fled into the desert where she had a place prepared by God.

Then I heard a loud voice in heaven say:

"Now have salvation and
power come,
and the Kingdom of our God
and the authority of his Anointed."

Alternate reading is Zechariah 2:14–17

RESPONSORIAL PSALM
Judith 13:18bcde, 19

℟. You are the high-est hon-or of our race.

Music: Owen Alstott, b. 1947, © 1977, 1990, OCP. All rights reserved.

▶ Blessed are you, daughter, by the
Most High God,
above all the women on earth;
and blessed be the LORD God,
the creator of heaven and earth. ℟.

▶ Your deed of hope will never
be forgotten
by those who tell of the might
of God. ℟.

GOSPEL ACCLAMATION

℟. Al-le-lu - ia, al-le-lu - ia, al - le - lu - ia.

Music: Owen Alstott, b. 1947, © 1977, 1990, OCP. All rights reserved.

(Omit if not sung)

▶ Blessed are you, holy Virgin Mary, deserving of all praise;
from you rose the sun of justice, Christ our God. ℟.

GOSPEL
Luke 1:39–47

Mary set out and traveled to the hill country in haste to a town of Judah, where she entered the house of Zechariah and greeted Elizabeth. When Elizabeth heard Mary's greeting, the infant leaped in her womb, and Elizabeth, filled with the Holy Spirit, cried out in a loud voice and said, "Most blessed are you among women, and blessed is the fruit of your womb. And how does this happen to me, that the mother of my

Lord should come to me? For at the moment the sound of your greeting reached my ears, the infant in my womb leaped for joy. Blessed are you who believed that what was spoken to you by the Lord would be fulfilled."

And Mary said:

"My soul proclaims the greatness
of the Lord;
my spirit rejoices in God
my savior."

Alternate reading is Luke 1:26–38

Tradition holds that Jesus walked from Pilate's praetorium to Golgotha (the Place of the Skull). The devotion known as "the way," or Stations of the Cross (Via Crucis), originated with pilgrims who walked the Via Dolorosa (the "way of tears") in Jerusalem. In 2001, the Congregation for the Discipline of the Sacraments issued the Directory on Popular Piety and the Liturgy (DPPL) and, when referring to this devotion, stated that "In the Via Crucis, various strands of Christian piety coalesce: the idea of life as being journey or pilgrimage; as a passage from earthly exile to our true home in Heaven; the deep desire to be conformed to the Passion of Christ, which imply that his disciples must follow behind their Master, daily carrying their own crosses (cf. Luke 9, 23)" (DPPL 133). For music, please see song #363.

1. **JESUS IS CONDEMNED TO DEATH.**
   Christ, help us to lead a better life and to seek your will.

2. **JESUS BEARS HIS CROSS.**
   Lord, we join you in your journey of suffering.

3. **JESUS FALLS FOR THE FIRST TIME.**
   Christ, help us who fall into sinful ways; teach us to rise with you.

4. **JESUS MEETS HIS MOTHER.**
   Lord, we implore your mother to console us who mourn.

5. **JESUS IS HELPED BY SIMON.**
   Christ, help as we try to do your work in our world.

6. **VERONICA WIPES HIS FACE.**
   Lord, help us as we help others.

7. **JESUS FALLS THE SECOND TIME.**
   Christ, teach us the healing power of penance.

8. **JESUS SPEAKS TO THE WOMEN.**
   Lord, help us to comfort those who have no one to help them.

9. **JESUS FALLS A THIRD TIME.**
   Christ, teach us the joy of obedience.

10. **JESUS IS STRIPPED OF HIS GARMENTS.**
    Lord, help us to model your life of holiness.

11. **JESUS IS NAILED TO THE CROSS.**
    Christ, draw us closer to you from this day forward.

12. **JESUS DIES ON THE CROSS.**
    Lord, we pray that you will be with us at our hour of death.

13. **HE IS TAKEN FROM THE CROSS.**
    Christ, open our hearts to the beauty of your love for us.

14. **HE IS LAID IN THE TOMB.**
    Lord, help us to walk in your ways all the days of our lives.

PRAYERS

1048 NIGHT PRAYER (COMPLINE)

Night Prayer is an occasion for the Christian to remember with sorrow the day's sin and failure and to pray for protection throughout the coming night.

VERSE AND RESPONSE

All make the sign of the cross.

HYMN

For music see #852–856

A penitential rite using the formulas of the Mass may be inserted here.

PSALMODY

Psalms and their antiphons may be taken from the proper of the day.

READING

HOMILY/PREACHING** *(optional)*

RESPONSORY

Presiding Minister/All: **Into your hands, Lord, I commend my spirit.**
Presiding Minister: You have redeemed us, Lord God of truth.
All: **I commend my spirit.**
Presiding Minister: Glory to the Father, and to the Son, and to the Holy Spirit.
All: **Into your hands, Lord, I commend my spirit.**

GOSPEL CANTICLE: SONG OF SIMEON

For music see #124, 125, 857

CONCLUDING PRAYER

The presiding minister says the concluding prayer.

BLESSING/CONCLUSION

Presiding Minister: May the all-powerful Lord grant us a restful night and a peaceful death.
All: **Amen.**

MARIAN ANTIPHON: SALVE REGINA *(For music see #485.)*

The Marian Antiphon "Regina Caeli," #416, is used during the Easter season; the antiphon "Alma Redemptoris Mater," #471, is used during the Advent season through the Presentation of the Lord. Other hymns approved by the Conference of Bishops may be used.

ANIMA CHRISTI

Soul of Christ, sanctify me; Body of Christ, save me; Blood of Christ, inebriate me; Water from the side of Christ, wash me; Passion of Christ, strengthen me; O good Jesus, hear me; Within your wounds hide me; Separated from you, let me never be; From the evil one protect me; At the hour of my death, call me; And close to you bid me; That with your saints, I may be, praising you forever and ever. Amen.

MEMORARE

Remember, O most gracious Virgin Mary, that never was it known that anyone who fled to your protection, implored your help, or sought your intercession, was left unaided. Inspired by this confidence, I fly unto you, O Virgin of virgins, my Mother. To you I come; before you I stand sinful and sorrowful. O Mother of the Word Incarnate! Despise not my petitions, but in your mercy hear and answer me. Amen.

HAIL, HOLY QUEEN

Hail, Holy Queen, Mother of Mercy, our life, our sweetness, and our hope! To you do we cry, poor banished children of Eve; to you do we send up our sighs, mourning and weeping in this vale of tears. Turn, then, most gracious advocate, your eyes of mercy toward us; and after this our exile, show unto us the blessed fruit of your womb, Jesus. O clement, O loving, O sweet Virgin Mary! Pray for us, O Holy Mother of God, that we may be made worthy of the promises of Christ.

ACT OF CONTRITION

O my God, I am heartily sorry for having offended you. I detest all my sins because of your just punishments. But most of all because they offend you, my God, who are all good and deserving of all my love. I firmly resolve, with the help of your grace to sin no more and to avoid the near occasions of sin. Amen.

REGINA COELI

O Queen of heaven, rejoice! Alleluia.
For He whom you did merit to bear,
  Alleluia.
Has risen, as He said, Alleluia.
Pray for us to God, Alleluia.
  ℣. Rejoice and be glad, O Virgin Mary.
  Alleluia.
  ℟. For the Lord has risen indeed.
  Alleluia.

Let us pray. O God, Who by the resurrection of Your Son, Our Lord Jesus Christ, has given joy to the whole world, grant, we beseech You, that through the intercession of the Virgin Mary, His Mother, we may attain the same joys of eternal life. Through the same Christ Our Lord. Amen.

ACT OF FAITH

O my God, I firmly believe that you are One God in Three Divine Persons, Father, Son, and the Holy Spirit; I believe that your Divine Son became man, and died for our sins, and that he will come again to judge the living and the dead. I believe these and all the truths which the Holy Catholic Church teaches, because you have revealed them, Who can neither deceive nor be deceived.

ACT OF HOPE

O my God, relying on your almighty power and infinite mercy and promises, I hope to obtain pardon of my sins, the help of your grace, and life everlasting, through the merits of Jesus Christ, my Lord and Redeemer.

ACT OF LOVE

O my God, I love you above all things, with my whole heart and soul, because you are all-good and worthy of all love. I love my neighbor as myself for the love of you. I forgive all who have injured me, and ask pardon of all whom I have injured.

The publisher sincerely thanks the authors, composers and owners or holders of copyright who have so kindly granted permission to use their material. Every effort has been made to determine and acknowledge owners and administrators of each copyright. The publisher regrets any oversight that may have occurred and will gladly make proper acknowledgment in future printings after written notice has been received.

Selections copyrighted by spiritandsong.com®, a division of OCP are owned and administered by OCP. All rights reserved. Selections copyrighted by Cooperative Ministries, Inc. are administered by OCP: exclusive agent. Selections copyrighted by Francisco (Kiko) Argüello are administered by OCP: exclusive agent. Selections copyrighted by Gooi en Sticht, bv., Baarn, The Netherlands, are administered by OCP: exclusive agent for English-language countries. Selections copyrighted by Willard Jabusch are administered by OCP. All rights reserved. Selections published by TRINITAS are owned and administered by OCP. All rights reserved.

For licensing information of all selections published or administered by OCP, please contact OCP's licensing agent: www.licensingonline.org.

Unauthorized reproduction of the material in this publication, by any means, or use of the individual pages herein, is a violation of the U.S. Copyright Law and the moral rights of the copyright owner. Permission to use, in any way, the material in this book must be obtained in writing from OCP and the copyright owner.

ABBAYE SAINT-PIERRE DE SOLESMES
F-72300 Sablé-sur-Sarthe
1 Place Dom Gueranger
Solesmes, 72300
France

ALFRED PUBLISHING CO., INC.
Chappell & Co., Inc.
J. Fischer & Bro.
Warner/Tamerlane
Publishing Corp.
PO Box 10003
Van Nuys, CA 91410-0003
(818) 891-5999
Fax (818) 891-2369

AUGSBURG FORTRESS
100 S. 5th St., #700
PO Box 1209
Minneapolis, MN 55440-1209
(800) 328-4648

THE BENEDICTINE FOUNDATION
OF THE STATE OF VERMONT, INC.
58 Priory Hill Rd.
Weston, VT 05161

CELEBRATION
c/o The Community of
Celebration Licensing
PO Box 309
Aliquippa, PA 15001
(724) 375-1510
Fax (724) 375-1138

CHAPPELL & CO., INC.
c/o Alfred Publishing Co., Inc.

CHURCH PUBLISHING, INC.
445 Fifth Ave.
New York, NY 10016
(800) 223-6629

COMISIÓN EPISCOPAL ESPAÑOLA
DE LITURGIA
Añastro, 1
28033 Madrid,
Spain

CONCACAN INC.
2500 Don Reid Dr.
Ottawa, ON K1H 2J2
Canada

CONFRATERNITY OF CHRISTIAN
DOCTRINE, INC. (CCD)
3211 4th St. NE
Washington, DC 20017

CONTINUUM INTERNATIONAL
PUBLISHING GROUP, LTD.
Burns & Oates, Ltd.
Mowbray & Co.
Tower Building
11 York Rd.
London, SE1 7NX
United Kingdom
011-44-(0)20-7922-0880

THE COPYRIGHT CO.
Abingdon Press
1025 16th Ave. S., Ste. 204
PO Box 128139
Nashville, TN 37212-8139

DAMEAN MUSIC
5329 Dijon Dr., Ste. 103
Baton Rouge, LA 70808-4378

EMI CMG PUBLISHING
Birdwing Music
Blue Raft Music
BMG Songs, Inc
Bud John Songs/Crouch Music
Meaux Mercy
Mountain Spring Music
Straightway Music
The Stuart K. Hine Trust
ThankYou Music
101 Winners Circle
Brentwood, TN 37027
(615) 371-4300

FABER MUSIC, LTD.
Bloomsbury House
74-77 Great Russell Street
London, WC1B 3DA
United Kingdom
011-44(0)1279-828900
Fax 011-44(0)1279-828901

JOYCE MACDONALD GLOVER
34405 S. Jefferson St., Apt. 837
Falls Church, VA 22041-3127

WILLIAM BOYD GROVE
109 McDavid Ln.
Charleston, WV 25311

RICHARD W. HILLERT
1620 Clay Court
Melrose Park, IL 60160

HOPE PUBLISHING CO.
The Hymn Society
The Jubilate Group
Stainer & Bell, Ltd.
The Stuart K. Hine Trust
380 S. Main Pl.
Carol Stream, IL 60188
(800) 323-1049
Fax (630) 665-2552

INTEGRITY MEDIA, INC.
Hillsong Publishing
Integrity's Hosanna! Music
Darlene Zschech
Attn: Jonathan Lane
1000 Cody Rd.
Mobile, AL 36695-3425
(251) 633-9000
Fax (251) 776-5036

INTERNATIONAL COMMISSION
ON ENGLISH IN THE LITURGY
CORPORATION (ICEL)
1100 Connecticut Ave NW, Ste. 710
Washington, DC 20036-4101
(202) 347-0800 Ext. 2
Fax (202) 347-1839

INTERNATIONAL LITURGY
PUBLICATIONS
PO Box 50476
Nashville, TN 37205
www.ilpmusic.org
(888) 898-SONG

JOHN IRELAND TRUST
20 Third Acre Rise
Oxford OX2 9DA
United Kingdom

JAN-LEE MUSIC
PO Box 1210
Penn Valley, CA 95946
(800) 211-8454

ANNE K. LECROY
2101 Christian Ln., Apt. 702
Johnson City, TN 37601-3254

EUGENE M. LINDUSKY
c/o Mary Catherine Lindusky
10101 52nd Dr. NE
Marysville, WA 98270

THE LITURGICAL PRESS
St. John's Abbey
PO Box 7500
Collegeville, MN 56321-7500
(800) 858-5450

LITURGY TRAINING PUBLICATIONS
3949 S. Racine Ave.
Chicago, IL 60609-2523
(800) 933-1800
Fax (800) 933-7094

LORENZ CORPORATION
PO Box 802
501 E. 3rd St.
Dayton, OH 45401-0802
(800) 444-1144
Fax (513) 223-2042

MRS. IRENE C. MUELLER
6402 Cheviot Rd., Apt. #8
Cincinnati, OH 45247

MUSIC SERVICES, INC.
  BMG Songs, Inc.
  Brentwood-Benson Music
    Publishing, Inc.
  CCCM Music
  Universal Music Group
5409 Maryland Way, Ste. 200
Brentwood, TN 37027
(615) 371-1320
Fax (615) 371-1351

NATIONAL CATHOLIC WELFARE
CONFERENCE, INC.
c/o United States Conference of
Catholic Bishops

HAROLD OBER ASSOC., INC.
425 Madison Ave.
New York, NY 10017

OXFORD UNIVERSITY PRESS
Attn: Simon Wright
Great Clarendon St.
Oxford, OX2 6DP
United Kingdom
011-44-(0)1865-556767
Fax 011-44-(0)1865-556646

ROLAND F. PALMER, SSJE
c/o Canon Peter D. Wilkinson
25 Government Unit 209
Victoria, BC V8V 2K4
Canada
(250) 385-4444

THE PILGRIM PRESS
700 Prospect Ave.
Cleveland, OH 44115-1100
(216) 736-3764
Fax (216) 736-2207

ROSALIND RUSBRIDGE
A. E. Rusbridge (Estate of)
c/o Bristol Church Housing
Association, Ltd.
11, Surrey St.
Bristol, BS2 8PS
United Kingdom
011-44-0117-973-6565

PETER J. SCAGNELLI
34 Arlington St.
Framingham, MA 01702-7343

E. C. SCHIRMER MUSIC CO.
c/o ECS Publishing
138 Ipswich St.
Boston, MA 02215-3534
(617) 236-1935
Fax (617) 236-0261

G. SCHIRMER, INC.
  J. Curwen & Sons, Ltd.
c/o Music Sales Corporation
1247 6th St.
Santa Monica, CA 90401
(310) 393-9900
Fax (310) 393-9925

SELAH PUBLISHING CO., INC.
4055 Cloverlea St.
PO Box 98066
Pittsburgh, PA 15227
(800) 852-6172
Fax (412) 886-1022

SHAWNEE PRESS, INC.
c/o Music Sales Corp.
257 Park Avenue South
New York, NY 10010
(212) 254-2100
Fax (212) 254-2013

DENNIS C. SMOLARSKI
Jesuit Community
Santa Clara University
Santa Clara, CA 95053

SOCIEDAD BÍBLICA CATÓLICA
INTERNACIONAL (SOBICAIN)
Protasio Gómez, 15
28027 Madrid,
Spain

SOCIETY OF THE SACRED HEART
Estate of Anne Carter
4120 Forest Park Ave.
St. Louis, MO 63108
(314) 652-1500
Fax (314) 534-6800

STANBROOK ABBEY
Wass
York, YO61 4AY
United Kingdom
011-44-(0)1905-830209
Fax 011-44-(0)1905-831737

WILLIAM G. STOREY
c/o Erasmus Books
1027 E. Wayne St.
South Bend, IN 46617

TWO-BY-TWO MUSIC
c/o spiritandsong.com®,
a division of OCP
5536 NE Hassalo
Portland, OR 97213
(800) 548-8749

UNITED STATES CONFERENCE OF
CATHOLIC BISHOPS
  Comisión Episcopal de Pastoral
    Litúrgica de la Conferencia del
    Episcopado Mexicano
  National Catholic Welfare
    Conference, Inc.
Permissions Department
USCCB Publishing
3211 4th St. NE
Washington, DC 20017-1994
(202) 541-3098
Fax (202) 541-3089

VERNACULAR HYMNS
Publishing Co.
PO Box 2304
Bakersfield, CA 93303

WALTON MUSIC CORPORATION
  Peace of Music Publishing AB
c/o Licensing Associates
935 Broad St. #310
Bloomfield, NJ 07003
(973) 743-6444
Fax (206) 426-6782

WARNER/TAMERLANE PUBLISHING
CORP.
c/o Alfred Publishing Co., Inc.

A.P. WATT, LTD.
20 John St.
London, WC1N 2DR
United Kingdom

WESTMINSTER-JOHN KNOX PRESS
100 Witherspoon St.
Louisville, KY 40202-1396
www.wjkpress.com
(502) 569-5060
Fax (502) 569-5018

THE WILLIS MUSIC COMPANY
7380 Industrial Rd.
PO Box 548
Florence, KY 41042
(859) 283-2050
Fax (859) 283-1784

WORD MUSIC GROUP, LLC
c/o Opryland Music Group
PO Box 128469
Nashville, TN 37212
(215) 587-3696
Fax (215) 587-3561

WORLD LIBRARY PUBLICATIONS
3708 River Rd., Ste. 400
Franklin Park, IL 60131-2158
www.wlpmusic.com
(800) 621-5197
Fax (888) 957-3291

METRICAL INDEX OF HYMN TUNES   1055

1056   SCRIPTURAL INDEX

TOPICAL INDEX   1057

INDEX OF SUGGESTED PSALMS 1059
FOR THE LITURGICAL YEAR

Suggested psalms for the church's three-year Lectionary cycle are listed below. Whenever possible, the psalm of the day or a seasonal (common) psalm has been indicated. If a suitable setting of the psalm is not available, a substitute has been recommended. These alternate settings are marked with an asterisk (*).

PROPER OF SEASONS

ADVENT SEASON

COMMON PSALM
27 Psalm 25: To You, O Lord
    (Joncas)
29 Psalm 25: To You, O Lord
    (Smith)
28 Psalm 25: To You, O Lord
    (Soper)
62 *Psalm 85: Let Us See
    Your Kindness
63 *Psalm 85: Lord, Let Us See
    Your Kindness (Schiavone)
64 *Psalm 85: Lord, Let Us See
    Your Kindness (Soper)

ADVENT I
A 103 Psalm 122: Let Us Go Rejoicing
    (Halligan)

102 Psalm 122: Let Us Go Rejoicing
    (Hurd)
B 60 Psalm 80: Lord, Make Us Turn
    to You
C 27 Psalm 25: To You, O Lord
    (Joncas)
29 Psalm 25: To You, O Lord
    (Smith)
28 Psalm 25: To You, O Lord
    (Soper)

ADVENT II
A 59 Psalm 72: Justice Shall Flourish
B 62 Psalm 85: Let Us See
    Your Kindness
63 Psalm 85: Lord, Let Us See
    Your Kindness (Schiavone)
64 Psalm 85: Lord, Let Us See
    Your Kindness (Soper)
C 104 Psalm 126: The Lord Has Done
    Great Things

ADVENT III
A 116 *Psalm 146: Praise the Lord,
    My Soul
B 121 Luke 1: Magnificat
120 Luke 1: My Soul Rejoices
C 118 *Isaiah 12: We Shall
    Draw Water

ADVENT IV
A 26 Psalm 24: Let the Lord Enter
B 66 Psalm 89: Forever I Will Sing
65 Psalm 89: Forever I Will Sing
    the Goodness of the Lord
C 60 Psalm 80: Lord, Make Us Turn
    to You

CHRISTMAS SEASON

COMMON PSALM
82 Psalm 98: All the Ends of the
    Earth (Canedo)

1060   LITURGICAL INDEX

SERVICE MUSIC FOR MASS

THE INTRODUCTORY RITES

Entrance Song (Gathering or Processional)
See also Liturgical Index, The Liturgical Year; Scriptural Index; Topical Index: Church, People of God, Praise, Thanksgiving, Unity

THE LITURGY OF THE EUCHARIST

Presentation and Preparation of the Gifts

The norms on the manner of singing [this song] are the same as for the Entrance chant. The purpose of this chant is to…foster the unity of those who have been *gathered, introduce their thoughts to the mystery of the liturgical season or festivity, and accompany the procession of the priest and ministers. Instrumental music is also appropriate. (Sing to the Lord, from #173, #142, #174)*

760 As We Gather at Your Table

Eucharistic Prayer

Preface Dialogue
152 Preface Dialogue
     (Roman Missal Chants)

Holy
209 Holy *(Belmont Mass)*
227 Holy *(Heritage Mass)*
189 Holy
     (Mass of Christ the Savior)
248 Holy *(Mass of Glory)*
179 Holy *(Mass of Renewal)*
199 Holy
     (Mass of Spirit and Grace)
219 Holy
     (Mass of the Resurrection)
153 Holy *(Roman Missal Chants)*
170 Sanctus *(Chant Mass)*
236 Santo/Holy *(Misa Santa Fe)*

We Proclaim Your Death
237 Anunciamos Tu Muerte/
     We Proclaim Your Death
     (Misa Santa Fe)
171 Post Consecrationem
     (Chant Mass)
210 We Proclaim Your Death
     (Belmont Mass)
228 We Proclaim Your Death
     (Heritage Mass)
190 We Proclaim Your Death
     (Mass of Christ the Savior)
249 We Proclaim Your Death
     (Mass of Glory)
180 We Proclaim Your Death
     (Mass of Renewal)
200 We Proclaim Your Death
     (Mass of Spirit and Grace)
220 We Proclaim Your Death
     (Mass of the Resurrection)
154 We Proclaim Your Death
     (Roman Missal Chants)

When We Eat this Bread
238 Cada Vez que Comemos/
     When We Eat This Bread
     (Misa Santa Fe)
211 When We Eat This Bread
     (Belmont Mass)
229 When We Eat This Bread
     (Heritage Mass)
191 When We Eat This Bread
     (Mass of Christ the Savior)
250 When We Eat This Bread
     (Mass of Glory)
181 When We Eat This Bread
     (Mass of Renewal)
201 When We Eat This Bread
     (Mass of Spirit and Grace)
221 When We Eat This Bread
     (Mass of the Resurrection)
155 When We Eat This Bread
     (Roman Missal Chants)

Save Us, Savior
239 Por Tu Cruz/Save Us, Savior
     (Misa Santa Fe)
212 Save Us, Savior
     (Belmont Mass)

230 Save Us, Savior
     (Heritage Mass)
192 Save Us, Savior
     (Mass of Christ the Savior)
251 Save Us, Savior
     (Mass of Glory)
182 Save Us, Savior
     (Mass of Renewal)
202 Save Us, Savior
     (Mass of Spirit and Grace)
222 Save Us, Savior
     (Mass of the Resurrection)
156 Save Us, Savior
     (Roman Missal Chants)

Doxology and Amen
213 Amen *(Belmont Mass)*
193 Amen
     (Mass of Christ the Savior)
203 Amen
     (Mass of Spirit and Grace)

Amen
172 Amen *(Chant Mass)*
231 Amen *(Heritage Mass)*
252 Amen *(Mass of Glory)*
183 Amen *(Mass of Renewal)*
223 Amen
     (Mass of the Resurrection)
240 Amén/Amen *(Misa Santa Fe)*
270 Danish Amen

The Communion Rite

The Lord's Prayer
6 Lord's Prayer
   (Camaldolese Monks, OSB)
157 Lord's Prayer
     (Roman Missal Chants)
173 Pater Noster *(Chant Mass)*

Lamb of God/Breaking of the Bread
271 Advent Lamb of God
174 Agnus Dei *(Chant Mass)*
273 Agnus Dei *(Honoré)*
241 Cordero de Dios/Lamb of
     God *(Misa Santa Fe)*
214 Lamb of God *(Belmont Mass)*
232 Lamb of God *(Heritage Mass)*
194 Lamb of God
     (Mass of Christ the Savior)
253 Lamb of God
     (Mass of Glory)
184 Lamb of God
     (Mass of Renewal)
204 Lamb of God
     (Mass of Spirit and Grace)
224 Lamb of God
     (Mass of the Resurrection)
272 Lamb of God
     (Missa Oecumenica)
158 Lamb of God
     (Roman Missal Chants)
789 Lamb of God/Taste and See
     (Kendzia)

Communion Song
See also Topical Index: Good Shepherd, Love for God, Love of God for Us, Paschal Mystery, Praise, Thanksgiving, Unity
670 Age to Age
604 All My Days
620 All the Earth
783 Amén. El Cuerpo de Cristo
697 Because the Lord Is
     My Shepherd
785 Behold the Lamb
780 Bread for the World

799 Bread of Life *(Cooney)*
788 Bread of Life *(Farrell)*
805 Bread of Life *(Fisher)*
665 Center of My Life
797 Come to Me and Drink
795 Come to the Lord
835 Companions on the Journey
454 Draw Near and Take the Body
     of the Lord
766 Gather the People
765 Gather Us Together
768 Gather Your People
791 Gift of Finest Wheat
723 God Is Love
792 God's Holy Gifts
777 Here at This Table
790 Holy Gifts
794 I Am the Living Bread
786 I Received the Living God
509 I Saw Water Flowing
779 In the Breaking of the Bread/
     Cuando Partimos el Pan
     del Señor
770 In This Place
789 Lamb of God/Taste and See
707 Litany of Peace
775 Look Beyond
718 Love One Another
834 Many and Great
693 My Soul Is Thirsting
793 One Bread, One Body
802 One Love Released
676 Only a Shadow
778 Our Blessing Cup
784 Pan de Vida
42 Psalm 34: Taste and See *(Dean)*
40 Psalm 34: Taste and See
     (Willcock)
39 Psalm 34: Taste and See/
     Gusten y Vean *(Reza)*
52 Psalm 63: My Soul Is Thirsting/
     As Morning Breaks
84 Psalm 100: We Are God's
     People *(Smith)*
83 Psalm 100: We Are His People
     (Friedman)
94 Psalm 116: Our Blessing Cup
     (Joncas)
95 Psalm 116: Our Blessing Cup/
     El Cáliz que Bendecimos
     (Cortez)
93 Psalm 116: Our Blessing-Cup/
     I Will Walk with the Lord/
     The Cup of Salvation
     (Soper)
112 Psalm 145: I Will Praise Your
     Name *(Walker)*
113 Psalm 145: I Will Praise Your
     Name/The Hand of the Lord
     (Smith)
115 Psalm 145: I Will Praise Your
     Name/The Hand of the Lord
     Feeds Us *(Soper)*
803 Sacramentum Caritatis
781 Seed, Scattered and Sown
798 Spirit and Grace
761 Table of Plenty
782 Taste and See *(Angrisano)*
796 Taste and See *(Hurd)*
774 The Supper of the Lord
787 To Be Your Bread
776 Ubi Caritas *(Hurd)*
710 Ubi Caritas *(Rosania)*
725 Unless a Grain of Wheat
     (Farrell)

LITURGY OF THE HOURS

MORNING PRAYER

Subtitles and alternate titles that differ from those used in Journeysongs, 3rd Edition *are given in italics.*

Hymns and Songs

Morning Prayer

Evening Prayer

Psalms

Canticles

Rites of Christian Initiation

DISMISSAL OF THE CATECHUMENS/ELECT

SCRUTINIES

Order of Christian Funerals

VIGIL FOR THE DECEASED

FUNERAL MASS

Eucharistic Exposition & Benediction

The Order of Mass

Mass Settings

Additional Service Music